THE CHEMISTRY OF WOOD

THE CHEMISTRY
OF WOOD

Edited by

B. L. BROWNING

The Institute of Paper Chemistry, Appleton, Wisconsin

1963

INTERSCIENCE PUBLISHERS

a division of John Wiley & Sons, New York • London

Preface

The field of wood chemistry is far from static, and developments of even less than a decade justify a fresh look at our concepts and state of knowledge in this important area. A new book on the subject must be anticipated with some trepidation, as it will inevitably be judged against a series of illustrious predecessors. The texts of Schorger (1926), Hawley and Wise (1926), Wise (1944), Wise and Jahn (1952), Hägglund (1928, 1939, 1951), and others have set enviably high standards which must serve as targets for later efforts. Monographs on cellulose by Heuser (1924, 1944) and by Ott and his associates (1943, 1955), on lignin by Brauns (1952, 1960), and many others on specialized topics have treated these subjects in such ample detail that attempts at compression may sometimes seem frustrating and futile.

Nevertheless, the prospective preparation of a new book has proved challenging, and the opportunity of participating in such an undertaking is not to be dismissed lightly. It has been our purpose to present the outstanding features of the chemistry of wood and its components in a text not too gargantuan for ready use and, at the same time, sufficiently detailed to serve as a reference text for those interested in the subject. If a publication must have a hypothetical audience, we would define ours to include the student, the young scientist in wood-using industries, and the scientist and technologist who may wish to have available critical if not exhaustive surveys of the topics included among the contents.

Two chapters in the present book represent something of an innovation in books devoted to wood chemistry and deserve special mention. One is the discussion of the development of woody tissue that takes place in the cambial zone. It is here that both wood and bark originate, and the end products can scarcely be discussed adequately or completely without some understanding of the biochemical processes that occur in the narrow zone where new material is formed. It is here, too, that our lack of understanding becomes embarrassingly evident, and so much needs to be learned. A chapter on bark may logically seem out of place in a book on the chemistry of wood, yet it is a truism that the tree cannot grow wood without bark. Both originate from the same cambial layer, and both must be dealt with when the trees are harvested in the forest. If bark has proved by and large to be less useful for commercial purposes, its ubiquitous presence and great quantity inspire study of possible utilization in ways not yet dreamed of.

I should like to acknowledge, here, my debt to the contributing authors, whose time and effort extracted from otherwise busy schedules have permitted synthesis of this volume. Thanks are due also to my associates and authors at The Institute of Paper Chemistry for reading many of the chapters and providing critical comments. Especial gratitude is expressed to Mr. J. G. Strange, President of The Institute of Paper Chemistry, for his encouragement and support. Many others have contributed in no small way to the preparation and publication of the book, and omission of specific mention in no way implies lack of sincere appreciation for efforts so willingly given.

B. L. Browning

Appleton, Wisconsin, 1963

Contributors

B. L. BROWNING	Senior Research Associate, The Institute of Paper Chemistry, Appleton, Wisconsin
M. A. BUCHANAN	Research Associate, The Institute of Paper Chemistry, Appleton, Wisconsin
G. H. CHIDESTER	Forest Products Laboratory, Forest Service, United States Department of Agriculture, Madison, Wisconsin
K. E. FREMER	Research Assistant, The Finnish Pulp and Paper Research Institute, Helsinki, Finland
J. F. HARRIS	Forest Products Laboratory, Forest Service, United States Department of Agriculture, Madison, Wisconsin
E. H. IMMERGUT	Interscience Publishers, a Division of John Wiley & Sons, Inc., New York, N. Y., and Polytechnic Institute of Brooklyn, Brooklyn, N. Y.
I. H. ISENBERG	Research Associate, The Institute of Paper Chemistry, Appleton, Wisconsin
WALDEMAR JENSEN	Professor, Managing Director of The Finnish Pulp and Paper Research Institute, Helsinki, Finland
R. E. KREMERS	Senior Research Associate, The Institute of Paper Chemistry, Appleton, Wisconsin

EDWARD G. LOCKE   Forest Products Laboratory, Forest Service, United States Department of Agriculture, Madison, Wisconsin

JEROME F. SAEMAN   Forest Products Laboratory, Forest Service, United States Department of Agriculture, Madison, Wisconsin

N. SANYER   Forest Products Laboratory, Forest Service, United States Department of Agriculture, Madison, Wisconsin

KYOSTI V. SARKANEN   Associate Professor of Wood Chemistry, University of Washington, Seattle, Washington (formerly Associate Professor, Cellulose Research Institute, State University College of Forestry at Syracuse University, Syracuse, New York

CONRAD SCHUERCH   State University College of Forestry, Syracuse University, Syracuse, New York

P. SIERILÄ   Research Assistant, The Finnish Pulp and Paper Research Institute, Helsinki, Finland

N. S. THOMPSON   Research Associate, The Institute of Paper Chemistry, Appleton, Wisconsin

V. WARTIOVAARA   Botanical Institute, University of Helsinki, Helsinki, Finland

Contents

CHAPTER 1

The Supply and Uses of Wood

B. L. Browning, *The Institute of Paper Chemistry, Appleton, Wisconsin*

Wood has always held a significant place in the human economy. It has served man as a structural material for his buildings, furnishings, tools, and weapons, and until recently as his only readily available fuel. Other parts of the tree—fruits, seeds, flowers, leaves, needles, and barks—have been utilized as food, and in decorations, clothing, and medicines. Although the manner of utilization has shifted during the centuries, the place of wood and other tree products in the economy has remained very important. Still further contributions of forests in a technological society lie in recreational usage and watershed control.

Wood represents one of the more important renewable natural resources, and the annual growth is sufficient to satisfy many essential needs indefinitely into the future. The major component of wood—cellulose—is one of the most abundant, naturally-occurring organic compounds.

About one third of the earth's land area is now forested. Much of the remaining area is represented by grasslands, desert, and arctic tundra which are unsuited to forest growth. Some other lands originally forested have been appropriated for agriculture because of favorable topography and fertile soil.

The total forest resources of the United States, of selected other regions, and of the world are given in Table I (4d). Much of the forest now growing is not useful at present because it lies in areas that are inaccessible; i.e., not within reach of exploitation by existing means of transport. In many regions only a portion of the total accessible forests is actually under exploitation or in use (yielding industrial wood and/or fuelwood). Extensive data on forest resources

TABLE I
Forest Resources of the World—1953

	United States (and Alaska)	Total North America	Central and South America	Europe	U.S.S.R.	World
Total land area[a]	2270	4975	5046	1184	5410	32635
Forested area[a]	784	1799	2135	336	1833	9593
Accessible forests[a,b]	509	917	775	329	1050	4591
Forests under exploitation[a,c]	509	710	194	321	867	2975
Growing stock, all species[d,e]	565	836	284	350	1166	3794
Softwood	388	601	35	219	1054	2047
Hardwood	177	235	249	131	112	1747

[a] Million acres.
[b] Forests now within reach of economic management or exploitation as sources of forest products.
[c] Forests yielding industrial wood and/or fuelwood.
[d] Billion cubic feet, including bark.
[e] On areas under exploitation.

and utilization of forest products are available in publications of the United States Forest Service (4) and of the Food and Agriculture Organization of the United Nations (2,3).

The growing stock includes live sawtimber and live poletimber trees. In the continental United States and Coastal Alaska the growing stock accounts for 86% of the total net volume of all timber. The remaining 14% is made up of cull trees, salvageable dead trees, and hardwood limbs (4a). Live sawtimber trees are those of commercial species that must contain at least one merchantable saw log and have minimum diameters at breast height of 9 inches for eastern softwoods and 11 inches for eastern hardwoods and all western woods. Live poletimber trees are below the size of sawtimber trees, but they must have a minimum diameter of 5 inches at breast height.

Two-thirds of the live sawtimber in the United States lies in the western states (Pacific Northwest, California, and Rocky Mountains). Douglas-fir is the predominant species, with ponderosa and Jeffrey pines, western hemlock, Sitka spruce, and the true firs representing other important species. The hardwoods are relatively unimportant in this region. The commercial forests of Coastal Alaska are principally western hemlock and Sitka spruce. In the northern states (New England, Middle Atlantic, Lake States, Central and Plains States) almost three-fourths of the available sawtimber is represented by hardwoods, of which the oaks are the most abundant; spruce, balsam fir, and white and red pines are the most important softwoods. In the southern states (South Atlantic, Southeast, and West Gulf States), the softwoods, chiefly the southern yellow pines, constitute about one-half of the sawtimber. The oaks account for a major part of the hardwood timber, although lumber from only the white and red oaks is highly esteemed (4b).

The net annual timber growth is greatest in the southern section of the United States, owing to the high growth rate of the southern yellow pines. The annual increment in growing stock of all species (in millions of cubic feet) in 1952 was estimated at 4660 in the North, 6810 in the South, 2750 in the West, and 32 in Coastal Alaska. The rate of sawtimber growth (as a percentage of timber volume) was 4.5% in the North, 6.7% in the South, and 0.8% in the West and Coastal Alaska (4c).

The total growth or gross annual increment of forests in use (in billions of cubic feet, including bark) is estimated at 29.0 in North America and 98.8 in the world (2c). The major portion of the growth in North America consists of coniferous woods (57%), whereas in the world's forests about one-half of the growth (51%) is represented by coniferous woods owing to the predominance of hardwoods in the tropical regions.

The world timber harvest in 1960 was estimated at 1732 million cubic meters or 61.2 billion cubic feet (not including bark) (3). The gross growth increment is not greatly in excess of current needs, and the consumption of wood may be expected to increase with an expanding world population and increasing technological development. The demand for industrial wood may be met partially by a shift from fuelwood in areas that are now largely undeveloped. Forests not used at present because of inaccessibility may be brought into production when this becomes economically feasible. The tropical regions now have a great unused potential of hardwoods.

In areas now under exploitation, reforestation of cutover and understocked areas, increased forest protection from fire and insect attack, and improved forest management can do much to increase the total wood supply (4). The genetic improvement of forest trees may lead not only to increased wood yield per acre, but to improvement of significant use properties (cf. Chapter 8). Much progress has already been made. In the United States the annual cut on the land in the public domain is controlled to furnish a continuous supply of timber. Nearly three-fourths of the commercial forest land in the United States is privately owned, and much of this is now managed for sustained yield. The productivity of farm and other small forests in private ownership is generally lower than that of the larger private holdings and the national forests (4).

The utilization of forest products varies widely. In regions with highly developed industries, only a minor portion of the timber harvest is consumed as fuelwood. In less developed areas the bulk of forest removals is represented by fuelwood. In Central America, South America, and Africa 80% or more of the total cut is utilized as fuel.

The uses of timber cut in the United States and Coastal Alaska on

TABLE II

Timber Cut from Growing Stock on Commercial Forest Land[a]
(United States and Coastal Alaska—1952)

Product	Softwood[b]	Hardwood[b]	Total[b]
Saw logs	5213	1607	6820
Pulpwood	1460	267	1727
Fuelwood	243	761	1004
Veneer logs and bolts	251	241	492
Posts	49	82	131
Hewn ties	32	77	109
Cooperage logs and bolts	29	76	105
Poles	101	< 1	101
Mine timbers	19	58	77
Piling	30	2	32
Other[c]	60	98	158
Totals	7487	3269	10756

[a] Does not include timber taken from dead and cull trees.
[b] Million cubic feet, not including bark.
[c] Including box and shingle bolts, excelsior bolts, turnery, dimension and handle stock, chemical wood, etc.

commercial forest land, in both private and public ownership, are given in Table II (4e). The most important converted forest product, in terms of both volume and value, is sawnwood. In areas supplying the pulp industry, pulpwood represents a significant proportion of the total harvest. Unsawn structural timber and other industrial woods occupy subordinate positions. The most notable changes in use distribution during the past several decades are the decreasing proportion of wood used as fuel, and the marked increase in the amount utilized as pulpwood.

The total pulpwood consumption in the United States during 1959

TABLE III

Some Production and Consumption Statistics (1)
(United States—1959)

Pulpwood consumption, thousands of cords	
Softwood	31,098
Hardwood	7,845
Total	38,943
Wood pulp production, thousands of tons[a]	
Special alpha and dissolving grades	1,092
Sulfite (bleached and unbleached)	2,447
Sulfate (bleached and unbleached)	13,780
Soda	480
Groundwood	3,187
Semichemical	1,906
Defibered or exploded	1,265
Screenings, etc.	100
Total	24,257
Paper and board production, thousands of tons[a]	
Paper	14,923
Paperboard	15,704
Wet machine board	143
Construction paper	3,281
Total	34,051
Papermaking fiber (other than wood pulp) consumption, thousands of tons[a]	
Waste paper	9,184
Other (including straw, rags, etc.)	1,026
Total	10,210

[a] Short tons of 2,000 pounds.

was 38.9 million cords (Table III). Wood pulp production by mills of the United States during the same year was 24.3 million tons, and paper and paperboard production amounted to 34 million tons (1). The production of dissolving pulps (chiefly for rayon, acetate, and cellophane) and some specially purified grades was 1.1 million tons.

A compilation of the major uses of wood obscures the diverse and commercially valuable materials extracted in smaller quantities from wood and bark, or derived as by-products in other industrial processes. Only a few may be mentioned as illustrative: naval stores (resins and turpentine) from the pines, tall oil obtained during recovery of sulfate pulping black liquors, dimethyl sulfide produced from sulfate pulping black liquors, an essential oil from eastern red cedarwood, vanillin from spent liquors in the sulfite pulping of softwoods, tannins from wood and tree barks, dihydroquercetin from Douglas-fir bark, and sugars, alcohols, and yeast derived from sulfite pulping liquors or wood hydrolyzates. (See also Chapters 7, 10, and 11.) The generic term "silvichemicals" has been used to represent chemicals derived from trees.

Barks, wood wastes, and by-products or wastes in manufacturing processes represent potential raw material sources of tremendous magnitude, and their efficient utilization presents an outstanding challenge for the technology of the future.

REFERENCES

1. American Paper and Pulp Association, *The Statistics of Paper*, 7th ed., New York, 1960.
2. Food and Agr. Organization U. N., (a) *World Forest Resources*, Rome, 1955; (b) *World Forest Products Statistics 1946–1955*, Rome, 1958; (c) *World Forest Inventory, 1958*, Rome, 1960.
3. Food and Agr. Organization U. N., *Yearbook of Forest Products Statistics*, Rome, 1961.
4. U. S. Dept. Agr., Forest Serv., *Timber Resources for America's Future*, Forest Resource Rep. No. 14, 1958; (a) p. 127, (b) p. 131, (c) p. 146, (d) p. 349, (e) p. 577.

CHAPTER 2

The Structure of Wood

I. H. Isenberg, *The Institute of Paper Chemistry, Appleton, Wisconsin*

It is appropriate that the chemist who is interested in the chemical composition, analysis, and properties of wood become familiar with the anatomical nature of this important, renewable natural resource. Wood is a heterogeneous material which, because of its complex biological nature, shows the effect of anatomical variation. This is frequently in contrast to the condition of the many homogeneous materials with which the chemist deals.

Wood is formed during the growth of certain plants, and as such, is comprised of plant cells, the majority of which have their principal axis oriented parallel to that of the stem. At one time each of these cells was alive and functioning; what remains in mature wood is a network of cell walls. The chemistry of the basic cell wall components, as well as the extraneous materials deposited in certain individual cells and their walls, is the chemistry of wood.

I. The Origin of Wood

Wood is obtained from the stems, roots, and branches of trees, shrubs, lianas (woody vines), and to a limited extent from certain herbaceous plants. These woody plants are seed-bearing plants or spermatophytes, although it should be mentioned that portions of certain ferns and fern allies (pteridophytes) are woody. The two subdivisions of the spermatophytes are the gymnosperms and angiosperms.

The gymnosperms exhibit a naked seed which is commonly subtended by a scale. The living gymnosperms are grouped into four plant orders of which the Coniferales is the most noteworthy, both from the point-of-view of number and economic value. The various members of this order are known as conifers, evergreens, or softwoods. The fruit of many species in this group is a cone, and hence the term conifer, or cone-bearer, is quite suitable. As several species have deciduous leaves, the term evergreen is rather misleading despite its frequent use. The term softwood has found favor particularly with the wood-user, and is commonly applied to the conifers in contrast to the broad-leaved trees or hardwoods. Physically, some softwoods are harder than certain hardwoods. To the neophyte this may seem very confusing. The widespread adoption of this terminology in the literature both here and abroad, however, makes its continued usage very probable.

The angiosperms have an ovary which encloses the ovules. The angiosperms are divided into two classes, the monocotyledons and the dicotyledons. Woody plants included among the monocotyledons are various palms and bamboos, of which there are numerous species. The dicotyledonous trees are known as broad-leaved trees, deciduous trees, or hardwoods. Since some temperate and many tropical species have persistent leaves, the term deciduous may not be appropriate. Again, some hardwoods are actually physically softer than certain species of softwoods.

Wood is not a homogeneous material with a uniform structure, but rather it is a tissue of very different kinds of cells which, in the living plant, perform three functions; namely, water conduction, metabolism (including the storage of reserve materials), and mechanical support. For each of these vital purposes there are definite cell forms (e.g., conducting cells tend to be long, empty, firm-walled, and well-pitted).

II. The Tree

A. THE PARTS OF A TREE

A tree is commonly considered to have three main parts—the crown, the stem, and the roots. Included in the crown are the foliage, the twigs, and the branches. The leaf is the factory of the tree; it is the organ in which food is manufactured by photosynthesis to furnish energy for the metabolism and growth of the tree. The process of photosynthesis which involves a combination of carbon dioxide and water in the presence of chlorophyll and light has not been completely elucidated, despite considerable research.

Although the branches and twigs of a tree are commonly considered to be part of the crown, they are actually extensions of the main stem and as such serve to conduct materials to and from the leaves. They are woody and have tissues similar to those of the stem. The leaves tend to be arranged on the twigs so that they receive the optimum amount of light.

The stem of the tree furnishes timber for the lumber mill or pulpwood bolts for the pulp mill. It is also called the trunk or bole. Economic considerations may govern the stem sizes used for sawlogs or pulpwood, but in small or large boles in the living tree the functions of the stem are mechanical support of the crown, conduction of water and mineral nutrients upward and elaborated foodstuffs downward, and storage.

It is easy to overlook the roots of the tree because the roots are usually underground. The root system is often as extensive as the crown, and it plays an important role in the life of the tree because it anchors the trunk in the ground, absorbs mineral nutrients (in solution) from the soil, transports these nutrients to the stem, and serves as a storage place for reserve foods. Roots form secondary xylem, or wood, as do the stems and branches.

B. GROWTH IN HEIGHT AND DIAMETER

In the springtime when the buds on the tree begin to swell and open, the lengthwise growth of the main stem and branches begins. The initiation of growth may vary with the species and climate (and in some cases it may be necessary for the leaves to be fairly well developed), but all extremities of the tree, above and beneath the surface of the ground, begin to extend. The apical meristem, a tissue capable of active cell division, forms the primary growth, or growth in length of the shoots and roots. Cell differentiation and complexity increases with distance from the tip. The primary growth which is laid down is about as thick as a lead pencil.

The first specialized cell type that develops once cells are formed from the apical meristem is the procambium, the precursor of the primary vascular tissue around the pith. At the termination of the primary growth this tissue has formed one of the most important parts of the plant—the cambium. The cambium is located between the wood and the bark, or more correctly at this stage, between the primary xylem and the primary phloem (Fig. 1A). When primary growth is completed at a particular level in the shoot, the cambium divides to create the new cells of secondary growth. Xylem cells are formed to the inside of the cambium and phloem cells to the outside,

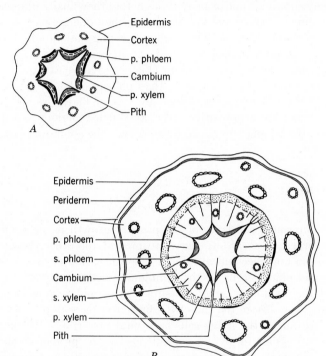

Fig. 1. Schematic drawings of transverse sections of a young pine twig (*Pinus strobus* L.), showing the arrangement of the tissues prior to, and after, secondary thickening. *A*—About one inch from the apical growing point; the primary tissues are complete, but secondary thickening has not begun. *B*—At the end of the growing season; secondary thickening is well advanced. (Reproduced from Brown, Panshin, and Forsaith, *Textbook of Wood Technology*, Vol. I, 1949, by permission of McGraw-Hill Book Co., Inc.).

however, in a division only one type is formed because the other daughter cell remains as the meristematic cambium cell. The formation of these secondary xylem cells between the cambium and the primary xylem forces the cambium outward and the diameter of the shoot increases (Fig. 1B). The cambium is inactive during the cool months of the year, but when growth resumes in warm weather additional cells are formed by the cambium—xylem to the inside adjacent to existing xylem cells, and phloem to the outside adjacent to previously formed phloem cells. The newly formed cambium derivative cells may subdivide one or more times before they finally differentiate into specific cell types and mature during the same growing season in which they were formed. This region of young undifferentiated cells is known as the cambial zone or layer in contradistinction to the original single layer, the cambium (Fig. 2). Each year about six to eight times more xylem cells form than phloem cells. As can be seen in Fig. 1 the phloem is surrounded by a layer known as the cortex. This is primarily a protective layer, and such functions as support, photosynthesis, and storage are secondary. The epidermis surrounds the cortex.

C. BARK

1. Periderm Formation

The outermost cell layer of the primary growth is the epidermis, which serves, to a certain degree, to protect the other tissues from desiccation and mechanical injury. The formation of new layers of xylem and phloem cells by the cambium and the consequent expansion of the stem exert great pressure on the epidermis causing it to rupture, often before the end of the first growing season. Prevention of desiccation of the living cells is of vital importance to the plant, and nature seems to prepare for this loss of the protective layer by forming a new layer, the periderm, a short distance from the epidermis in the cortex (Fig. 1B). The periderm originates as isolated patches, but eventually it unites into a layer.

Continued formation of cells from the cambium increases the pressure on the outer parts of the stem, with subsequent rupture occurring locally. At these places new periderm layers are formed to provide protection. Within a few years this phenomenon penetrates to the secondary phloem in most species, and is described as a deep periderm formation. In most trees the periderm is shaped somewhat like a clamshell, with its apex toward the center of the tree. Overlapping of these many layers provides the required protection. In the periderm of nearly all trees, small areas have loosely arranged cells with abundant, small, intercellular spaces. These areas, known as lenticels, are conspicuous as dots or slits on twigs. With the formation of deep

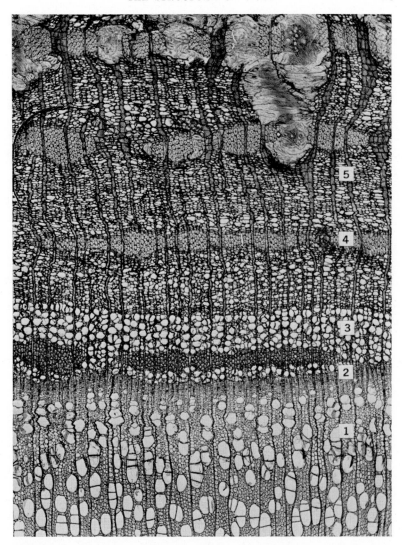

Fig. 2. Transverse section of aspen (*Populus tremuloides* Michx.), showing (1) the sapwood, (2) active cambium, (3) bark including sieve tubes, (4) stone cells, and (5) phloem parenchyma. Magnification 45X. (Photomicrograph by J. D. Hankey.)

periderm, new lenticels are formed by the specialized functioning of local areas in the phellogen.

2. Division of the Bark

It is customary in describing a tree that has reached the stage of deep periderm formation to refer to the tissues inside the cambium layer as wood, and to those to the outside as bark. Only a few of the highlights of the anatomy of bark will be mentioned at this time, as this subject is given more attention in Chapter 12.

Casual observation of the cross section of the tree stem shows that the bark is usually divided colorwise into two parts. The actual dividing line is the innermost, or most recently formed, periderm. The tissue to the outside is often darker and the cells are dead so that the region no longer functions physiologically. This is the outer, dead bark or rhytidome. The lighter colored tissue between the last-formed periderm and the cambium is living and physiologically

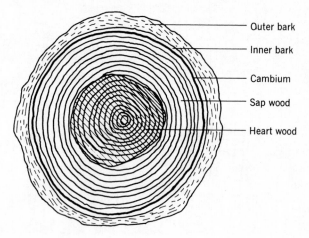

Fig. 3. Schematic drawing of a transverse section of a mature tree stem, showing the outer bark, inner bark, cambium, sapwood, and heartwood. The annual growth rings are also shown in the wood portion.

active. It is known as the inner, living bark (Fig. 3). A familiar exception to the color orientation just noted is the white birch with its chalky, or creamy white, outer bark and a pinkish inner bark.

a. Periderm

The periderm layer is composed of three kinds of cells: phellogen, phellem, and phelloderm. The phellogen, or cork cambium, arises by stimulation of existing parenchyma cells of the inner bark and becomes meristematic, i.e., capable of subdivision. By subdivision during the growing season it forms phellem or cork cells to the outside, or phelloderm cells to the inside. The proportion of each cell-type formed is relatively constant for a particular species. The phellem, because of its corky nature, prevents the cells exterior to it from performing their life processes. When maturity is reached the phellem cells die and then function only in a protective manner.

b. Outer Bark

The outer dead bark is a collection of the cells which originally existed in the inner living bark plus the various old periderm layers spaced at irregular distances. Externally the bark may show fissures, plates, scales, etc., and a variety of colors, usually the darker ones. Young trees, or the younger parts of old trees, which have not experienced deep periderm formation are rather smooth. In thickness, bark varies in different species and trees, and in parts of the same tree.

c. Inner Bark

The inner bark, which is usually rather narrow, contains conducting cells, storage cells, and, in some cases, strengthening cells. These are the various types of cells found in the secondary phloem. The most characteristic cell of the secondary phloem is the sieve cell in coniferous trees or the sieve tube member in dicotyledonous trees. This cell is adapted to the conduction of the elaborated food and serves in this fashion particularly during the first year of its life. Later it may be crushed and become nonfunctioning. Actually, the sieve tube member is one cell in a series known as a sieve tube. These elements are arranged end to end, with the common walls being sieve plates. Accompanying the sieve tube (and intimately connected with it) is a series of short parenchymatous cells—the companion cells.

In addition to the conducting cells, the secondary phloem contains parenchyma cells which serve for storage, some of which eventually are stimulated to become phellogen. Ray parenchyma cells are also always present.

Certain species of trees have strengthening cells in their bark.

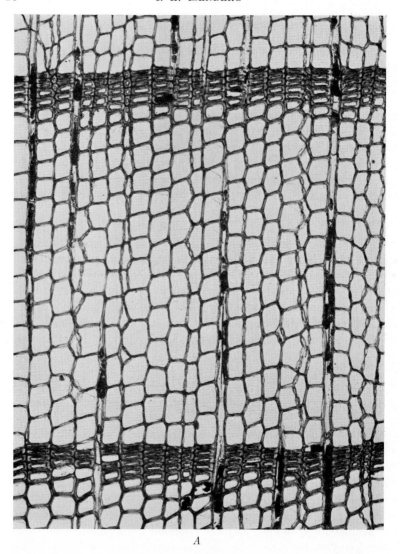

A

Fig. 4. Redwood heartwood [*Sequoia sempervirens* (D. Don) Endl.], showing extraneous deposits in longitudinal and ray parenchyma cells. Magnification: 100X. *A*—Transverse section. *B*—Radial section.

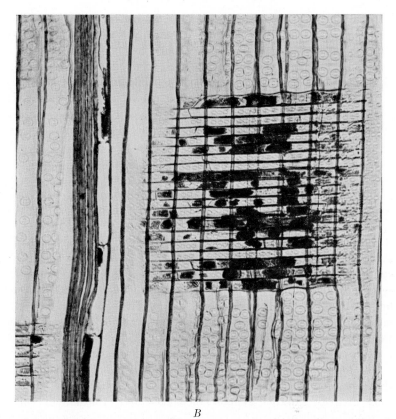

B

Redwood, and many of the cedars, have tangential rows of long fibers. Basswood and other dicotyledonous trees contain phloem fibers. Other types of sclereids or stone cells are found in barks of many trees and shrubs (Fig. 2). Further discussion will be found in plant anatomy texts to which the reader is referred (4, 5).

D. SAPWOOD AND HEARTWOOD

When a tree is young, the wood that is added year after year to the trunk and branches continues to function in sap conduction and storage of reserve food, as well as in the support of the tree crown. This wood, known as sapwood, is physiologically active in that at least a part of the tissue is alive and is in communication with the cambium and inner bark. Eventually, as the years pass and the trunk increases in girth, the inside tissue surrounding the pith dies. This core of dead wood in the center of the stem is known as heartwood (Fig. 3); it provides only mechanical support.

The initiation of the formation of heartwood varies greatly in different species and in the same species under different site conditions. Once formation starts in a tree at a given height, it progresses toward the outside. The tree, of course, maintains a layer of sapwood under the bark to provide for the necessary sap conduction. The sapwood varies from only a few growth rings in some species to nearly 200 in others. In a given tree the sapwood is usually at its widest when the plant is young, and narrows as the tree increases in diameter; accordingly, it is wider in the upper portions of the trunk than toward the base. Within a species the more vigorous trees appear to have the most sapwood.

In a great majority of species the formation of heartwood is made evident because of an appreciable darkening of the tissue so that it contrasts with the lighter-colored sapwood (see Table V). However, certain of the commonly used species such as spruce (*Picea* sp.), true fir (*Abies* sp.), hemlock (*Tsuga* sp.), aspen and poplar (*Populus* sp.) normally do not show a darkening of the heartwood. In some species where formation requires many years, the smaller trees, such as are used in pulping, may be composed entirely of sapwood.

The formation of heartwood is still an enigma. What stimulates the formation, when does it begin, is there a periodicity, and why do some areas of sapwood remain unchanged and eventually become surrounded by heartwood? These are some of the intriguing questions that still remain unanswered. A particular growth ring may occur in the sapwood at one place and in the heartwood elsewhere.

In the heartwood various colored organic compounds may infiltrate the cell walls and, if copious, may even accumulate in the cell cavities as amorphous materials (Fig. 4). The extraneous components of wood are discussed in Chapter 7.

III. The Anatomy of Wood

A. GENERAL DESCRIPTION OF WOOD

1. Planes of Orientation

In order to obtain the proper spatial concept of the structure of wood the stem form of trees must be considered. A log may be pictured, with good approximation, as a truncated cone through which three sections may be cut perpendicular to each other. These are the transverse, or cross section, at right angles to the stem axis; the radial section, parallel to the axis on a radius of the stem; and the tangential section, parallel to the axis and perpendicular to the radius. These planes are denoted by x, r, t, respectively.

2. Growth Increments

The formation of wood by the cambium (Fig. 2) takes place during late spring, summer, and possibly early autumn in most of the temperate zones. The cambium is dormant during the remainder of the year. This seasonal growth is usually evident as a layer of tissue which is more or less noticeable in the various planes of the wood. It is termed a growth layer or, because of its characteristic appearance in transverse section, an annual ring.

3. Springwood and Summerwood

The growth layer is apparent owing to the difference in the growth of the early-formed cells and the late-formed cells in the increment. The earlywood, or springwood, cells generally are thinner-walled and of larger diameter than the latewood, or summerwood, cells (Figs. 4A and 5A). The transition may be gradual (Fig. 5) or abrupt (Fig. 4) in passing from springwood to summerwood. Macroscopically the structural difference may be reflected in physical properties and thus delineate the increment layer.

4. Wood Ray

The ray is a tissue which has its principal direction oriented radially in the tree. When observed in radial section it has been likened to a ribbon (Figs. 4B and 5C). The chief function of the ray in the sapwood is to transport materials in solution to and from the cambium and inner bark. The rays also serve as storage places for reserve food. Wood rays are formed in the first layer of secondary tissue, and are extended as new layers are added unless injury interferes. As the diameter of the woody stem increases, new ray initial cells form in the cambium so that the characteristic spacing of the wood rays for the species is maintained. This spacing may be several rays per millimeter in the tangential direction, as observed in the cross section. When viewed in tangential section the rays are seen in sectional view

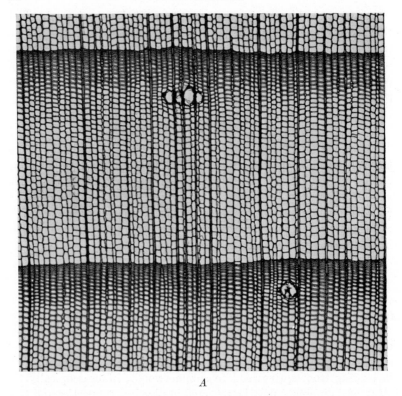

A

Fig. 5. White spruce wood *Picea glauca* (Moench) Voss. Magnification: 50X.
A—Transverse section. B—Tangential section. C—Radial section.

so that the height and width are apparent (Fig. 5B). Rays may be low
or high and narrow or wide; the height usually exceeds the width.
Certain species exhibit considerable variation. In the oaks, beech,
and sycamore the wide rays are quite noticeable (Fig. 6). In red
alder (*Alnus rubra* Bong.) several narrow rays, separated by single
layers of fibrous cells, are so closely spaced as to appear to the unaided
eye of the observer as a single wide ray—an aggregate ray. Like the
oak-type, or compound ray, it is of diagnostic value because it is not
common in occurrence.

When viewed in tangential section there are several rays per square
millimeter (Fig. 5B). As mentioned, the size varies as does the
distribution which may be random (a common condition in American
woods) or aligned in rows (storied rays).

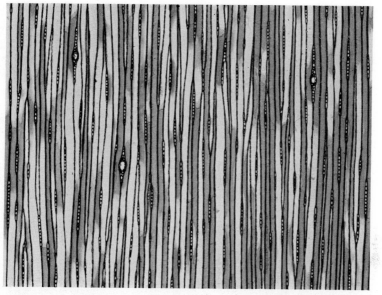

B

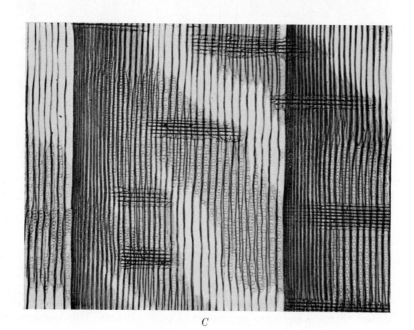

C

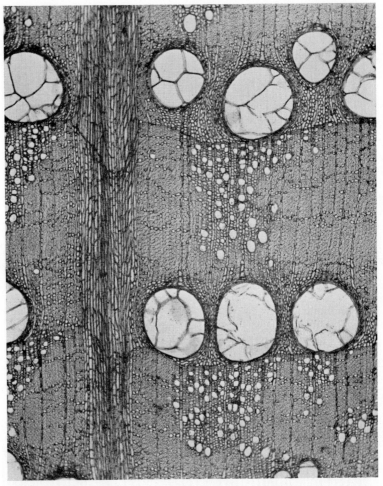

Fig. 6. Transverse section of post oak (*Quercus stellata* Wagenh.), showing broad oak-type ray and tyloses in large springwood pores. Magnification: 50X.

5. Parenchyma

The cells which serve for storage, and are therefore alive while in the sapwood, collectively form a parenchymatous system in the wood. These cells are comparatively short and usually thin-walled.

The parenchyma of wood consists of ray, longitudinal, and epithelial (if resin passages are present) parenchyma. The wood rays are composed either entirely or largely of ray parenchyma cells. The longitudinal parenchyma extends along the grain of the wood as strands of cells which may, or may not, be grouped further into larger masses of tissue. The larger masses may be readily visible to the observer, and even individual strands sometimes show particularly because of the dark contents of the cells in certain species (Fig. 4). Epithelial parenchyma constitute a narrow band of cells surrounding resin passages and usually are not visible without magnification (Fig. 5).

6. Prosenchyma

A large majority of the wood cells formed by the cambium layer during a given year lose their protoplasts before the end of the growing season in which they were laid down, and thereafter function only to provide sufficient strength to the stem and as a means of conduction. These cells are usually greatly elongated in the longitudinal direction and are collectively known as prosenchyma.

7. Resin Canals

The resin canal is a tubular intercellular spacing surrounded by a sheathing of small parenchymatous cells, the epithelial cells (Figs. 5A and 5B). These canals occur both longitudinally and horizontally in the wood of four genera of American conifers—pine (*Pinus*), spruce (*Picea*), larch (*Larix*), and Douglas-fir (*Pseudotsuga*). The longitudinal canals are larger in diameter than the horizontal canals in the same species. The horizontal canals occur only in the wood rays, and only in a relatively small proportion of them.

The size of canals of different species varies. In frequency they are considerably more numerous in pines than in the other genera. In addition to the normal resin canals, so-called traumatic resin canals occur not only in the above-mentioned species, but also in other conifers such as true firs (*Abies*) and hemlock (*Tsuga*). These wound canals are usually longitudinal.

8. Texture and Grain

Two terms often used when discussing wood are texture and grain. Texture is concerned with the size and quality of wood cells—fine- and coarse-textured, even- and uneven-textured, smooth- and harsh-textured.

Grain refers to the alignment and sorting of wood cells. Wood may be straight-grained, spiral-grained, interlocking-grained, curly-grained, or wavy-grained. Sorting of the cells is usually linked with the width of the growth layer, because it frequently differs in wide and narrow rings. Even- and uneven-grained are common terms used in discussing changes of transition in the growth ring.

B. THE STRUCTURE OF CONIFEROUS WOOD

1. General

The cells of the wood of the conifers have their longest axis oriented either longitudinally or radially. The cell types which have their longest axis with the grain are the tracheid, the wood parenchyma, and the epithelial cells surrounding the longitudinal resin canals. The ray tracheid, the ray parenchyma, and the horizontal epithelial cell have their principal axis in the radial direction; these occur only in the wood rays. A particular species need not contain all of these types. The simplest wood from the anatomical viewpoint has only longitudinal tracheids and ray parenchyma cells. In Table I are listed some of the anatomical features characteristic of several important American softwood species. Proportions of cell types in softwoods are given in Table II.

2. Tracheid

The coniferous tracheid is an extremely long, linear cell that may be as much as 75 times longer than its diameter; it tapers to a blunt end as viewed radially, and to a relatively sharp tip as seen tangentially. In cross sections of wood, tracheids appear as polygonal cells that are arranged in radial rows (Figs. 4A and 5A). In the springwood they are rectangular or hexagonal and in the summerwood they are rectangular or even tablet-like toward the outer margin of the growth ring. The tracheids of greatest radial diameter often are produced when growth first starts in the spring. Springwood is composed of relatively thin-walled tracheids with a wide lumen or cell cavity.

a. Pitting

(1) Inter-Tracheid Pitting

The radial walls of the tracheids, and, in some species, the tangential walls of the outermost summerwood tracheids and the adjoining walls of the first-formed springwood tracheids, show markings due to pits or thin areas in the cell wall. Most conspicuous are the pits which lead to complementary pits in contiguous longitudinal tracheids. In the springwood tracheids these are large and doughnut-shaped (Fig. 4B). The bordered pits (Fig. 11) on the radial walls of the tracheids may be crowded or distant, with a tendency for the crowding to occur toward the ends of the tracheid. The pits are arranged in longitudinal series. Crosswise in the cell, there may be one pit in the wall at a given height, or several in a transverse row. The uniseriate condition prevails on the radial walls of summerwood tracheids and is the most common type in springwood tracheids (Fig. 5C). In some species, however, the paired condition or even three or four pits will be found in the broad springwood tracheids (Fig. 4B). Uniformity need not occur over the entire length of the tracheid. Transverse rows of intertracheid pits are indicative of coarseness of texture.

Tangential pitting is confined to the last few rows of summerwood tracheids and the inner wall of the first-formed springwood tracheid. It is found in all coniferous woods but those of the hard pines (*Diploxylon*) (red pine, *Pinus resinosa* Ait., is an exception). These pits are always smaller than the bordered pits on the radial walls, usually round, and rather widely spaced.

(2) Cross-Field Pitting

Each longitudinal tracheid makes connection for liquid transfer with several wood rays by means of pits. As was noted, the rays of coniferous woods are composed of ray parenchyma, ray tracheids, or of both cell types. Where the longitudinal tracheid makes contact with a ray tracheid, small bordered pits are in evidence. The nature of the pitting from ray parenchyma to longitudinal tracheid, especially in the wide springwood tracheid, is of help in wood or fiber identification. These pits are located in a region which has been termed, for convenience, a ray crossing or cross-field. A cross-field is the area bordered by the horizontal walls of a ray cell and the vertical walls of the adjacent axial tracheid.

Several well-defined types of cross-field pits in conifers are recognized (Fig. 7). (*1*) Windowlike, or fenestriform, in the wood of the soft pines and red pine in this country and in Scotch pine (*P. sylvestris* L.) of Europe; (*2*) pinoid, more numerous, smaller, and more variable in size, in the woods of other native pines; (*3*) piceoid, or piciform, generally elliptical, in the woods of spruce, larch, and Douglas-fir; (*4*) taxodioid, in the woods of the Taxodiaceae and also in the true

TABLE I

Important Anatomical Features of American Softwoods

Species	Transition from springwood to summerwood	Resin canals	Epithelial cell walls	Ray parenchyma pitting	Ray tracheid location	Ray tracheid wall	Longitudinal wood parenchyma
Eastern white pine (*Pinus strobus* L.)	G	N; L	Thin	W	M; I	S	X
Western white pine (*P. monticola* Dougl.)	G	N; L	Thin	W	M; I	S	X
Sugar pine (*P. lambertiana* Dougl.)	G	N; VL	Thin	W	M; I	S	X
Red pine (*P. resinosa* Ait.)	More or less abrupt	N; Med	Thin	W	M; I	D	X
Jack pine (*P. banksiana* Lamb.)	More or less abrupt	N; Med	Thin	Pin	M; I	D	X
Longleaf pine[a] (*P. palustris* Mill.)	A	N; L	Thin	Pin	M; I	D	X
Virginia pine (*P. virginiana* Mill.)	A	N; L	Thin	Pin	M; I	D	X
Ponderosa pine (*P. ponderosa* Laws.)	A	N; VL	Thin	Pin	M; occasionally I	D	X
Lodgepole pine (*P. contorta latifolia* Wats.)	More or less abrupt	N; Med	Thin	Pin	M; I	D	X
Tamarack (*Larix laricina* K. Koch)	A	Sp; Med	Thick	Pic	M	S	Absent or terminal and very sparse

Species						
Western larch (*L. occidentalis* Nutt.)	A	Sp; Med	Thick	Pic	M	S	Absent or terminal and very sparse
Black spruce[b] (*Picea mariana* B.S.P.)	G	Sp; Med	Thick	Pic	M	S	X
Sitka spruce (*P. sitchensis* Carr.)	G	Sp; Med	Thick	Pic	M	S	X
Douglas-fir (*Pseudotsuga taxifolia* Britt.)	A	Sp; Med	Thick	Pic	M	S	Absent or terminal and very sparse
Eastern hemlock (*Tsuga canadensis* Carr.)	A	X	X	C	M	S	Absent or terminal and very sparse
Western hemlock (*Tsuga heterophylla* Sarg.)	More or less gradual	X (traumatic)	X	C	M	S	Absent or terminal and very sparse
Balsam fir (*Abies balsamea* Mill.)	G	X (traumatic)	X	T	X (M, if present)	S	X
White fir[c] (*Abies concolor* Lindl.)	G	X (traumatic)	X	T	X	X	Absent or terminal and very sparse
Noble fir (*Abies procera* Rehd.)	More or less gradual	X (traumatic)	X	T	X	X	Absent or terminal and very sparse
Redwood (*Sequoia sempervirens* Endl.)	A	X (traumatic)	X	T	X (M, if present)	X	Metatracheal-diffuse
Southern cypress (*Taxodium distichum* Rich.)	More or less abrupt	X	X	T or C	X	X	Metatracheal-diffuse
Incense-cedar (*Libocedrus decurrens* Torr.)	G	X	X	C	X (occasional M)	X	Metatracheal-diffuse

(continued)

TABLE I (*continued*)

Important Anatomical Features of American Softwoods

Species	Transition from springwood to summerwood	Resin canals	Epithelial cell walls	Ray parenchyma pitting	Ray tracheid location	Ray tracheid wall	Longitudinal wood parenchyma
Northern white-cedar (*Thuja occidentalis* L.)	More or less gradual	X	X	T	X (occasional M)	X	Metatracheal-diffuse
Western red-cedar (*Thuja plicata* D. Don)	More or less abrupt	X	X	T	X (occasional M)	X	Metatracheal
Port-Orford-cedar (*Chamaecyparis lawsoniana* Parl.)	More or less gradual	X	X	C	X (very rarely M)	X	Metatracheal-diffuse
Alaska yellow-cedar (*C. nootkatensis* Spach)	More or less abrupt	X	X	C	M	S	Metatracheal-diffuse
Atlantic white-cedar (*C. thyoides* B.S.P.)	More or less gradual	X	X	C	X (occasional M)	X	Diffuse or zonate
Eastern red-cedar (*Juniperus virginiana* L.)	Gradual to rather abrupt	X	X	C	X	X	Metatracheal-diffuse

[a] Other southern pine species which are similar are shortleaf (*P. echinata* Mill.), loblolly (*P. taeda* L.), slash (*P. elliottii* Engelm.), pitch (*P. rigida* Mill.), and pond (*P. rigida serotina* (Michx.) Loud.).

[b] Other spruce species which are similar are red (*P. rubens* Sarg.), white (*P. glauca* Voss), and Engelmann (*P. engelmanni* Engelm.).

[c] Other true fir species which are similar are silver (*A. amabilis* Forbes), grand (*A. grandis* Lindl.), and alpine (*A. lasiocarpa* Nutt.).

Symbols: X—absent or void; G—transition gradual; A—transition abrupt; N—resin canals numerous; Sp—resin canals sparse; L—resin canals large; VL—resin canals very large; Med—resin canals medium; W—cross-field pitting windowlike; Pin—cross-field pitting pinoid; Pic—cross-field pitting piceoid; C—cross-field pitting cupressoid; T—cross-field pitting taxodioid; M—ray tracheids marginal; I—ray tracheids interspersed; S—ray tracheid wall smooth; D—ray tracheid wall dentate.

TABLE II

Cell Type Proportions and Fiber Dimensions in Several American Softwoods

Species	Proportions of cells, per cent volume				Longitudinal tracheid dimensions			
	Tracheids	Rays	Longitudinal parenchyma	Resin canals	Length, mm.			Tangential diameter, μ, range
					Av.	Min.	Max.	
Eastern white pine	94.0	5.3		0.7	3.0	1.6	5.0	25–35
Sugar pine	94.0	5.5		0.5	5.9	1.6	7.9	40–50
Longleaf pine	90.8	8.4		0.8	4.9	1.6	6.9	35–45
Ponderosa pine	93.0	6.7		0.3	3.6	1.5	5.0	35–45
Tamarack	89.0	10.0	0.9	0.1	3.6	1.7	5.6	25–35
Black spruce	94.8	5.0		0.2	3.3	1.3	4.9	25–30
Sitka spruce	92.5	7.2		0.3	5.6	3.6	7.3	35–45
Douglas-fir	92.5	7.3		0.2	3.9	1.7	7.0	35–45
Western hemlock	91.2	8.8			4.2	1.8	6.0	30–40
Balsam fir	94.3	5.7			3.5	1.9	5.6	30–40
Redwood	91.2	7.8	1.0		6.1	2.9	9.3	50–65
Western red-cedar	93.1	6.9	Trace		3.5	1.4	5.9	30–40

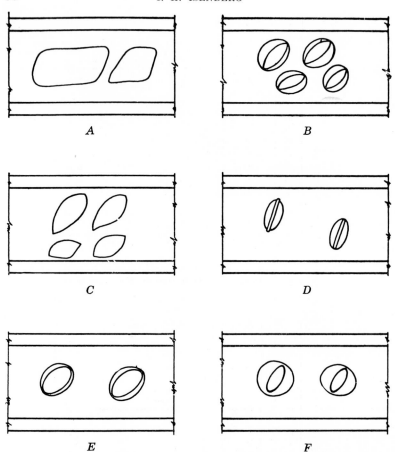

Fig. 7. Types of pit-pairs occurring in the cross-fields of coniferous woods.
A—Windowlike or fenestriform. *B* and *C*—Pinoid, with and without border.
D—Piceoid. *E*—Taxodioid. *F*—Cupressoid. (Reproduced from Brown, Panshin,
and Forsaith, *Textbook of Wood Technology*, Vol. I, 1949, by permission of
McGraw-Hill Book Co., Inc.)

firs (*Abies*) and in *Thuja* species; (*5*) cupressoid, similar to piceoid
but aperture is included and elliptical, in the woods of all cupres-
saceous genera except *Thuja*.

b. Spiral Thickening

A feature known as spiral thickening sometimes occurs on the inner
surface of the cell wall next to the lumen in prosenchyma cells. In

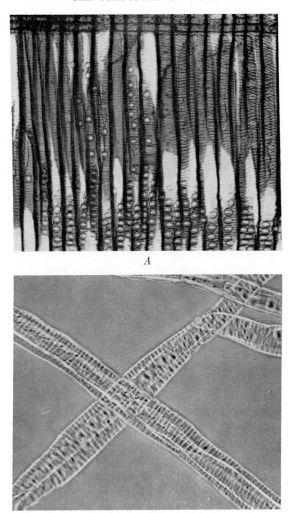

A

B

Fig. 8. Spiral thickening in tracheids of Douglas-fir [*Pseudotsuga taxifolia* (Poir) Britt.]. *A*—Radial section of wood. Magnification: 100X. *B*—Early springwood tracheids as seen with phase-contrast. Magnification: 150X.

coniferous woods this feature is found principally in the longitudinal tracheids of certain species. The outstanding examples in American woods are in Douglas-fir (Fig. 8) and in *Taxus*. Several such spirals extend along the inner surface of the wall at the same time, ascending usually in a clockwise direction. The angle of the helices within a species varies considerably, but the spacing of the coils of the spirals is more or less constant within certain limits in a given wood.

C. THE STRUCTURE OF DICOTYLEDONOUS WOOD

1. General

The cells of the wood of the dicotyledonous species, similar to those of coniferous woods, are oriented either longitudinally or radially. The hardwoods differ greatly from the softwoods because they contain vessels (known as pores in cross section), have little (if any) radial alignment of the longitudinal cells when viewed in cross section, are more complex in structure with several more cell types possible, and have rays which show more variability in width. Proportions of various cell types in hardwoods are given in Table III.

a. Porous Woods

In a specialized sense the term porous is used to describe the presence of pores (vessels in cross section) in the wood of the dicotyledonous species. In contrast, coniferous wood, which does not possess such features is termed nonporous. All woods are porous, of course, in the sense of possessing air space.

If the springwood pores are much larger than those in the remainder of the growth layer the hardwood is considered to be ring-porous (Figs. 6 and 9A). On the other hand, a rather uniform size of the pores throughout the growth ring (even though there is a slight decrease in size of the pores to the outside of the ring) results in a diffuse-porous wood (Figs. 9B and 9C). There are species in which the condition is intermediate; such woods are known as semi-ring-porous.

2. Vessels

The vessel is an axial tube-like system of indeterminate length composed of individual cells which have coalesced end to end. These individual components are known as vessel members or elements. A portion of the cell wall at or close to each end of the vessel member is dissolved to leave an opening known as a perforation. If the perforation plate contains one large opening, it is known as a simple perforation, or, if it is ladderlike in appearance with several undissolved bars, it is termed scalariform (Fig. 10). This variation in the type of

TABLE III

Cell Type Proportions and Fiber Dimensions in Selected American Hardwoods

Species	Proportions of cells, per cent volume				Cell dimensions			
	Vessels	Fibers	Longitudinal parenchyma	Rays	Vessel length Av., mm.	Fiber length Av., mm.	Fiber diameter range, μ	Wall
Quaking aspen	33.8	55.1	Trace	11.1	0.67	1.04	10–27	Thin to medium thick
Black willow	38.1	54.5	Trace	7.4	0.42	1.1	16–32	Thin to moderately thick
Yellow birch	21.4	65.8	2.0	10.8	0.84	1.85	20–36	Thin to moderately thick
Beech	31.0	44.0	5.0	20.0	0.61	1.2	16–22	Thick
Chestnut	39.8	46.8	1.5	11.9	0.58	1.0	16–34	Thin
American elm	48.0	34.7	6.0	11.3	0.22	1.5	14–26	Moderately thick to thick
Cucumber magnolia	38.6	47.5	Trace	13.9	0.72	1.6	28–40	Thin to moderately thick
Yellow-poplar	36.6	49.2	Trace	14.2	0.89	1.9	24–40	Thin to moderately thick
Sweetgum	54.9	26.8	Trace	18.3	1.32	1.7	20–40	Moderately thick
Sugar maple	21.0	61.1	Trace	17.9	0.41	0.8	16–30	Thin to moderately thick
Basswood	55.6	36.1	2.2	6.1	0.43	1.1	24–36	Thin
Black tupelo	38.4	45.0	Trace	16.6	1.11	1.8	20–32	Moderately thick to thick
Black ash	11.6	69.4	7.0	12.0	0.27	1.3	12–22	Thin to fairly thick

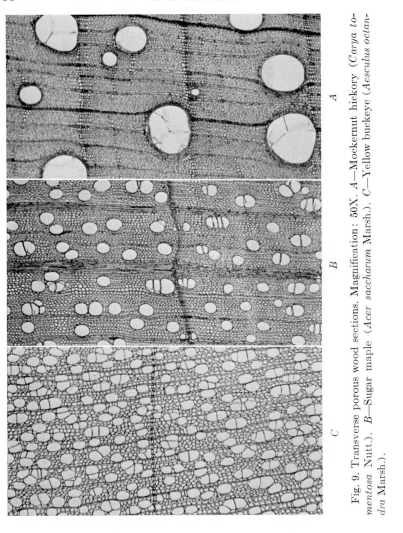

Fig. 9. Transverse porous wood sections. Magnification: 50X. A—Mockernut hickory (*Carya to-mentosa* Nutt.). B—Sugar maple (*Acer saccharum* Marsh.). C—Yellow buckeye (*Aesculus octandra* Marsh.).

perforation is of value in wood or pulp identification and is one of the details in Table IV which lists the anatomical features of various important American hardwoods. Vessel member lengths are given in Table III.

In some species, such as the ashes, black locust, hickories, osage-orange, and certain of the oaks, the vessels become plugged with

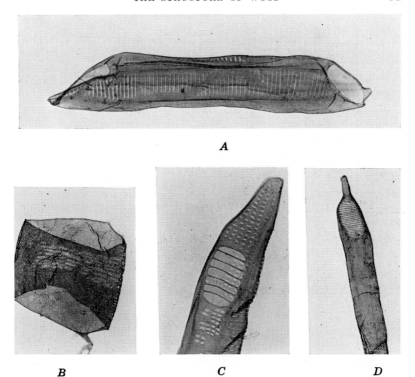

A

B   *C*   *D*

Fig. 10. Vessel members of several species showing perforations. Magnification: 130X. *A*—Cucumber magnolia (*Magnolia acuminata* L.), simple. *B*—Southern red oak (*Quercus falcata* Michx.), springwood, simple. *C*—Yellow poplar (*Liriodendron tulipifera* L.), scalariform. *D*—Sweetgum (*Liquidambar styraciflua* L.), scalariform. (Reproduced from *The College Textbook of Pulp and Paper Manufacture*, Vol. I, 1958, by permission of the Technical Association of the Pulp and Paper Industry.)

ingrowths (known as tyloses) from adjacent living parenchyma cells, before the change from sapwood to heartwood is completed (Fig. 6).

3. Other Cell Types

Additional longitudinal cells which may occur in the hardwoods and contribute to their complexity are tracheids, fibers, and longitudinal parenchyma cells. The transverse cells are ray parenchyma cells.

TABLE IV

Important Anatomical Features of Several American Hardwoods

Species	Pore arrangement	Vessel perforation	Vessel pitting	Ray width	Ray composition	Parenchyma arrangement
Butternut (Juglans cinerea L.)	SR	S	Orb to ang	1–4 Ser	Homo to het	Meta & meta-diff
Black walnut (Juglans nigra L.)	SR	S	Orb to ang	1–5 Ser	Homo to het	Meta & meta-diff
True hickories (Carya species)	R	S	Orb to ang	1–5 Ser	Homo to het	Meta, meta-diff, & ter
Pecan hickories (Carya species)	SR	S	Orb to ang	1–5 Ser	Homo to het	Meta, meta-diff, & ter
Cottonwood (Populus species)	SR to D	S	Orb to ang	Uniser	Essentially homo	Ter
Quaking aspen[a] (Populus tremuloides Michx.)	D	S	Orb to ang	Uniser	Essentially homo	Ter
Black willow (Salix nigra Marsh.)	SR to D	S	Orb to ang	Uniser	Het	Ter
Birch (Betula species)	D	Sc	Orb to ang	1–5 Ser	Homo	Meta-diff, para, & ter
Red alder (Alnus rubra Bong.)	D	Sc	Orb to ang	Uniser & aggregate	Homo	Para, meta-diff, & occasionally ter
Beech (Fagus grandifolia Ehrh.)	D	Essentially S	Oval to el	1–5 ser & 15–25 ser	Homo to het	Meta & meta-diff

		Essentially S				
Chestnut (Castanea dentata Borkh.)	R	S	Orb to el	Uniser	Homo	Para & meta-diff
Tan-oak (Lithocarpus densiflora Rehd.)	D	S	Orb	Uniser, aggregate, & broad oak-type	Essentially homo	Para, meta, & meta-diff
Live oak (Quercus virginiana Mill.)	D	S	Orb to oval	1–3 ser, aggregate, & broad oak-type	Essentially homo	Para, meta-diff, & meta
Red oaks^b (Quercus species)	R	S	Orb to oval	Uniser, part biser, & 12–30 + ser	Homo	Para, meta-diff, & usually meta
White oaks^c (Quercus species)	R	S	Orb to oval	Uniser, part biser, & 12–30 + ser	Homo	Para, meta-diff, & usually meta
American elm (Ulmus americana L.)	R	S	Orb or ang	1–7 Ser	Essentially homo	Para & meta-diff
Hackberry (Celtis occidentalis L.)	R	S	Orb or ang	1–13 Ser	Essentially het	Para & meta-diff
Red mulberry (Morus rubra L.)	R	S	Orb to ang	1–8 Ser	Homo to het	Para & meta-diff
Osage-orange (Maclura pomifera Schneid.)	R	S	Orb to ang	1–6 Ser	Essentially homo	Para, para-con, & ter
Cucumber magnolia (Magnolia acuminata L.)	D	S	Linear	1–5 Ser	Homo to het	Ter

(continued)

TABLE IV (*continued*)

Important Anatomical Features of Several American Hardwoods

Species	Pore arrangement	Vessel perforation	Vessel pitting	Ray width	Ray composition	Parenchyma arrangement
Southern magnolia (*Magnolia grandiflora* L.)	D	Sc	Linear	1–5 Ser	Homo to het	Ter
Yellow-poplar (*Liriodendron tulipifera* L.)	D	Sc	Oval or ang	1–5 Ser	Homo to het	Ter
Sweetgum (*Liquidambar styraciflua* L.)	D	Sc	Orb to linear	1–3 Ser	Homo to het	Para & meta-diff
Sycamore (*Platanus occidentalis* L.)	D	S & Sc	Oval to orb	1–14 Ser	Homo	Para & meta-diff
Black cherry (*Prunus serotina* Ehrh.)	SR	S	Oval to ang	1–6 Ser	Homo to het	Para, meta-diff, & ter
Black locust (*Robinia pseudoacacia* L.)	R	S	Orb to ang	1–7 Ser	Homo to het	Para, para-con, & ter
Sugar maple (*Acer saccharum* Marsh.)	D	S	Orb to ang	3–8 Ser & 1–3 Ser	Essentially homo	Ter, para, & meta-diff
Red maple (*Acer rubrum* L.)	D	S	Orb to ang	1–5 Ser	Essentially homo	Ter, para, & meta-diff
Yellow buckeye (*Aesculus octandra* Marsh.)	D	S	Orb to ang	Uniser	Homo to het	Ter & para
Basswood (*Tilia americana* L.)	D	S	Ang	1–6 Ser	Essentially homo	Ter & meta

Black tupelo (*Nyssa sylvatica* Marsh.)	D	Sc	Rect to linear	1-4 Ser	Het	Para & meta-diff
Water tupelo (*Nyssa aquatica* L.)	D	Sc	Rect to linear	1-4 Ser	Het	Para & meta-diff
White ash (*Fraxinus americana* L.)	R	S	Orb to short oval	1-3 Ser	Homo	Para, para-con, & ter
Black ash (*Fraxinus nigra* Marsh.)	R	S	Orb to short oval	1-3 Ser	Homo	Para & ter
Catalpa (*Catalpa speciosa* Ward.)	R	S	Orb	1-6 Ser	Homo to het	Para & para-zonate

[a] Bigtooth aspen (*P. grandidentata* Michx.) is similar.

[b] The important species of red oaks in the United States are northern red (*Q. rubra* L.), black (*Q. velutina* Lam.), Shumard (*Q. shumardii* Buckl.), scarlet (*Q. coccinea* Muench.), pin (*Q. palustris* Muench.), and willow (*Q. phellos* L.).

[c] The important species of white oaks in the United States are white (*Q. alba* L.), bur (*Q. macrocarpa* Michx.), overcup (*Q. lyrata* Walt.), post (*Q. stellata* Wangenh.), swamp chestnut (*Q. michauxii* Nutt.), chestnut (*Q. prinus* L.), and swamp white (*Q. bicolor* Willd.).

Symbols: D—diffuse-porous wood; R—ring-porous wood; SR—semi-ring-porous wood; S—simple perforation; Sc—scalariform perforation; Ang—angular pitting; El—elliptical pitting; Orb—orbicular pitting; Rect—rectangular pitting; Ser—seriate; Biser—biseriate; Uniser—uniseriate; Homo—homogeneous rays; Het—heterogeneous rays; Con—confluent parenchyma; Meta—metatracheal parenchyma; Meta-diff—diffuse metatracheal parenchyma; Para—paratracheal parenchyma; Para-zonate—paratracheal zonate parenchyma; Ter—terminal parenchyma.

a. Tracheids

Tracheids in the hardwoods are of two types: the vascular tracheid and the vasicentric tracheid. The vascular tracheid resembles the individual members of small vessels with which it is associated, but unlike the vessel member it does not have perforations. These cells occur in relatively few genera of American woods, e.g., *Ulmus* and *Celtis*. Spiral thickening is common in vascular tracheids.

The vasicentric tracheid resembles a short coniferous tracheid with lateral walls copiously pitted with bordered pits. This cell type does not occur in all species, but it does abound in the proximity of the large springwood vessels of certain ring-porous woods such as the oaks (*Quercus*) and chestnut (*Castanea*) where it shows evidence of distortion.

b. Fibers

The fibers in hardwoods are of two types: fiber tracheids and libriform fibers. Both types are typical fibrous cells but the pitting is considerably less pronounced than in the softwood tracheid. This is very likely because the fibers in hardwoods serve mainly as supporting cells, and the vessels conduct the liquids while the softwood tracheids must accomplish both functions. The two types of hardwood fibers are not readily distinguishable, but the libriform fibers possess simple pits which are usually smaller than the bordered pits of the fiber tracheids. Libriform fibers generally have a smaller diameter and a narrower lumen. Although this may make their walls appear thicker than those of fiber tracheids, it is not necessarily the case. Both fiber types may occur in the same wood and the transition may be so gradual that the separation is chiefly arbitrary.

c. Longitudinal Parenchyma

By far the most common type of longitudinal parenchyma in porous woods is strand parenchyma in which the short cells are arranged in rows along the grain of the wood. Such a row is formed through the further division of a longitudinal cell arising from a fusiform initial in the cambium. The strands of longitudinal parenchyma are much shorter in hardwoods than in conifers.

Longitudinal parenchyma is distributed in rather characteristic arrangements in the growth layer as seen in the transverse section. These arrangements are of sufficient uniformity to permit species identification in certain timbers. Three general types and several modifications of them are recognized. (*1*) metatracheal parenchyma is arranged in concentric layers and is not associated with the pores; (*2*) paratracheal parenchyma is grouped around the pores; and (*3*) terminal parenchyma is located at the margin of the growth ring. These terms are used in Table IV. Also used are the terms metatracheal-diffuse to indicate scattered arrangement rather than zonate and paratracheal-confluent to denote extensions from one pore to the next. Volumetrically, American hardwoods usually have less than 18% of their wood in longitudinal parenchyma, but in some tropical hardwoods the amount may surpass 50%.

d. Wood Rays

The wood rays of hardwoods are more variable in width and in height as compared with those of softwoods. Although some species have rays only one cell wide (Fig. 9C) (as do those that feature the softwoods), and others are characterized by rays two cells in width, most species possess multiseriate rays (Fig. 9B) (Table IV). Among American woods maximum ray width occurs in oaks where some rays are 30 or more cells wide (Fig. 6).

The rays of hardwoods are composed of parenchyma cells. These cells may be oriented with their long axis radial (procumbent) or longitudinal (upright). A ray composed wholly of one arrangement of cell, usually procumbent, is known as homogeneous, and one composed of cells oriented in both directions as heterogeneous. Certain hardwoods possess rays with transverse gum canals but no American species seem to be in this class.

e. Gum Canals

Certain tropical hardwoods possess normal gum canals either of the longitudinal or the radial type, but the two kinds rarely occur in the same wood. These gum canals are surrounded by epithelial cells. Longitudinal gum canals occur sporadically in sweetgum (*Liquidambar styraciflua* L.) but appear to be the result of injury. Normal gum canals are not found in American timbers.

D. VARIATION IN FIBER LENGTH

Fiber length data for various species are presented in accompanying tables. In Table II the average length, as well as the minimum and maximum lengths, for tracheids of several American softwoods are given. Average values listed range from 3.0 mm. for eastern white pine to 6.1 mm. for redwood. Undoubtedly, other species could be found with shorter or longer average lengths, but it is obvious that the softwood tracheids are relatively long. Actually the fusiform initials in the cambium from which these tracheids are derived are also relatively long because the increase in length of the tracheid after it begins as a daughter cell averages about 25%.

Table III gives average fiber lengths for several American hardwoods. These range in value from 0.8 mm. for sugar maple to 1.9 mm. for yellow-poplar. As these values are representative it is apparent that the hardwood fibers are in general a great deal shorter than the softwood tracheids. It is interesting that the fusiform initials of the hardwoods are so short that an increase of as much as three or four times may take place during formation of the relatively short fibers just noted. This is in remarkable contrast to the lengths and change that occur in the coniferous woods.

It is apparent from this discussion that the mean tracheid length of softwoods, and the mean fiber tracheid and libriform fiber lengths of hardwoods, varies among species. As might be expected the lengths vary among the individual stems of the same species in the same and in different timber stands. Factors such as suppression and spacing have been found to affect tracheid length.

Many studies during the last 80 years with various species of trees have shown that there is a gradual increase in mean fiber length from the initial growth layer outwards until a more or less constant length has been reached. Further, there is a variation with height in the tree which shows a steady increase from the stump, until at a fixed height the maximum length is reached and then the size decreases toward the tip.

Within the growth layer it has been reported that for those hardwoods with definite growth rings, the latewood fibers are considerably longer than the earlywood fibers. In various softwoods the summerwood tracheids are slightly longer than those of the springwood, although there is an occasional contradiction to this pattern.

E. CELL WALL STRUCTURE

Each of the countless millions of cells in wood has arisen from the division of specialized meristematic cells in the cambium. At the time of division a cambial or primary wall is laid down by the protoplast.

Each of these living cells possesses a limiting wall enclosing a cell cavity or lumen in which the vital protoplasm is located. Upon the death of the cell the protoplasm is either absorbed or it dries up.

The cells in wood are cemented together by intercellular substance or true middle lamella which, in mature wood, is predominantly ligneous in nature. The primary wall is basically cellulosic, although by the time the tracheid or fiber has matured it has become heavily lignified. The fibrils, or small physical units, of the primary wall are oriented in a random manner but tend toward the transverse direction.

After the formation of the primary wall by cell division, the cell grows and forces the cell wall to enlarge. During this step in the life history of the cell the first evidence of the formation of the secondary wall appears. Soon the secondary wall thickening is in process. One of the most important features of the primary wall is that its surface growth is not accompanied by a marked increase in thickness; the secondary wall, on the other hand, increases in thickness, but does not grow in area. The thickness of the primary wall is of the order of a few tenths of a micron.

The secondary wall is basically cellulosic, but on cell maturity it contains some of the lignin present in the wood, possibly 25% of the total amount. As a rule the secondary walls of tracheids and fibers consist of three layers that may vary in thickness, and that can be distinguished under the microscope because of differences in chemical composition and in the orientation of the cellulose microfibrils. It is worthwhile to draw attention to the fact that the middle (S_2) layer consists nearly always, and the outer (S_1) layer rather often, of thinner layers with identical or only slightly different orientation. The outer (S_1) and inner (S_3) layers, if one is present, are about the same thickness and are relatively thin. The structure is fibrillar and the fibrils are oriented at an angle approaching the perpendicular to the longitudinal fiber axis. The middle layer, whose thickness varies and actually is the controlling factor in the thickness of the cell wall, is also fibrillar in nature, with the fibrils aligned at a small angle with the fiber axis (6, 11, 12, and 17). (For further details, see Chapter 4, Section II-A.)

1. Pits

During the formation of the secondary wall, voids are left which form pits limited by the primary wall membrane. Usually a comple-

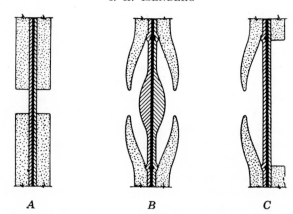

A   B   C

Fig. 11. Schematic drawings illustrating various types of pit-pairs. *A*—Simple pit-pair in sectional view (the intercellular substance is indicated by solid black, the primary wall by crosshatching). *B*—Bordered pit-pair in sectional view with the compound torus in the medial position. *C*—Half-bordered pit-pair in sectional view; there is no evidence of a compound torus. (Reproduced from Brown, Panshin, and Forsaith, *Textbook of Wood Technology*, Vol. I, 1949, by permission of McGraw-Hill Book Co., Inc.)

mentary pit is formed directly opposite on the other side of the inter-cellular substance in the adjacent cell, and a pit-pair is the result. These thin areas facilitate passage of materials in solution between the cells. It is unnecessary to discuss parts of the pit in detail, except to note that the pit cavity is the recess in the secondary wall, the opening of the pit into the cell lumen is called the pit aperture, and the pit membrane closes the pit at the outer end. Two general categories of pit structure are recognized: simple or bordered. In a simple pit, the pit cavity does not change very much in various distances into the secondary wall, whereas bordered pits possess cavities that narrow more or less abruptly near the cell lumen.

The pit-pairs which result from formation of complementary pits in contiguous cells may be of three kinds depending on the cell types involved: (*1*) simple, (*2*) bordered, or (*3*) half-bordered (Fig. 11).

IV. Some Physical Properties of Wood

A. SPECIFIC GRAVITY

Specific gravity of wood is a measure of the weight of wood substance contained in a unit volume of wood. It is the ratio, usually expressed decimally, between the ovendry weight of the wood and the weight of an equal volume of water at a specified temperature. Water at its greatest density (4°C.) is virtually a universal standard. Since the volume of wood changes below a critical point upon drying (the fiber saturation point; see Chapter 9, Section I-D), it is necessary to refer to the moisture condition when mentioning the specific gravity of wood. A common method of expressing specific gravity of wood is ovendry weight at green volume.

Some workers prefer to refer to this as the apparent specific gravity of wood, as the specific gravity of the cell wall substance itself is in the neighborhood of 1.53 as determined by the water-displacement method. The air space in the cell cavities of wood governs whether wood will float. If enough air space is replaced with water, even the lightest wood will sink. Of course, a wood which has a specific gravity of 1.00 or more will sink.

Most of the commercial woods in the United States have a specific gravity of 0.35 to 0.65 on a green volume basis. Because many wood users prefer to think of the weight of wood in their operations, average weights for some species of American woods are listed in Table V, expressed as ovendry weight in pounds per cubic foot of wood on a green volume basis. The lightest woods in the world are about one-sixth as heavy as cork and the heaviest nearly six times as weighty. The view that all tropical woods are heavy and hard is false, and actually the weight distribution is about the same as that among woods occurring in the temperate zones.

It should be noted that the frequency distribution of specific gravity within the wood of a particular species approaches a normal probability curve. Variation in specific gravity reflects differences in cell structure, especially cell-wall thickness, within a species. In general, most of this variation seems to be due to position in the tree, the age at which the wood is produced, and the structural design of the stem. Growth rate, whether due to position of the tree in the stand or to site, may have an effect under certain conditions, but its effect normally is much less than that of the above factors. Although much emphasis has been placed on growth rate, serious limitations on its usefulness as a measure of wood density are now recognized.

B. MOISTURE CONTENT

The affinity of wood for water is common knowledge. The affinity is very great when the wood is ovendry, and falls to zero when the

TABLE V

Density and Color of American Woods

Species	Density, lb./cu. ft., Oven-dry wt./ green vol.	Color of heartwood
Eastern white pine	21	Cream to light or reddish brown
Western white pine	22	Cream to light or reddish brown
Sugar pine	22	Light brown to pale red-brown
Red pine	27	Light red to orange or reddish brown
Jack pine	24	Reddish tinge
Longleaf pine	34	Shades of yellow and orange to reddish brown
Shortleaf pine	29	Shades of yellow and orange to reddish brown
Loblolly pine	29	Shades of yellow and orange to reddish brown
Slash pine	35	Shades of yellow and orange to reddish brown
Pond pine	31	Shades of yellow and orange to reddish brown
Virginia pine	26	Shades of yellow and orange to reddish brown
Ponderosa pine	24	Yellowish to light red- to orange-brown
Lodgepole pine	24	Light yellow to pale yellow-brown
Tamarack	31	Yellowish brown
Western larch	30	Russet or reddish brown
Black spruce	25	White to pale yellow
Red spruce	24	White to pale yellow
White spruce	22	White to pale yellow
Engelmann spruce	20	White to pale yellow
Sitka spruce	23	Light pinkish yellow to pale brown
Douglas-fir (coast form)	28	Yellowish to deep red
Douglas-fir (Rocky Mt. form)	25	Yellowish to deep red
Eastern hemlock	24	Buff to light brown
Western hemlock	24	Light yellowish brown
Mountain hemlock	27	Pale reddish brown
Balsam fir	21	Whitish to pale brown
Silver fir	22	Whitish to light brown

(continued)

TABLE V (*continued*)

Species	Density, lb./cu. ft., Oven-dry wt./ green vol.	Color of heartwood
Noble fir	22	Light yellowish brown
Grand fir	23	Whitish to light brown
White fir	22	Whitish to light brown
Alpine fir	19	Whitish to light brown
California red fir	23	Light yellowish brown
Redwood	24	Light red to deep reddish brown
Southern cypress	26	Yellowish to light or dark brown, reddish brown
Incense-cedar	22	Reddish to dull brown
Northern white-cedar	18	Straw brown
Western red-cedar	19	Reddish to dull brown
Port Orford cedar	25	Yellowish white to pale yellowish brown
Alaska cedar	26	Bright clear yellow
Atlantic white-cedar	19	Light brown with reddish tinge
Eastern red-cedar	27	Brick red to deep reddish brown
Butternut	22	Chestnut brown
Black walnut	32	Light to rich chocolate brown
Hickory	40	Reddish brown
Cottonwood	22	Grayish white to light grayish brown
Aspen	22	Whitish, creamy to light, grayish brown
Black willow	21	Pale reddish or grayish brown
Birch	34	Reddish brown
Red alder	23	Light brown with reddish tinge
Beech	39	Reddish brown
Chestnut	25	Grayish brown to brown
Tan oak	36	Dark reddish brown
Live oak	57	Dull brown to gray brown
Red oaks	32–38	Reddish brown
White oaks	36–40	Dark brown
American elm	29	Light brown to brown
Hackberry	31	Yellowish gray
Red mulberry	37	Russet brown
Osage-orange	47	Golden yellow
Cucumber magnolia	27	Greenish yellow

(*continued*)

48   I. H. ISENBERG

TABLE V (*continued*)

Density and Color of American Woods

Species	Density, lb./cu. ft., Oven-dry wt./ green vol.	Color of heartwood
Southern magnolia	29	Greenish yellow
Yellow-poplar	24	Greenish yellow
Sweetgum	27	Reddish brown
Sycamore	29	Dark or reddish brown
Black cherry	29	Light to dark reddish brown
Black locust	41	Golden brown
Sugar maple	35	Light reddish brown
Red maple	31	Light reddish brown
Buckeye	21	Creamy white to yellowish white
Basswood	20	Pale brown
Tupelo	29	Pale to moderately dark brownish gray
White ash	34	Light brown
Brown ash	28	Grayish brown to brown
Catalpa	24	Grayish brown

wood substance is saturated at about 30% moisture content (fiber saturation point). Above the fiber saturation point wood can still take up water by absorption or capillary action until the cell cavities are filled with liquid water ("free water"). Adsorbed moisture (taken up by the cell walls) affects all the properties of wood, whereas the free water does not. One commonly encountered phenomenon affected by water is the dimensional stability of wood. Dry wood swells in contact with water until the fiber saturation point is reached; the swelling is proportional to the cell-wall moisture content. (See also Chapter 9.)

As a general rule denser woods shrink more across the grain than do lighter ones. Heavier pieces also shrink more than lighter pieces of the same species. Hardwoods generally shrink more than softwoods. Species, however, do not always conform to the general pattern. For example, basswood is a light wood, but it shrinks considerably more than black cherry, a moderately heavy wood. The total longitudinal shrinkage of normal wood is much less than either the radial or tangential shrinkage, only 0.1 to 0.3% of the swollen wood dimension.

Moisture content of wood is commonly expressed as a percentage based on the ovendry weight, and thus a moisture content of more than 100% is not unusual. Since chemists, however, often base the moisture content on the original weight of material, the safest practice is to specify which basis is used.

C. WEIGHT OF WOOD

The weight of wood is dependent on the amount of wood substance present, on the weight of infiltration products in the wood, and on the weight of the included moisture. The amount of cell wall substance per unit of volume varies according to the size of the cells, the thickness of the cell walls, and the number of cells present of different types.

The infiltration products found in wood are both mineral and organic. The mineral types, which remain when wood has been ashed, usually total less than 1% of the weight of the wood. The organic extraneous components, however, may be scanty or copious. The compounds comprising the organic infiltrates include diverse materials which may be chemically complex. These include gums, resins, tannins, dyes, phenols, etc., some of which have considerable economic value. These compounds are discussed in some detail in Chapter 7.

The amount of moisture present in wood can vary to a considerable degree. As the moisture displaces air in the wood the moisture content greatly influences the weight of a given piece of wood.

V. Defects in Wood

A. NATURAL

The natural defects in wood are those abnormalities which are due to growth and environment. Natural defects include knots, reaction wood, compression failures, brashness, spiral and diagonal grain, shakes, frost injuries, pitch defects, bark pockets, mineral streaks, chemical stains, and floccosoids. Many of these defects are of limited occurrence or have such slight effect as to be of little direct interest to the chemist. It is worthwhile, however, to discuss in more detail knots, reaction wood, pitch defects, and bark pockets so that these defects may be recognized.

1. Knots

A knot is an embedded branch base. The branch has developed from a lateral bud and has a cambium layer which is continuous with that of the larger stem from which it was formed. The portion of the branch which is embedded while the branch is alive (and consequently, forms a continuous fiber connection between stem and branch), is termed an intergrown or tight knot. If the branch dies the cambium ceases to function and no new wood is formed on the branch. Wood continues to grow on the stem and while the branch remains attached it is encased by the growing trunk forming an encased or loose knot. If bark remains on the dead branch it is included around the knot. The presence of knots has an important bearing on the quality and value of wood. The encased knot and the fibers of the trunk are not continuous, and consequently, the distortion of the grain around the knot is less than for intergrown knots. The encased knot, if surrounded by bark and dirt, is more bothersome in pulp manufacture than the intergrown knot. Knots generally have a higher lignin content than the surrounding wood and are also more difficult to penetrate with liquor than normal wood. Hence, knots tend to be underpulped in the cooking process and appear in the screenings from chemical pulps.

2. Reaction Wood

Wood with more or less distinctive anatomical characters (formed typically in parts of leaning or crooked stems and in branches) which has somehow been disturbed, is designated as reaction wood. In conifers this abnormal wood develops on the underside of leaning trunks and branches; it is called compression wood. In the hardwoods the abnormal wood forms generally on the upperside of leaning trunks and branches and is known as tension wood.

a. Compression Wood

As observed in logs, compression wood is usually indicated by the presence of relatively wide eccentric growth rings which appear to contain an abnormally large proportion of summerwood at the point of greatest eccentricity (Fig. 12). This disproportionate amount of summerwood causes the tissue to be redder than normal, and to have rather a lifeless appearance. Typical compression wood is 15 to 40% heavier than normal wood; the summerwood tracheids tend to be

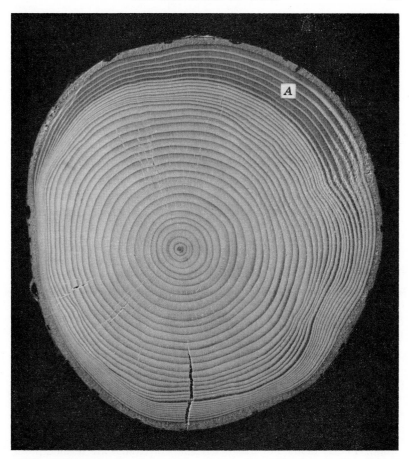

Fig. 12. Transverse section of balsam fir log (*Abies balsamea*), showing general appearance of compression wood (*A*). Magnification: 7/8X.

more circular than in normal wood; intercellular spaces are visible in the summerwood of compression wood and generally lacking in normal wood; the fibrils of the middle layer of the secondary wall of compression wood tracheids make a greater angle with the fiber axis than do those in normal wood; although the summerwood tracheid walls have about the same thickness, those of the springwood are slightly thicker than those of normal wood; the tracheids of compression wood are frequently shorter than comparable ones from normal wood; and the lignin content has been found to be higher and the cellulose content lower in compression wood as compared to normal wood.

b. Tension Wood

Tension wood is usually found on the upper side of a leaning stem of hardwood trees or on a branch, and is generally associated with eccentricity of growth, with the wider growth rings on the tension side. The amount of tension wood present varies considerably even where its presence is expected. It may be found as a dense, partially concentric band extending over several growth rings, or as scattered or irregularly grouped fibers. It is not nearly as definite as is compression wood of conifers.

The main features of tension wood are fibers with a characteristic thick, highly refractive, inner layer, often termed a gelatinous layer, which gives a cellulose reaction with various staining reagents; marked reduction in the size and number of vessels in comparison with neighboring normal wood; higher average density than normal wood; slightly lower lignin content and higher cellulose and pentosan content than normal wood; abnormally high longitudinal shrinkage; and a "wooliness" appearing on machined surfaces.

3. Pitch

A number of defects known as pitch, pitch streaks, and pitch pockets may occur in the softwoods which normally possess resin canals, although they may develop in any coniferous wood if the cambium is injured. These defects develop as a result of excessive resin accumulation so that resin-soaked patches or streaks are found in the wood. Poorly defined or irregularly shaped patches are termed pitch, sharply defined areas are called pitch streaks, and injury-caused cavities filled with resin are known as pitch pockets.

4. Bark Pockets

Bark pockets are small patches of bark that are embedded in wood owing to the death of a small area of the cambium and the closing over of new cambium from the surrounding areas.

B. FOREIGN ORGANISMS

Tremendous destruction results annually from the ravages of fungi and insects in the forest and the woodyard. Different species exhibit wide variation in their resistance to attack. Although no native wood is immune, a number of them possess superior durability (e.g., cedars, redwood, and southern cypress). Under favorable conditions for attack the sapwood of all native species is susceptible, but the heartwood is frequently less susceptible largely because of the presence of certain extraneous substances, such as essential oils, tannins, and phenolic components (see Chapter 3, Section II-C). Additional contributing factors for increased durability of the heartwood may be lower moisture content, poorer penetrability, blocking of the cell cavities by gums, resins, and protrusions such as tyloses (Fig. 6) in the hardwood vessels and tylosoids in the resin canals. Obviously, in many instances the proportion of heartwood in the logs may be important in controlling wood losses.

1. Fungi

Fungi inhabiting wood are separated into two groups: (1) wood-destroyers which attack and disintegrate cell walls to obtain the necessary nourishment, and (2) wood-stainers and molds which utilize food materials stored in cell cavities and have little, if any, disintegrating effect. The growth of the fungus depends on favorable temperature, oxygen, adequate moisture, and suitable food. Absence or elimination of any of these requirements prevents or greatly curtails the growth of the fungus. For example, underwater storage of pulpwood causes air in cell cavities to be replaced with water to the point of inhibition of fungal attack. Wood becomes infected either by means of spores produced during the fruiting stage of the fungus or by the direct migration of mycelium from a source of previous infection. The use of sanitary methods and good housekeeping in the woodyard is extremely helpful in controlling the spread of decay.

Wood-destroying fungi are conveniently divided into those producing white rots and those producing brown rots. The wood-staining fungi, as their name implies, tend to discolor wood, especially the sapwood.

2. Insects

In addition to the countless numbers of defoliators, weevils, beetles, and other insects which prey on living trees, there are many wood-boring insects that cause a large loss. Some of these wood-borers infest both living and dead trees, and also inflict damage on logs, unseasoned lumber, bolts of wood, and cordwood. Sapwood and heartwood are equally susceptible, as are softwood and hardwood species. The chief damage results from the larval borings with the resulting pinholes and grub holes. Spraying studies with benzene hexachloride (BHC) on stacked bolts indicate that losses can be minimized with proper precautions.

Termites (sometimes incorrectly called "white ants") can be bothersome in the woodyard and in buildings or other structures because of their use of wood for shelter and food.

3. Marine Borers

Marine wood borers are mollusks and crustaceans which live in salt and brackish water and inflict heavy damage on submerged wooden structures or parts exposed at low tide. The teredos or shipworms (species of *Teredo* and *Bankia*) and other forms of mollusk (*Martesia* sp.) as well as the genera of crustaceans (*Limnoria*, *Sphaeroma*, and *Chelura*) are of special concern to industries and other organizations that have seacoast docks and piers. Several tropical timbers such as greenheart (*Ocotea rodiaei* (Schomb.) Mez.) have heartwood which is unusually resistant to marine borer attacks. Teak (*Tectona grandis* L. f.) and jarrah (*Eucalyptus marginata* Sm.) are also of importance.

REFERENCES

1. Brown, H. P., A. J. Panshin, and C. C. Forsaith, *Textbook of Wood Technology*, Vol. 1, McGraw-Hill, New York, 1949; Vol. II, 1952.
2. Canada Department of Resources and Development, Forestry Branch, Forest Products Laboratories Division, *Canadian Woods, Their Properties and Uses*, Ottawa, 1951.
3. Desch, H. E., *Timber, Its Structure and Properties*, 3rd ed., Macmillan, London, 1953.
4. Eames, A. J., and L. H. MacDaniels, *An Introduction to Plant Anatomy*, 2nd ed., McGraw-Hill, New York, 1947.
5. Esau, K., *Plant Anatomy*, Wiley, New York, 1953.
6. Frey-Wyssling, A., *Die pflanzliche Zellwand*, Springer, Berlin, 1959.
7. Greguss, P., *Identification of Living Gymnosperms on the Basis of Xylotomy*, Akad. Kiado, Budapest, 1955.
8. International Association of Wood Anatomists (Committee on Nomenclature), "International Glossary of Terms Used in Wood Anatomy," *Trop. Woods*, **No. 107**, 1 (October, 1957).
9. Isenberg, I. H., *Pulpwoods of the United States and Canada*, 2nd ed., The Institute of Paper Chemistry, Appleton, Wis., 1951.
10. Jane, F. W., *The Structure of Wood.*, A. & C. Black, London, 1956.
11. Kallmes, O., *Tappi*, **43**, 143 (1960).

12. Kerr, T., and I. W. Bailey, "The Cambium and Its Derivative Tissues. X. Structure, Optical Properties and Chemical Composition of the so-called Middle Lamella," *J. Arnold Arboretum, (Harvard Univ.)*, **15**, 327 (1934).
13. Kollmann, F., *Technologie des Holzes und der Holzwerkstoffe*, Vol. I, 2nd ed., Springer, Berlin, 1951.
14. Little, E. L., *Check List of Native and Naturalized Trees of the United States (including Alaska)*, Agricultural Handbook No. 41, U. S. Government Printing Office, Washington, D.C., 1953.
15. Phillips, E. W. J., "The Identification of Coniferous Woods by Their Microscopic Structure," *J. Linnean Soc., London*, **52**, 259 (1941).
16. Record, S. J., *Identification of the Timbers of Temperate North America*, Wiley, New York. 1934.
17. Roelofsen, P. A., *The Plant Cell Wall*, Borntraeger, Berlin, 1959.
18. Tiemann, H. D., *Wood Technology, Constitution, Properties and Uses*, 3rd ed., Pitman, New York, 1951.
19. Trendelenburg, R., *Das Holz als Rohstoff*, edited by H. Mayer-Wegelin, 2nd ed., Carl Hanser Verlag, Munich, 1955.
20. U. S. Dep. Agr., Forest Serv., *Wood Handbook, Basic Information on Wood as a Material of Construction with Data for its Use in Design and Specification*, Agricultural Handbook No. 72, U. S. Government Printing Office, Washington, D.C., 1955.

CHAPTER 3

The Composition and Chemical
Reactions of Wood

B. L. BROWNING, *The Institute of Paper Chemistry, Appleton, Wisconsin*

I. Chemical Composition

The chemical composition of wood is complex. The woody tissue is made up of many chemical components which are distributed nonuniformly as the result of anatomical structure, and which are not present in simple physical admixture. Consequently, the chemical behavior of wood cannot be deduced in detail from the properties of the component substances.

The greater part of the wood substance is composed of materials of high molecular weight, and wood has been aptly described as an interpenetrating system of high polymers. The separation and isolation of these polymers without significant modification is a difficult and challenging undertaking, and much future research will be necessary to elucidate fully their nature and properties.

A. CLASSES OF COMPOUNDS PRESENT IN WOOD

The components that are present generally in woods can be classified chemically in the following way.

Carbohydrates. The carbohydrates are represented chiefly by the polysaccharides, which account for roughly three-fourths of the wood substance. They include cellulose, the group of cold water-insoluble noncellulosic polysaccharides commonly designated as hemicelluloses, starch, pectic substances, and water-soluble polysaccharides such as the arabinogalactans. Cellulose is the major wood component, and amounts to approximately one-half the wood weight. Sugars occur in the sap and in developing tissues, but are negligible components in mature woody tissues.

(The prefixes *arabo-* and *arabino-*, e.g., *arabo*galactan and *arabino*-galactan, are both used in the literature to designate the arabinose part in polysaccharides containing this sugar unit. The latter prefix is used in the text throughout this book.)

Phenolic substances. Aromatic materials characterized by the presence of phenolic hydroxyl groups (partly methylated) comprise a diverse group of substances which amount to about 20 to 30% of the woody tissue. The greater part of the phenolic substances comprise the system known as lignin, which is generally of high molecular weight and insoluble in common solvents. Some of the phenolic substances are soluble in water or organic solvents, e.g., the tannins, phlobaphenes, coloring matters, and lignans. Others can be removed by acid or alkaline hydrolysis of the wood.

Terpenes. The terpenes and terpenoid compounds include volatile constituents (e.g., in turpentine) and the resin acids. This group amounts to about 5% in the softwoods, but is very small or practically absent in the hardwoods.

Aliphatic acids. The higher fatty acids occur in all woods, mostly as their esters. Acetic acid combined as an ester with a portion of the polysaccharides is present to the extent of 1 to 5%.

Alcohols. These include aliphatic alcohols and sterols.

Proteins. Proteins represent a significant portion of the developing tissue, but in mature wood the amount as judged by the nitrogen content is only approximately 1%.

Inorganic constituents. The inorganic constituents amount to less than 0.5% in most woods of the temperate zone, although a few woods and particularly those of the tropics may have ash contents of 1 to 5% or more.

Many other organic substances occur in wood, usually in small amounts and in many instances in only a few genera or species. Among these may be included cyclic polyhydric alcohols (cyclitols), aldehydes, hydrocarbons, and alkaloids. Dibasic acids are of common occurrence, usually as their calcium salts (e.g., calcium carbonate and calcium oxalate).

B. SEPARATION OF WOOD COMPONENTS

Separation of the components of wood is required in analysis and for studies of the properties of the isolated fractions. No fully satisfactory methods have been devised, and much of wood chemistry is concerned with methods for isolation and purification of the component substances. The isolation of components according to a classification of the chemical classes listed above is generally not feasible.

The general composition of mature wood as established by conventional methods of examination is shown in idealized outline in Fig. 1. The application of chemical methods does not yet permit exact and complete separation of the components as indicated by a scheme of this kind.

The major portion of wood is composed of polysaccharides and lignin. These constitute the *cell wall* components and, together with the smaller quantity of intercellular material, they form the basis of the physical structure of wood.

It is customary to differentiate the cell wall components from the *extraneous* components (see Chapter 7), which are not considered an essential structural part of wood. The extraneous components include

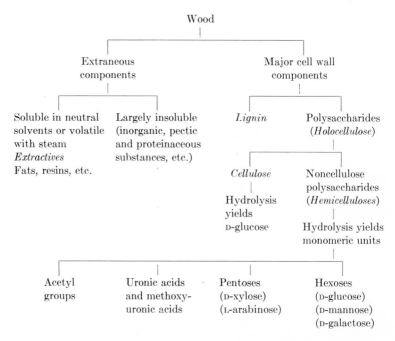

Fig. 1. Idealized outline of wood components.

the substances that are soluble in neutral organic solvents and in cold water, or are volatile with steam and are called the *extractives* (121). The wood from which the extractives have been removed is designated *extractive-free* wood. The distinction between the extractives and cell wall material is difficult to define experimentally in the case of some borderline materials.

Materials such as proteins, pectic substances, and inorganic compounds are minor constituents in mature wood. They are partially or wholly insoluble in solvents used to remove the extractives. It is convenient to include them among the extraneous components, although it should be pointed out that they participate actively in the physiological activity of the developing tissue and remain as a part of the wood structure in the mature tissue.

The extractive-free wood is composed of lignin and polysaccharides. The polysaccharides include cellulose (see Chapter 4), which ideally yields only D-glucose on hydrolysis, and the noncellulose polysaccharides which yield chiefly sugars other than D-glucose.

The complete hydrolysis by acids of wood polysaccharides yields the sugars D-glucose, D-mannose, D-galactose, D-xylose, and L-arabinose, and in some woods a small amount of L-rhamnose. Separation of the sugars produced by hydrolysis can be effected in a reasonably satisfactory manner by the methods of paper chromatography.

In addition to sugar units, the noncellulose polysaccharides contain uronic acid (6-hexuronic acid) and monomethyl uronic acid units as characteristic constituents. Hydrolysis to the monomeric uronic acids is difficult to achieve without a considerable destruction of the acids. After hydrolysis, some of the uronic acid units remain as aldobiouronic or other acids, in which the uronic anhydride moiety is combined with one or more sugar units (usually D-xylose). The total content of uronic acid units (uronic anhydride) can be determined by the amount of carbon dioxide produced upon decarboxylation by boiling 12% hydrochloric acid.

The sugars are combined as polymers with the loss of one molecule of water per sugar molecule, for the greater part as long linear chains. (It is proper to speak of a polysaccharide as being composed of sugar units; e.g., cellulose is made up of D-glucose units and yields D-glucose on hydrolysis. However, statement that a polysaccharide contains certain sugars is not uncommon. In such cases, it should be understood that the polysaccharide *does not contain* the simple sugars, but that these sugars are produced upon hydrolysis.)

The polysaccharide chains can be separated to some degree into fractions having fairly well defined sugar ratios, e.g., arabinogalactan, glucomannan, etc. Homopolymers, i.e., chains yielding only one kind of sugar on hydrolysis, are (except for cellulose) uncommon in wood, although they are found frequently in other plant materials. The separation and isolation of the polysaccharide polymers is difficult and cannot be accomplished quantitatively.

The polysaccharide fraction of wood is isolated as a preparation from extractive-free wood by removal of the lignin through some appropriate process of delignification. When the lignin is removed with minimal loss of polysaccharides, the product is called *holocellulose* (160). Common laboratory procedures for isolation of holocellulose are based on (*1*) alternate chlorination and extraction with an alcoholic solution of an organic base such as monoethanolamine (191) or (*2*) treatment with an acidified aqueous solution of sodium chlorite to yield *chlorite holocellulose* (100,198). The chlorine-monoethanolamine procedure is preferred for quantitative isolation of holocellulose.

Ideally, an isolation of holocellulose should accomplish a complete removal of lignin without loss of polysaccharides or chemical attack on the polysaccharidic components. This is difficult to achieve experimentally, and in practice no procedure has been devised which is capable of removing the lignin completely without some attack on the polysaccharides. Nevertheless, procedures for the isolation of holocelluloses have proved indispensable in many avenues of investigative work.

The noncellulose polysaccharides are largely soluble in alkalies, and the materials dissolved have been called the *hemicelluloses* (169) (see Chapter 5). Experimentally, the hemicelluloses are removed from polysaccharide preparations such as holocellulose by extraction with aqueous solutions of alkalies, e.g., 18% sodium hydroxide solution. The insoluble residue is called *alpha-cellulose*. It is not possible to dissolve all materials which yield sugars other than D-glucose. The tenacious retention of nonglucose sugar units by the cellulose which remains insoluble after the alkaline extraction has led to some disagreement as to the true nature of "wood cellulose," and some workers have preferred to distinguish between wood cellulose and cotton cellulose (cf. 199).

The acetyl groups (CH_3CO) are combined as esters of acetic acid with the noncellulose polysaccharides, and are removed as acetic acid by acid or alkaline hydrolysis. They remain in holocellulose preparations, but preparations such as alpha-cellulose that have been subjected to alkaline treatment during isolation no longer contain acetyl groups.

Lignin cannot be isolated as a pure substance of definite composition. It is known to be primarily aromatic in nature, and for the greater part its structure appears to be based on phenylpropane (C_6C_3) units (see Chapter 6). Lignin is insoluble in acids under conditions which effect hydrolysis of the polysaccharides, and the usual methods for direct determination of lignin (e.g., treatment with sulfuric acid according to the Klason method) are based on weighing the insoluble lignin remaining after the acid hydrolysis. On the other hand, lignin is more easily solubilized by oxidizing agents than are the polysaccharides, and many processes of delignification are based on oxidative removal of the lignin.

Whether or not lignin and the polysaccharides are linked chemically, by some kind of lignin-carbohydrate bonds, has remained an unanswered question for many years. Recent evidence has been adduced to support the view that a portion of the noncellulose polysaccharides are bound chemically to at least a part of the lignin (19,129,139) (see also Chapter 5, Section VI, Chapter 6, Section II-C, and Chapter 10, Section II-A-3).

C. ANALYSES OF WOOD

1. Composition of the Whole Wood

Wood is markedly nonuniform in composition. The major gross differences in composition can be assigned to variations among species, although considerable variability within species arises because of genetic factors and ecological conditions of growth. Within a single tree, the composition varies with height in the stem and the distance from the pith. The compositions of twigs and rootwood differ from those of the stem. Moreover, characteristic differences are observed in sapwood and heartwood, springwood and summerwood, and, on a microscopic scale, within the individual cells. All these considerations emphasize the nonuniformity of wood and attest the care which must be taken in assessing statements of composition.

Many analyses of wood have been reported (e.g., ref. 39). Although these analyses have served to delineate the major constituents of wood, it should be pointed out that many analytical methods represent empirical procedures for isolation of groups of related substances rather than of a single molecular species. Because of this, analyses of wood frequently lack the precision and specificity expected in methods of quantitative analysis.

The most rigorous evaluation of analytical data is represented by *summative analyses*, in which the analyst aims to account for all constituents present by a summation that ideally should total 100% if no constituents have been overlooked and there is no overlapping.

Summations may be taken over groups of constituents defined by proximate analysis, or over all the individual components that are amenable to isolation or analysis.

The simplest summative analysis is that in which the extractives are isolated, as is the extractive-free wood from which the extractives have been removed. The summation of these two proximate fractions usually totals very closely to 100%. Possible errors may arise from loss of volatile constituents that are not included in either fraction, and from the retention of organic solvents by the wood which cannot be completely removed even by prolonged ovendrying at 100°C. As much as 1 to 2% of a polar organic solvent such as ethyl alcohol may be retained by the wood, and removal can be effected only by displacement with water (138,197) (cf. also Chapter 9, Section II-B).

The summative analysis may be extended to include the cell wall components—holocellulose and lignin. A summation that includes extractives, lignin, holocellulose, and ash ideally accounts for all constituents of wood. Many workers prefer to use pre-extracted (extractive-free) wood and to report summative analyses on the extractive-free basis.

Disregarding the ash content, which is justifiable for most woods of the temperate zone having low ash contents, the sum of holocellulose and lignin should equal 100% of the extractive-free wood. Indeed, such summations have been used in establishing the validity of both the holocellulose and lignin procedures. Summations of ash, extractives, holocellulose, and lignin for several woods have been found to total 99.3 to 101.1% (5,65).

However, further studies of analytical separations have shown that neither the holocellulose nor the lignin procedure is beyond criticism, and it appears that the excellence of many summations is fortuitous and due to the approximate balancing of experimental errors. It has been found that losses of polysaccharides always occur in the isolation of holocellulose by either the chlorine–monoethanolamine or the chlorite method (93,103,181,186) and, on the other hand, residual contents of ash, nitrogen, chlorine, and degradation products of lignin are not negligible (11,38,181). In the determination of lignin, there is no assurance that the isolated lignin exactly represents in quantity the *protolignin*, i.e., the lignin as it exists in wood.

A breakdown of components of the holocellulose leads to further summations. On treatment of the cellulose preparation with alkaline solutions, the hemicelluloses are largely dissolved and can be recovered by acidification of the alkaline solution and addition of ethyl alcohol. The alkali-resistant cellulose, or alpha-cellulose, is isolated and weighed. Table I and Summation A of Tables II and III illustrate summative analyses arrived at in this way.

A summation that includes alpha-cellulose and constituents of the hemicelluloses (xylan, mannan, and uronic anhydride) is illustrated by Summation B in Tables II and III. The xylan, mannan, and uronic anhydride are determined on the original wood, and the isolated alpha-cellulose is corrected for the small quantities of these components that remain with it.

The figure for CH_2 is found by subtracting from the total content of methoxyl groups (OCH_3) in the wood the content of these groups found by analysis in the isolated lignin. The difference is presumed to represent the methoxyl groups combined with uronic acids as ethers, and is calculated as the equivalent CH_2 which represents the increment in weight when a hydroxyl group is methylated.

With the advent of improved methods for separation of sugars by chromatographic procedures, it has become possible to express the composition of the carbohydrate fraction of wood in terms of component sugars. This approach avoids any assumption as to the association of the sugar units in polymers that are made up of more than one kind of sugar unit, and permits a simple statement of carbohydrate composition. Of necessity, any information concerning the polymer composition is lost, and just such information is necessary in understanding many aspects of wood composition. The advantage of analysis for sugars is, of course, retained by analysis of fractions separated by alkaline extraction or by other processes.

An example of summative analysis in which component sugar polymers are included is given in Table IV. It should be understood that the reported polymers, such as glucan and xylan, represent only a calculation of the sugars obtained after total hydrolysis to the corresponding value for the anhydro sugar basis, and implies no statement concerning the mode of linkage of these units into polysaccharide chains. Also, it should be noted that the data for sugar composition in Table IV represent analytical values proportionally adjusted so that the sum of sugars equals 100% less the percentages of nonsugar constituents.

TABLE I

Summative Analysis of Canadian Woods (46) (all values in per cent)

Species	Soluble in alcohol–benzene	Soluble in hot water[a]	Ash	Acetyl	Lignin	Alpha-cellulose	Hemi-celluloses	Total
Red pine (Pinus resinosa)	9.7	1.8	0.2	1.9	23.4	47.8	15.1	99.9
Tamarack (Larix lariciana)	3.1	7.9	0.3	1.6	24.8	49.5	13.3	100.5
Basswood (Tilia americana)	6.3	1.3	0.6	5.9	17.2	45.0	22.9	99.2
White elm (Ulmus americana)	2.2	1.3	1.1	5.0	23.4	47.2	18.5	98.7
Black ash (Fraxinus nigra)	3.4	1.3	0.7	5.3	18.6	47.4	21.2	97.9
Yellow birch (Betula lutea)	3.4	0.7	0.3	5.4	18.8	42.6	26.6	97.8
Beech (Fagus grandifolia)	2.0	0.7	0.4	5.3	22.2	43.6	23.6	97.8
Sugar maple (Acer saccharum)	2.7	1.0	0.4	4.6	21.1	46.8	22.2	98.8

[a] After extraction with alcohol–benzene.

TABLE II

Summative Analysis of Woods (26,201,202) (per cent of extractive-free dry wood)

Constituent	Douglas-fir	Western hemlock	Loblolly pine	Black spruce	Western red-cedar	Monterey pine	Southern red oak	Black tupelo
Ash	0.3	0.5	0.3	0.4	0.3	0.2	0.2	0.7
Acetyl	0.6	1.2	1.1	1.1	0.5	1.4	3.3	3.7
Lignin	28.4	30.4	29.5	28.0	32.5	26.5	25.2	25.8
Summation A								
Alpha-cellulose	57.2	51.6	55.0	51.5	52.7	54.8	45.7	46.5
Hemicellulose	14.1	15.5	15.3	17.4	14.6	16.4	23.3	23.4
Total[a]	100.6	99.2	101.2	98.4	100.6	99.3	97.7	100.1
Summation B								
Alpha-cellulose[b]	48.3	44.5	46.6	45.6	47.5	45.3	43.7	45.6
Mannan[c]	5.4	4.1	4.7	8.0	5.1	11.7	20.0	17.1
Xylan	6.2	7.3	10.1	10.5	8.1	9.3	4.5	4.7
Uronic anhydride	2.8	5.0	3.8	4.1	4.2	3.4	0.6	0.9
CH_2[d]	0	0.2	0.2	0.2	0.2	0.1		
Total[a]	92.0	93.2	96.3	97.9	98.4	97.9	97.5	98.5

[a] Including ash, acetyl, and lignin.

[b] Corrected for mannan, xylan, and uronic anhydride.

[c] By the phenylhydrazine method; the figures are probably low.

[d] Calculated from methoxyl not in lignin.

TABLE III

Summative Analysis of Tropical Woods (203) (per cent of unextracted dry wood)

Constituent	*Couratari pulchra* (tauary)	*Eschweilera sagotiana* (kakeralli)	*Dicorynia paraensis* (angelique)	*Tectona grandis* (teak)	*Swietenia macrophylla* (mahogany)	*Ocotea rodiaei* (greenheart)
Total extractives[a]	5.3	5.8	5.4	15.1	16.3	9.5
Ash	0.8	0.6	0.6	1.4	0.6	0.2
Acetyl	1.1	1.4	1.1	1.1	1.1	1.1
Lignin	31.0	29.1	31.6	30.5	24.1	31.2
Summation A						
Alpha-cellulose	47.3	49.0	45.2	37.0	40.2	44.7
Hemicellulose	14.3	13.4	14.7	12.2	16.0	13.2
Total[d]	99.8	99.3	98.6	97.3	98.3	99.9
Summation B						
Alpha-cellulose[b]	45.1	46.4	42.6	33.9	37.2	38.5
Mannan	1.2	0.2	0.3	1.4	1.4	4.9
Xylan	12.5	13.2	12.0	11.7	10.9	10.0
Uronic anhydride	3.8	4.1	4.2	3.8	4.5	3.9
CH_2[c]	0.2	0.3	0.3	0.1	0.5	0.4
Total[d]	101.0	101.1	98.1	99.0	96.6	99.7

[a] Soluble in ether (or chloroform), 50% alcohol, acetone, and water (at 80°C).
[b] Corrected for ash, lignin, mannan, xylan, and uronic anhydride.
[c] Calculated from methoxyl not in lignin.
[d] Including extractives, ash, acetyl, and lignin.

2. Comparison of Softwoods and Hardwoods

Although the composition in either the softwood or hardwood classes shows considerable variation among species, certain characteristic differences serve to differentiate the softwoods as a group from the hardwoods (cf. 39).

In woods of the temperate zones, the extractives soluble in organic solvents are consistently higher in the softwoods. Among the extractives, the resin acids constitute a significant fraction in the softwoods, whereas their presence has not been shown or they are very minor constituents in the hardwoods. The volatile constituents are small in most hardwoods and in many softwoods, but they occur in some softwoods in considerable quantities.

In the carbohydrate portion the most striking difference is in the mannan and xylan fractions. The mannan content of the softwoods is in the range of 10 to 15%, but it rarely exceeds 2 to 3% in hardwoods. On the other hand, the xylan content of hardwoods is from 12 to 20% or even higher, whereas in softwoods the xylan content rarely exceeds 10%.

The lignin content varies from about 23 to 33% in the softwoods and from about 16 to 25% in the hardwoods. Because hardwood lignins have a higher content of methoxyl groups than the lignins of the softwoods, the methoxyl content of the whole wood does not reflect the greater content of lignin in the softwoods.

3. Tropical Woods

Hardwoods of the tropics differ in many characteristics from those of the temperate zone. The amounts of extractives and ash are relatively higher and the acetyl contents lower in the tropical woods. The lignin content is in the range of softwoods rather than the temperate zone hardwoods (204). Some recent data are given in Table V (cf. 166,204).

4. Comparison of Sapwood and Heartwood

The compositional differences in sapwood and heartwood have been investigated extensively (5,44,65,136,158). In the softwoods, the heartwood generally contains more extractives and less lignin and cellulose than the sapwood, whereas the heartwood and sapwood of the hardwoods do not show consistent differences. The acetyl content is consistently higher in the sapwood than in the heartwood in both

TABLE IV

Composition of North American Woods (per cent of extractive-free wood)

Species	Glucan	Mannan	Galactan	Xylan	Arabinan	Uronic anhydride	Acetyl	Lignin	Ash
Hardwoods									
Trembling aspen (*Populus tremuloides*)	57.3	2.3	0.8	16.0	0.4	3.3	3.4	16.3	0.2
Beech (*Fagus grandifolia*)	47.5	2.1	1.2	17.5	0.5	4.8	3.9	22.1	0.4
White birch (*Betula papyrifera*)	44.7	1.5	0.6	24.6	0.5	4.6	4.4	18.9	0.2
Yellow birch (*Betula lutea*)	46.7	3.6	0.9	20.1	0.6	4.2	3.3	21.3	0.3
Red maple (*Acer rubrum*)	46.6	3.5	0.6	17.3	0.5	3.5	3.8	24.0	0.2
Sugar maple (*Acer saccharum*)	51.7	2.3	< 0.1	14.8	0.8	4.4	2.9	22.7	0.3
Sweetgum[a] (*Liquidambar styraciflua*)	39.4	3.1	0.8	17.5	0.3			23.7	0.2
White elm (*Ulmus americana*)	53.2	2.4	0.9	11.5	0.6	3.6	3.9	23.6	0.3
Southern red oak[a] (*Quercus falcata*)	40.6	2.0	1.2	19.2	0.4	4.5	3.3	23.9	0.8

Softwoods

Balsam fir (*Abies balsamea*)	46.8	12.4	1.0	4.8	0.5	3.4	1.5	29.4	0.2
Eastern white-cedar (*Thuja occidentalis*)	45.2	8.3	1.5	7.5	1.3	4.2	1.1	30.7	0.2
Eastern hemlock (*Tsuga canadensis*)	45.3	11.2	1.2	4.0	0.6	3.3	1.7	32.5	0.2
Jack pine (*Pinus banksiana*)	45.6	10.6	1.4	7.1	1.4	3.9	1.2	28.6	0.2
White pine (*Pinus strobus*)	44.5	10.6	2.5	6.3	1.2	4.0	1.3	29.3	0.2
Loblolly pine[a] (*Pinus taeda*)	45.0	11.2	2.3	6.8	1.7	3.8	1.1	27.7	0.3
Douglas-fir[a] (*Pseudotsuga taxifolia*)	43.5	10.8	4.7	2.8	2.7	2.8	0.8	31.5	0.4
Black spruce[a] (*Picea mariana*)	47.9	10.5	[b]	8.0	[b]	4.1	1.1	28.0	0.4
White spruce (*Picea glauca*)	46.5	11.6	1.2	6.8	1.6	3.6	1.3	27.1	0.3
Tamarack (*Larix laricina*)	46.1	13.1	2.3	4.3	1.0	2.9	1.5	28.6	0.2

a Data supplied through the courtesy of the Forest Products Laboratory; others from reference 185.
b Galactan included with glucan, and arabinan included with mannan.

TABLE V

Composition of Some Woods from the Amazon Basin (123) (all values in per cent)

Species	Alcohol–benzene extract	Hot water extract	Ash	Lignin[a]	Pentosans[a]	Holocel-lulose[a]	Alpha-cellulose
Pau mulato (*Qualea dinizii*)	2.4	3.0	0.8	28.3	13.9	69.3	48.3
Abiurara (*Lucuma dissepala*)	1.8	2.1	1.0	24.8	16.8	73.8	47.6
Breu branco (*Protium heptaphyllum*)	2.1	4.8	0.6	27.4	17.2	70.1	48.7
Imbauba (*Crecropia juranyana*)	3.2	6.2	0.8	24.8	17.4	69.3	49.2

[a] On extractive-free wood.

softwoods and hardwoods (200). The compounds that characterize the extractives of a species often are concentrated by deposition in the heartwood, with smaller amounts in the sapwood (cf. 59).

5. Comparison of Springwood and Summerwood

Summerwood is quite consistently higher in cellulose and lower in lignin than the springwood (13,159). The cell walls, which are largely cellulose, are thicker in summerwood than in springwood and the proportion of lignin contributed by the middle lamella is correspondingly less.

6. Composition of Abnormal Wood Growths

Reaction wood (cf. Chapter 2, Section V-A-2) differs from normal wood in both composition and physical properties. Compression wood contains more lignin and less cellulose than normal wood (51, 80,106,108). The lignin appears to have a lower methoxyl content than the lignin of normal wood (80,106). It has been shown that the formation of compression wood in pine takes place under experimental conditions in stems subjected to a centrifugal force approximating gravity (172).

Tension wood of deciduous trees contains less pentosans and lignin and more cellulose than normal wood (45,101,110,171). In *Eucalyptus goniocalyx*, the galactose yield after hydrolysis was much higher than in normal wood (171), and the properties of the lignin differed from those of normal wood lignin (171). The "opposite wood" (the opposite side of the branch or stem) in contrast to tension wood, contained more pentosans and lignin, and less cellulose than did the wood outside the zones of abnormal growth (20).

Application of microspectrographic methods indicated that the secondary cell wall in both the tension wood of European (red) beech and the compression wood of spruce contain very small amounts of lignin (122). Microscopic observations suggest that tension wood fibers are characterized by a lignin-free "gelatinous layer" as a lining of the lumen (107). The "gelatinous layer" has been shown to be highly crystalline (52,194).

7. Ultimate Analysis

The greater part of wood is composed of carbon, hydrogen, and oxygen. Nitrogen is present to the extent of about 0.2% from proteinaceous residues originating during the early growth of the cells.

If the wood contains alkaloids, the nitrogen content may be significantly higher. Some typical values for ultimate analysis of woods are given in Table VI.

TABLE VI

Ultimate Analysis of Woods[a] (190) (all values in per cent)

Constituent	Larch	Pine	Spruce	Oak	Beech
Carbon	49.6	50.2	50.0	49.2	48.9
Hydrogen	5.8	6.1	6.0	5.8	5.9
Nitrogen	0.2	0.2	0.2	0.4	0.2
Oxygen	44.2	43.4	43.5	44.2	44.5
Ash	0.2	0.2	0.3	0.4	0.5

[a] Sapwood.

II. The Chemical Reactions of Wood

A. THE ACTION OF CHEMICALS ON WOOD

Wood is remarkably resistant toward the action of solvents and chemicals. No solvent is known which is capable of dissolving wood without concomitant chemical attack. In part, this resistance may be attributed to the complex structure of associated high polymers, as the application of a solvent or chemical reagent which is capable of effecting dissolution of one of the components may be without effect on others. This selectivity is illustrated by the difference in behavior of the lignin and carbohydrate systems, which is evidenced in the many (and oftentimes fortunate) ways by which one of these types of components can be removed while leaving the other largely intact.

1. The Action of Neutral Solvents

Wood is essentially unattacked at ordinary temperature by neutral organic solvents and by cold water, which dissolve only those constituents of the wood that are classed among the extractives. The rate of solution depends largely on diffusion processes which govern the transfer of soluble materials from the solid wood particles to the solvent. Extraction is relatively rapid if the wood is finely divided, and the amount of material dissolved does not increase significantly upon prolonged contact with fresh portions of the solvent.

The amount of material dissolved by water increases significantly

as the temperature is increased. This is not attributed to a temperature coefficient of solubility (183), as the amount of solvent normally
used is sufficient in quantity to insure that saturation is not reached
except in the case of a few borderline materials having very slight
solubility.

A more important consideration is the increase in acidity caused by
hydrolysis of the acetyl groups to acetic acid in the presence of hot
water. The pH of the extract may be as low as 3.5 to 4.5. Thus, the
effect is that of extraction with a weakly acid solution, and hydrolysis
products of polysaccharides and lignin appear in the solution.

In contrast to the action of cold water, the amount of material
dissolved increases continuously as the time of extraction with hot
water is prolonged. In extraction of jack pine wood (74) the amount
of material dissolved by cold water was only about 1%, and little
additional material was removed when the extraction time was extended to 72 hours. On the other hand, the amount soluble in boiling
water was 2% after 3 hours and increased to 28% after 200 hours.

A 50-day aqueous extraction at 100°C. of coniferous groundwood
reduced the carbohydrates from 61.9 to 49.8%, and the lignin content
from 28.7 to 25.3% (1). Treatment of wood with cold 28.5% hydrochloric acid caused comparable losses in 10 hours. Treatment of oak
wood sawdust with boiling water dissolved 32.0% after 500 hours and
65.6% after 1000 hours (206). The pentosans were attacked most
rapidly. Because hot water dissolves both carbohydrates and lignin,
the material removed has been called "soluble wood" (115). At least
a portion of the soluble materials appears to be present as a lignin–
carbohydrate complex (116).

At higher temperatures (ca. 150 to 175°C.) the increase in solubility
with time of treatment is still more pronounced, and 20 to 30% of the
wood is dissolved in a few hours. Aqueous hydrolysis of black gum
wood at 160°C. (120 minutes) removed 28.4% of the wood weight and
reduced the hemicellulose content by nearly 70% (17). The final pH
was 3.6. The effect of water, or of dilute acids, at temperatures in the
range of 150 to 170°C. is utilized in *prehydrolysis*, which is applied as
an initial step in the commercial pulping of woods (particularly hardwoods), when it is desired to reduce the content of hemicelluloses in
the resultant wood pulp (see also Chapter 10, Section V-E).

The larger part of the dissolved materials consists of polysaccharides, but a considerable amount of aromatic material appears in the
extract, and this has its origin in substances which would appear in

the lignin by conventional means of examination of the untreated wood. The action of water at 150 to 175°C. leads to the formation of hydrolysis or degradation products such as sugars, uronic acids, furfural, and nonvolatile organic acids from the carbohydrates (102, 154,177). Aromatic compounds such as coniferyl aldehyde, vanillin, vanillic acid, and other aldehydes, ketones, and acids appear as degradation products of lignin (102). The simple aromatic compounds can be extracted from the aqueous phase with ether and be identified after chromatographic separations (71,180). A part of the dissolved lignin can be rendered insoluble by a secondary hydrolysis at 100°C with 2% sulfuric acid (177).

Cellulose is more resistant than other wood components, but it is not wholly immune to attack. When present alone, it is hydrolyzed and partially dissolved by water at temperatures in the range of 100 to 225°C., at a rate which depends on the hydrogen ion concentration even at the low acidities existing between pH 5 and 8 (143).

Further increases in temperature, from about 170° up to 200°C., lead to a progressively more severe action of water on wood. The amount of wood that becomes soluble increases rapidly, and the carbohydrates are more strongly attacked (163). The condensation of lignin is shown by the decreased yield of vanillin on nitrobenzene oxidation (116). The pentosans are partially converted to furfural, which condenses with the lignin to alter the character of the remaining wood (163). At the same time, the insoluble lignin is changed so that it becomes partially soluble in solvents such as dioxane and alcohol.

The effect of water is utilized in the formation of wood or wood fiber boards in which temperatures up to 200°C. or higher are reached during formation. The hydrolysis or degradation products of carbohydrates and lignin that appear in the water-soluble portion can react further, or partially condense to yield substances contributing to the properties of the product (109,163,164). In the Asplund process, wood chips are mechanically defiberized in the presence of moisture at 160 to 180°C. (130). The combination of mechanical action, partial solubility of wood constituents in water, and secondary reactions at higher temperatures are essential features of the process. In the Masonite process wood chips are subjected to steam at temperatures up to 280°C., and at pressures up to 1000 pounds per square inch for times of 10 seconds or less. Soluble products are formed from the wood, and some of these are combined and condensed by secondary reactions to yield wood fiber products of characteristic and valuable properties (23). At high temperatures and in the presence of water the lignin becomes softened and partially plasticized. The separation of fibers by mechanical action while the lignin is in this condition is aided, and the binding or bonding capacity of the product when subjected to heat and pressure is enhanced.

The action of neutral organic solvents is not greatly increased on raising the temperature to ca. 100°C., but reaction of alcohols with the lignin occurs at ca. 150 to 170°C. and a considerable portion of the lignin dissolves. Alcohol–water mixtures dissolve much of the lignin from hardwoods and a portion of the lignin from softwoods at elevated temperatures (10). The action of alcohols and phenols is enhanced by the presence of catalysts (e.g., mineral acids), and at elevated temperatures dissolution of the major portion of the lignin occurs. The treatment of wood with ethanol–hydrochloric acid results in entrance of ethyl groups into the lignin (cf. Chapter 6, Section IV-B).

Treatment of *Eucalyptus regnans* with methanol at 150°C. extracted lignin without addition of an acid catalyst, but the formation of volatile esters indicated liberation of acid from the wood (22). Sprucewood heated at 150°C. with methanol or ethanol in the absence of mineral acids yielded alkylated lignins (21).

2. The Action of Acids

Wood exhibits considerable resistance to hydrolysis by dilute acids at ordinary temperature, and tanks constructed of wood give satisfactory service in contact with dilute aqueous solutions of mineral acids. More concentrated acids, e.g., 60% sulfuric acid or 37% hydrochloric acid attack wood rapidly with hydrolysis of the polysaccharides. At higher temperatures (ca. 100°C.) even dilute mineral acids (e.g., 2 to 3% sulfuric or hydrochloric acids) produce rapid hydrolysis of a major portion of the hemicelluloses. The cellulose is attacked more slowly, presumably because of its partly crystalline nature.

The hydrolysis of wood in the laboratory for production of sugars or isolation of lignin employs hydrolyzing concentrations of mineral acids (e.g., 72% sulfuric, 41 to 42% hydrochloric, or 85% phosphoric acid). The polysaccharides are hydrolyzed rapidly, and subsequent dilution and heating of the solution results in formation of the simple sugars in yields of 90 to 95% of the theoretical amount. Some loss of sugars during hydrolysis occurs because of reversion reactions (14,

182) and degradation to furan-type compounds. Lignin is left as an insoluble residue after the hydrolysis, but it is altered in character by the acid treatment.

The maximum yield of reducing sugars depends upon the time, temperature, and acid concentration during the treatment with strong acid, and upon these same factors during the treatment with the weaker acid existing after dilution. The optimum conditions for isolation of lignin also depend upon these factors, but are not necessarily identical with those for obtaining maximum yields of sugars.

Many investigations of hydrolysis have been carried out, but no universally applicable conditions of hydrolysis have been established and the investigator still is required to find the best conditions for his specific material by systematic variation of time, temperature, and acid strength. Typical conditions when sulfuric acid is employed are hydrolysis with 72% acid for 2 hours at 20°C., or 0.6 hour at 30°C. followed by heating in 3 to 4% acid for 4 hours at 100°C., or for 1 hour at 120°C. under pressure. The yield of reducing sugars depends on the time of hydrolysis with dilute acid. It usually reaches a maximum and then decreases because of reversion and degradation of sugars.

Wood hydrolysis by commercial processes yields sugars which are commercially recoverable for food purposes, or which are utilized for yeast production or fermentation to alcohols and acids. In such processes, the amount of acid used is an important cost factor, and the treatment is usually carried out with dilute acids under pressure (cf. Chapter 11).

The hydrolysis of wood and polysaccharides follows a first order reaction. The kinetics of hydrolysis have been studied by several investigators (e.g., 96,111,114,165). An extensive review of wood hydrolysis has been presented by Harris (83).

3. The Effect of Bases

Solutions of strong bases (e.g., sodium, potassium, or calcium hydroxides) dissolve a considerable quantity of wood substances even at ordinary temperature. The major attack occurs on the carbohydrates, of which the less resistant are dissolved. A portion of the lignin also dissolves and aromatic substances appear in the extract. The extractives are removed for the greater part by alkaline solutions. No wholly selective solution of wood components takes place, and alkaline extracts are chemically very heterogeneous.

Solutions of sodium hydroxide are effective in removing pentosans from hardwoods, and about 80% of the pentosans are extracted from birchwood meal with 12% sodium hydroxide solution at 80°C. (146). Extraction of pentosans is less complete from some hardwoods and is relatively slight from softwoods (24,147).

Treatment of wood by alkaline hydrolysis with N-sodium hydroxide at ca. 100°C. yields a number of simple aromatic substances in the extract. From hardwoods, these include vanillin, syringaldehyde, vanillic acid, and syringic acid. One or more species yield in addition p-hydroxybenzaldehyde, p-hydroxybenzoic acid, p-coumaric acid, and ferulic acid (144,150,151). Vanillic acid is the major carboxylic acid in the alkaline hydrolyzate of softwoods (144).

At higher temperatures (e.g., 100 to 180°C.) a much greater amount of material is dissolved. In commercial pulping of wood by the soda process (cf. Chapter 10), the wood is digested with ca. 4% sodium hydroxide solution, which removes the greater part of the lignin and a large fraction of the hemicelluloses. Alkaline hydrolysis of glycosidic linkages can occur under drastic conditions, e.g., 10% aqueous sodium hydroxide at 170°C. (128), and some depolymerization which occurs in alkaline pulping may arise from hydrolysis.

The polysaccharides are sensitive to oxidation under alkaline conditions, and in addition they undergo depolymerization and rearrangement. Saccharinic and other acids account for the major portion of the dissolved polysaccharides in alkaline spent liquors (73). The degradation of hemicelluloses in alkaline solutions at elevated temperatures appears to proceed by the stepwise elimination of end groups (47).

4. The Action of Salts

Aqueous solutions of neutral salts have scarcely more effect on wood from ordinary temperatures to 100°C. than does water alone. Acid salts, such as calcium and zinc chlorides, produce acid by hydrolysis and lead to hydrolytic deterioration. Similarly, solutions of salts which become basic upon hydrolysis have the general action of other alkaline solutions. At temperatures in the range of 170°C. even neutral salts show strong hydrolytic effects (cf. 83).

Aqueous solutions of salts such as sodium xylenesulfonate, sodium salicylate, and sodium benzoate ("hydrotropic" solutions) dissolve the major portion of the lignin from hardwoods and lesser amounts from softwoods at elevated temperatures (137). Wood pulps are obtained in approximately 50% yield, and with a low lignin content

when hardwoods are digested with sodium xylenesulfonate for 5 to 10
hours at 150 to 160°C. (75,118,141). About 65% of the lignin was
removed when aspen wood was heated with a 40% sodium benzoate
solution for 8 hours at 160°C. (187). Sodium cymenesulfonate has
been reported as the most effective (most hydrotropic) of this group
of solutions (140). The lignin can be largely precipitated from the
spent hydrotropic solutions by diluting with water and boiling (75).
The lignin can be recovered and the solution prepared for reuse. The
pulping of softwoods with hydrotropic solutions is incomplete. (See
also Chapter 10, Section VI, and Chapter 11, Section III-B.)

Two salts are of especial interest because of their commercial
utilization in pulping processes, namely, sodium sulfide and sodium
or other sulfites. Bisulfites, bisulfites with excess sulfurous acid, and
normal or monosulfites have been utilized in several pulping processes
(Chapter 10, Section IV). Sodium sulfide, in conjunction with sodium
hydroxide, is employed in the sulfate or kraft process (Chapter 10,
Section V). It has been postulated that the acid anions HSO_3^- and
HS^- are the effective delignifying agents, although in neither instance
has the mechanism been completely established. In any event, the
main reaction is one involving dissolution of the lignin; reaction with
the carbohydrates may be considered a side reaction and it is an undesirable one if it proceeds too far.

5. Oxidizing Agents

Atmospheric oxygen is without effect on wood at ordinary temperatures, and in the absence of decay wood articles remain essentially
unaltered for thousands of years. At higher temperatures pyrolysis
occurs, and above the ignition temperature combustion takes place
in the presence of air.

The action of oxidizing agents such as chlorine, hypochlorites, and
chlorine dioxide consists primarily of reaction with the lignin to form
soluble chlorinated and oxidation products. Premethylation of the
wood with diazomethane inhibits the oxidation reaction (3).

Wood is reactive generally toward strong oxidizing agents such as
potassium permanganate, chromic acid, chloric acid, hydrogen peroxide, sodium peroxide, and strong nitric acid. The reactions are not
confined to the lignin, as the carbohydrates are partially oxidized
with the formation of carbonyl and carboxyl groups, and with simultaneous depolymerization. Under more drastic conditions of reagent
concentration and temperature the entire woody tissue is broken

down progressively to simpler compounds, and finally to carbon dioxide, oxalic acid, volatile acids, and other degradation products.

When dilute solutions of strong oxidizing agents are used, chemical reaction may be more restricted, e.g., when hydrogen peroxide is applied under optimal conditions it is an effective bleaching agent for groundwood, and no extensive reaction occurs with either the lignin or polysaccharides.

The action of periodic acid on wood differs from that of other oxidizing agents in attacking primarily the polysaccharides, leaving "periodate lignin" as an insoluble residue (157,193). Several alternate treatments with acid periodate solution and boiling water are required to dissolve the carbohydrate fragments produced by the oxidation.

The oxidation of lignin with nitrobenzene and with cupric oxide in alkaline solutions converts a significant portion of the lignin in softwoods to vanillin and in hardwoods to vanillin and syringaldehyde, together with lesser quantities of other aromatic oxidation products (see Chapter 6). The reactions are applicable generally to wood and to other lignified tissues. This relatively mild oxidation procedure has proved a valuable technique in lignin chemistry (see Chapter 6, Section II-B).

6. Reducing Agents

Sodium borohydride has limited action on wood, the chief reaction being apparently the reduction of carbonyl groups. It has been applied in the bleaching of mechanical pulp (135). As a component of the pulping liquor in the sulfite and sulfate digestion of wood it appears to alter the nature of the pulping process (86). Sodium hydrosulfite (sodium dithionite) is used as a reducing bleach for some mechanical pulps, in which it improves the whiteness by reaction with coloring matters of the wood.

7. Hydrogenation

The reaction of wood with hydrogen gas under pressure is the most extensively studied type of reducing reaction. In the presence of a suitable catalyst a complex mixture of gaseous and liquid products is produced (98). Raney nickel is a superior catalyst (32,81,153), although preparations of copper, iron, chromium, molybdenum, zinc, and cobalt also promote hydrogenation (98). (See also Chapter 6, Section II-A, and Chapter 11, Section III-E.)

In order to carry out the hydrogenation the wood is suspended in a suitable liquid medium. When the liquid is water, concomitant hydrogenation and hydrolysis take place and the process is one of *hydrogenolysis* (81). Other liquids used include ethanol–water (1:1) and dioxane. Many workers prefer to use a liquid which dissolves most of the products of reaction.

The hydrogenation of wood produces a complex mixture of compounds. The relative amounts of these compounds depend upon the kind and amount of catalyst, the temperature, and other factors. The hydrogenation of lignin above 250°C. leads to the formation of compounds containing a chain of three carbon atoms bound to a C_6 ring. At temperatures below about 215°C. "hydrolignin" or "hydrol lignin" is obtained along with the simpler compounds (105).

Hydrogenation of ezomatsu (*Picea jezoensis*) wood flour in dilute alkali with Raney nickel yielded hydrolignin and various cyclohexanol derivatives (78). Mild hydrogenation of maple wood in the presence of Raney nickel yields a product from which chloroform-soluble hydrogenated (hydrol) lignin can be isolated (32). A more extensive treatment results in destructive hydrogenation with the formation of relatively simple organic compounds (153).

Hydrogenation in the presence of sodium hydroxide yields a cellulose-containing pulp and soluble aromatic products derived from the lignin (176). When the sapwood of aspen was hydrogenated with Raney nickel in dioxane–water (1:1) containing 3% sodium hydroxide for 2 to 3 hours at 165 to 175°C. and 3000 pounds hydrogen pressure, 51% of the wood remained as pulp. The soluble fractions included 4-hydroxy-3-methoxyphenylethane, 4-hydroxy-3,5-dimethoxyphenylethane, and 2-(4-hydroxy-3,5-dimethoxyphenyl)ethanol (152).

High-pressure hydrogenation of maple wood yielded propylcyclohexane derivatives such as 4-*n*-propylcyclohexanol and 3-(4-hydroxycyclohexyl)propanol-1 (48,84,85). These compounds have their origin in the lignin and their formation is considered evidence for the presence of phenylpropane units in the lignin structure. With mild alkaline hydrogenation, guaiacyl and syringyl compounds are obtained (18). Dihydroconiferyl and dihydrosinapyl alcohols were isolated after hydrogenolysis of young maple wood (35).

When Douglas-fir wood was hydrogenated for 4 hours at 250 to 290°C. and 3700 to 4600 pounds per square inch maximum hydrogen pressure, more than 50% of the wood was obtained as nonaqueous distillable liquids (81). Wood can be finally completely liquefied in the presence of Raney nickel to yield pale yellow, transparent solutions (77). Wood can be converted completely to gases and liquids by hydrogenation in the presence of tetralin at 325 to 350°C. without the need for other catalyst, and some hydrogenation occurs with tetralin alone (25).

8. Formation of Esters and Ethers

a. Nitration

Wood reacts with nitric acid in the presence of dehydrating acids to form nitrates of both lignin and carbohydrate components (99). The nitrated wood can be fractionated by solvents to yield fractions which largely represent the nitrates of cellulose, hemicelluloses, and lignin, respectively (126).

Nitration with a mixture of nitric acid, phosphoric acid, and phosphoric anhydride (62:26:10 w/w) yields a cellulose nitrate with little or no degradation (2,91). When applied to wood, the cellulose component can be isolated with a molecular weight close to that of the cellulose in the wood (184). The yield of cellulose nitrate, corrected to the equivalent weight of cellulose, is in reasonable agreement with the amount of alpha-cellulose isolated from delignified wood by alkaline extraction (184).

The nitration of wood has been accomplished by reaction with anhydrous dinitrogen pentoxide (55). Spruce sawdust has been nitrated with a mixture of nitric acid, acetic acid, and acetic anhydride (33). After addition of concentrated nitric acid to wood meal suspended in acetic acid, a nitrolignin can be recovered from the solution (188).

Wood reacts readily upon heating with nitric acid in either aqueous or alcoholic solution, with the formation of soluble nitrated lignin (27,28,79). Most of the hemicelluloses also are dissolved, but the cellulose is mainly unattacked except for the decrease in molecular weight resulting from hydrolysis. Kürschner and co-workers (120) have studied the action of alcoholic nitric acid on wood in a series of investigations. The method has been applied for the quantitative determination of cellulose in woods by heating the wood meal with a mixture of nitric acid and methanol under reflux. Part of the dissolved lignin is precipitated upon pouring the alcoholic solution into water.

b. Alkylation

Alkyl groups are introduced into wood by appropriate procedures and form alkyl ethers with the hydroxyl groups of both the carbohydrates and lignin. Alkylation (especially methylation) is a very common procedure in the study of carbohydrates and lignin. The alkylation of wood is less common, although it is sometimes carried out to characterize the amount and kind of hydroxyl groups present before the separation of wood components.

Methylation of beechwood and sprucewood with dimethyl sulfate yields methylated wood containing about 38 to 40% methoxyl groups (29,30,31,66,90,189,192). Isolation of lignin from methylated sprucewood by acid hydrolysis yields lignin with a methoxyl content greater than that of lignin from unmethylated wood, but some methoxyl groups appear to be removed from the lignin by the hydrolysis (29). Methylation with methanol and hydrochloric acid and with diazomethane (which reacts only with acidic hydroxyl groups) introduce less methoxyl groups.

Ethyl and hydroxyethyl (98) and benzyl (92) ethers have also been prepared. The wood ethers retain the original structure of the wood and are relatively insoluble in organic solvents.

c. Esterification

In addition to formation of inorganic esters such as the nitrate, the hydroxyl groups of wood components can be esterified with organic acids.

Treatment of pine and beech woods with acetic anhydride and sulfuric acid gives acetylated products containing 41 to 42.2% of acetyl groups (69,94). Nearly all hydroxyl groups in both lignin and carbohydrates are esterified by this procedure, although some of the hemicelluloses are dissolved. The acetylated wood becomes soluble in organic solvents only after acid hydrolysis, which simultaneously effects removal of some acetyl groups. Finely ground beech wood was acetylated with acetic anhydride and pyridine to yield a product containing 40% acetyl groups and that was soluble in organic solvents (90).

When birchwood is heated under reflux with glacial acetic acid for 100 hours, the solution contains a complex mixture of "acetic lignins" and the carbohydrates are partially acetylated (15). A mixture of glacial acetic acid and acetic anhydride containing 6 to 10 volume per cent of sulfuric acid dissolves wood after extended treatment, but the carbohydrates are extensively degraded and the lignin is sulfonated (67,68,127). The cell wall components of wood are esterified by mono- and dicarboxylic acids in the presence of molar quantities of trifluoro-acetic anhydride (9a).

B. THERMAL DECOMPOSITION OF WOOD

The ready combustion of wood forms the basis of extensive use of wood as a fuel, and at the same time it is a factor in use as a structural material because of fire hazards. Heating in the absence of oxygen leads to pyrolysis, which produces a variety of volatile products and ultimately leaves a residue of charcoal.

The effect of heat at temperatures below those required to initiate combustion and pyrolysis produces slow degradative changes and a decrease in the strength properties of the wood. The rate of change is a function of temperature, and data obtained by accelerated heat aging permit calculation of durability at ordinary temperatures by application of the Arrhenius equation (179).

1. Calorific Value

a. Total Heating Value

The heat of combustion of wood is closely equivalent to the weighted mean values of the wood components. It can also be deduced approximately from the elementary composition of the wood. The calorific values of woods of various species do not vary greatly, and are in the neighborhood of 8500 to 9000 B.T.U. per pound of dry

TABLE VII

Fuel Values of Woods (149)

Wood type	B.T.U./lb., dry wood basis
Pine	8836
Oak	8556
Hickory	8448
Cherry	8623
Birch	8458
Poplar	8640

wood. The heat values are somewhat larger in softwoods because of the presence of greater proportions of lignin and resins, both of which contain smaller percentages of oxygen than do the polysaccharides. The values given in Table VII may be considered typical.

The heating value of Canadian woods per airdry cord varies from 15.5 to 32.0 million B.T.U. for hardwoods and from 15.5 to 26.5 million B.T.U. for softwoods (43,53). (Typical values are given in

TABLE VIII

Heating Value of Canadian Woods (43)
(Gross calorific value in millions of B.T.U. per airdry cord)

Hardwoods	B.T.U.	Softwoods	B.T.U.
Black ash		Red-cedar, western	
(*Fraxinus nigra*)	22.6	(*Thuja plicata*)	16.8
Aspen		Douglas-fir	
(*Populus tremuloides*)	17.7	(*Pseudotsuga taxifolia*)	24.3
Beech		Fir, balsam	
(*Fagus grandifolia*)	27.8	(*Abies balsamea*)	15.5
Birch, white		Larch, eastern	
(*Betula papyrifera*)	23.4	(*Larix laricina*)	24.0
Elm, white		Pine, white	
(*Ulmus americana*)	24.5	(*Pinus strobus*)	17.1
Hickory, shagbark		Spruce, white	
(*Carya ovata*)	30.6	(*Picea glauca*)	16.2
Maple, red			
(*Acer rubrum*)	24.0		
Oak, white			
(*Quercus alba*)	30.6		

Table VIII.) The variations are accounted for largely by differences in weight per cord.

b. Effect of Moisture on Calorific Value

The heat value, as determined in a calorimeter, is not affected by the moisture content of the wood if it is calculated on the dry basis. Any water evaporated during combustion is condensed and its latent heat is recovered. However, when wood is used as fuel heat is absorbed for heating and vaporization of the water, and for heating the water vapor to the final temperature of the flue gases. Hawley (87) has calculated that wood with a heating value of 8600 B.T.U. per pound of dry wood has a value of 3670 B.T.U. per pound of wet wood (containing 100% water on the dry basis). The heat value of the wet wood is almost 7400 B.T.U. per pound when corrected to the dry basis. Wood with 200% water (dry basis) still has a net B.T.U. value of 6100 B.T.U. per pound of dry wood, but in practice wood containing water in excess of this amount is not usable as fuel because of the difficulty in maintaining combustion.

2. Ignition Temperature

The ignition temperature usually defined in comparing fire resistance of woods is that at which wood gives off volatile products which can be ignited from an external source of higher temperature, e.g., a pilot flame. It may be as low as 228°C. (145), although results are variable and dependent on conditions of testing. Wood density and the presence of volatile extractive components influence the production of combustible products. The migration of inorganic components to the surface with deposition during drying reduces the surface flammability.

"Fire-test" methods for wood have been widely studied, and many have been established on a national basis (cf. 64). Methods of test for surface flammability of wood have been examined by the Forest Products Laboratory (40). A.S.T.M. Standard E84 (4) describes a fire test chamber for classifying building materials as to fire hazard.

The autogeneous or self-ignition temperature has been defined as the lowest initial temperature from which, under favoring conditions, a material will heat spontaneously until glow or flame occurs (8). It is influenced primarily by the conditions under which the decomposition reactions become exothermic. The temperature at which self-ignition takes place is dependent on the testing apparatus, control of ambient temperature, specimen size, rate of heating, and other factors. Many difficulties have been experienced in determination and specification of an unique "ignition temperature."

The temperature reached by a combustible material depends on a critical heat balance that exists during the heating. Self-ignition is possible only when the rate of heat generation within the material exceeds the rate at which heat is lost to the surroundings. A critical size of specimen exists above which self-heating proceeds at a given temperature (76). The ignition temperature appears to be established most reliably as the temperature at which the condition of self-heating is reached. The temperature then rises sharply to that of self-initiated combustion, unless the specimen size is so small that the generated heat is rapidly dissipated.

The ignition temperatures reported for wood and wood components show wide variations. The temperature at which the decomposition of wood becomes exothermic appears to be in the range of 270 to 280°C. (54,87,112). Ignition temperatures as low as 190 to 230° (34, 41,113) and as high as 475 to 555°C. (49) have been reported. No doubt these variations result from differences in size and degree of subdivision of the specimen (76), rate of heating (54), and the extent of removal of volatile products produced by decomposition.

3. Fire-Retardant Treatments

Treatments are designed to modify wood so as to be fire-resistant or fire-retardant rather than fireproof, as no feasible treatment prevents the combustion of wood at high temperature in the presence of oxygen. Treatments are of two types: (1) a protective coating is applied to retard combustion, and (2) the wood is treated with impregnating materials.

Fire-retardant paints present a surface coating which hinders the spread of flame and affords some protection in preventing rapid spread of a fire during its early stages. The most effective chemical fire-retarding impregnant is ammonium phosphate, because it prevents afterglow as well as flaming. Ammonium sulfate, borax, boric acid, zinc chloride, and other salts are used with monobasic or dibasic ammonium phosphate in a variety of formulations (43,95).

The combustible properties of wood treated with flame-retarding agents are tested according to A.S.T.M. standards (4) by the crib test (E160) and the fire-tube apparatus (E69). The wood is heated with a burner under carefully specified conditions and the percentage loss in weight is determined after all flaming and glowing have ceased.

4. Pyrolysis

a. The Course of Pyrolysis

The thermal decomposition of wood, when carried out in the absence of oxygen, results in the production of combustible and non-combustible gases and vapors, and a residue of charcoal remains. The products possess commercial value, and form the basis of the wood distillation industry (72,88). Thermal decomposition also occurs during the combustion of wood and establishes the nature of the combustion process.

Wood is stable toward heat, except for loss of hygroscopic water, up to about 100°C. As the temperature is further increased, carbon dioxide, carbon monoxide, hydrogen, and water are formed by the chemical decomposition of the wood constituents.

Between 100 and 250°C. decomposition causes the wood to darken in color and lose its strength, although the structure is retained. At higher temperatures, up to 500°C., carbonization occurs and additional volatile materials are lost. The reaction (in the absence of air) becomes exothermic at about 275 to 280°C. The decomposition reactions of lignin and cellulose become exothermic at about 270 and 300°C., respectively (175). Pyrolysis of alpha-cellulose at about 300°C., and of lignin at about 400°C. has been reported (119). Hemicelluloses decompose at a considerably lower temperature (117,142).

The pyrolysis is largely completed at about 500°C. (16), and the residue of wood charcoal remains. However, charcoal produced at this temperature still gives off a considerable quantity of noncondensable gases on further heating at 800°C. (16).

In the range of wood distillation or carbonization the products formed can be classed broadly as noncondensable gases, pyroligneous liquor, insoluble tar, and charcoal. The products obtained by laboratory pyrolysis over the range of 250 to 350°C. were approximately 27.5% water, 10% noncondensable gases, 2% acids and methanol, 5% dissolved tar, and 8% settled tar. Over the range of 350 to 450°C. the products were 4% water, 3% noncondensable gases, 2% settled tar, and 0.5% acids and methanol (16). The noncondensable gases consisted largely of carbon dioxide and carbon monoxide, with smaller quantities of hydrogen and hydrocarbons.

Thermogravimetric investigations of pyrolysis (58,133), in which the weight of a specimen is recorded during the pyrolysis reactions, permit accurate determination of weight changes and facilitate study of the changes taking place. Thermal differential analysis (173) indicates that considerable interaction between components of wood takes place during pyrolysis.

b. Compounds Produced by Pyrolysis

The drastic character of the reactions occurring during wood carbonization or destructive distillation gives rise to a large number of chemical compounds. More than 200 compounds isolated after pyrolysis of resinous woods, bark, cellulose, pentosans, and lignin have been listed (72) and undoubtedly many others not yet identified are present.

Although the origin of all the products of thermal decomposition cannot be assigned to individual components of the original wood, it is known that each of the major components yields characteristic decomposition products. Thus, levoglucosan (1,6-anhydroglucose) results from pyrolysis of cellulose, furan derivatives from pentoses, and an assortment of aromatic substances from lignin. The origin of much of the acetic acid is attributed to the acetyl groups in the wood. At the elevated temperatures prevailing, secondary reactions of many types take place. The final products represent not only a wide variety of substances, but the proportions of these substances are variable depending upon the conditions existing during the decomposition reactions. Because of the complexity of the reactions and the extensive degradation to a diversity of compounds of relatively low molecular weight, the term "molecular debris" has been applied to the products (72).

C. THE DURABILITY OF WOOD

1. Resistance of Wood to Chemicals

Because wood is resistant to many chemicals it is widely utilized as a structural material in which such resistance is essential. Tanks, pipelines, and cooling towers constructed of wood normally give satisfactory service. Wood is resistant to salt solutions and to aqueous solutions of dilute acids and bases at ordinary temperatures. At the boiling point deterioration may take place and the wood is unsuitable for such applications. The durability varies considerably with the species. The heartwoods of cypress, southern yellow pine, Douglas-fir, and redwood are recommended for water tanks, and all except the last for tanks where resistance to chemicals is important (205).

Oxidizing agents cause rapid deterioration because of their reaction with lignin. In the use of wood for cooling towers, for example, the concentration of chlorine introduced as an algacide must be maintained at not more than one part per million (97).

Selected values for breaking strength of wood after exposure to a number of chemicals selected from the data of Ross (161) are given in

Table IX. Cold water and neutral salts were without significant effect.

TABLE IX

Effect of Acids and Bases on the Durability of Wood

Treatment	Percentage retention of wet breaking strength				
	Douglas-fir	Ponderosa pine, heart-wood	Western hemlock	Redwood	Cypress
Sulfuric acid, 5%, 105 days	91	90	92	86	84
Hydrochloric acid, 5%, 71 days	67	64	68	65	66
Nitric acid, 5%, 72 days	65	71	67	77	80
Acetic acid, 20%, 94 days	94	67	87	78	77
Hydrochloric acid, 1%, 36 hours[a]	59	53	47	58	59
Sodium hydroxide, 1%, 87 days	51	43	59	34	54
Sodium hydroxide, 1%, 36 hours[a]	42	53	47	43	53
Water, 80 hours[a]	76	67	76	77	85

[a] Boiling temperature, others at room temperature.

2. Weathering of Wood

Boards exposed to the weather without a protective coating develop a gray luster with roughening and checking of the surface. The effect of weathering is confined to the surface (104). In the absence of decay, actual erosion of the wood is very slow and may amount to no more than 0.0025 inch per year (205). The changes occurring at the surface are attributed to oxidation of the cellulose and lignin under the influence of light and moisture.

The effect of light does not extend much below the surface. Absorption of ultraviolet radiation is complete in a few thousandths of an inch. Only about 0.02% of visible radiation and 0.28% of infrared radiation penetrates to 0.1 inch in larchwood. The penetration into darker woods, such as redwood, is much less. The brown layer on weathered wood may be 0.1 inch deep. It is postulated that browning is caused by ultraviolet radiation and that rain water carries the soluble colored matter into wood as far as the wet line (36).

The deterioration of wood is accelerated by the presence of acid sprays or vapors (37), and under severe conditions the wood is broken down rapidly. Urban or industrial atmospheres in which the content of sulfur dioxide, either alone or in combination with ammonia, reaches significant proportions contribute to rapid deterioration of the wood (42).

Deterioration is accelerated in the presence of many metals and their salts. Wood loses tensile strength and chemical stability after it has been exposed to moisture and air in the presence of iron (61,134). The hemicelluloses are converted to products soluble in sodium hydroxide solutions (134). Calcium carbonate reacts with the acids and suppresses the amount of iron acquired by the wood. It has been reported (170) that titanium dioxide acts as a catalyst in the light damaging of cellulose.

3. The Decay of Wood

a. Causes of Decay

The disintegration of wood by decay is caused by the growth of fungi in the wood tissues under suitable conditions. Temperatures in the range of 20 to 35°C., and a pH in the range of 4.5 to 7 are favorable for growth. The water content must be close to, or above, the fiber saturation point (about 20 to 100% water based on dry wood), but no growth takes place if the pores are completely filled with water and oxygen is excluded. Many "fossil woods" have been preserved for thousands and sometimes millions of years, with little or no decay and relatively minor chemical modification because the wood was nearly, or completely, saturated with water.

Although a wide variety of fungi are capable of causing decay, the rots produced fall mainly into two classes—the brown and white rots, which are differentiated by the color and the nature of attack during early and intermediate stages of decay. In the brown rots, which are also called "destructive" rots, the carbohydrates are preferentially attacked and the lignin is little affected. The white or "corrosive" rots consume both carbohydrates and lignin. Some fractions of the pentosans appear to be more resistant to attack than the cellulose (9).

Rot fungi of the *Chaetomium* type differ in their effect on wood constituents from the *Basidiomycetes* which produce the common brown and white rots, and result in a "soft rot" (167). *Chaetomium globosum* attacks chiefly the polysaccharide cell wall constituents, which are removed in amounts proportional to the quantities present in the wood. Lignin is not markedly attacked until decay is well advanced.

The increased solubility in hot 1% sodium hydroxide solutions is often used as a diagnostic of decay. The increase in alkaline solubility resulting from decay is more marked in woods attacked by brown rots than in those affected by white rots. Woods attacked by *Chaetomium* rots resemble those after attack by the white rots with regard to resistance to solution in 1% sodium hydroxide solutions.

Although lignin is less affected than the polysaccharides by the brown rots, some lignin is destroyed (9). The lignin that remains becomes partially soluble in ethanol–benzene and in aqueous alkaline solutions, and is easily sulfonated (9,57,125). The lignin appears to be changed from the original protolignin in several respects, and the yield of vanillin after nitrobenzene oxidation is decreased (9,125).

Carbohydrates appear to be destroyed through hydrolysis by enzymes and acids produced by the fungi, whereas lignin decomposition apparently occurs by an oxidative process (50,70,124,196). Of the *Basidiomycetes*, organisms that form peroxidase are believed in general to attack preferentially the heartwood, whereas organisms that produce laccase prefer sapwood (131).

A number of fungi produce discoloration or staining without causing decay or rot in their final stages of activity. Both heartwood and sapwood may be affected. Sapwood staining fungi feed upon the food reserves stored in the ray and wood parenchyma cells rather than upon the cell wall substance.

Bacteria do not attack wood directly to any great extent, although they may increase the rate of growth of fungi (42). Bacterial attack on cellulose and other polysaccharides occurs readily, and it is not inhibited by the presence of wood or of isolated lignin in the medium. Finely ground wood also is attacked. The resistance of wood to bacterial action is attributed to the effect of lignin in mechanically preventing the close approach of the organism to the cellulose, which is a prerequisite for action of the bacterial enzymes. Attack on sapwood of *Pinus ponderosa* and *P. lambertiana* by anaerobic bacteria, including *Aerobacillus polymyxa*, has been reported (56).

b. Resistance to Decay

Woods vary greatly in resistance to decay, although no wood is wholly immune. No species produces a durable sapwood. The heartwoods vary from those that are highly resistant to those which decay easily. The relative resistances of seasoned sapwood and heartwood are reversed from those in the standing tree, in which the sapwood shows the greater resistance to decay owing to a generally higher moisture content that is above the optimum for fungal growth.

The greatest durability among the North American hardwoods is shown by the heartwoods of Osage-orange, catalpa, chestnut, black locust, red mulberry, black walnut, and sassafras. The more durable softwoods include the heartwoods of the yews, most of the cedars, baldcypress, the junipers, and redwood.

Low decay resistance is shown by aspen, basswood, birches, cottonwood, the red oaks, and willows among the hardwoods, and hemlocks, spruces, and true firs among the softwoods (63,95).

Many of the tropical woods are highly resistant to decay (82). Examples are camphorwood (*Ocotea usambarensis*), Indian ebony (*Diospyros melanoxylon*), greenheart (*Ocotea rodiaei*), lignumvitae (*Guaiacum officinale*), purpleheart (*Peltogyne* spp.), Honduras rosewood (*Dalbergia stevensonii*), and teak (*Tectona grandis*).

The natural resistance of many woods to decay is attributed to the deposition in heartwood of materials inhibitory or toxic to fungi. These materials are mostly phenolic compounds, and for the greater part they are soluble in water or organic solvents or are steam-volatile and, thus, are classed among the extractives. The distribution varies from tree to tree, and with location in the stem, giving rise to considerable variability in resistance, even within the same species (cf. 132). When the effective extractives are soluble in water, they may be removed by leaching and the wood then becomes subject to decay.

Only a few of the chemical compounds which give rise to decay resistance have been identified. The durability of a number of hardwoods is due to materials removed by hot water extraction (89,168). Tannin-containing water-soluble extractives were shown to account for the resistance to decay of redwood (*Sequoia sempervirens*) heartwood (174). Pinosylvin and pinosylvin monomethyl ether, which occur in the heartwood of pines, are toxic to some test fungi (155,156). Components of the steam-volatile oil from incense-cedar heartwood, particularly *p*-methoxythymol, are highly active (7). The hot water extract of western red-cedar (*Thuja plicata*) was found to be toxic to *Lentinus lepideus* (178). One of the most toxic substances known to occur in wood is γ-thujaplicin, which has been isolated from western red-cedar (6,60,132). It should be noted that not all phenolic compounds are highly toxic to fungi, e.g., pinoresinol appears to possess little toxicity (156) and gallic and ellagic acids were found in many Eucalyptus species, but they were not toxic at levels existing in the wood (162).

c. Wood Preservation

The decay of wood in the forest, in storage after cutting, and in use represents a large economic loss. Decay during use takes place under favorable conditions for growth of fungi unless a preservative treatment is applied. Many treatments have been used, particularly with the object of utilizing species which otherwise are not durable, and a large wood preservation industry has developed.

The most widely used preservatives are based on coal-tar creosote, usually modified with coal tar and petroleum oils (43,62,95). Others of commercial importance are formulations which may include chlorinated phenols, chromated zinc chloride, acid copper chromate, copper naphthenate, chromated zinc arsenate, chromated copper arsenate, mercuric salts, or sodium fluoride (62,63,95). Many dyestuffs are effective (195). Water-insoluble preservatives are preferred to avoid loss from the wood by leaching. Chemical modification of wood to destroy or inactivate nutrients required by fungi has been suggested (12). A listing of recommended practices and specifications for wood preservation has been compiled (148).

REFERENCES

1. Abadie-Maumert, F. A., *Papeterie*, **77**, 255 (1955); *Chem. Abstracts*, **49**, 9271 (1955).
2. Alexander, W. J., and R. L. Mitchell, *Anal. Chem.*, **21**, 1497 (1949).
3. Alfredsson, B., *Svensk Papperstidn.*, **60**, 489 (1957).
4. American Society for Testing Materials, *ASTM Standards*, Philadelphia.
5. Anderson, A. B., *Ind. Eng. Chem.*, **36**, 662 (1944).
6. Anderson, A. B., and E. C. Sherrard, *J. Am. Chem. Soc.*, **55**, 3813 (1933).
7. Anderson, A. B., E. Zavarin, and T. C. Scheffer, *Nature*, **181**, 1275 (1958).
8. Anon., *J. Franklin Inst.*, **234**, 492 (1942).
9. Apenitis, A., H. Erdtman, and B. Leopold, *Svensk Kem. Tidskr.*, **63**, 195 (1951).
9a. Arni, P. C., J. D. Gray, and R. K. Scougall, *J. Appl. Chem.*, **11**, 157 (1961).

10. Aronovsky, S. I., and R. A. Gortner, *Ind. Eng. Chem.*, **28**, 1270 (1936).
11. Atchison, J. E., *Paper Trade J.*, **116**, No. 22, 23 (1943).
12. Baechler, R. H., *Forest Prods. J.*, **9**, 166 (1959).
13. Bailey, A. J., *Ind. Eng. Chem., Anal. Ed.*, **8**, 52 (1936).
14. Ball, D. H., and J. K. N. Jones, *J. Chem. Soc.*, **1958**, 33.
15. Bell, A., and G. F. Wright, *J. Am. Chem. Soc.*, **72**, 1495 (1950).
16. Bergström, H., *Svensk Papperstidn.*, **60**, 115 (1957).
17. Bernardin, L. J., *Tappi*, **41**, 491 (1958).
18. Bhattacharya, A., E. Sondheimer, and C. Schuerch, *Tappi*, **42**, 446 (1959).
19. Björkman, A., *Ind. Eng. Chem.*, **49**, 1395 (1957).
20. Bland, D. E., *Holzforschung*, **12**, 36 (1958).
21. Bland, D. E., G. Billek, K. Gruber, and K. Kratzl, *Holzforschung*, **13**, 6 (1959).
22. Bland, D. E., E. A. Hanson, C. M. Stewart, and A. J. Watson, *J. Council Sci. Ind. Res.*, **20**, 553 (1947).
23. Boehm, R. M., *Tech. Assoc. Papers*, **23**, 387 (1940); *Ind. Eng. Chem.*, **22**, 493 (1930).
24. Booker, E., and C. Schuerch, *Tappi*, **41**, 650 (1958).
25. Boomer, E. H., G. H. Argue, and J. Edwards, *Can. J. Research*, **13B**, 337 (1935).
26. Brasch, D. J., and L. E. Wise, *Tappi*, **39**, 581 (1956).
27. Brauns, F. E., "The Chemistry of Lignin," in *Wood Chemistry*, L. E. Wise and E. C. Jahn, eds., Reinhold, New York, 1952.
28. Brauns, F. E., *The Chemistry of Lignin*, Academic Press, New York, 1952; Brauns, F. E., and D. A. Brauns, *The Chemistry of Lignin*, Supplement Volume, Academic Press, New York, 1960.
29. Brauns, F. E., *J. Am. Chem. Soc.*, **68**, 1721 (1946).
30. Brauns, F. E., and H. Hibbert, *Can. J. Research*, **13B**, 78 (1935).
31. Brauns, F. E., and J. J. Yirak, *Paper Trade J.*, **125**, No. 12, 55 (1947).
32. Brewer, C. P., L. M. Cooke, and H. Hibbert, *J. Am. Chem. Soc.*, **70**, 57 (1948).
33. Brissaud, L., and S. Ronssin, *Assoc. tech. ind. papetière, Bull.*, **1953**, 107.
34. Brown, C. R., *Quart. Natl. Fire Protection Assoc.*, **28**, 135 (1934); *Chem. Abstracts*, **29**, 344 (1935).
35. Brown, S. A., and A. C. Neish, *J. Am. Chem. Soc.*, **81**, 2419 (1959).
36. Browne, F. L., and H. C. Simonson, *Forest Prods. J.*, **7**, 308 (1957).
37. Browning, B. L., and L. O. Bublitz, *Ind. Eng. Chem.*, **45**, 1516 (1953).
38. Browning, B. L., and L. O. Bublitz, *Tappi*, **36**, 452 (1953).
39. Browning, B. L., and I. H. Isenberg, "Analytical Data and Their Significance," in *Wood Chemistry*, L. E. Wise and E. C. Jahn, eds., Reinhold, New York, 1952.
40. Bruce, H. D., and V. P. Miniutti, *U. S. Dept. Agr., Forest Serv., Forest Prod. Lab., Report No.* 2907, 1957.
41. Buchanan, M. A., *Tappi*, **35**, 209 (1952).
42. Campbell, W. G., "The Biological Decomposition of Wood," in *Wood Chemistry*, L. E. Wise and E. C. Jahn, eds., Reinhold, New York, 1952.
43. *Canadian Woods, Their Properties and Uses*, Can. Dep. Resources and Development, Forestry Branch, Forest Products Lab., Ottawa, 1950.

44. Chidester, G. H., and J. N. McGovern, *Tech. Assoc. Papers*, **23**, 322 (1940).
45. Chow, K Y., *Forestry*, **20**, 62 (1946); *Bull. Inst. Paper Chem.*, **19**, 462 (1949).
46. Clermont, L. P., and H. Schwartz, *Pulp Paper Mag. Can.*, **53**, No. 6, 142 (1952).
47. Collier, R. W., *Tappi*, **43**, 15 (1960).
48. Cooke, L. M., J L. McCarthy, and H. Hibbert, *J. Am. Chem. Soc.*, **63**, 3056 (1941).
49. Costa, D., G. Costa, P. Batti, S. Valussi, and E. Susa, *Riv. combustibili*, **10**, 101 (1956); *Chem. Abstracts*, **50**, 15,080 (1956).
50. Cowling, E. B., *U. S. Dep. Agr., Forest Serv., Forest Prod. Lab. Rept. No. 2116* (1958); (a) *U. S. Dep. Agr., Forest Serv., Tech. Bull. No. 1258* (1961).
51. Dadswell, H. E., and L. F. Hawley, *Ind. Eng. Chem.*, **21**, 973 (1929).
52. Dadswell, H. E., and A. B. Wardrop, *Holzforschung*, **9**, 97 (1955).
53. Data Sheet Q-8, *Pulp Paper Mag. Can.*, **60**, No. 9, T262 (1959).
54. Edwards, P. W., and R. W. Harrison, *Ind. Eng. Chem., Anal. Ed.*, **2**, 344 (1930).
55. Elias, W. E., and L. D. Hayward, *Tappi*, **41**, 246 (1958).
56. Ellwood, E. L., and B. Ecklund, *Nature*, **183**, 1206 (1959).
57. Enkvist, T., E. Solin, and U. Maunula, *Paperi ja Puu*, **36**, 65 (1954).
58. Erdey, L., F. Paulik, and J. Paulik, *Acta Chim. Acad. Sci. Hung.*, **10**, 61 (1956); *Chem. Abstracts*, **51**, 6304 (1957).
59. Erdtman, H., "Phenolic and Other Extraneous Components of Coniferous Heartwoods," in *Wood Chemistry*, L. E. Wise and E. C. Jahn, eds., Reinhold, New York, 1952; *Progr. in Org. Chem.*, **1**, 22 (1952).
60. Erdtman, H., and J. Gripenberg, *Acta Chem. Scand.*, **2**, 625 (1948).
61. Farber, E., *Ind. Eng. Chem.*, **46**, 1968 (1954).
62. Farber, E., *Ind. Eng. Chem.*, **48**, No. 3, 7A (1956).
63. Forbes, R. D., ed., *Forestry Handbook*, Ronald Press, New York, 1955.
64. Fourth Conference on Wood Technology, *Final Report*, Madrid, Spain, Food and Agr. Organization U. N. (1958): F. Kollmann, *Svensk Papperstidn.*, **63**, 208 (1960).
65. Freeman, R. D., and F. C. Peterson, *Ind. Eng. Chem., Anal. Ed.*, **13**, 803 (1941).
66. Freudenberg, K., and R. Kraft, *Chem. Ber.*, **83**, 530 (1950).
67. Friese, H., *Ber.*, **63B**, 1902 (1930).
68. Friese, H., and H. Glassner, *Ber.*, **70B**, 1473 (1937).
69. Fuchs, W., *Ber.*, **61B**, 948 (1928).
70. Gadd, O., *Paperi ja Puu*, **39**, 363 (1957).
71. Goldschmid, O., *Tappi*, **38**, 728 (1955).
72. Goos, A. W., "The Thermal Decomposition of Wood," in *Wood Chemistry*, L. E. Wise and E. C. Jahn, eds., Reinhold, New York, 1952.
73. Green, J. W., *Tappi*, **39**, 472 (1956).
74. Green, J. W., and R. L. Leaf, Jr., *Tappi*, **35**, 468 (1952).
75. Gromovs, V. and P. Odincovs, *Bumazh. Prom.*, **32**, No. 6, 11 (1957); *Chem. Abstracts*, **52**, 3330 (1958).
76. Gross, D., and A. F. Robertson, *J. Research Natl. Bur. Standards*, **61**, 413 (1958).

77. Hachihama, Y., S. Jodai, K. Sawai, and M. Nakayama, *J. Soc. Chem. Ind. Japan*, **47**, 218 (1944); *Chem. Abstracts*, **43**, 8675 (1949).
78. Hachihama, Y., S. Jodai, and M. Takeda, *J. Soc. Chem. Ind. Japan*, **47**, 215 (1944); *Chem. Abstracts*, **43**, 8675 (1949).
79. Hachihama, Y., and J. Okabe, *Technol. Repts. Osaka Univ.*, **6**, 171 (1956); *Chem. Abstracts*, **51**, 8432 (1957).
80. Hägglund, E., and S. Ljunggren, *Svensk Kem. Tidskr.*, **45**, 123 (1933).
81. Hallonquist, E. G., *Ind. Eng. Chem.*, **43**, 1427 (1951).
82. *Handbook of Hardwoods*, G. Brit., Dep. Sci. Ind. Research, Forest Prods. Research, H. M. S. O., London, 1956.
83. Harris, E. E., "Wood Hydrolysis," in *Wood Chemistry*, L. E. Wise and E. C. Jahn, eds., Reinhold, New York, 1952.
84. Harris, E. E., J. D'Ianni, and H. Adkins, *J. Am. Chem. Soc.*, **60**, 1467 (1938).
85. Harris, E. E., J. Saeman, and E. C. Sherrard, *Ind. Eng. Chem.*, **32**, 440 (1940).
86. Hartler, H., *Svensk Papperstidn.*, **62**, 467 (1959).
87. Hawley, L. F., "The Combustion of Wood," in *Wood Chemistry*, L. E. Wise and E. C. Jahn, eds., Reinhold, New York, 1952.
88. Hawley, L. F., *Wood Distillation*, Chem. Catalog Co., New York, 1923.
89. Hawley, L. F., L. C. Fleck, and C. A. Richards, *Ind. Eng. Chem.*, **16**, 699 (1924).
90. Hess, K., K. P. Jung, and K. E. Heumann, *Naturwissenschaften*, **27**, 770 (1939).
91. Heuser, E., and L. Jörgensen, *Tappi*, **34**, 57 (1951).
92. Hilpert, R. S., and O. Peters, *Ber.*, **70B**, 108, 514 (1937).
93. Holmberg, C. V., and E. C. Jahn, *Paper Trade J.*, **111**, No. 1, 33 (1940).
94. Horn, O., *Ber.*, **61B**, 2542 (1928).
95. Hunt, G. M., and G. A. Garratt, *Wood Preservation*, 2nd ed., McGraw-Hill, New York, 1953.
96. Iglesias, C. D., *Anales fac. cienc. fis y matemat*, **4**, 99 (1955); *Chem. Abstracts*, **51**, 2269 (1957).
97. *Interim Report N*, California Redwood Association, San Francisco, 1958.
98. Jahn, E. C., "The Chemical Behavior of Wood," in *Wood Chemistry*, L. E. Wise and E. C. Jahn, eds., Reinhold, New York, 1952.
99. Jahn, E. C., and S. Coppick, *Ind. Eng. Chem.*, **33**, 678 (1941); **35**, 890 (1943).
100. Jayme, G., *Cellulosechemie*, **20**, 43 (1942).
101. Jayme, G., and M. Harders-Steinhäuser, *Das Papier*, **4**, 104 (1950).
102. Jayme, G., and K. Reimann, *Das Papier*, **12**, 44 (1958).
103. Jayme, G., K. Storch, E. Kerler, and G. Schwab, *Papier-Fabr.*, **37**, 57 (1939).
104. Jemison, G. M., *J. Forestry*, **35**, 460 (1937).
105. Jodai, S., *J. Soc. Chem. Ind. Japan*, **47**, 962 (1944); *Chem. Abstracts*, **43**, 8675 (1949).
106. Johnsen, B., and R. W. Hovey, *J. Soc. Chem. Ind.*, **37**, 132T (1918).
107. Jutte, S. M., *Holzforschung*, **10**, 33 (1956).
108. Klason, P., *Cellulosechemie*, **4**, 81 (1923).
109. Klauditz, W., and G. Stegman, *Holz Roh- u. Werkstoff.* **13**, 434 (1955).
110. Klauditz, W., and I. Stolley, *Holzforschung*, **9**, 5 (1955).

111. Kobayashi, T., and Y. Sakai, *Bull. Agr. Chem. Soc. Japan*, **20**, 1 (1956); *Chem. Abstracts*, **51**, 12,485 (1957).
112. Kobe, K. A., and F. L. Goin, *Ind. Eng. Chem.*, **31**, 1171 (1939).
113. Kollmann, F., *Holz Roh- u. Werkstoff*, **18**, 193 (1960).
114. Korol'kov, I. I., Z. A. Tyagunova, E. A. Ivlieva, V. I. Ryabovich, and L. M. Papashnikov, *Gidroliz. i Lesokhim. Prom.*, **11**, No. 6, 3 (1958); *Chem. Abstracts*, **53**, 711 (1959).
115. Kratzl, K., *Mitt. Österr. Ges. Holzforsch.*, **2**, 135 (1950); *Chem. Abstracts*, **46**, 8365 (1952).
116. Kratzl, K., and H. Silbernagel, *Monatsh. Chem.*, **83**, 1022 (1952).
117. Kudo, K., and E. Yoshida, *Mokuzai Gakkaishi*, **3**, 125 (1957); *Chem. Abstracts*, **51**, 18,587 (1957).
118. Kunugi, T., and K. Uchida, *J. Chem. Soc. Japan, Ind. Chem. Sect.*, **56**, 634 (1953); *Chem. Abstracts*, **48**, 12,404 (1954).
119. Kuriyama, A., *Mokuzai Gakkaishi*, **4**, 30 (1958); *Chem. Abstracts*, **52**, 12,397 (1958).
120. Kürschner, K., and G. Hostomský, *Holzforschung*, **12**, 142 (1958).
121. Kurth, E. F., *Ind. Eng. Chem., Anal. Ed.*, **11**, 203 (1939).
122. Lange, P. W., *Svensk Papperstidn.*, **57**, 525 (1954).
123. Lauer, K., *Tappi*, **41**, 334 (1958).
124. Lawson, L. R., and C. N. Still, *Tappi*, **40**, No. 9, 56A (1957).
125. Leopold, B., *Svensk Kem. Tidskr.*, **63**, 260 (1951).
126. Lewin, M., and J. A. Epstein, *Tappi*, **41**, 240 (1958).
127. Lieser, T., and V. Schwind, *Ann.*, **532**, 104 (1937).
128. Lindberg, B., *Svensk Papperstidn.*, **59**, 531 (1956).
129. Lindgren, B. O., *Svensk Papperstidn.*, **61**, 669 (1958).
130. Lowgren, U., *Tech. Assoc. Papers*, **24**, 432 (1941).
131. Lyr, H., *Planta*, **46**, 408 (1955); *Chem. Abstracts*, **50**, 5079 (1956).
132. MacLean, H., and J. A. F. Gardner, *Forest Prods. J.*, **6**, 510 (1956).
133. Madorsky, S. L., V. E. Hart, and S. Straus, *J. Research Natl. Bur. Standards*, **56**, 343 (1956).
134. Marian, J. E., and A. Wissing, *Svensk Papperstidn.*, **63**, 47, 98, 130, 174 (1960).
135. Mayer, W. C., and C. P. Donofrio, *Tappi*, **43**, No. 1, 238A (1960).
136. McGovern, J. N., and G. H. Chidester, *Tech. Assoc. Papers*, **22**, 617 (1939).
137. McKee, R. H., *Ind. Eng. Chem.*, **38**, 382 (1946).
138. Mease, R. T., *Ind. Eng. Chem., Anal. Ed.*, **5**, 317 (1933).
139. Merewether, J. W. T., *APPITA Proc.*, **5**, 226 (1951); *Holzforschung*, **11**, 65 (1957).
140. Migita, N., J. Nakano, S. Hirai, and C. Takatsuka, *Sen-i Gakkaishi*, **12**, 632 (1956); *Chem. Abstracts*, **51**, 8429 (1957).
141. Migita, N., J. Nakano, and Y. Ito, *J. Japan. Forest. Soc.*, **36**, 343 (1954); *Chem. Abstracts*, **50**, 3758 (1956).
142. Mitchell, R. L., R. M. Seborg, and M. A. Millett, *J. Forest Prods. Research Soc.*, **3**, No. 4, 38 (1953).
143. Mithel, B. B., G. H. Webster, and W. H. Rapson, *Tappi*, **40**, 1 (1957).
144. Nakano, J., A. Ishizu, and N. Migita, *J. Japan. Wood Research. Soc.*, **4**, No. 1, 1 (1958).

145. Narayanamurti, D., and J. George, *Current Sci. (India)*, **27**, 22 (1958); *Chem. Abstracts*, **52**, 10,571 (1958).

146. Nelson, R., and C. Schuerch, *J. Polymer Sci.*, **22**, 435 (1956).

147. Nelson, R., and C. Schuerch, *Tappi*, **40**, 419 (1957).

148. *Northeastern Wood Utilization Council, Bulletin No. 44*, (1955).

149. Parr, S. W., and C. N. Davidson, *Ind. Eng. Chem.*, **14**, 935 (1922).

150. Pearl, I. A., D. L. Beyer, and B. Johnson, *Tappi*, **41**, 255 (1958).

151. Pearl, I. A., D. L. Beyer, B. Johnson, and S. Wilkinson, *Tappi*, **40**, 374 (1957).

152. Pepper, J. M., C. J. Brounstein, and D. A. Shearer, *J. Am. Chem. Soc.*, **73**, 3316 (1951).

153. Pepper, J. M., and H. Hibbert, *J. Am. Chem. Soc.*, **70**, 67 (1948).

154. Plath, E., and L. Plath, *Holz Roh- u. Werkstoff*, **13**, 226 (1955).

155. Rennerfelt, E., *Svensk Botan. Tidskr.*, **1943**, 83; *Chem. Abstracts*, **38**, 5656 (1944).

156. Rennerfelt, E., *Acta Chem. Scand.*, **3**, 1343 (1949).

157. Ritchie, P. F., and C. B. Purves, *Pulp Paper Mag. Can.*, **48**, No. 12, 74 (1947).

158. Ritter, G. J., and L. C. Fleck, *Ind. Eng. Chem.*, **15**, 1055 (1923).

159. Ritter, G. J., and L. C. Fleck, *Ind. Eng. Chem.*, **18**, 608 (1926).

160. Ritter, G. J., and E. F. Kurth, *Ind. Eng. Chem.*, **25**, 1250 (1933).

161. Ross, J. D., *Forest Prods. J.*, **6**, 34 (1956).

162. Rudman, P., *Holzforschung*, **13**, 112 (1959).

163. Runkel, R. O. H., and K.-D. Wilke, *Holz Roh- u. Werkstoff*, **9**, 260 (1951).

164. Runkel, R. O. H., and H. Witt, *Holz Roh- u. Werkstoff*, **11**, 457 (1953).

165. Savard, J., *Inds. aliment et agr. (Paris)*, **74**, 469 (1957); *Chem. Abstracts*, **51**, 18,591 (1957).

166. Savard, J., A. Besson, and S. Morize, *Analyse chimique des bois tropicaux*, Centre Technique Forestier Tropical, Nogent-sur-Marne, 1954; J. R. Istas, E. L. Raekelboom, and R. Heremans, *Study of Some Congo Woods*, Publs. inst. natl. étude agron. Congo Belge, Sér. Tech. No. 59, 1959.

167. Savory, J. G., and L. C. Pinion, *Holzforschung*, **12**, 99 (1958).

168. Scheffer, T. C., H. G. Lachmund, and H. Hopp, *J. Agr. Research*, **68**, 415 (1944); *Chem. Abstracts*, **38**, 4770 (1944).

169. Schulze, E., *Ber.*, **24**, 2277 (1891).

170. Schurz, J., and E. Kienzl, *Faserforsch. u. Textiltech.*, **9**, 513 (1958).

171. Schwerin, G., *Holzforschung*, **12**, 43 (1958).

172. Scott, D. R. M., and S. B. Preston, *Forest Science*, **1**, 178 (1955).

173. Sergeeva, V. N., and A. Vaivads, *Latvijas PSR Zinātņu Akad. Vēstis*, **1954**, No. 9, 103; *Chem. Abstracts*, **49**, 5831 (1955).

174. Sherrard, E. C., and E. F. Kurth, *Ind. Eng. Chem.*, **25**, 300 (1933).

175. Smith, K. N., *Tappi*, **42**, 869 (1959).

176. Sobolev, I., and C. Schuerch, *Tappi*, **41**, 545 (1958).

177. Sohn, A. W., and P. O. Lenel, *Das Papier*, **3**, 109 (1949).

178. Sowder, A. M., *Ind. Eng. Chem.*, **21**, 981 (1929).

179. Stamm, A. J., *Ind. Eng. Chem.*, **48**, 413 (1956).

180. Stanek, D. A., *Tappi*, **41**, 601 (1958).

181. Thomas, B. B., *Paper Ind.*, **26**, 1281 (1945); **27**, 374 (1945).

182. Thompson, A., K. Anno, M. L. Wolfrom, and M. Inatome, *J. Am. Chem. Soc.*, **76**, 1309 (1954).
183. Thompson, J. O., J. J. Becher, and L. E. Wise, *Tappi*, **36**, 319 (1953).
184. Timell, T. E., *Tappi*, **40**, 25, 30 (1957).
185. Timell, T. E., *Tappi*, **40**, 568 (1957); *Pulp Paper Mag. Can.*, **59**, No. 8, 139 (1958).
186. Timell, T. E., and E. C. Jahn, *Svensk Papperstidn.*, **54**, 831 (1951).
187. Traynard, P., and A. Eymery, *Holzforschung*, **9**, 172 (1955); **10**, 6, 43 (1956).
188. Traynard, P., and A. Robert, *Assoc. tech. ind. papetière, Bull.*, **5**, 401 (1951); *Bull. soc. chim. France*, **1952**, 746.
189. Urban, H., *Cellulosechemie*, **7**, 73 (1926).
190. *U. S. Dep. Agr., Forest Serv., Forest Prods. Lab., Tech. Note No. 235*, 1952.
191. Van Beckum, W. G., and G. J. Ritter, *Paper Trade J.*, **105**, No. 18, 127 (1937).
192. Wacek, A. v., *Ber.*, **61B**, 1604 (1928).
193. Wald, W. J., P. F. Ritchie, and C. B. Purves, *J. Am. Chem. Soc.*, **69**, 1371 (1947).
194. Wardrop, A. B., and H. E. Dadswell, *Australian J. Botany*, **3**, 177 (1955).
195. Weaver, J. W., E. B. Jeroski, and I. S. Goldstein, *Forest Prods. J.*, **9**, 372 (1959).
196. Wiertelak, J., and T. Dominik, *Polish Agr. Forest Ann.*, **36**, 369 (1936); *Chem. Abstracts*, **30**, 7812 (1936).
197. Wiertelak, J., and I. Garbaczówna, *Ind. Eng. Chem., Anal. Ed.*, **7**, 110 (1935).
198. Wise, L. E., *Ind. Eng. Chem., Anal. Ed.*, **17**, 63 (1945).
199. Wise, L. E., *Tappi*, **41**, No. 9, 14A (1958).
200. Wise, L. E., and E. C. Jahn, *Wood Chemistry*, Reinhold, New York, 1952, p. 1272.
201. Wise, L. E., and J. Pickard, *Tappi*, **38**, 618 (1955).
202. Wise, L. E., and E. K. Ratliff, *Anal. Chem.*, **19**, 459 (1947).
203. Wise, L. E., R. C. Rittenhouse, E. E. Dickey, O. H. Olson, and C. Garcia, *J. Forest Prods. Research Soc.*, **2**, No. 5, 237 (1952).
204. Wise, L. E., R. C. Rittenhouse, and C. Garcia, *Proc. Forest Prods. Research Soc.*, **5**, 239 (1951).
205. *Wood Handbook, U. S. Dep. Agr. Forest Serv., Forest Prods. Lab., Handbook No. 72*, 1955.
206. Zaĭtseva, A. F., and N. I. Nikitin, *J. Applied Chem. U.S.S.R.*, **24**, 392, 427 (1951); *Chem. Abstracts*, **46**, 4785 (1952).

CHAPTER 4

Cellulose

E. H. Immergut, *Interscience Publishers, a Division of John Wiley & Sons, Inc., New York, N. Y.* and *Polytechnic Institute of Brooklyn, Brooklyn, N. Y.*

I. Chemical Structure

A. NATURE OF CELLULOSE

The chemistry of cellulose began in 1838 with the work of Payen (170), who realized that the cell wall of plants is not one uniform chemical substance peculiar to each species, as had hitherto been thought on the basis of differing carbon contents. Instead, he felt that the variation in the analytical results was due to differences in "incrusting or ligneous matter" and incomplete removal of the latter, prior to analysis. Payen, therefore, began to extract the plants under more severe conditions and, from his results, finally arrived at the conclusion that the fibrous tissue of all young plant cells consists of one uniform chemical substance: a carbohydrate comprised of glucose residues and isomeric with starch (C, 44.4%; H, 6.2%), which he named cellulose.

In spite of opposition, especially by Fremy (57), Erdman (46) and, later, Cross and Bevan (31), who believed that in the plant the cellulose, lignin, pectin, and fatty material merged into one another by insensible chemical gradations, the concept of Payen and also of Schulze (194), which defined cellulose as the carbohydrate portion of the cell wall derived exclusively from glucose and resembling cotton cellulose in its physical and chemical properties, finally won out. (Among workers concerned more with technical utilization, the fibrous delignified pulps, which still contain hemicelluloses, are often called celluloses after the terminology of Cross and Bevan.)

B. MACROMOLECULAR STRUCTURE OF CELLULOSE

The concept of cellulose as a linear macromolecule consisting of anhydroglucose units (or more specifically, anhydro-β-glucopyranose units) was not evolved until the early 1920s. It resulted from the knowledge gained through the development of several related sciences, such as the advances made in the chemistry of the simple sugars, in x-ray diffraction, and in colloid chemistry. Through the development of the methylation method (106) it could be shown that the hydroxyl groups in cellulose occupied the 2, 3, and 6 positions of each anhydroglucose unit. This information ruled out the previously proposed structures, except that proposed by Hibbert (90) (shown in Fig. 1). Other steps, such as the demonstration of a

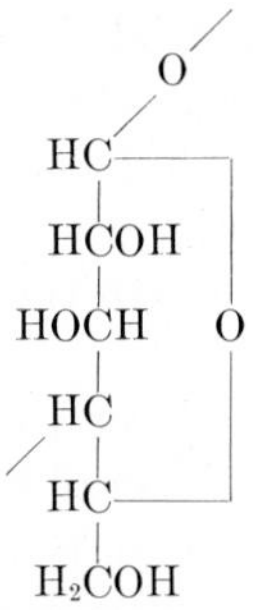

$$
\begin{array}{c}
\overset{/}{O} \\
HC\!\!-\!\!-\!\!-\!\!-\!\!\rceil \\
| \\
HCOH \\
| \\
HOCH \quad O \\
| \\
HC \\
/ \\
HC\!\!-\!\!-\!\!-\!\!-\!\! \\
| \\
H_2COH
\end{array}
$$

Fig. 1. Hibbert's formula for cellulose (repeat n times for main-valence molecule).

6-membered ring structure for glucose (23,71) and the proof that cellobiose was a 4-glucopyranosylglucose (74,235), then led the way to the representation of cellulose as a linear *macromolecule* (210) consisting of a large number of hexose units (see Fig. 1) linked together by main-valence glucosidic links.

However, at that time not enough experimental evidence was available to decide conclusively in favor of the linear macromolecule concept. As a result, another theory commonly called the "association theory," or "micellar theory" received much support (83,146). It was based on the idea that cellulose was a colloidal substance and, therefore, consisted of aggregates (or micelles) of smaller molecules rather than a single, long, main-valence chain. The opponents of the macromolecular theory, Karrer, Hess, and others (86,113), were supported in their view by a number of experimental observations, most of which, however, could equally well have been interpreted on the basis of a long-chain linear macromolecule. (Fig. 1, for n sufficiently large.)

After 1927, however, evidence favoring the linear chain structure began to accumulate as follows.

(1) Degradation studies permitted the isolation of the crystalline compounds corresponding to $n = 3$, $n = 4$, and $n = 5$ in Fig. 1.

(2) The kinetics of the reaction showed that the degradation consisted of random scission of equivalent bonds in a linear chain molecule.

(3) Hydrolysis of trimethyl cellulose yielded a small amount of 2, 3, 4, 6-tetramethylglucose. corresponding to one of the end groups in Fig. 1.

(4) The amount of this material showed that the chain molecules must consist of several hundred anhydroglucose units.

(5) Improvements in the techniques for studying macromolecules in solution (viscosity, osmotic pressure, ultracentrifuge) yielded information about the chain length that was in agreement with end group results and x-ray data.

The fact that no reproducible or conclusive evidence in favor of the "association theory" had been obtained, together with the new experimental results definitely in agreement with the macromolecular concept, established the latter concept on a firm basis, and it became almost universally accepted after 1932.

Once the macromolecular or chain structure of cellulose had been accepted in preference to the idea of soaplike aggregates of low-molecular weight material, it was possible to define the chemical structure of these chains more closely. Of primary importance here is the question of uniformity.

C. UNIFORMITY OF CELLULOSE

1. Does Cellulose Consist Exclusively of Glucose Units?

Although it was known that all celluloses, when treated with strong acids, decomposed to form glucose, it still had to be shown that this was really a quantitative reaction. For this purpose, cotton (the purest form of cellulose) was submitted to hydrolytic degradation under various conditions by different workers. Monier-Williams (156) was able to isolate a 90.7% yield of crystalline glucose by using concentrated sulfuric acid. Irvine and Hirst (107) first acetylated the cotton and then, by subsequent methanolysis, obtained a crystalline equilibrium mixture of methyl α- and β-glucopyranosides, which accounted for 95.5% of the cellulose. As the furfural test for pentosans was negative, and no other compounds besides the methylglucoside could be detected, this was accepted as conclusive evidence that pure cellulose contains only glucose residues.

With the establishment of chromatography (e.g. 20) as a powerful method for the separation and identification of sugars, it became possible to study the hydrolysis products of different celluloses in order to determine their chemical composition. By use of this technique, Dymmling, Giertz, and Rånby (43) were able to confirm that a very pure form of cellulose, such as ramie, yields only glucose upon hydrolysis.

Chromatography is of even greater value, however, in investigating the chemical constitution of different wood species and pulps (42,43, 68,180,218), as it permits quantitative determination and identification of the noncellulosic polysaccharides which play such an important role in determining the properties of pulp and the products made therefrom (e.g., cellophane, rayon).

2. Does Each Cellulose Chain Contain the Same Number of Glucose Units?

Although early workers often observed considerable variations in alkali solubility with different samples of cellulose, they could not explain this phenomenon as the samples appeared to be chemically identical.

Then, Berl and Klaye (13), by working with cellulose nitrates that were obtained from degraded and undegraded cotton, found that solutions from the undegraded cotton exhibited higher viscosities than solutions from a degraded sample. This led to the opinion that cellulose must exist in different molecular sizes, and that the viscosity of solutions of cellulose or cellulose derivatives increased with the size of the chain molecules.

Later it was also found that, on adding successive portions of a nonsolvent to a solution of cellulose or a cellulose derivative (such as cellulose nitrate or cellulose acetate), the precipitated fractions showed markedly different solution properties (e.g., viscosity, solubility, etc.), but no detectable chemical difference.

The most soluble fractions were found to have the lowest molecular weight (number average as determined by osmotic pressure), whereas the least soluble had the highest (142). Since cellulose had been shown to consist of linear chains of glucose units, this meant that different cellulose chains were made up of different numbers of glucose residues, and that each original cellulose sample contained a spectrum of cellulose chains of different length.

3. What Is the Nature of the Linkages between the Glucose Units?

The glucosidic bond could be either an α- or a β-glucosidic bond and, furthermore, it might be attached to the 4 or 5 position in the adjacent hexose unit, thus leaving uncertain whether the hexose units had a 1, 4- or a 1, 5-cyclic structure. In order to clarify these points, intermediate products obtained during the degradation of cellulose to glucose had to be studied.

The early work of Franchimont (55,56), and later confirmations by Skraup (203) and Willstätter and Zechmeister (230), showed that a disaccharide—cellobiose—is formed as an intermediate in the hydrolytic degradation of cellulose to glucose, and that cellobiose further decomposes to glucose as the reaction is carried to completion.

The fact that cellobiose was resistant to yeast maltase (204), but was readily hydrolyzed to glucose by emulsin (48,183) showed that the linkage between the two glucose units must be a β- rather than an α-glucosidic link.

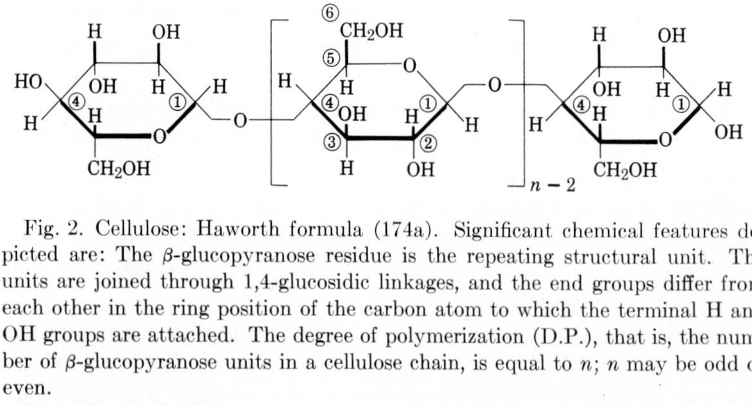

Fig. 2. Cellulose: Haworth formula (174a). Significant chemical features depicted are: The β-glucopyranose residue is the repeating structural unit. The units are joined through 1,4-glucosidic linkages, and the end groups differ from each other in the ring position of the carbon atom to which the terminal H and OH groups are attached. The degree of polymerization (D.P.), that is, the number of β-glucopyranose units in a cellulose chain, is equal to n; n may be odd or even.

Stereochemical relationships are emphasized by heavy and light lines in the formalized three-dimensional perspective formula. Heavy lines in the rings indicate those portions nearest the observer. Heavy vertical bonds join to the ring the substituent groups which lie above the plane of the ring; light bonds, those which lie below. Thus, the completely *trans* arrangement of the ring substituents —that is, hydroxyl groups, primary alcohol groups and glucosidic linkages—is evident. The Haworth-type formula also shows that adjacent rings are turned 180° to each other but does not show the puckered arrangement of the six atoms in the ring.

More recent confirmation of the β-glucosidic structure of cellulose has been obtained by comparison of the infrared absorption spectrum of cellulose and starch with their α and β oligomers (8). Thus, it was found that all the low molecular weight β-glucosidic compounds, and also cellulose, showed an absorption maximum at 891 ± 7 cm.$^{-1}$ (11.2 μ), whereas the compounds containing α-glucosidic links do not.

Zechmeister and Toth (234) also prepared cellotriose, cellotetraose, and another sugar, which was probably cellopentaose. This series has recently been extended to celloheptaose by Wolfrom and coworkers (231). They then submitted their cellotriose to acetolysis, obtaining cellobiose octaacetate. This showed that cellotriose was a cellobiosyl glucose, and suggested that the entire series of oligosaccharides was probably made up of anhydro-β-glucopyranose units linked together in an open chain. This is well represented in terms of Haworth's structural formula (70,72), shown in Fig. 2, which has been confirmed by both x-ray and methylation results.

The position of the glucosidic link in cellobiose was determined by Zemplén, Haworth, Hirst, and their collaborators (73,74) through the preparation of derivatives according to classical organic methods. This work proved conclusively that the glucosidic bond in cellobiose was a 1,4 rather than 1,5 bond, and that cellobiose was, therefore, 4(β-D-glucopyranosyl)D-glucopyranose.

4. Are All the Linkages in Cellulose Identical?

This question has been answered in the affirmative as the result of extensive studies by Freudenberg and others who used a number of different approaches. We shall discuss these briefly.

a. Chemical Proof

The preparation and identification of the methylated derivatives of glucose, cellobiose, cellotriose, cellotetraose, and cellulose by the classical methods of organic chemistry provide chemical proof (58,59) of the β-glucosidic structure of cellulose.

b. Polarimetric Proof

Freudenberg and co-workers (58) showed that the observed optical rotations of cellulose, cellulose acetate, and methylated cellulose, in different solvents, agreed very well with the values calculated from the respective short-chain intermediates (cellobiose and cellotriose), assuming that all chain units were β-anhydroglucose units. This polarimetric proof was confirmed for cellopentaose and also for cellohexaose and celloheptaose (231).

c. Kinetic Proof

Freudenberg, Kuhn, and co-workers subjected cellulose to acid hydrolysis and showed that if it were assumed that all the glucosidic bonds in cellulose were equivalent (correction was made for the somewhat faster rate of cleavage of the bond adjacent to the reducing end of the chain molecules) it was possible to account quantitatively for the cause of the changes in optical rotation and in reducing power during the hydrolysis (59,60,125).

d. Static Proof

This method involves determining the amounts of the various oligosaccharides formed during acid hydrolysis. Thus, the low yields of the intermediate compounds were satisfactorily explained on the basis of a mathematical treatment by Kuhn (124), which assumed that all glucosidic bonds are equivalent. The high yield of cellobiose octaacetate was also accounted for by the fact that the ready crystallization of this material from solution protected it from further degradation.

5. "Weak" Bonds

Owing to the large size of the cellulose molecule, a small number of nonglucosidic bonds are extremely hard to detect. This casts a shadow of doubt on the "proofs" discussed above, which were not sensitive enough to show that 100%, rather than only 99%, of the glucosidic bonds in cellulose were equivalent. Furthermore, in Kuhn's mathematical treatments, it was always assumed that the initial cellulose chains were all of the same length; this assumption, however, is not correct.

Attempts to eliminate these uncertainties have yielded valuable information on the molecular weight distribution of cellulose (see Section II-C-3), as well as on the kinetics of cellulose degradation (see Section III-D-1), and further, reduced the limit of error in Freudenberg's kinetic proof from perhaps 1% to about 0.1% of the glucosidic bonds in cellulose. These investigations have, however, also given rise to a heated controversy over the presence or absence of "weak" bonds in cellulose; to date, the controversy has not been settled conclusively. Recent evidence seems to favor the point of view that in the native state there are no "weak" bonds but, rather, that subsequent treatments of the cellulose may introduce groups, such as $C{=}O$ groups, which may "sensitize" the adjacent β-glucosidic bonds (178).

D. NATURE OF THE HYDROXYL GROUPS

Denham and Woodhouse (37) and, later, Irvine and Hirst (108) prepared methyl ether derivatives of cellulose, and found that the highest methoxyl content they could achieve was about 43%, from which they concluded that the derivative they had prepared corresponded to the trimethyl ether (OCH_3, 45.6%). Subsequent refinements improved the technique to the point where now it is possible to prepare almost completely methylated cellulose (OCH_3, ca. 45%). This information, together with the well-known experimental findings that the highest cellulose nitrate was a trinitrate (33) and the highest cellulose acetate was a triacetate (167), demonstrated conclusively that each glucose residue in cellulose must contain three hydroxyl groups.

Denham and Woodhouse, and Irvine and Hirst, also showed that on submitting their trimethylcellulose to hydrolytic degradation the final product was a simple crystalline trimethyl glucose. This proved that the three methoxyl groups occupied the *same* positions in every glucose unit; if they were otherwise arranged, isomeric trimethyl-glucoses would have been isolated.

The actual locations of the three hydroxyl groups turned out to be the 2, 3, and 6 positions. Thus, it was shown that the trimethyl glucose obtained by degradation of fully methylated cellulose contained unsubstituted hydroxyl groups in the 4 and 5 positions and, therefore, the anhydro-β-glucopyranose units of cellulose must have their hydroxyl groups in the 2, 3, and 6 positions.

The hydroxyl groups in cellulose can also be studied with regard to their characteristic bands in the infrared absorption spectrum (e.g., 17,52,123,137) and, in fact, it is even possible to differentiate between those that are hydrogen-bonded and those that are free. Thus, there are fundamental OH stretching bands at 1.5 and 2.0 μ which are characteristic of hydrogen-bonded hydroxyl groups, whereas free hydroxyl groups would have corresponding bands at

1.44 and 2.02 μ. Marrinan and Mann (137) have shown, in this manner, that at least in the crystalline regions of cellulose all the hydroxyl groups are hydrogen-bonded.

The question of hydrogen bonding has recently been studied extensively by Liang and Marchessault (127,128) who used polarized infrared spectra. They concluded that the most likely hydrogen bonds in native cellulose are the following: (1) *intra*molecular hydrogen bonding between the C_3 hydroxyl and the ring oxygen of contiguous glucose units, and (2) *inter*molecular hydrogen bonding between the C_6 hydroxyl and a bridge oxygen of a neighboring chain. (See also Section II-B-1.)

E. THE END GROUPS OF THE CELLULOSE MOLECULE

Haworth's formula (see Fig. 2) shows that the two terminal glucose residues not only differ from the glucose residues forming the chain itself, but also differ from each other. One contains a reducing hemiacetal group and is, therefore, known as the *reducing end group*, whereas the other contains an extra secondary hydroxyl group and is known as the *nonreducing end group*, which is shown in Fig. 3.

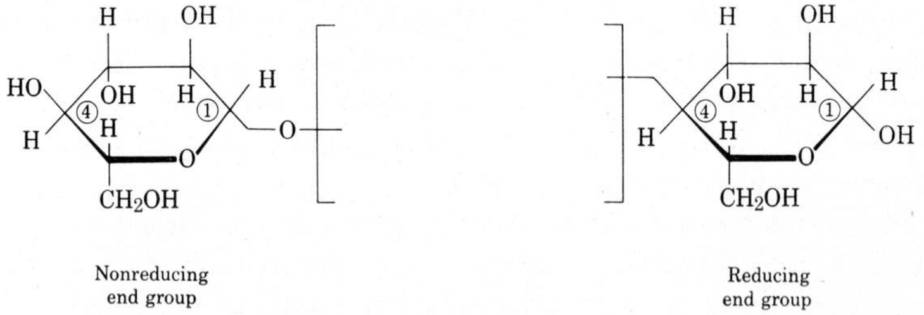

Nonreducing
end group

Reducing
end group

Fig. 3. Cellulose end groups.

The reducing end group has never been isolated in any of the degradation studies; the nonreducing end group, however, has been isolated by Haworth and Machemer (75) in the form of crystalline, 2, 3, 4, 6-tetramethyl glucose. These end groups are present in native cellulose, and they are also obtained during strictly hydrolytic cleavage where, for each glucosidic bond cut, two new end groups—one of each type—will appear. For this reason, the determination of end groups has been used as a means of measuring the molecular weight of cellulose as well as for following the course of hydrolytic degradation. Degradation by other than hydrolytic means (e.g., oxidative), however, may result in the formation of entirely different types of end groups.

F. CARBOXYL GROUPS IN CELLULOSE

The acidic nature of unpurified cellulose is due to the presence of substances such as lignin and polyglucuronic acids, which occur together with the cellulose. It is also believed that in the plant the oxidation of cellulose to polyglucuronic acid may occur to a degree. By further decarboxylation, xylan may be formed, as shown in Fig. 4.

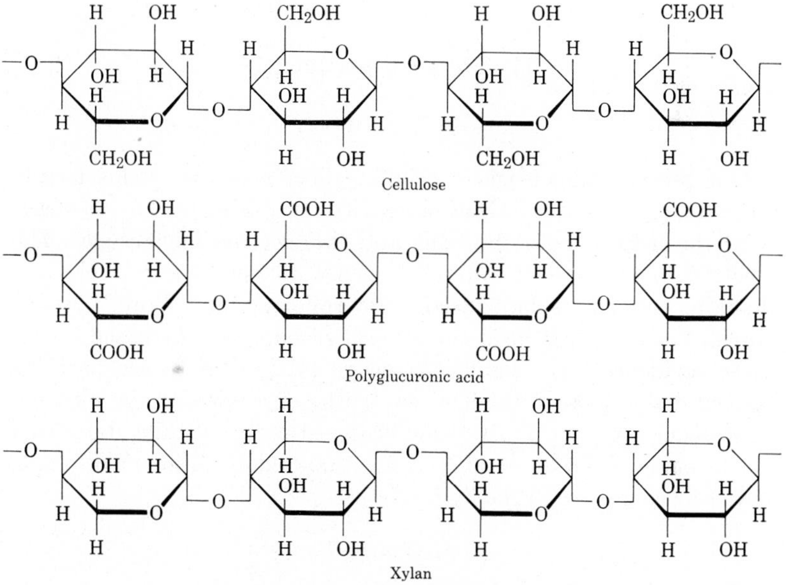

Fig. 4. Chain formulas of cellulose and related substances.

Whether there really are carboxyl groups in pure, native cellulose has never been conclusively decided, due to the difficulty of purifying the cellulose without causing oxidation. However, current opinion favors the hypothesis that true native cellulose contains no carboxyl groups, and that the carboxyl-containing materials should be more correctly classified as hemicelluloses.

The industrial importance of carboxyl groups in cellulose results from the peculiar properties imparted to pulp by even a small number of them. These groups may also give rise to the yellowing of pulp if stored after bleaching (97), and they also seem to play a role in hydrolytic degradation (178).

The amount of carboxyl groups present in different cellulose preparations is sometimes used as an indication of the degree of damage to cotton and other textile materials from bleaching. Extensive work by Ant-Wuorinen and co-workers (3) has led to the development of reliable methods for determining the carboxyl group content of different celluloses. Here, again, the infrared absorption spectrum may be used to determine the presence of carboxyl groups through the characteristic $C{=}O$ absorption band at 5.7 to 5.8 μ (53).

II. Physical Structure

A. MORPHOLOGY

Our present knowledge of cellulose fiber structure stems largely from the results of investigations carried out during the last 20 years, with the help of both the light and the electron microscope. The electron microscope has literally opened to our eyes a whole new domain, termed "submicroscopic morphology" by Frey-Wyssling which, hitherto, had been the subject of suppositions based on indirect evidence. The light microscope permits us to see particles having dimensions of about a few tenths of a micron; the electron microscope provides direct vision of fine-structure details, down to a resolution of about 30 to 50 A. (i.e., a 100-fold extension of resolving power as compared to the light microscope).

1. Macrostructure

When viewed under the light microscope, except for some minor details, all cellulose fibers have essentially the same structure. This structure consists of (1) a *primary wall*, which is quite thin (ca. 0.1 μ in thickness) and contains mostly noncellulosic substances such as waxes and pectin, (2) a *secondary wall*, which may vary in thickness (ca. 1 to 4 μ), depending on the maturity of the fiber, and which contains almost all the cellulose present in the fiber (ca. 95% by weight), and (3) the *lumen*, or central canal which, usually, is quite narrow (especially with the bast fibers), and is composed mainly of proteinaceous materials.

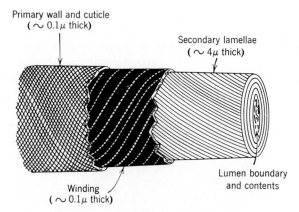

Primary wall and cuticle
(∿ 0.1μ thick)

Secondary lamellae
(∿ 4μ thick)

Lumen boundary
and contents

Winding
(∿0.1μ thick)

Fig. 5. Schematic representation of structural parts of cotton fiber (221).

Of all the naturally occurring cellulosic materials, cotton has been the most thoroughly microscopically investigated fiber (27,92,184, 185,221), and a fairly complete picture of its morphology has been established. Figure 5 schematically illustrates the position and general features of the different fiber elements of cotton.

Whereas the cotton plant produces only one type of fiber, wood is made up of many different fibers or cells (see Figs. 6 and 7). These are

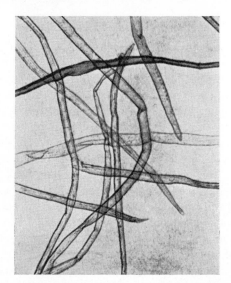

Fig. 6. Cells from a softwood (92). Magnification × 50.

held together by an isotropic, noncellulosic layer (mostly pectin and lignin) called the middle lamella. Similar to cotton, the individual cells consist of a thin primary wall (0.5 μ), a thick secondary wall that may be subdivided into an outer, central, and inner zone, and a lumen or central canal that is large and empty. A schematic cross section of wood fiber cells is shown in Fig. 8. The secondary wall

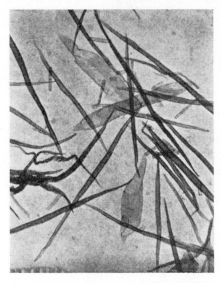

Fig. 7. Cells from a hardwood (92). Magnification $\times$ 50.

consists of concentric layers in which the cellulose is present in the form of fibrils. These are usually oriented in this manner: those in the outer and inner zones are transverse to the fiber axis, while those in the central zone are roughly parallel to the fiber axis (220,228). This arrangement gives rise to the ballooning effects, similar to those found with cotton, observed on swelling the fibers in alkali.

Contrary to the cotton fiber, the secondary wall of wood also contains a considerable amount of lignin, probably as a sheath around each individual fibril rather than as a sheet between two layers of fibrils. This view is supported by the micrographs in Fig. 9, which show sections of wood specimens before and after removal of lignin and hemicellulose from the cellulose framework (190). The composition of different cell-wall layers of deciduous and coniferous wood fibers has also been determined recently by Meier (145), and

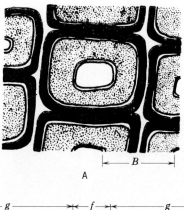

A

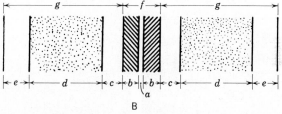

B

Fig. 8. The compound cell wall of wood fibers (93a). Key: A, cross section of fiber; B, section of two adjacent cell walls; a, intercellular substance; b, primary (cambial) wall; c, outer layer secondary wall; d, central layer secondary wall; e, inner layer secondary wall; f, compound middle lamella; g, complete secondary wall.

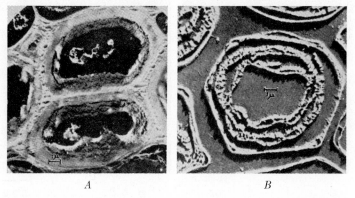

A   B

Fig. 9. Electron micrographs of wood fiber sections (190). The sections are cut from willow tree at right angles to the fiber axis; before (A) and after (B) lignin and hemicellulose were removed from the cellulose framework. Magnification 3500 ×.

information about the chemical composition of the middle lamella, the primary wall, and the secondary wall is now available.

2. Fine Structure

From observations obtained with the light microscope, the general conclusion can be drawn that in native celluloses, regardless of origin,

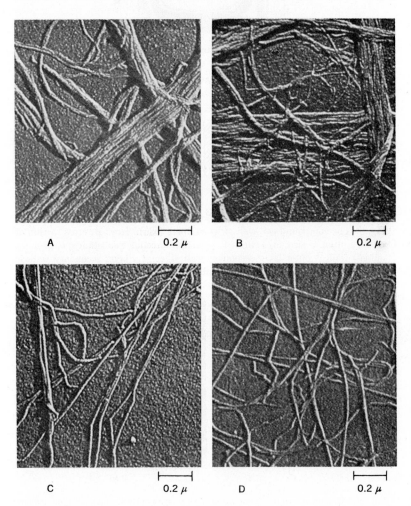

A   0.2 μ   B   0.2 μ

C   0.2 μ   D   0.2 μ

Fig. 10. Electron micrographs (47,000 ×). *A*, Egyptian cotton; *B*, spruce wood pulp; *C*, animal cellulose (tunicin); and *D*, bacterial cellulose (*acetobacter xylinum*). (Courtesy of B. G. Rånby.)

the cellulose is present in the form of fibrils. These fibrils were found to approximate a few tenths of a micron in diameter (i.e., near the limit of resolution of the light microscope) and, therefore, nothing further could be said about their detailed structure. With the aid of the electron microscope, however, the fine structure of the fibrils is visible, and it is found that they are composed of still finer microfibrils, about 100 A. in diameter and of indefinite length (115,143,175) (see Figs. 10A, B, C, and D).

The diameter of these microfibrils has been the subject of some controversy because other investigators (62,174) have reported diameters as large as 200 to 400 A. The larger values may, however, be the result of aggregation of several microfibrils into what appears to be a single filament. On the electron micrographs of highest resolution, it can be seen that, although such filaments are quite common, they clearly resolve themselves into individual microfibrils (diameter about 100 A.) if their course is followed for some distance. It has been found that the average diameter of the microfibrils apparently depends on the origin of the cellulose and increases in the order: wood < cotton < bacterial cellulose < animal cellulose < ramie (175). This order runs parallel to the increasing resistance of these celluloses toward hydrolytic degradation, as well as with other properties depending on crystallinity and orientation of the cellulose under consideration.

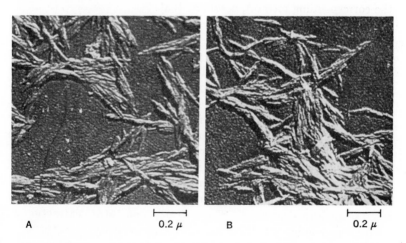

A   0.2 μ   B   0.2 μ

Fig. 11. Electron micrographs (47,000 ×) of A, hydrolyzed cotton, and B, hydrolyzed wood pulp.

The observed microfibrils have been called "micelle-strings" by Rånby (175), which is a suitable term, in view of the correlation with x-ray results from which it was estimated that the crystalline *micelles* (see Section II-B-2b) in native celluloses were ca. 50 to 70 A. wide and had a minimum length of 300 to 600 A. (76). Recent small-angle x-ray scattering experiments have also given a value of about 60 A. for the width of the micelles or crystallites (122). If the micelle-strings are assumed to be circular in diameter (see, however, ref. 61), then a diameter of 100 A. would correspond to a micelle or micro-crystallite of 240 cellulose chains.

With regard to the length of the cellulose micelles, the electron microscope has also yielded some informative data. Thus, upon heterogeneous hydrolytic degradation of native cotton and wood cellulose, the micelle-strings seen in Figs. 10A and 10B are broken down into cigar-shaped rodlets of lengths varying from about 300 to about 700 A. (see Figs. 11A and 11B) (101).

In general, the wood celluloses exhibit shorter hydrolysis particles than the cotton celluloses, but the pretreatment undergone by the material before hydrolysis also affects the length. The width of these hydrolysis particles corresponds to that of the original micelle-strings, and their length corresponds not only with the previously cited x-ray data, but also checks very well with the length calculated from the osmotically determined number-average degree of polymerization (of the corresponding nitrate), assuming that:

$$\text{chain length} = (\overline{\text{DP}})(5.15 \text{ A.})$$

where 5.15 A. is the length of a glucose unit (101). This indicates that the hydrolysis has removed the amorphous regions from the micelle-strings, leaving behind the resistant portions (i.e., the micro-crystallites or micelles).

The *arrangement* and *orientation* of the micelle-strings in the various morphological units of native cellulose fibers has also been made visible with the help of electron microscopy. Thus, fragments of primary wall, winding, secondary wall, and lumen have been isolated from cotton fibers and examined in the electron microscope (184,185, 221) and, in general, the conclusions obtained from light optical microscopy are confirmed. The *primary wall*, after extraction of waxes and pectic materials, appears to be a crisscross network of microfibrils or micelle-strings, the outer surface appearing to contain microfibrils oriented roughly parallel to the fiber axis, the inner sur-

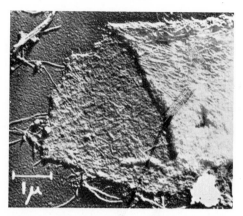

Fig. 12. Electron micrograph (11,000 ×) of the primary wall of a cotton fiber (161).

face microfibrils with transverse orientation (see Fig. 12). The first layer of the secondary wall, i.e., *the winding*, shows extended areas of highly oriented microfibrils, separated by regions of coarse microfibrils interlaced with some at right angles to them (see Fig. 13).

Fig. 13. Electron micrograph (11,500 ×) of single thickness of winding from raw cotton fiber (221).

The *secondary wall* shows very highly parallel orientation of the microfibrils in the form of lamellas (see Fig. 14), which is also the case in the secondary wall of flax, ramie, and wood pulp fibers (e.g., 161,166,233). The lumen shows no fibrillar structure at all, but only a series of granules can be distinguished (21).

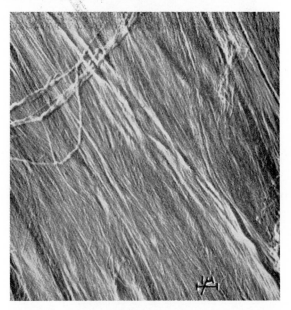

Fig. 14. Electron micrograph (5,000 ✕) of portion of secondary wall (185).

Wood fibers have been extensively studied in the electron microscope (143,161,227) and show a similar fine structure to that of cotton fibers. Thus, there is a primary wall (thickness ∼0.1 μ) in which the microfibrils or micelle-strings form an interwoven network. The secondary wall is apparently made up of three well-defined entities: adjacent to the primary wall, there is a transition layer (Übergangs-lamelle; thickness ∼0.2 μ), which consists of layers of microfibrils crossing each other and making an angle of 40 to 50° with the fiber axis; the central layer (thickness ∼1 to 5 μ) consists of highly parallel microfibrils, making an angle of only a few degrees (e.g., Preston finds 18°) with the fiber axis; the third subdivision consists of a layer (thickness ∼0.1 μ), adjacent to the lumen, where the microfibrils are lying parallel to the fiber axis. This layer has been called "tertiary wall," and it can be clearly made visible by exposing the wood fiber to a fungus specific for cellulose, which will dissolve the cellulose of the secondary wall but leave behind the tertiary wall (143). The tertiary wall surface, forming the wall of the central canal or lumen, is covered with granules with the softwood tracheids, and is smooth with hardwood fibers.

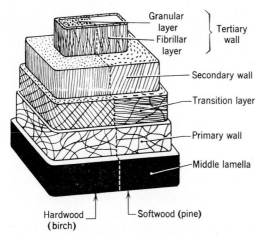

Fig. 15. Model of fine structure of hardwood (left half) and softwood (right half) fibers (143).

A comparison of the fine structure of wood fibers is shown in Fig. 15.
The middle lamella, which is the part between two adjacent wood fibers, has no fibrillar structure and consists mainly of lignin (5).

B. MOLECULAR STRUCTURE

1. Crystal Structure

X-ray diffraction techniques had been applied to cellulose as early as 1913, when Nishikawa and Ono (165) showed that the x-ray diagrams of cellulose consisted of definite diffraction rings. This led to the conclusion that cellulose must contain small crystallites oriented parallel to the fiber axis. The systematic and more widely known work of Herzog and Jancke (85) not only put the analysis of the x-ray diagrams on a more quantitative basis, but showed that with a number of native celluloses of widely different origin the x-ray reflections corresponding to the different lattice planes were at identical positions in the diagram and these celluloses must, therefore, have

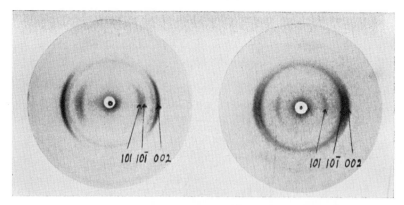

Figs. 16 and 17. X-ray diagrams of cotton (95a). Left, native (Cellulose I); right, mercerized (Cellulose II).

identical crystalline structures. It has since been shown that all native celluloses (with the possible exception of the marine plant *Halicystis*) have essentially the same type of x-ray diagram and therefore the same crystal structure, which is known as *Cellulose I*.

When the cellulose chains are all oriented more or less in a single direction, as in the case of a cotton fiber, a so-called x-ray fiber diagram results. An example of a typical x-ray fiber diagram of *Cellulose I* is shown in Fig. 16 (Fig. 17 shows the corresponding diagram for *Cellulose II*).

The strongest reflections are those corresponding to the 101, 10$\bar{1}$, and 002 lattice planes (see Fig. 18), which have been marked in all the x-ray diagrams. Table I (147), gives the corresponding reflection angle (2θ) and lattice plane spacings (*d*-values).

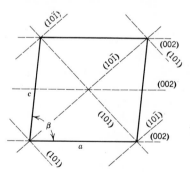

Fig. 18. Principal paratropic planes in Cellulose I (232).

TABLE I

Equatorial Reflections of Native Cellulose (147)

Lattice plane		Reflection angle	Lattice plane spacing
Miller	Herzog	(2θ; degrees)	(d-values)
101	A_1	14.6	6.05 A.
10$\bar{1}$	A_2	16.2	5.45 A.
002	A_4	22.6	3.92 A.

The lattice plane spacings may also be determined by means of electron diffraction. Thus, when fast electrons interact with the electrostatic field of an atomic nucleus, they are scattered, and the resulting diffracted electron beams are intense even from a crystalline layer containing few lattice planes. The electron diffraction diagram of a polycrystalline substance such as cellulose forms a system of concentric rings, similar to an x-ray powder diagram. Figure 19A shows an electron diffraction diagram of native wood cellulose (176).

Using Bragg's law and having determined the wave length of the electrons from diffraction diagrams of substances containing known lattices (e.g., magnesium oxide, graphite, gold, etc.), the lattice plane spacings can be calculated. Very good agreement between x-ray and electron diffraction results may be obtained.

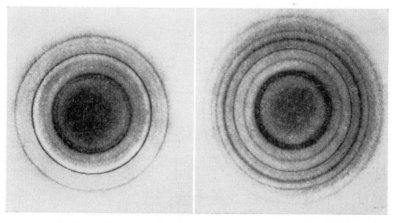

Fig. 19. Electron diffraction diagrams of *A*, native, and *B*, mercerized, wood cellulose (176).

The quantitative interpretation of the x-ray data in order to establish a *crystallographic unit cell* for cellulose was first undertaken by Polanyi (171) and then by Sponsler (206). Meyer and Mark (148,149), however, were the first to postulate a monoclinic unit cell which, after revision by Meyer and Misch (150,151) and confirmation by the results of Gross and Clark (67), became the accepted unit cell for native cellulose (*Cellulose I*).

$a =$ 8.2 A.
$b =$ 10.3 A.   (identity period along the fiber axis)
$c =$ 7.9 A.
$\beta =$ 84°   (according to current crystallographic usage β should be $180 - 84 = 96°$)

The Meyer-Misch unit cell of *Cellulose I* (see Fig. 20) contains four glucose residues (calculated on the basis of 1.57 as the specific

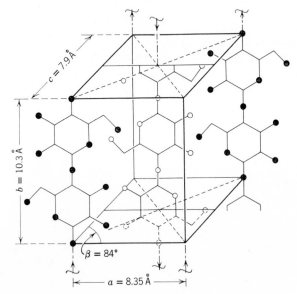

Fig. 20. Unit cell of Cellulose I (149–151).

gravity of cellulose), and each glucose ring of the chain is rotated through 180° with respect to its neighbors, thus obeying the screw-axis requirement corresponding to the x-ray fiber diagram. The glucose residues are all linked to each other through 1,4 linkages as required by the chemical evidence. For the distance between carbon atoms, 1.54 A. was used and, for the distance between carbon and oxygen atoms, 1.35 A. The planes of the glucose units lie in the *ab* plane of the unit cell which gives the strongest diffraction lines, and the axes of the cellulose chains lie along the *b* axis, with each chain having the symmetry of a diagonal screw axis. There are two sets of chains, corresponding to the two independent sets of screw axes and, it is believed, as indicated in the figure, that they run in opposite directions.

The distances between the atoms of the different chains in the Meyer-Misch unit cell determine the nature of the forces which hold the cellulose lattice together. Thus, the glucose residues along the *b* axis are held together by main valence bonds (i.e., the 1,4-β-glucosidic bonds). Along the *a* axis the anhydroglucose rings are separated by a distance of 2.5 A., and hydrogen bonding may, therefore, occur quite readily. Along the *c*-axis the nearest distance between atoms is about 3.1 A. and, therefore, in this direction, the lattice may be held together by van der Waals forces.

In recent years, however, evidence has started to accumulate that indicates that the Meyer and Misch unit cell is *not* a correct representation of crystal structure of *Cellulose I*. Thus, Honjo and Watanabe (94) have obtained electron diffraction diagrams of *Valonia ventricosa* cellulose which show certain reflections that cannot be indexed on the basis of the Meyer and Misch unit cell, but would require *a* and *c* axes twice as long as those shown in Fig. 20 and a space group symmetry different from P2$_1$ which had been selected by Meyer and Misch. These findings were confirmed more recently by Fisher and Mann (49), who further concluded that the unit cell must have triclinic symmetry even though it has a monoclinic shape ($\alpha = \gamma = 90°$, $\beta \neq 90°$) and that, therefore, it must belong to space group P1.

Also for ramie, on the basis of x-ray intensity measurements, Jones (110) found that the observed intensities do not correspond to the ones calculated for the Meyer-Misch unit cell. However, in this case it seems that the larger dimensions required for the unit cell of *Valonia ventricosa* are not required.

It remains to be seen whether the Meyer-Misch unit cell is also inadequate for wood cellulose, but the fact that it cannot be reconciled with crystallographic results and stereochemical considerations for *Valonia ventricosa* and for ramie indicates that further work with refined techniques is also required in the case of wood cellulose.

Apart from the unit cell dimensions it is, of course, of interest to determine the exact position of all the atoms in the cellulose unit cell and to find out the location of the hydrogen bonds. Such information can readily be obtained for pure crystalline compounds from x-ray work alone. However, native cellulose, even in its purest forms such as bacterial cellulose or ramie, is still not a pure crystalline substance and, therefore, the x-ray information must be combined with information from other sources. Infrared absorption spectra using polarized radiation have proved especially valuable in this respect.

Thus, Tsuboi (222) showed that the polarized infrared spectra, especially in the 2700 to 3100 cm.$^{-1}$ region, cannot be interpreted in accordance with the orientation of the CH_2 groups in the crystal structure proposed by Meyer and Misch. To obtain better agreement between the infrared results and the crystal structure, Tsuboi suggests rotation of the CH_2OH group of each glucose unit around the C_5—C_6 bond by about 45° from the position shown in Fig. 21, which is a spatial representation of the Meyer-Misch cell with the anhydro-

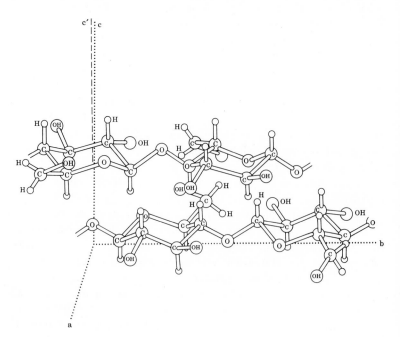

Fig. 21. Representation of the Meyer-Misch unit cell after Tsuboi (222).

glucose units in the preferred "armchair" conformation. It should be pointed out, however, that Mann and Marrinan (134) have questioned this suggestion on the basis that all the C—H bonds cannot be exactly perpendicular to the *ab* plane, that they are in fact inclined toward each other, which causes coupling between vibrations of different CH groups and will therefore affect the infrared spectrum.

Perhaps the most detailed assignment of bonds in the infrared spectrum is that of Liang and Marchessault (128,129) for bacterial cellulose. Their results are shown in Tables II and III, which represent the two important regions of the cellulose spectrum. Especially the 3 μ region of the spectrum, which is shown in Fig. 22, yields

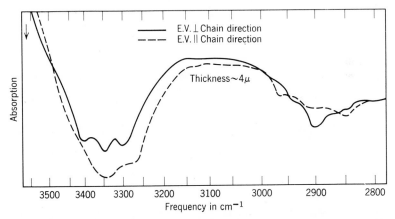

Fig. 22. Absorption spectrum of cellulose, using polarized infrared radiation (127.)

considerable information about the hydrogen bonds in native cellulose. Thus, Liang and Marchessault conclude that there is *intra*molecular hydrogen bonding between the C_3 hydroxyl group of one glucose residue and the ring oxygen of the next residue. They also propose two sets of *inter*molecular hydrogen bonds: in the 101 plane the C_6 hydroxyls of the antiparallel chains are joined to the bridge oxygens of the adjacent parallel chains; in the 10$\bar{1}$ plane the C_6 hydroxyls of the parallel chains are hydrogen-bonded to the bridge oxygens of the adjacent antiparallel chains. These different hydrogen bonds are shown in Fig. 23.

The final proof of the crystal structure of cellulose will probably result from current work by Rånby (177), Manley (133), and others,

TABLE II

Infrared Spectrum of Cellulose I (2800–3550 cm.$^{-1}$) (128)

Frequency, cm.$^{-1}$

Valonia or bacterial cellulose	Ramie cellulose	Polari- zation	Interpretation
2853	2853	$\parallel$	CH$_2$ sym. stretching
2870	2870	$\perp$	
2897		$\perp$	CH stretching
	2910	$\perp$	
2914		$\perp$	
2945	2945	$\perp$	CH$_2$ antisym. stretching
2970	2970	$\parallel$	CH stretching
3245	—	$\parallel$	
3275	3275	$\parallel$	
3305	3305	$\perp$	OH stretching (intermolecular hydrogen bonds in 101 plane)
3350	3350	$\parallel$	OH stretching (intramolecular hydrogen bonds)
3375	3375	$\parallel$	
3405	3405	$\perp$	OH stretching (intermolecular hydrogen bonds in 101 plane)
—	3450	$\parallel$	Cellulose II impurity?

who have been able to isolate *single crystals* of cellulose by precipitation of cellulose derivatives, e.g., cellulose acetate (see Fig. 24), from dilute solution and subsequent regeneration of the cellulose. Such a lamellar single crystal consists of folded cellulose chains, and x-ray or electron diffraction work should lead to complete clarification of the crystal structure.

Modifications of the Crystal Structure

Besides the crystal lattice of native cellulose (*Cellulose I*), several modifications of the crystal structure have been reported, the most important one being *Cellulose II*, which is found in "hydrate," "mercerized," and regenerated cellulose. The subject of mercerization will be treated also in Section III. Consequently it may suffice at this point to say that, on treating Cellulose I with strong

TABLE III

Infrared Spectrum of Native Cellulose (640–1700 cm.$^{-1}$) (129)

Frequency cm.$^{-1}$	Relative intensity	Polarization	Assignment
663	m	⊥	} OH out-of-plane bending
~700	m	⊥	
~740	sd	⊥?	CH$_2$ rocking?
~800	sd	⊥?	ring breathing (β)
895	w	‖	antisymmetrical out of phase stretching
985	sd	⊥?	
1000	sd	‖?	
1015	m	‖	} C—O stretching
1035	s	‖	
1058	s	‖	
1110	s	‖	antisymmetrical in phase ring stretching
1125	sd	‖	
1162	s	‖	antisymmetrical bridge oxygen stretching
1205	w	⊥	OH in-plane bending?
1235	w	‖	
1250	w	⊥	
1282	m	‖	CH bending
1317	m	⊥	CH$_2$ wagging
1336	m	⊥	OH in-plane bending
1358	m	‖	
1374	m	‖	CH bending
1430	m	‖	CH$_2$ bending
1455	sd	⊥	OH in-plane bending
~1635	—	—	adsorbed H$_2$O

alkali, which is subsequently washed out, a change in the crystal structure to Cellulose II occurs. This transformation is evident from a comparison of the x-ray and electron diffraction diagrams of mercerized (Cellulose II) and native (Cellulose I) cellulose, shown in Figs. 16, 17, and 19.

The change that occurs in the crystal lattice in the transition from Cellulose I to Cellulose II is perhaps best illustrated by Fig. 25 (Andress (2)).

The conformation of the cellulose chains in the Cellulose II structure and the position of the hydrogen bonds have been studied recently by Mann and Marrinan (135) and by Marchessault and

Liang (136). Figure 26 shows the arrangement of the hydrogen bonds in Cellulose II proposed by Mann and Marrinan.

Other polymorphic forms of cellulose have been reported, such as *Cellulose III* and *Cellulose IV;* however, it is possible that these

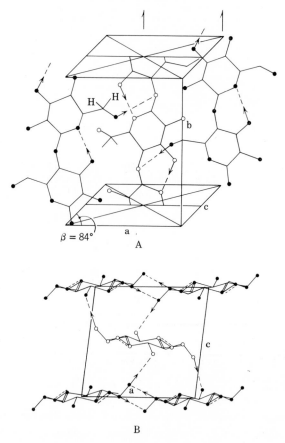

Fig. 23. Hydrogen bonds of Cellulose I (128). *A*, arrangement of CH_2OH groups in cellobiose unit; and *B*, hydrogen bonds in Cellulose I unit cell.

are not true polymorphic forms but only somewhat disordered versions of Celluloses II and I, respectively. The similarity of the corresponding unit cell dimensions, as summarized in Table IV, might appear to lend some support to this suggestion.

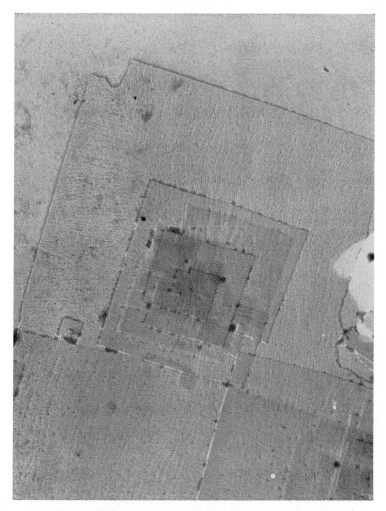

Fig. 24. Cellulose acetate single crystals (14,500 ×) (133).

It should be pointed out, however, that Marrinan and Mann (138) have shown that the infrared spectra of Cellulose III, prepared from Celluloses I or II, are not identical, and neither are the spectra of Cellulose IV, prepared from Cellulose I (via Cellulose III) and Cellulose II. This implies that differences in the molecular packing are involved, rather than differences in the degree of perfection of

TABLE IV

The Unit Cell Dimensions of Polymorphic Forms of Cellulose[a]

		Dimensions			
		a	b	c	β
Cellulose	Type of cell	Angstroms			(degrees)
I	Monoclinic	8.2	10.3	7.9	83
II	Monoclinic	8.0	10.3	9.1	62
III	Monoclinic (hexagonal)	8.6	10.3	8.6	60
IV	Orthorhombic	8.1	10.3	7.9	90

[a] After Wellard (229).

crystals having the same basic molecular arrangement. The behavior of *Cellulose III$_I$* and *Cellulose III$_{II}$* (i.e., Cellulose III, derived from Celluloses I and II, respectively) toward water, which shows that

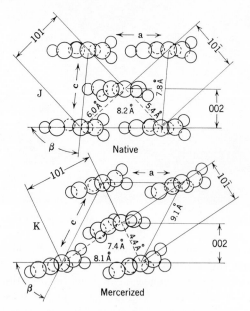

Fig. 25. View down *b* axis of unit cell of native (Cellulose I) and mercerized (Cellulose II) cellulose, showing the location of the *a* and *c* axes, angle β, and the 101, 10$\overline{1}$, and 002 planes (2,95a).

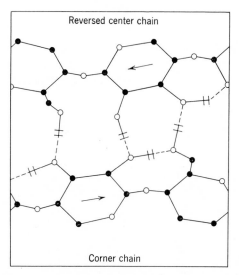

Fig. 26. Suggested arrangement of hydrogen bonds in Cellulose II (135).

these materials revert to their respective starting materials, further supports this concept.

2. Crystallinity

a. Crystalline and Amorphous Regions

Cellulose consists of crystalline (highly ordered) as well as amorphous (disordered) regions. These regions do not have clearly defined boundaries, but there seems to be a transition from an orderly arrangement of the cellulose chains in a three-dimensional crystal lattice (such regions have been called *microcrystallites* or *micelles*) to a disordered or amorphous state, where the cellulose chains show much less orientation with respect to each other. With different celluloses, the relative amounts of material in the microcrystallites and in the amorphous regions, as well as the degree of order within the microcrystallites, are not the same. Thus, the lattice order for wood, cotton, animal, and algal (from *Valonia* algae) cellulose increases in the sequence stated (175). This is shown in Fig. 27, which presents the photometer curves obtained by measuring the intensities of the reflections on the x-ray powder diagrams (179).

Various attempts have been made to determine the "degree of

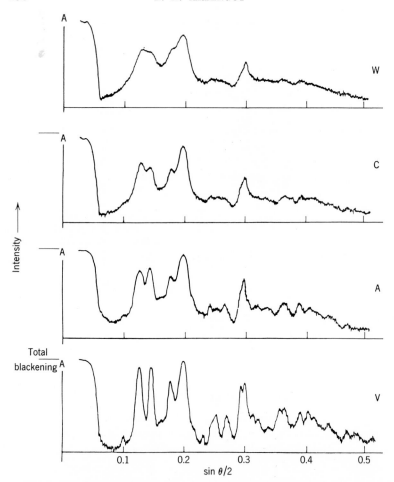

Fig. 27. Photometer curves of x-ray powder diagrams of different native cell-uloses (179). Curves with intensity vs. sin θ/2 of wood (*W*), cotton (*C*), animal (*A*), and algal (*V*, *Valonia*) cellulose, showing sharper reflections, i.e., a better lattice order, in the order given.

crystallinity," i.e., the relative amounts of cellulose in the crystalline (ordered) and amorphous (disordered) regions.

Thus, by comparison of the photometer curves, which show the intensities of the x-ray powder diagrams of native (ramie) and re-generated (rayon—Hermans filament) cellulose and, assuming that crystalline cellulose produces only discrete x-ray reflections whereas amorphous cellulose gives only background scattering, Hermans and Weidinger (80–82) obtain the following results: purified native cellulose (wood, cotton, ramie) is found to be 69 to 71% crystalline; mercerized cellulose, 48% crystalline; and regenerated cellulose fibers (viscose), 38 to 40% crystalline.

In the Hermans-Weidinger method, a certain amount of arbitrariness is involved in the drawing of the amorphous background curve, and the results are, therefore, not absolute. For this reason, Ant-Wuorinen (4) has proposed another method of evaluating the photometer curves of the x-ray diagrams, which yields a function called the "crystallinity index." However, the crystallinity index is characteristic of the degree of lateral order within the crystallites rather than of the amount of crystalline material. It is found to correspond fairly well with results of water sorption measurements.

Other methods for determining the degree of crystallinity in cellulose are based either on physical properties, such as density (78), water sorption (95), or the exchange with heavy water, D_2O (63), or on chemical reactions involving the transformation of cellulose into derivatives (e.g., mercerization to alkali-cellulose, see Section III), or its degradation (e.g., hydrolysis).

It should be realized that several of these methods do not measure crystallinity directly, but only the accessibility of the cellulose toward a reagent, which is an indirect way of determining crystallinity based

TABLE V

Crystallinity and Accessibility Measurements on Cellulose (179)

	Per cent			
	Crystallinity (X-ray diffraction)	Crystallinity (D_2O exchange)	Non-accessibility (HCl-$FeCl_3$)	Non-accessibility ($4N$ HCl)
Wood pulp (hot alkali refined)	70	54	92	—
Cotton linters (chemical grade)	70	—	95	88–89
Cotton	69–71	79	91	86
Mercerized cotton	48	—	84	68
Regenerated cellulose (viscose rayon)	38–40	34	73	62–69

on the assumption that only the amorphous regions are accessible. A further complication is that the accessibility depends on the lateral order within the microcrystallites as well as on the total amount of crystalline material.

Although all the above methods yield crystallinity values of the same relative order (see Table V), the x-ray results are usually somewhat higher than the results based on D_2O accessibility measurements. The hydrolysis results also give somewhat higher crystallinity values because a certain amount of recrystallization of cut chains is possible (e.g., 196). We may conclude from the results of the various methods that the amount of crystalline material and the lateral order within the microcrystallites usually runs in the order: cotton > wood pulp > mercerized cellulose > regenerated cellulose.

b. Dimensions of the Microcrystallites

The dimensions of the crystalline regions (microcrystallites or micelles) and how these are arranged in the cellulose fibers are questions that still lack a universally accepted answer.

Several methods have been used to determine the *size* of the microcrystallites. The first attempt was made by Herzog (84) and by Hengstenberg and Mark (76), who estimated the dimensions of the crystalline regions from the width of the x-ray interferences (the width increases with decreasing crystallite size). Since the lines due to lattice planes perpendicular to the fiber axis were found to be less wide than those due to planes parallel to the fiber axis, these authors concluded that the crystalline regions must be long and rodlike. They calculated for the microcrystallites in ramie a diameter of about 60 A. For viscose rayon, they calculated a crystallite diameter of about 40 A. and a length of at least 300 A.

X-ray scattering at *small angles* (less than 3°) also yields information about microcrystallite size. The interpretation of the small-angle x-ray diagrams has been the subject of considerable controversy and there is still some uncertainty as to whether the small-angle x-ray diagram yields information about the particle size or about the interparticle distance.

Although all the different interpretations yield results of about 40 to 100 A., showing some variation with the type of cellulose under investigation, the Kratky-Porod treatment (121,172), from a theoretical point of view, seems to be the one most applicable for dry cellulose. Heyn (88,89) has shown, however, that if the cellulose fibers are subjected to swelling in about 5% sodium hydroxide (both lower and higher concentrations are not suitable) the interparticle interference is eliminated, and particle size may be calculated successfully. The effect of such swelling on the small-angle x-ray diagram is shown in Fig. 28 (89).

Fig. 28. Small angle x-ray scattering by jute (89). Original size, distance from sample to film, 20 cm. Beam focused with curved crystal. (a) Fiber in dry state; (b) fiber swollen in water; (c) fiber swollen in 5 per cent sodium hydroxide; and (d) fiber swollen in 10 per cent sodium hydroxide.

Electron microscopy has provided us with a means for making the microcrystallites or micelles visible and obtaining direct information as to their shape and dimensions. Thus, if cellulose is subjected to hydrolytic degradation to remove the nonresistant (amorphous) cellulose, and then examined in the electron microscope, one sees particles (see Figs. 11A and 11B) whose width is roughly the same as that of the original cellulose microfibrils, i.e., about 100 A. (see Section II-A-2), and whose length is usually between 300 A. and 800 A., depending on the conditions of hydrolysis and the cellulose starting material. Some evidence also indicates that these particles are flat rather than of circular diameter and that they are perhaps best represented schematically in terms of Frey-Wyssling's picture (61) shown in Fig. 29.

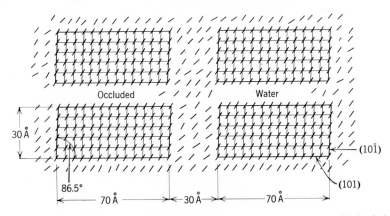

Fig. 29. Model of cross-sectional structure of cellulose elementary fibrils (microfibrils or "micelle strings") (61).

Although the exact length of the microcrystallites does not seem to be too meaningful, as it depends on the conditions of removal of the nonresistant portion of the cellulose, it should be pointed out that this length seems to check very well with the actual length of the cellulose molecules obtained by nitration and subsequent dissolution of these microcrystallites (101).

c. Orientation of the Microcrystallites

The problem of how the microcrystallites are oriented in the cellulose fiber has been investigated in several ways.

By a comparison of x-ray diffraction diagrams and photomicrographs for several different celluloses, it has been possible to show that the long axis of the cellulose microcrystallites must lie parallel to the axis of the fibrils visible in the light microscope (173,200).

The electron microscope has shown that the fibrils visible in the light microscope are made up of still finer microfibrils of about 100 A. in width (see Section II-A-2) and, by comparison with x-ray diffraction diagrams, it was shown that the orientation of these microfibrils in the cell wall corresponds to the orientation of the microcrystallites (185).

The small-angle x-ray scattering technique has also provided information about the orientation of the microcrystallites with respect to the fiber axis. The usefulness of this method has been demonstrated, especially, by the extensive work of Heyn (88,89) with cotton, bast, leaf, and regenerated fibers and of Wardrop with wood fibers (227). Figure 30 (88) shows how the small-angle x-ray diagram varies with

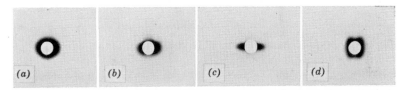

Fig. 30. Small angle scattering of monofilaments of regenerated cellulose (88). (*a*) No stretch or torsion; (*b*) low stretch; (*c*) high stretch; and (*d*) torsion.

differences in the orientation of the microcrystallites with respect to the fiber axis.

Still another way of obtaining information about the orientation of the microcrystallites or micelles and the lattice order within them is from measurements of the optical birefringence. Thus, in an anisotropic body, where the electrons of the medium are not distributed at random, the interaction between them and the light waves passing through the body will occur to a different extent in different directions. This means that in the direction of highest electron density, the light will be slowed down most and the refractive index will be a maximum. If we consider a cellulose microcrystallite as a uniaxial crystal, then the refractive index along its optical axis will be the maximum refractive index, n_γ, and the one in a direction perpendicular to the optical axis will be the minimum refractive index, n_α.

The birefringence is the numerical difference $(n_\gamma - n_\alpha)$ between the maximum and the minimum refractive indices, and its magnitude provides a measure of the degree of lateral order within the fiber. This is illustrated in Table VI (79).

TABLE VI

Birefringence of Native and Regenerated Cellulose Fibers (79)

Fiber	$n_\gamma - n_\alpha$
Ramie	0.069
Flax	0.054
Cotton	0.046
Agave perfoliata	0.017
Viscose rayon (10% stretch)	0.053
Viscose rayon (80% stretch)	0.074
Viscose rayon (120% stretch)	0.088

C. SOLUTION PROPERTIES

1. Solubility of Cellulose

With a nonpolar, noncrystalline (amorphous) polymer (e.g., polystyrene), it is relatively simple to find a solvent which will swell and then dissolve it. With a crystalline, but nonpolar polymer (e.g., polyethylene), or a polar, but noncrystalline polymer (e.g., polymethylmethacrylate), it is still not difficult to find a suitable solvent. However, with a polar *and* crystalline high polymer, such as cellulose or nylon, the problem of finding a solvent is a serious one. Thus, cellulose, because of its relatively stiff long-chain molecules, shows a strong tendency to crystallize and, once crystallized, the polar OH groups hold the chains together through a lateral network of hydrogen bonds.

From thermodynamics we know that for dissolution to occur spontaneously, the change in free energy, ΔF, must be negative for this process, i.e.,

$$\Delta F = \Delta H - T\Delta S < 0$$

However, for cellulose in the presence of a low-molecular solvent, both the heat and the entropy terms are unfavorable:

ΔH is *positive* and *large;* i.e., a considerable amount of energy (heat) must be put into the system to overcome the attractive forces between the cellulose molecules.

ΔS is *positive*, as it should be, but its magnitude is relatively *small*. This is because the gain in entropy of the cellulose molecules, in the transition from a fairly orderly solid state to a more or less disordered state in solution, is small because even in the dissolved state the cellulose chains are quite stiff and cannot assume as many configurations as a flexible macromolecule.

In spite of these unfavorable conditions, it is possible to bring cellulose into solution by *direct* and by *indirect* methods. The direct method consists of dispersing the cellulose in a single operation in solvents such as cuprammonium hydroxide, cupriethylenediamine, concentrated mineral acids, and certain tetraalkylammonium bases; however, this method causes transformation of the cellulose into an addition compound. In the indirect methods, the cellulose is first converted to a derivative by substitution of some of its hydroxyls with bulky and nonhydrogen-bonding groups, such as nitro, acetyl, or xanthate groups. The resulting compound is then dispersed in a suitable solvent (e.g., cellulose nitrate in acetone). In both cases, the cellulose molecule has been modified, and this must be taken into account in any subsequent study of the solution properties.

The "direct" process of swelling and dissolution of cellulose may be pictured as follows. At first the swelling agent penetrates the amorphous regions where the chain molecules are less closely packed. This occurs without any change in the x-ray diagram since the swelling is only "*inter*micellar"; i.e., the crystalline regions do not swell, only the material between them (e.g., cellulose swollen in water). If the affinity of the swelling agent for the cellulose molecules is very great (i.e., if more energy is given off on mixing of the two species than must be put in to overcome the cohesive forces within each species), then also the crystalline regions will be penetrated, and "*intra*micellar" swelling occurs, with a resulting change in the x-ray diagram as a new cellulose lattice is formed. There are then two possibilities: (*1*) only the stoichiometrical number of molecules required to form the addition compound penetrates the cellulose lattice and no further swelling occurs because the cohesive forces in the new lattice, although not as great as in the original lattice, are still too great to be overcome (e.g., cellulose in concentrated sodium hydroxide), or (*2*) the penetration of the lattice of the newly formed addition compound continues until it dissolves and a homogeneous solution is obtained (e.g., cellulose in concentrated phosphoric acid). This is known as "unlimited swelling," and only liquids that can bring about this state are true solvents.

Solvents for cellulose may be divided into the following classes. *Basic solvents.* These include some copper complexes, such as cuprammonium hydroxide $[Cu(NH_3)_4](OH)_2$ (e.g., 19) and cupri-ethylenediamine $[CuEn_2](OH)_2$ (e.g., 19), and quaternary ammonium bases, e.g., $[(C_2H_5)_4N]OH$ (e.g., 120) or dibenzyldimethylammonium hydroxide (Triton F) (14).

Acidic solvents. This category includes strong mineral acids, such as 72% sulfuric acid, 44% hydrochloric acid, 85% phosphoric acid (e.g., 44), and acids of intermediate strength, such as formic acid-zinc chloride mixtures.

Salts. Concentrated aqueous solutions of certain salts also act as solvents for cellulose. The solvent action will be greatest with a salt whose cation binds many water molecules and whose anion binds few. Thus, the solvent power increases in the order: $Ca^{2+} < Li^+ < Zn^{2+}$ for the cation and, for the anion, such ions as I^-, CNS^-, HgI_4^{2-}, and ZnO_2^{2-} are recommended. One of the best solvents in this group seems to be an aqueous solution of beryllium perchlorate (39). Many salts will only dissolve the cellulose at higher temperature, e.g., calcium thiocyanate and, in such cases, solution is apparently effected only after some degradation.

It is generally found that the process of dissolving the cellulose in a certain solvent is facilitated by swelling the sample first in a more dilute solution and, then, adding the concentrated reagent to obtain a solvent of the desired final concentration (215).

In all the solvents listed above, cellulose is degraded to a certain extent, depending on experimental conditions, especially temperature and presence or absence of oxygen (for attempts to find a nondegrading solvent, see, e.g., ref. 152). This is due to the unfortunate fact that the forces that are responsible for dissolving the cellulose also promote the formation of intermediate complexes that catalyze degradation. For this reason, a direct study of the behavior of cellulose in solution is extremely difficult, and one usually prefers to convert the cellulose to a derivative that will be soluble in nondegrading solvents (e.g., cellulose acetate or nitrate in ethyl acetate or acetone).

2. *Molecular Weight, Size and Shape*

With cellulose, as with other macromolecules, the physical and, in particular, the mechanical properties of the final products, such as fibers, paper, cellophane, etc., depend to a great extent on the molecular weight—i.e., the length—of the chain molecules. For this reason it is not surprising that the molecular weight of cellulose has been the subject of much research during the last few decades. However, unusual difficulties have been encountered. First, there is the difficulty of isolating the native cellulose from its source without causing any degradation and, then, of purifying it from noncellulosic substances, again without degradation. This question has been studied with great care by Schulz and Marx (193). Second, cellulose is insoluble in all common organic and aqueous solvents, dissolving only in strong bases, strong acids, and concentrated salt solutions which, owing to their corrosive nature, make the usual physicochemical techniques extremely difficult or even inapplicable. Furthermore, as soon as one has finally succeeded in getting the cellulose into solution, it begins to degrade rather rapidly, and the worker is, therefore, faced with the problem of measuring a nonequilibrium molecular weight or chain length. Finally, if he decides to avoid some of these difficulties and converts the cellulose to a more soluble derivative, there is the problem of carrying out this chemical transformation without attendant degradation.

From the above it can be seen that any data on cellulose molecular weight should be accepted with caution, not only because of inherent difficulties with the measurement techniques but because of the susceptibility of dissolved cellulose toward degradation. It might also be pointed out that the interpretation of solution properties assumes *complete* molecular dispersion of the cellulose sample and, unless this is the case, the data will of necessity be misleading. Fortunately, solution property measurements, for theoretical reasons that require extrapolation to zero concentration, are usually carried out at concentrations below 1% (1 g. cellulose/100 ml. of solution) where the cellulose may be assumed to be molecularly dispersed.

There are a number of physicochemical methods for the determination of the molecular weight of a high-polymeric substance, and these will now be treated briefly with emphasis on their applicability to cellulose. (The end-group method has been mentioned earlier in Section I-E.)

The different methods do not all give the same molecular weight because cellulose is a polymolecular material, i.e., the molecules do not all have the same size. Therefore, different average molecular weights are obtained, depending on the relation between the measured property and the chain length.

a. Number-Average Molecular Weight

For cellulose solutions, direct determination of the number-average molecular weight by osmotic pressure measurements is very difficult for two reasons: (*1*) the usual cellulosic semipermeable membranes tend to dissolve in the solvent in which the measurements are carried out; and (*2*) by the time the first osmotic pressure readings are obtained, the cellulose sample may already have undergone considerable degradation. Although some successful attempts have been made to overcome these difficulties (104,225), further work along these lines is required before such measurements can be carried out in a routine manner.

Usually the cellulose is converted to the trinitrate by nondegradative methods (e.g., 1) and the osmotic pressure is determined on solutions of the nitrate in such solvents as acetone, ethyl or butyl acetate, etc. (e.g., 102,112,162,164). Conversion to cellulose acetate and other derivatives has also been used as a means of bringing about solubility in common organic solvents, and osmotic pressure studies of such derivatives have been carried out (e.g., 132,214).

Some cellulose degrees of polymerization obtained from osmotic pressure measurements of cellulose nitrate solutions are shown in Table VII.

TABLE VII

Number-Average Degree of Polymerization of Cellulose (102)

Type of cellulose	$\overline{DP}_n$
Cotton lint[a]	1750–3350[b]
Cotton linters	900–1750
Wood pulp	650–1250
Regenerated cellulose	100–500

[a] In the reference cited, note that the original publication should read "Cotton lint" instead of "Cotton linters" for samples MS40 to MS48 in Table II, p. 2484.

[b] $\overline{DP}_n$ values up to 5000 have been reported in the literature (93,164).

b. Weight-Average Molecular Weight

Whereas osmotic pressure measurements give information about the *number*-average molecular weight of the solute (i.e., the polymer), the light-scattering technique permits determination of the *weight*-average molecular weight and, in addition, provides information

about the size and shape of the polymer molecules; in certain cases
it also provides information about the polydispersity (see also
Section II-C3). An example of light-scattering results in the form
of a "Zimm Plot" (169,236) for solutions of cellulose nitrate in acetone
is shown in Fig. 31 (93).

Attempts to apply the light-scattering method directly to solutions
of cellulose have thus far met with little success. One reason is again
the degradation problem: by the time the cellulose is dissolved and

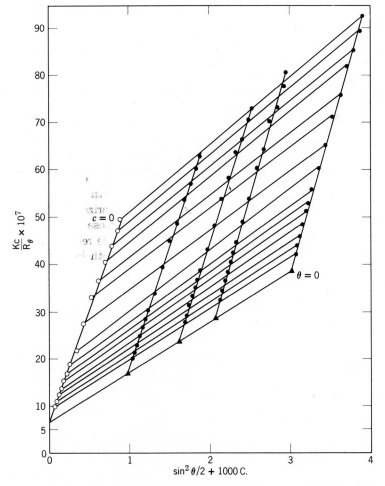

Fig. 31. Light scattering data for cellulose nitrate in acetone at 25°C. (93).

the solutions have been filtered to remove dust particles and any undissolved material, considerable degradation has occurred, and the molecular weight and size obtained are meaningless as absolute quantities. Secondly, the nondegrading solvents for cellulose are mostly colored and, therefore, the increase in scattering due to the cellulose molecules is slight as compared to the scattering of the solvent. In one case where the solvent is colorless and degradation rather slow—that of phosphoric acid—interpretation of the results is rendered difficult by the fact that as a function of time the solutions become increasingly fluorescent with a resulting increase in the intensity of the scattered light (25).

With cellulose derivatives, however, the light-scattering technique has yielded very interesting information, especially as to size, shape, and polydispersity. Thus, already the early measurements of Stein and Doty (212) on solutions of cellulose acetate, and of Badger and Blaker (6) on cellulose nitrate solutions, showed that the light-scattering technique could be used to determine molecular weights. These, being weight-averages, were found to be higher than the number-average molecular weights obtained from osmotic pressure measurements. A comparison of the length of the molecules, as calculated from dissymmetry measurements, with their "contour length," which is equal to the degree of polymerization times the length of the monomer unit (5.15 A. for the glucose unit), revealed that cellulosic chains are too stiff and rodlike to be represented by a random (or Gaussian) coil model. Later work with improved tech-

TABLE VIII

Degree of Coiling of Different Polymers with Same Extended Length (99)

Polymer	Solvent	Temperature (°C.)	L (A.)	$\sqrt{\bar{r}^2}$ (A.)	$L/\sqrt{\bar{r}^2}$ Coiling ratio
Hevea rubber.	Toluene	25	5000	309	16.2
Polystyrene	Toluene	25	5000	410	12.2
Cellulose acetate	Acetone	25	5000	877	5.7
Cellulose nitrate	Acetone	25	5000	1120	4.5

L = contour length.

$\sqrt{\bar{r}^2}$ = root-mean-square end-to-end distance (experimental values from dissymmetry measurements).

niques (11,40,93) has confirmed the earlier conclusions that cellulose chain molecules in solution are considerably stiffer and more extended than vinyl polymers of comparable contour length (i.e., length of the molecule in its fully extended state). This is illustrated in Table VIII.

It is believed that for cellulose nitrate there is a transition from rigid rods to flexible coils at degrees of polymerization between 400 and 500, and that at DPs about 1000 the chains are Gaussian. For other cellulose derivatives, such as cellulose acetate, there will be similar transitions but, since cellulose acetate is somewhat more flexible, they will occur already at lower DPs.

The polydispersity of cellulose derivatives may be determined in an approximate manner by comparing the light-scattering weight-average molecular weight with the number-average molecular weight from osmotic pressure measurements. For most unfractionated samples, the ratio of $\overline{M}_w$ to $\overline{M}_n$ is $\cong$ 2, as with vinyl polymers; however, unlike the latter, the cellulose derivatives do not show a significant decrease in polydispersity upon fractionation. Thus, a reduction of $\overline{M}_w/\overline{M}_n$ below 1.4 seems very difficult to achieve. This is probably due to the fact that the fractionation of cellulose derivatives is a function of degree of substitution as well as of chain length.

Some representative light-scattering results (93) for cellulose nitrate in acetone are shown in Table IX.

TABLE IX

Molecular Weight and Size of Cellulose Nitrate
Determined by Light Scattering

Sample No.	$\overline{M}_n$	$\overline{M}_w$	$\sqrt{\overline{r_n^2}}$ (A.)	$\sqrt{\overline{r_z^2}}$ (A.)
Cb	(45,000)[a]	77,000	(271)	380
Ca	(52,000)	89,000	(344)	540
Bb	213,000	360,000	(868)	1350
Ba	234,000	400,000	(955)	1500
A[8]	424,000	850,000	1250	2165
A	775,000	2,300,000	1760	3080

[a] All values in parentheses have been calculated by Holtzer, Benoit, and Doty (93) on the basis of certain polydispersity assumptions.

c. Other Molecular Weight Averages

With the development of the ultracentrifuge by Svedberg and his collaborators (213), it became possible to subject macromolecular solutions to centrifugal fields sufficiently strong to cause sedimentation of the macromolecules. Depending on the magnitude of the centrifugal field, the ultracentrifuge may be used either to determine the sedimentation velocity of the solute molecules or their ultimate equilibrium distribution. In both cases, the ultracentrifuge provides not only an average molecular weight, but also considerable information about the molecular weight distribution. If it were not such an intricate and costly instrument, the ultracentrifuge would probably be used to the same extent as a light-scattering photometer in the study of high-polymer solutions.

(1) Sedimentation Velocity

Sedimentation velocity measurements, in combination with diffusion measurements, permit calculation of the molecular weight, M, according to Svedberg's equation:

$$M = RTs/D(1 - V\rho)$$

where R is the gas constant; T is the absolute temperature; s and D are the sedimentation and diffusion constants, respectively; V is the partial specific volume of the solute; and ρ is the density of the solution. This relation, however, is only valid at infinite dilution. Therefore, s and D must be determined by suitable extrapolation to zero concentration before a molecular weight calculation may be attempted. For cellulosic materials the extrapolation of the sedimentation constant to $c = 0$ can be carried out with reasonable accuracy; the concentration dependence of the diffusion constant, however, is quite nonlinear, especially for the higher molecular-weight samples, and the diffusion measurements should, therefore, be carried out at very low concentrations and in poor solvents.

Another important complication arises because of polydispersity: both s and D will have distributions, and the type of average of the molecular weight obtained from the Svedberg equation will depend on the method used in the evaluation of s and D and also on the molecular-weight distribution and shape of the sample. In general, both s and D are evaluated as weight-averages, and the Svedberg relation therefore yields $\overline{M}_{ww}$, which usually lies between $\overline{M}_w$ and $\overline{M}_n$ (199). Some characteristic values for cellulose nitrates in acetone (98) are shown in Table X. (See also Refs. 153, 160, and 163 for other investigations on the sedimentation behavior of cellulose in the form of one of its derivatives.)

TABLE X

Sedimentation and Diffusion Results for Cellulose Nitrate (98)

Nitrate sample[a]	25°C. $[\eta]$ acetone	$S_0 \cdot 10^{13}$	$D_0 \cdot 10^7$ (cm.^{2} sec.$^{-1}$)	$\overline{M}_{ww}$
Viscose rayon	1.45	10.5	9.74	45,000
Viscose rayon	3.6	15.6	5.42	120,000
Viscose rayon	6.8	20.0	3.54	235,000
Wood pulp	7.1	20.1	3.35	250,000
Wood pulp	12.7	24.0	2.17	460,000
Cotton linters	16.3	28.0	1.89	620,000
Chemical cotton	21.0	29.5	1.52	810,000
Cotton lint	25.3	33.0	1.38	1,000,000

[a] Nitrogen content: 13.74 to 13.98%.

Direct measurements on cellulose itself are again beset by difficulties: corrosive solvents, and degradation of the cellulose during dissolution and during the experiment. Gralén (66) has carried out sedimentation and diffusion measurements of cellulose in cuprammonium; however, his degrees of polymerization are unusually high (DP's of 11,000 to 36,000 for native celluloses) and it is, therefore, likely that the solutions exhibit a polyelectrolyte effect in the extrapolation of s and D to zero concentration. However, more recent work by Vink (224) with solutions of cellulose in cupriethylenediamine indicates that useful results can be obtained even without conversion of the cellulose to a derivative.

With regard to the polymolecularity of cellulose samples, the sedimentation velocity ultracentrifuge presents a means of obtaining a direct picture of this important characteristic of the material. Thus, the shape of the concentration gradient curve, made visible by the optical system of the ultracentrifuge, will give the general features of the frequency function of the molecular weights, i.e., the molecular weight distribution curve.

(2) Sedimentation Equilibrium

When weaker centrifugal fields are applied to a polymer solution, an equilibrium distribution of the polymer over the length of the cell is eventually set up. This type of experiment permits determination of the weight-average molecular weight, the z-average molecular weight, and the molecular-weight distribution of the sample.

For cellulose and cellulose derivatives, the sedimentation equilibrium technique has been applied by Kraemer (118), who showed
that the ratio of the measured DP (degree of polymerization) to the
intrinsic viscosity was a constant for cellulose in cuprammonium, for
secondary cellulose acetate in acetone, and for cellulose nitrate in
acetone.

(3) Viscosity

The viscosity-average molecular weight is based on Staudinger's
discovery that, for a "polymerhomologous series," i.e., a series of
polymers differing *only* in chain length but *not* in composition or
structure, the dilute solution viscosity increases with the molecular
weight or DP. This may be expressed by the simple relation:

$$[\eta] = K_m M$$

or
$$\mathrm{DP} = K_v[\eta]$$

where $[\eta]$, usually expressed in deciliters per gram, is the intrinsic
viscosity (or limiting viscosity number), K_m or K_v are so-called
Staudinger constants, and M is the molecular weight of the polymer.

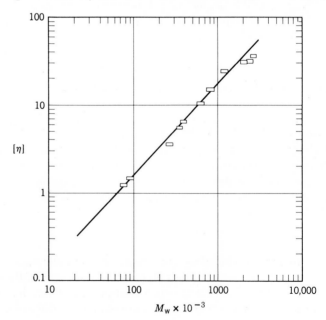

Fig. 32. Log $[\eta]$ vs. log $\overline{M}_w$ for cellulose nitrate in acetone at 25°C. (93).

In order to calculate M from experimental viscosity data, it is necessary to determine K_m, which is usually done by calibrating the intrinsic viscosity with a series of samples of known molecular weight.
The viscosity method is, therefore, *not an absolute method* like the
osmotic pressure or light-scattering methods described in the foregoing sections, and its widespread use is only due to the relative
simplicity and rapidity with which viscosity measurements can be
carried out and the low cost of conventional viscometers. It should
be emphasized, however, that the molecular weight obtained by use of
the Staudinger equation, or the more widely applicable relation:

$$[\eta] = KM^a$$

is a *viscosity-average* molecular weight which, for unfractionated
samples, is essentially equal to the *weight-average* molecular weight.
Correlation of $[\eta]$ with $\overline{M}_n$, unless the samples are all perfect fractions
(i.e., $\overline{M}_v = \overline{M}_w = \overline{M}_n$), or all have the same relative molecular
weight distribution, is, therefore, not a very correct procedure, and a
correlation of $[\eta]$ with $\overline{M}_w$, as shown in Fig. 32, should be used instead.
Due to the fact that the light-scattering technique is a relative new-
comer to the molecular-weight determination field and requires somewhat expensive equipment, most of the existing correlations between
$[\eta]$ and M, have been carried out using $\overline{M}_n$-values and the resulting
constants (see Table XI) should, therefore, be used with caution. A
further consideration should be the fact that the degree of substitution of a cellulose derivative will have an effect on the intrinsic
viscosity and that, therefore, the constants in Table XI should not be
used without checking the degree of substitution for which they have
been established.

For cellulose and cellulose derivatives, the intrinsic viscosity is
usually determined from measurements of the specific viscosity at
several concentrations and extrapolation to zero concentration according to the equation:

$$ln(\eta_{sp}/c) = ln[\eta] + k^1[\eta]c$$

Some representative viscosity curves for cellulose nitrate in acetone
are shown in Fig. 33. (For other viscosity data, see Refs. 51,140,
224.)

As indicated on Fig. 33, the viscosity measurements have been
corrected for the effect of the rate of shear by extrapolation to zero

TABLE XI

Intrinsic Viscosity—Molecular Weight Constants for Cellulose
and Cellulose Derivatives (99)

Material	Solvent	Frac-tions	K_v	$K \cdot 10^5$	a	Aver-age
Cellulose	Cuprammonium	—	260	—	—	$\overline{M}_w$
Cellulose	Cuprammonium	—	—	8.5	0.81	?
Cellulose	Cuprammonium	—	230	—	—	$\overline{M}_w$
Cellulose	Cuene	—	170	—	—	$\overline{M}_w$
Cellulose	Cuene	±	124–156[a]	13.3	0.90	$\overline{M}_n$
Cellulose nitrate	Acetone	±	88–110[a]	11.0	0.91	$\overline{M}_n$
Cellulose nitrate	Acetone	+	—	9.8	0.91	$\overline{M}_w$
Cellulose nitrate	Acetone	±	200	—	—	$\overline{M}_w$
Cellulose nitrate	Acetone	+	98–122[a]	—	—	$\overline{M}_n$
Cellulose nitrate	Acetone	—	77–100[a]	—	—	$\overline{M}_n$
Cellulose nitrate	Acetone	+	111	—	—	$\overline{M}_a$
Cellulose nitrate	Acetone	—	91	—	—	$\overline{M}_n$
Cellulose nitrate	Ethyl acetate	+	—	6.7	0.99	$\overline{M}_n$
Cellulose nitrate	Ethyl acetate	+	80	4.8	0.99	$\overline{M}_n$
Cellulose nitrate	Ethyl acetate	±	62	3.8	1.03	$\overline{M}_n$
Cellulose nitrate	Ethyl lactate	±	71	12.2	0.92	$\overline{M}_n$
Cellulose nitrate	Butyl acetate	±	—	21.0	0.71	$\overline{M}_w$
Cellulose dinitrate	Acetone	+	230	19.1	0.79	$\overline{M}_n$
Cellulose acetate	Acetone	?	—	14.9	0.82	$\overline{M}_n$
Cellulose acetate	Acetone	+	150	24	0.80	$\overline{M}_n$
Cellulose acetate	Acetone	—	230	—	—	$\overline{M}_w$
Cellulose acetate	Acetone	+	—	9.0	0.90	$\overline{M}_n$
Cellulose acetate butyrate	Acetone	+	—	13.7	0.83	$\overline{M}_n$
Cellulose acetate butyrate	Acetic acid	+	—	14.6	0.83	$\overline{M}_n$
Cellulose tributyrate	Butanone	+	—	39.8	0.91	$\overline{M}_n$
Cellulose tricaprylate	Toluene	+	—	47.8	0.81	$\overline{M}_n$
Ethyl cellulose (DS 2.5) 80/20	Toluene/ethanol	?	135	—	—	$\overline{M}_n$
Ethyl cellulose (DS 2.5) 80/20	Toluene/ethanol	?	300	—	—	$\overline{M}_w$
Sodium carboxy methyl cellulose	Water	—	120	—	—	$\overline{M}_w$

[a] Where two K_v values are listed, the first one applies to samples of DP below 400 to 500, and
the second one to samples of higher DP.

shear gradient. Such an extrapolation is especially important for the
higher molecular-weight samples ($\overline{DP}_n > 900$ for cellulose nitrate in
acetone; $DP_n > 1300$ for cellulose in cupriethylenediamine) (18,105,
216).

The intrinsic viscosity also lends itself to determinations of molecular size by application of one or more of the newer hydrodynamic
theories, such as the Brinkman-Debye-Bueche theory (15,36), the

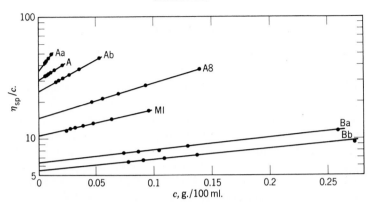

Fig. 33. Log η_{sp}/c vs. c (at zero gradient) for cellulose nitrate in acetone at 25°C. (93).

Kirkwood-Riseman theory (116), and the Fox-Flory theory (50,54). For cellulose and cellulose derivatives of intermediate DP, (600 < $\overline{DP}_n$ < 2500), the Kirkwood-Riseman treatment seems to give end-to-end distances which are in better agreement with the experimental end-to-end distances determined from light scattering than either of the ones calculated by use of the other theories (98,99). This is shown in Table XII.

TABLE XII

End-to-end Distances in Angstroms of Cellulose Nitrates in Acetone (98,99)

Nitrate sample origin	$\overline{DP}_n$	L (fully extended) a	R K-R b	R_s B-D-B c	R F-F d	R_0 (without interactions) e	Rexptl. (light scattering) f
Viscose rayon	300	1550	518	349	271	184	710
Wood pulp	650	3350	765	566	440	270	920
Wood pulp	1250	6480	1062	855	652	370	1120
Cotton linters	1750	9000	1254	1040	803	440	1245
Chemical cotton	2300	11900	1450	1247	964	510	1350
Cotton lint	2700	13900	1560	1392	1080	550	1430

a L = 5.15 A. × $\overline{DP}_n$.
b Calculated using Kirkwood-Riseman parameters, b = 30 A.; ζ = 11.9 × 10^{-10}.
c Calculated using Debye-Bueche parameters, ϕ = 0.30, σ = 1.9.
d Calculated using K = 3.71 × 10^{-3} and R = αR_0.
e Calculated using Benoit's expression for cellulosic "random coils," R_0 = 10.5$(\overline{DP}_n)^{1/2}$.
f Calculated from dissymmetry measurements assuming the polydisperse coil model.

3. Molecular Weight Distribution

The physical properties of a cellulosic material, be it a fiber, a film, or any other product, depend not only on the average molecular weight but also, to a large extent, on the molecular weight distribution. It is, therefore, very important from a technical point of view to obtain a measure of the molecular weight distribution of various cellulosic materials. From the point of view of the physical chemist, this is also a very important problem, because the molecular weight distribution and assumptions relating to it are involved in all the relations between molecular weight and various solution properties. Such relations are rigorous only for homogeneous materials and the chemist, therefore, attempts either to prepare homogeneous samples, or to eva'uate the nonhomogeneity, i.e., polydisperity of the sample, and take this into account in subsequent calculations. The method most commonly employed to achieve either of these aims is fractionation (29).

a. Fractionation

Cellulose and its derivatives may be separated into fractions either by precipitation fractionation, or by solution fractionation, of which the former is generally preferred where large fractions are desired.

The *precipitation* method may be applied either by addition of a nonsolvent, by removal of solvent, or by addition of solvent-nonsolvent mixtures. The first precipitation fractionation of a cellulosic material was carried out in 1920 by Duclaux and Wollman (41) on solutions of cellulose nitrate in acetone. Since then, the technique of nondegradative conversion of cellulose to cellulose nitrate and subsequent precipitation fractionation has developed to the stage where it has been proposed as a standard method for the cellulose industry (155). Direct fractionation of cellulose dissolved in cuprammonium has been achieved by Battista and Sisson through addition of *n*-propyl alcohol and other reagents (10) and, more recently, by Sihtola and co-workers (198).

Solution fractionation, which relies on the progressive extraction from the sample of fractions of increasing chain length as the extracting solvent becomes a "better" solvent (i.e., through a change in composition or in temperature), has also been applied to cellulose and cellulose derivatives (e.g., 38). Although it was shown by Desreux (38) that much better resolution can be obtained by the precipitation method, a modification of the solution technique due to Baker and Williams (7), where the polymer is deposited on a substrate in a column, yields, in a much shorter time, fractions that are as sharp as those obtainable by precipitation.

From the fractionation data and characterization of the fractions, it is possible to construct an "integral distribution curve" and, from that, to draw the "differential distribution curve," which shows the relative amounts of the different molecular weight species present in the original sample. Distribution curves of a large number of native celluloses of different origin were obtained in this manner by Schulz and Marx (193; see also 217). The reproducibility of such curves is usually not very good for cellulose derivatives, due to the fact that fractionation occurs not only with respect to molecular weight, but also with respect to degree of substitution. From this point of view it is also easily understood why it is so difficult to obtain sharp fractions with cellulosic materials.

b. Estimation of Molecular Weight Distribution without Separation into Fractions

Fractionation, even with the simpler vinyl polymers, is a rather long and tedious procedure, especially if refractionation of the individual fractions is undertaken. Attempts have therefore been made, in cases where no need for the actual fractions existed from a preparative point of view, to obtain an estimate of the polymolecularity of a sample without actual separation into fractions.

(1) Turbidity Titration

This method, developed by Morey and Tamblyn (158), is based on the progressive increase of the turbidity of a dilute polymer solution on the addition in small increments of a precipitating agent. It was applied by these authors to cellulose acetate butyrate and, subsequently, by Oth (168) to cellulose nitrate. The method, after calibration with fractions of known molecular weight, gives the integral molecular weight distribution curve of the sample directly from the results of a single titration run.

A variation of this is the observation of the cumulative volume of precipitate corresponding to the addition of successive portions of nonsolvent to a dilute solution of the polymer. This technique has been applied to a study of regenerated cellulose dissolved in caustic soda (28).

(2) Sedimentation

Sedimentation in the ultracentrifuge, if the influence of diffusion may be neglected and upon suitable extrapolation to zero concentration, provides a direct picture of the differential molecular weight distribution curve. Methods for interpreting the sedimentation diagrams of cellulose and cellulose derivatives to obtain a quantitative value for the polydispersity of the sample have been described in the literature (66,114).

(3) Diffusion

Diffusion measurements have been used by Gralén (66) for an estimation of the polymolecularity of cellulose, cellulose nitrate, and cellulose xanthate.

(4) Chromatography

Chromatography has been applied to this problem by Claesson (26) and Brooks and Badger (16). These authors have adsorbed cellulose nitrate onto different substrates, such as carbon, or potato starch. From frontal analysis diagrams of this system, upon extrapolation to zero concentration, a picture of the molecular weight distribution curve is obtained.

(5) Other Methods

Among other methods that have been investigated in order to obtain information about the molecular weight distribution of cellulose and cellulose derivatives are: *flow birefringence* (186), *electron microscopy* (101), and *dielectric dispersion* (189). A simple comparison of different molecular weight averages, e.g., weight-average and number-average, will also provide a rough measure of the polydispersity of the sample.

III. Cellulose Reactions—Cellulose Derivatives

A. REACTIVITY OF CELLULOSE

1. Influence of Structure

The reactions of cellulose with different organic and inorganic reagents are governed, to a large extent, by its physical structure.

Cellulose is a fibrous material, composed of individual fibers that may be subdivided into microfibrils which, in turn, consist of aggregates of cellulose chain molecules passing through crystalline (ordered) and amorphous (disordered) regions. Each cellulose chain is made up of a large number of anhydroglucopyranose units with three hydroxyl groups (one primary group and two secondary groups) per ring. It is, therefore, clear that, in the formation of cellulose derivatives, the problem of the *accessibility* or *availability* of the hydroxyl groups is an important one. Thus, if the reagent cannot penetrate the fiber at all, i.e., if the fiber is completely nonswelling in the reaction medium, only a topochemical or surface reaction will occur. If the reagent is able to penetrate between the microfibrils and into their amorphous regions, the extent and rate of reaction will increase greatly, but the reaction product will still be rather nonuniform, because no reaction could occur with hydroxyl groups of the crystalline regions. If, however, the reagent is able to penetrate both the amorphous and the crystalline regions of the microfibrils, a fairly uniform reaction product is obtained. It is, therefore, one of the most important objectives in the manufacture of cellulose derivatives to make all of the OH groups available to the reagent.

However, even if all of the cellulose hydroxyl groups are available for reaction, there must still be a certain degree of heterogeneity in the product, due to the fact that substitution occurs at random along the chain and some anhydroglucose units may have reacted, while others may not have reacted. Furthermore, since there are three different hydroxyl groups available for reaction on each anhydroglucose unit (see Fig. 34), there are theoretically eight possible ways

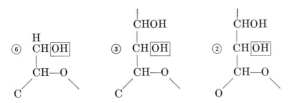

Fig. 34. Structural comparison of the different hydroxyl groups (6, 3, and 2) in cellulose (179).

of substitution per monomer unit: no substitution at all; three different monosubstitution products (substitution of the OH group in the 2, 3, or 6 position); three different disubstitution products (the 2,6,

3,6, and 2,3 derivatives); and the 2,3,6-trisubstituted derivative. Assuming that the three different hydroxyl groups have the same reactivity toward the substitution reagent and that the groups which are already substituted do not have any influence on the reactivity of those which have not yet reacted, Spurlin (207) calculated the statistical over-all distribution of substituents along the cellulose chain for degrees of substitution (DS) between 0.0 and 3.0. The distribution curves obtained are shown in Fig. 35, and illustrate the

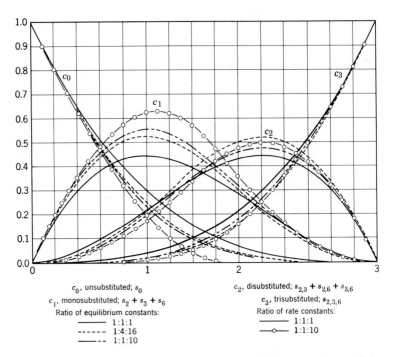

Fig. 35. Theoretical over-all distribution of substituent groups in cellulose (207). Abscissa: Average number of substituents per anhydroglucose unit. Ordinate: Fraction of total number of anhydroglucose units substituted as indicated.

fact that a cellulose derivative of an intermediate over-all degree of substitution always contains a certain amount of unsubstituted, monosubstituted, disubstituted, and trisubstituted anhydroglucose units. The figure also shows that differences in the reactivity of the 2-, 3-, and 6-hydroxyl groups do not greatly affect the over-all distribution of substituents on the different anhydroglucose units. Experimental investigation of the relative reactivities of the three hydroxyl groups seems to indicate that, in general, the primary OH group in the 6 position is substituted most readily, i.e., it is the most reactive of the three hydroxyl groups (e.g., 30). In spite of this inherent heterogeneity, we may define a *"uniform"* reaction product as one where every hydroxyl group has had an equal amount of exposure to the reagent. In order to bring all the hydroxyl groups in contact with the reagent involved, either the cellulose is dissolved (usually via an intermediate addition compound), or it is swollen to such an extent that the reagent can penetrate between the individual cellulose chains and, eventually, if the reaction is permitted to go to equilibrium, gain access to all OH groups. In either case, the first step involves swelling, i.e., forcing the cellulose chain molecules apart by breaking the hydrogen bonds between the OH groups of adjacent chains and introducing in their place molecules of the swelling agent.

2. Swelling

The swelling of cellulose may be subdivided into two types: *"inter*crystalline," and *"intra*crystalline." The former refers to cases where the swelling agent penetrates into the *amorphous* regions of the cellulose microfibrils and into the regions *between* the microfibrils, whereas the latter refers to the penetration and swelling of the *crystalline* regions of the microfibrils.

The most familiar case of intercrystalline swelling is the swelling of cellulose in water. If a bone-dry cellulose is exposed to an atmosphere containing water vapor, cross-sectional swelling of the fiber takes place as soon as adsorption of water molecules begins. As the relative humidity (RH) is increased to 100% and water sorption continues, the diameter of the fiber may increase by about 20–25%. If the fiber conditioned to 100% RH is then immersed in water, a further, very large increase in swelling occurs, e.g., increasing the fiber diameter by perhaps another 25% (e.g., 157). The final water swelling varies from fiber to fiber, and is related to the crystallinity and orientation of the sample. The longitudinal water swelling of cellulose fibers is usually very small for highly oriented fibers, but larger for unoriented materials such as wood fibers, and one may therefore use the anisotropy of swelling as a measure of orientation (77).

Intercrystalline swelling can also be brought about by a number of organic liquids: e.g., methanol, ethanol, aniline, benzaldehyde, nitrobenzene, and several others. In general, the higher the polarity of the liquid, the greater the amount of swelling produced but, in all the above-mentioned examples, swelling is less than with water. To achieve intercrystalline swelling of cellulose beyond the extent of water swelling, aqueous solutions of acids, bases, or salts must be used, although aqueous solutions of certain organic compounds, such as thiourea or resorcinol, are also effective.

An important characteristic of intercrystalline swelling is that the x-ray diagram of the original cellulosic material remains unchanged except for the superposition of the diagram of the swelling agent. If, on the other hand, intracrystalline swelling also occurs, the x-ray diagram undergoes definite changes corresponding to the modification of the cellulose lattice by the swelling agent. It should be pointed out that intercrystalline and intracrystalline swelling overlap to some extent, just as in cellulose the amorphous regions are not completely disordered and the crystalline regions are not completely ordered.

Intracrystalline swelling may be brought about by the use of concentrated solutions of most strong acids, strong bases, and a few salts. It is possible to distinguish between two types of intracrystalline swelling: limited and unlimited. Thus, in certain cases, where the swelling reagent is a very strong complexing agent and has bulky groups, the adjacent chains are pushed so far apart that gradual dissolution of the cellulose occurs, i.e., the swelling is *unlimited*. In other cases, the swelling reagent combines with the cellulose in certain stoichiometric proportions, forming a crystalline swelling or addition compound with a well-defined x-ray diagram of its own. If, on further addition of swelling reagent this compound gradually dissolves, then it is again a case of unlimited swelling, but if no further expansion of the cellulose lattice occurs, the swelling is known as *limited* intracrystalline swelling.

B. CELLULOSE ADDITION REACTIONS

1. Formation of Addition Compounds

The importance of cellulose addition or swelling compounds lies in the fact that they exhibit greatly enhanced reactivity toward chemical reagents and that more or less homogeneous cellulose derivatives can be prepared from them. The reason for the greater reactivity is that the hydrogen bonds between adjacent cellulose chains have been broken during the swelling treatment and molecules of the swelling agent have been introduced instead. In such a swollen structure a chemical reagent can diffuse freely and, therefore, come into contact with all the hydroxyl groups.

For the formation of these addition compounds, a minimum concentration of the swelling reagent is required, which depends on the type of reagent, the temperature, and the physical structure of the cellulose sample. For example, the minimum concentration required for formation of alkali cellulose (mercerization) is less, the smaller and more hydrated the metal ion (87), the lower the temperature, and the lower the size and lattice order of the crystalline regions of the cellulose (175).

In order to picture the formation of a cellulose addition compound from a chemical point of view, it is perhaps best to regard acids and bases as proton donors and proton acceptors, respectively. Thus, the hydronium ions (H_3O^+) of the acid and the hydroxyl ions (OH^-) of the base are capable of breaking the hydrogen bonds between the

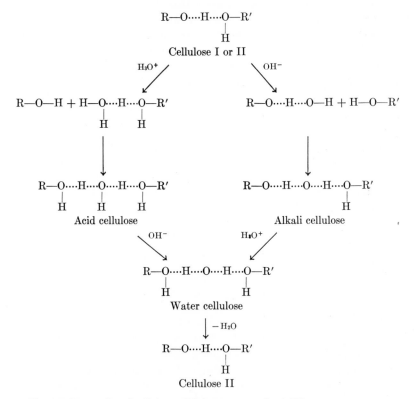

Fig. 36. Formation of cellulose addition compounds of different proton content (R indicates the glucose residue) (179).

cellulose hydroxyl groups and forming their own hydrogen bonds with them, as shown in Fig. 36. The counterions will follow into the lattice, due to electrostatic attraction, and intracrystalline swelling results. As was pointed out previously, if the counterions are very bulky as, for example, with the quaternary ammonium bases, the cellulose chains are pushed so far apart that the cellulose dissolves. The expansion of the lattice in the formation of the addition compounds occurs almost entirely in the direction normal to the 101 planes, as can be shown by comparison of the x-ray diagrams of the original cellulose (*Cellulose I*) and the addition compound. Cellulose addition compounds are not stable except in the presence of the swelling reagent and, upon removal of excess reagent, the *Cellulose II* lattice (mercerized or regenerated cellulose) is formed. These transformatiors are also indicated in Fig. 36 in terms of the chemical changes taking place. It is apparent from this reaction scheme that the presence of the correct amount of water is of great importance: there should be sufficient water to permit ionization of the reagent to occur, but not enough for competition between the cellulose hydroxyls and the water molecules for the reagent (H_3O^+ or OH^-) to prevent formation of the addition compound.

2. Types of Addition Compounds

The addition compounds of cellulose may be divided into four main groups: alkali celluloses, acid celluloses, amine celluloses, and salt celluloses. In the present discussion only a few representative examples can be given, but a careful compilation of known cellulose addition compounds has been carried out by Rånby and Rydholm (179) and should be consulted for further references on this subject.

a. Alkali Celluloses

The formation of alkali cellulose, from a technical point of view, is one of the most important of all cellulose reactions. It is used in industry in two ways: (1) to improve the luster and tensile strength of cotton fibers and yarns by the process known as "*mercerization*," and (2) as an intermediate step in the formation of cellulose xanthate, from which viscose rayon and cellophane are produced.

Mercerization, named after John Mercer, who discovered the process in 1844, involves the treatment of cotton fibers with a caustic soda solution of about 12 to 18% concentration (e.g., 139). The corresponding changes occurring in the cellulose lattice are the transitions from *Cellulose I* to alkali or soda cellulose and upon subsequent

washing from soda cellulose to *Cellulose II*. A sample is considered
completely mercerized, if after the caustic treatment and subsequent
washing the x-ray diagram only shows the presence of the *Cellulose II*
lattice. As was already indicated in the previous section, a minimum
concentration of caustic soda in the aqueous reagent is required to
bring about mercerization and, once this concentration is reached,
the uptake of sodium hydroxide by the cellulose and the phase
transformation to the new lattice occurs over a very narrow concentration interval. This fact, together with the previously mentioned effect
of the cellulose order-disorder structure on the minimum caustic soda
concentration required for mercerization, is illustrated in Fig. 37
(175).

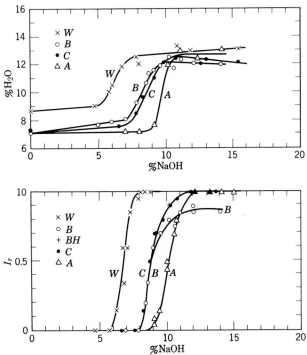

Fig. 37. Phase transition diagrams for mercerization of different celluloses
with caustic soda solutions at 0°C. (175). *W* is wood, *B* bacterial, *C* cotton, and *A*
animal cellulose, *BH* is bacterial cellulose hydrolyzed in hot dilute sulfuric acid.
The upper graph shows increases of water adsorption (at 65% relative humidity)
by the cellulose after alkali treatment, and the lower graph shows intensity ratios
I_r of selected x-ray reflections ($I_r = 0.0$ for native and 1.0 for completely mercerized cellulose). The wood cellulose had the lowest and the animal cellulose the
highest resistance to mercerization.

It should be pointed out that at high concentrations of sodium hydroxide (> 21%) a different addition compound, *Alkali Cellulose II*, with a higher molar ration of NaOH to H_2O in the cellulose lattice, is formed (e.g., 188) and that, by controlling temperature and concentration of the NaOH solution, a number of different crystalline alkali celluloses can be obtained from the same native cellulose (205). The actual chemical composition of these different alkali celluloses has not yet been established with certainty, but the majority of investigators agree that alkali cellulose is an addition compound of the form $R_{cell.}(OH) \cdot NaOH$ rather than a true alcoholate of the form $R_{cell.}(ONa)$, and that *Alkali Cellulose I*, as obtained under normal mercerization conditions (12 to 18% NaOH), may be represented by the formula $(C_6H_{10}O_5)_2 \cdot NaOH$ for the repeat unit.

The treatment of cellulose with alkali is even more important as an intermediate step in the preparation of viscose than for mercerization purposes. Thus it was discovered in 1892 by Cross, Bevan, and Beadle (32) that, on treating alkali cellulose with carbon disulfide, cellulose xanthate is obtained which, when dissolved in dilute alkali, gives a viscous, orange-yellow solution. This solution, called *viscose* by its discoverers and still known by that name, can be extruded into an acid bath to give fibers or films of regenerated cellulose, which are known as rayon and cellophane, respectively.

Alkali cellulose is also used as an intermediate product in the preparation of a number of important cellulose ethers, such as methyl, ethyl and carboxymethyl cellulose.

It is interesting to note that although alkali cellulose is an addition compound and not a true alcoholate of cellulose, its reactions with alkyl halides to form ethers and with acid anhydrides and acid chlorides to form esters, are typical of those of a metal alcoholate.

Of considerable importance among the alkali celluloses are also the *cuprammonium-* and *cupriethylenediamine-cellulose complexes*. About a hundred years ago, it was discovered by Schweizer(195) that when copper hydroxide is dissolved in aqueous ammonia, a solution results (sometimes called Schweizer's solution) that is capable of dissolving cellulose. This discovery was important for two reasons: it made possible the study of the cellulose molecule in solution in a medium where, at least in the absence of oxygen, relatively little degradation occurs. (Cuprammonium hydroxide is still one of the most important solvents used for characterization of industrial celluloses by viscosity measurements.) Furthermore, Schweizer's discovery became the basis of the cuprammonium rayon industry, which produces filaments of regenerated cellulose by forcing a cuprammonium solution of cellulose through a spinneret into a coagulation bath.

Several structures have been proposed for the cuprammonium-cellulose complex, of which perhaps the one proposed by Jolley (109), which applies also to the cupriethylenediamine-cellulose complex, is to be preferred:

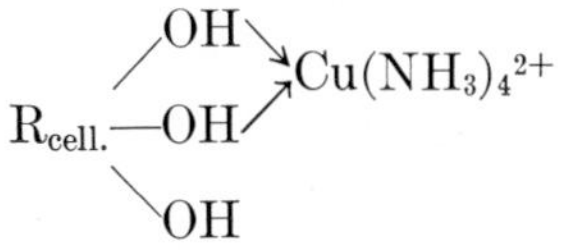

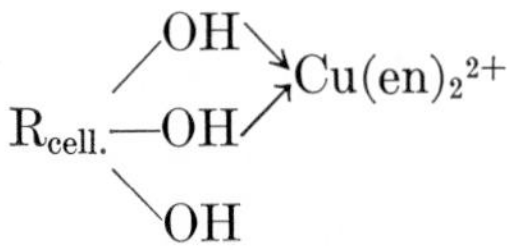

$$R_{cell.}-OH \begin{matrix} OH \\ \\ OH \end{matrix} Cu(NH_3)_4{}^{2+}$$

$$R_{cell.}-OH \begin{matrix} OH \\ \\ OH \end{matrix} Cu(en)_2{}^{2+}$$

In the above structures, which refer to the dissolved complexes, the ratio of copper to cellulose is 1:1 (i.e., one atom of copper combined with *one* anhydroglucose unit); however, it is found that, on isolation of the complex compound from solution (this has only been achieved from the cupriethylenediamine solution thus far), the ratio of copper to cellulose becomes 1:2 (i.e., one atom of copper combined with *two* anhydroglucose units) (219).

b. Acid Celluloses

Perhaps the most well-known of the acid addition compounds is the so-called *Knecht compound*, $[C_6H_{10}O_5 \cdot HNO_3]_n$ (117), which is formed on treating cellulose with approximately 61% nitric acid, or as an intermediate in the esterification of cellulose with more concentrated nitric acid.

c. Amine Celluloses

Whereas ammonium hydroxide does not form an addition compound with cellulose, liquid ammonia forms two different ammonia celluloses (I and II, depending on temperature of formation).

The alkyl amines also form addition compounds similar in nature to *Ammonia Cellulose* I (34). With the larger alkyl groups, such as amyl, hexyl or heptyl, the cellulose lattice is expanded to such an extent that the distance between the 101 planes may be from two to three times its original value. With these bulky reagents, it is necessary to preswell the cellulose lattice with smaller swelling agents, e.g., ammonia or one of the lower alkyl amines.

d. Salt Celluloses

Certain concentrated salt solutions, such as zinc chloride, lithium thiocyanate, etc., cause intracrystalline swelling and sometimes, also, dissolution of the cellulose. To explain this in terms of the scheme shown in Fig. 36, one must assume either that some hydrolytic breakdown of the cellulose occurs with formation of H_3O^+ ions, which then swell the lattice, or that the cations of the salts are very highly hydrated and can interact with the cellulose hydroxyl groups in this form.

3. Inclusion Compounds

The previous sections have dealt with cellulose addition compounds where, in every case, the swelling reagent was distributed in fixed stoichiometric amounts throughout the cellulose lattice and was interacting with the cellulose hydroxyl groups through hydrogen bonds. However, it is also possible to prepare cellulose compounds which are highly reactive, i.e., which have readily available OH groups, even in a medium of quite *poor* swelling ability. This is achieved by first swelling the cellulose with a good swelling agent (e.g., concentrated sodium hydroxide) and, then, successively replacing the sodium hydroxide molecules with an organic compound that serves to keep the cellulose lattice expanded and, yet, does not compete for hydroxyl groups with the final esterification or etherification reagent. Thus, it is possible to treat cellulose with concentrated sodium hydroxide in order to expand the lattice, then to displace the sodium hydroxide with water, the water with methanol, and the methanol with such compounds as pyridine, benzene, cyclohexane or acetic acid. The resulting compounds are known as "inclusion celluloses" because the organic compound (benzene, pyridine, etc.), which by itself would be unable to swell the cellulose lattice, is actually "included" in the cellulose lattice. These compounds are highly reactive starting materials in the formation of chemical derivatives. Staudinger and co-workers (208,209,211) and Krässig (119,120) have prepared a number of inclusion celluloses, and have investigated their behavior in esterification with acetic anhydride-benzene and other acetylation reagents. Table XIII summarizes some of their results, and clearly demon-

TABLE XIII

Acetylation of Inclusion Celluloses (211)[a]

Cellulose	Acetyl content (%)	
	After 1 hour	After 24 hours
Mercerized cellulose, vacuum dried (40°C.)	—	0.9
Mercerized cellulose, acetic acid included	22.0	44.9
Mercerized cellulose, benzene included	25.7	45.0
Mercerized cellulose, pyridine included[b]	—	14.0

[a] Conditions: acetylated with acetic anhydride-benzene with H_2SO_4 catalyst at 60°C.

[b] Acetic anhydride-pyridine acetylation reagent used.

strates the enhanced reactivity of the inclusion celluloses. Graft-copolymers (Section III-C4) of cellulose have been prepared by "including" the monomer into the cellulose (96).

C. SUBSTITUTION REACTIONS

1. Esterification

Cellulose esters may be divided into two groups: inorganic esters and organic esters.

a. Inorganic Esters

Certain strong inorganic acids, such as nitric acid, sulfuric acid, and phosphoric acid, react directly with cellulose to give the respective esters, whereas other strong acids, such as perchloric acid and other halogen acids, do not esterify cellulose. Those strong acids that do are characterized by their ability to form crystalline addition compounds with cellulose, their ability to dissolve cellulose when they are present in sufficiently concentrated solution, and the fact that their esters do not hydrolyze in a normal manner in alkali. Of the inorganic esters of cellulose, by far the most important one is cellulose nitrate.

Cellulose nitrate is usually prepared by treating cellulose with a mixture of nitric acid, sulfuric acid, and water (22% HNO_3, 66% H_2SO_4, and 12% H_2O, for maximum nitration). The sulfuric acid acts as a dehydrating agent, but will also give rise to the formation of some cellulose sulfate as an unavoidable side product. The nitration reaction may be written as follows:

$$HONO_2 + H^+ \rightleftharpoons \underset{H}{HO^+NO_2} \rightleftharpoons NO_2^+ + H_2O$$

$$NO_2^+ + HOR_{cell.} \rightleftharpoons \underset{H}{NO_2O^+R_{cell.}} \rightleftharpoons NO_2OR_{cell.} + H^+$$

And the sulfation side reaction may be written:

$$SO_3 + HOR_{cell.} \rightleftharpoons SO_3OR_{cell.} \rightleftharpoons {}^-SO_3OR_{cell.} + H^+$$
$$H$$

The extent to which maximum nitration is hindered by the sulfation reaction is determined by the amount of water and of sulfuric acid present in the reaction medium. If the sulfuric acid is replaced by the weaker phosphoric acid, more complete nitration is possible, and cellulose degradation is kept to a minimum. In some commercial nitrations, where intermediate degrees of substitution are desirable, a reaction medium with higher water content is used (e.g., 21% HNO_3, 61% H_2SO_4, and 18% H_2O). The degree of substitution (DS), or nitrogen content, is determined by the composition of the reaction medium (24,154) as illustrated in Fig. 38.

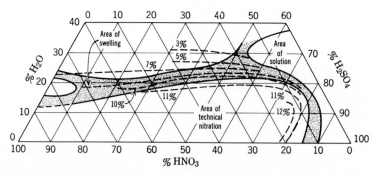

Fig. 38. Effect of dipping acid composition on the nitrogen content of cellulose nitrate (154).

The commercial preparation of cellulose nitrate involves the following operations: shredding and drying of the cellulose, nitration with mixed acid, removal of the spent acid by centrifugation, stabilization by boiling and treatment with hard water or weak organic bases, viscosity control (reduction of chain length is achieved by means of acid hydrolysis) and, finally, water removal by displacement with ethanol.

The end uses of the cellulose nitrate obtained are determined by its physical and mechanical properties and these, in turn, depend on the degree of polymerization (DP) and the DS (see Table XIV).

TABLE XIV

Commercial Grades of Cellulose Nitrate (179)

DS	% Nitrogen	DP	Solvents	Applications
2.4–2.8	12.0–13.5	2000	Acetone	Explosives
2.0–2.3	~11.8	500	Esters	Films, cements
1.9–2.3	~11.5	200	Esters (high DS) Ethanol (low DS) Ether-alcohol	Lacquers
1.0–2.0	~11.0	500	Ethanol	Plastics

b. Organic Esters

Esterification of cellulose may also be brought about by organic acids, acid anhydrides, and acid chlorides.

Of the organic acids, formic acid is the only one which is capable of direct esterification of cellulose to any appreciable extent. Other organic acids, even at their boiling point, give only products with very low DS. However, if these acids are converted to anhydrides, they readily esterify cellulose to high degrees of substitution. In this type of esterification mineral acids or salts, such as magnesium perchlorate, are used as catalysts.

Acid chlorides of most organic acids will also esterify cellulose in a basic medium such as pyridine or sodium hydroxide. In certain cases, however, the products obtained are not the desired esters, and special techniques must be used to avoid side reactions.

Of the organic cellulose esters, such as the acetate, butyrate, etc., and several mixed esters (see a comprehensive list by Rånby and Rydholm (179) and the detailed sections of Chapter IX in Ott-Spurlin eds., *Cellulose and Cellulose Derivatives*, Interscience, New York, 1954), the acetate is by far the most important one from a commercial point of view.

Cellulose acetate. The acetylation of cellulose, which is usually carried out by treating the cellulose with acetic anhydride in the presence of acetic acid and sulfuric acid (e.g., 131), may be described by the following reactions:

$$CH_3COOH + H^+ \rightleftharpoons CH_3CO\overset{+}{O}H \rightleftharpoons CH_3\overset{+}{C}O + H_2O$$
$$H$$

$$CH_3\overset{+}{C}O + HOR_{cell.} \rightleftharpoons CH_3CO\overset{+}{O}R_{cell.} \rightleftharpoons CH_3COOR_{cell.} + H^+$$
$$\phantom{CH_3CO + HOR_{cell.} \rightleftharpoons CH_3COO}H$$

And, again, a certain amount of sulfation occurs as a side reaction:

$$SO_3 + HOR_{cell.} \rightleftharpoons SO_3\overset{-}{O}R_{cell.} \rightleftharpoons SO_3OR_{cell.} + H^+$$
$$\phantom{SO_3 + HOR_{cell.} \rightleftharpoons SO_3O}H$$

Whereas in all other technical processes for the production of cellulose derivatives the cellulose maintains its fiber structure, in the usual acetylation process the material dissolves after esterification has occurred. The esterification reaction occurs in a heterogeneous manner because cellulose does not form an addition compound with acetic acid as it does with $H_3\overset{+}{O}$-forming acids.

The acetylation of cellulose is carried out in several steps. The cellulose first undergoes a pretreatment, usually with acetic acid, either alone or in presence of an esterification catalyst, to make the material more reactive. The presence of catalyst results in considerable viscosity reduction and the pretreatment therefore presents a means for regulation of the molecular weight of the final product. The next step is the addition of the acetylation reagent consisting of acetic anhydride, catalyst (H_2SO_4), unless the latter has been added during the pretreatment, and a diluent, usually acetic acid or methylene chloride. This must be done slowly and at low temperature, and cooling should be maintained during the early stages of the acetylation to avoid excessive temperature rises. The esterification to the triacetate is complete when all the cellulose has gone into solution.

However, the *triacetate* or *primary* acetate is soluble only in a few solvents, such as glacial acetic acid, methylene chloride, or chloroform, and it has only recently become a commercially important material. In order to obtain an acetone-soluble product, it is necessary to saponify some of the acetyl groups (usually about one out of six). Aqueous acetic acid is therefore added to reverse the acetylation and, at the same time, to remove any combined sulfate. This hydrolysis is carried out at constant temperature (about 40°C.) until a product of the desired acetyl content is obtained. The latter, known as *secondary* acetate, is then precipitated from solution by addition of water or dilute acetic acid, washed to remove acetic acid, and dried.

Cellulose acetate has replaced cellulose nitrate in a number of applications because of its lower flammability. It is used largely in the manufacture of films, lacquers, plastic compositions, and fibers. Table XV describes some of the application of different grades of cellulose acetate.

TABLE XV

Commercial Grades of Cellulose Acetate (179)

DS	Solvents	Applications
1.8–1.9	Water-propanol-chloroform	Composite fabrics
2.2–2.3	Acetone	Lacquers and plastics
2.3–2.4	Acetone	Acetate rayon
2.5–2.6	Acetone	X-ray and safety films
2.8–2.9	Methylene chloride-ethanol	Insulating foils
2.9–3.0	Methylene chloride	Fabrics (e.g., "Arnel")

2. Etherification

Cellulose ethers are formed when cellulose, in the presence of alkali, or as alkali cellulose, is treated with alkyl or arylalkyl halides or sulfates, with ω-halocarboxylic acids or their salts, with alkene oxides, or with olefins activated by polar substituents. In certain cases, such as in the reaction of aldehydes with cellulose, the etherification may also be acid-catalyzed.

Some of the more important etherifying agents and the corresponding cellulose ethers are: methyl chloride or dimethyl sulfate → methyl cellulose (MC); ethyl chloride or diethyl sulfate → ethyl cellulose (EC); chloroacetic acid or its sodium salt → carboxymethyl cellulose (CMC); ethylene oxide → hydroxyethyl cellulose (HEC); and acrylonitrile → cyanoethyl cellulose.

The most common etherification reaction is perhaps the interaction between an alkyl halide and cellulose in alkaline medium. This reaction may be written as follows:

$$R_{cell.}OH \cdot NaOH + R'Cl \rightarrow R_{cell.}OR' + NaCl + H_2O$$

Although the etherification would also be consistent with the reaction of the cellulose hydroxyl group in its alcoholate form:

$$R_{cell}.OH + OH^- \rightleftharpoons R_{cell}.O^- + H_2O$$
$$R_{cell}.O^- + R'Cl \rightleftharpoons R_{cell}.OR' + Cl^-$$

At the present time the most important cellulose ether is probably *carboxymethyl cellulose* (CMC) or, rather, its water-soluble sodium salt, which finds wide application as a textile and paper size and as a thickening agent for aqueous media. Its preparation may be summarized by the following reaction:

$$R_{cell}.OH + ClCH_2COONa + NaOH \rightarrow R_{cell}.OCH_2COONa$$
$$+ NaCl + H_2O$$

with the formation of sodium glycolate occurring as a side reaction. The preparation of carboxymethyl cellulose, which is more or less characteristic of the preparation of cellulose ethers, is usually carried out batchwise, although there is a trend toward continuous processes. The first step involves the formation of alkali cellulose and, with carboxymethylation but not other etherification reactions, this may be carried out in the same operation as the etherification. The etherification with monochloroacetic acid or its sodium salt is complete in a few hours at temperatures of 40–60°C. (temperatures above 70°C. are not used in order to avoid degradation). The crude product obtained may be purified from sodium chloride and sodium glycolate by treatment with alcohol-water mixtures or by conversion of the NaCMC to the insoluble free acid form.

The determining factors in etherification reactions are the ratios of alkali to cellulose, alkali to water, and cellulose to alkylating agent.

TABLE XVI

Variation of Solubility of Cellulose Ethers with Degree of Substitution (164a)

Solubility	Methyl cellulose, DS	Ethyl cellulose, DS	Sodium carboxymethyl cellulose, DS
4 to 8% NaOH	0.1–0.6	0.5–0.7	0.05–0.25
Cold water	1.3–2.6	0.7–1.3	0.3–0.8
Increasing in alcohol	2.1–2.6	1.4–1.8	2.0–2.8
Increasing in solvents	2.4–2.7	1.8–2.2	—
Increasing in hydrocarbons	2.6–2.8	2.7–2.9	—

These factors will also determine the DS of the product and, through the DS, its solubility characteristics and applications. The variation of solubility of cellulose ethers with DS is illustrated for the most important cellulose ethers in Table XVI.

Table XVI also illustrates the fact that the nature of the substituents influences the solubility behavior. The generalization may be made that: the bulkier the substituent, the lower the DS required to attain water solubility. Furthermore, with increasing DS, the more hydrophobic the substituent, the lower the DS at which water solubility is lost again. However, cellulose ethers with only hydrophilic substituents never lose their water solubility even at high DS.

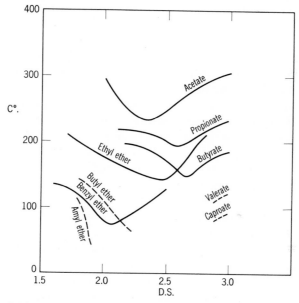

Fig. 39. Melting points of cellulose derivatives as functions of the degree of substitution (179).

The effect of DS and substituent nature on other properties such as melting behavior is also evident. This is shown for a number of cellulose ethers and esters in Fig. 39.

3. Xanthation

Cellulose xanthate is by far the most important cellulose derivative. Although cellulose xanthate is an ester (the ester of dithiocarbonic acid), the xanthation reaction is very similar to an etherification. Thus, on treating alkali cellulose with carbon disulfide, the following reaction may be written:

$$R_{cell}.OH \cdot NaOH + CS_2 \xrightarrow{OH^-} R_{cell}.OCSSNa + H_2O$$

with the hydrolysis of CS_2 occurring as a side reaction.

The cellulose xanthate is important, not as such, but as an intermediate in the manufacture of rayon, cellophane, and other forms of regenerated cellulose by the *viscose process*.

The first step in xanthation, as in the preparation of cellulose ethers, is the formation of alkali cellulose, usually obtained by treating cellulose sheets (wood pulp) with 18% sodium hydroxide at about 15–30°C. After removal of excess alkali, the material is shredded and left to "age," i.e., it is left to undergo alkaline oxidative degradation with resulting decrease in degree of polymerization from about 1000 to about 200 to 400. Xanthation is then carried out by reaction with carbon disulfide in rotating drums at about 20–35°C. for about 3 hours. The resulting cellulose xanthate has a DS of approximately 0.5. In the preparation of regenerated cellulose, the xanthate is then dissolved in aqueous sodium hydroxide to give an orange solution known as "viscose," which is left to "ripen." During the ripening, the xanthate probably becomes more dispersed (but not molecularly!), migration of the xanthate groups occurs, resulting in a more homogeneously substituted product. The final steps then consist of filtration and deaeration of the viscose and regeneration of the cellulose by extrusion of the viscose into an acid coagulation medium. These various steps and the corresponding chemical reactions have been reviewed recently by Sisson (201).

Xanthation to higher degrees of substitution than required in the viscose process may be carried out by treating the cellulose with certain tetraalkylammonium solutions instead of with sodium hydroxide before reaction with carbon disulfide (130).

4. Formation of Graft- and Block-Copolymers of Cellulose

In recent years two new types of macromolecules, known as graft-copolymers and block-copolymers, have been synthesized. [Review papers on this subject can be found in the literature (69,100,223).] Their structure may be described as follows: a *graft-copolymer* consists of a chain of monomer units of type A, to which there are attached branches containing monomer units of a different type, B; on the other hand, a *block-copolymer* is a linear chain molecule, which consists of segments or "blocks" of monomer units differing from each other by the fact that one block is made up of type A monomer units and another block of type B monomer units. Fig. 40 illustrates this.

(a)
```
                        AAAAAAAAAAAAA
                          B       B
                          B       B
                          B       B
                          B       B
                          B       B
                                  B
                                  B
                                  B
```

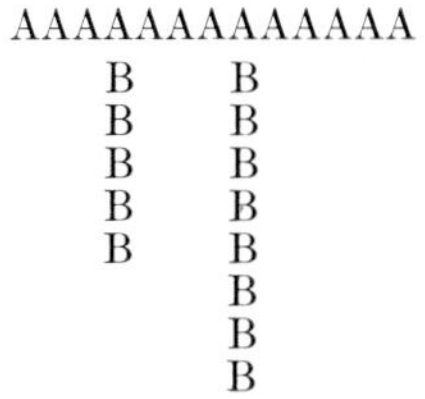

(b)
```
            AAAAAAABBBBBBBBBB

      AAAAAAABBBBBAAAAAAAABBBBBB
```

Fig. 40. Structure of (a) graft-copolymers, and (b) block-copolymers.

A large number of graft- and block-copolymers, where both A and B represent vinyl type monomers, have already been prepared but, until recently, few cases of graft- or block-copolymers involving cellulose chains have been reported. The following reactions are representative of some that have been used thus far in the preparation of graft- and block-copolymers of cellulose:

(1) Reaction of cellulose with *ethylene oxide* (159):

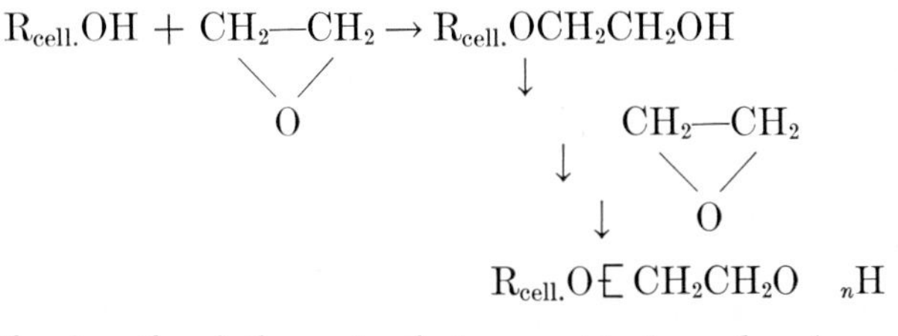

$$R_{cell.}OH + CH_2{-}CH_2 \rightarrow R_{cell.}OCH_2CH_2OH$$

$$\diagdown \diagup$$
$$O \qquad\qquad\qquad\quad \downarrow$$

$$CH_2{-}CH_2$$

$$\downarrow \qquad \diagdown \diagup$$
$$\downarrow \qquad O$$

$$R_{cell.}O{-}[CH_2CH_2O{-}]_n H$$

As the length of the polyethylene oxide branches increases, the product becomes water soluble.

(2) Reaction of cellulose with *β-propiolactone* (182):

$$R_{cell.}O{-}[CH_2CH_2COO{-}]_n H$$

Graft-copolymers of the above type have been prepared by treating alkali-swollen cellulose with dilute solutions of β-propiolactone in inert solvents such as xylene.

(*3*) Reaction of cellulose with *vinyl monomers:*

(*a*) It is possible to prepare a cellulose sample containing peroxidic groups which, when heated in the presence of a vinyl monomer, will decompose leaving free radicals on the cellulose chain. These can then initiate polymerization of the vinyl monomer, with resulting formation of polyvinyl branches on the cellulose chain.

An example of this type has been reported by Jahn and coworkers (226), who have prepared the *ortho*-chlorobenzyl ester of cellulose which, on standing in air, forms hydroperoxide groups and, on subsequent heating in styrene, forms a graft-copolymer.

A graft-copolymer based on a similar principle may be prepared by preparing the cumene ester of cellulose (12), oxidizing the latter to a polyhydroperoxide, and heating in the presence of monomer.

(*b*) By submitting ethyl cellulose or other cellulose derivatives to mechanical shear (35) in the presence of a vinyl monomer, such as methyl methacrylate, a block-copolymer of ethyl cellulose and polymethyl methacrylate can be prepared.

(*c*) By irradiation of cellulose and cellulose derivatives in the presence of vinyl monomers with high energy electrons or gamma rays, block- and graft-copolymers have been prepared (96).

(*d*) By irradiation of regenerated cellulose by ultraviolet light in the presence of a photosensitizer and vinyl monomer, graft-copolymers can be prepared (65).

(*e*) By treatment of cellulose with ozone and subsequent heating in the presence of certain monomers, graft-copolymers can be prepared (126).

D. DEGRADATION REACTIONS

The fact that cellulose degrades under a variety of circumstances is important from several points of view.

For the manufacturer of cellulosic products, degradation is both helpful and undesirable. Thus, a certain amount of degradation, such as that which occurs during the aging of alkali cellulose, is desirable, since it provides an important means of controlling the properties of the final product. However, once the final product is obtained, degradation must be kept at a minimum to avoid deterioration of physical properties such as strength.

Degradation reactions also provide information regarding the chemical and physical structure of cellulose, e.g., regarding the existence of "weak links" and the amount and size of the ordered and disordered regions in cellulose.

There are several types of degradation, which may be divided into four main classes: (*1*) hydrolytic; (*2*) oxidative; (*3*) microbiological; and (*4*) mechanical. Of these, only the first three classes, which are perhaps the most important ones, will be briefly treated here. (For detailed treatment of the different types of cellulose degradation, see Refs. 47,64,97,141, and 202).

1. Hydrolytic Degradation

This type of degradation refers to the scission of the cellulose acetal links, i.e., the β-glucoside bonds, by acid:

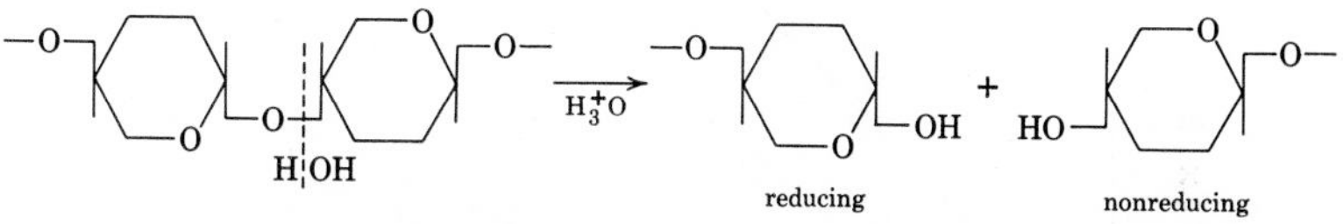

The resulting increase in reducing power of the reaction mixture presents a way of following the kinetics of this type of degradation.

The hydrolysis may be *homogeneous* or *heterogeneous*, depending on whether or not the cellulose is soluble in the reaction medium. Thus, in concentrated phosphoric acid, which is a solvent for cellulose, homogeneous hydrolytic degradation occurs, whereas in concentrated sulfuric or hydrochloric acid, the cellulose is not soluble and the degradation is heterogeneous in nature.

(*1*) *Heterogeneous* hydrolysis occurs in almost all acid-catalyzed technical reactions of cellulose, since these are nearly always carried out with the cellulose maintaining its fibrous structure. In such a case, one finds an initial rapid degradation until a so-called "leveling-off DP" has been attained (9), corresponding to hydrolysis of the cellulose in the amorphous regions, which are more readily penetrated by the acid reagent. This readily hydrolyzable material usually constitutes about 10–12% by weight of the cellulose sample. The hydrolysis rate then decreases to a new, lower value, corresponding to the degradation of the crystalline or ordered regions. Although heterogeneous hydrolysis is thus useful for determination of order-disorder ratios in different cellulosic materials, the effect of physical structure renders a kinetic interpretation of the results unreliable. This effect of physical structure may, however, be eliminated by a preliminary nondegrading alkali treatment (9).

(2) *Homogeneous* hydrolysis eliminates the effect of fiber inhomogeneity and permits the study of hydrolysis rates in solution. Such studies have shown that the kinetics of the reaction is zero order with respect to time. It is also found that the rate of hydrolysis, determined by measuring the change in $1/\overline{DP}_n$ as a function of hydrolysis time, does not change with time [see Fig. 41 (103)]. Since

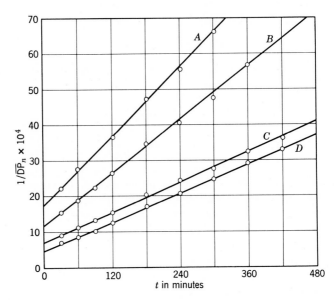

Fig. 41. Hydrolysis of cotton linters and sulfite pulp in 80% H_3PO_4 at 25°C. (103). (Samples A and B are cotton linters, and samples C and D are sulfite pulp).

$1/\overline{DP}_n$ is a direct measure of the number of chain breaks, this means that there is no evidence to support the existence of so-called "weak links" or "Lockerstellen" postulated by Schulz and Husemann (191, 192) and by Pacsu (91). Fig. 41 shows, however, that the rate of hydrolysis of the wood cellulose is about twice that of the cotton cellulose. This is in agreement with the earlier results of Jörgensen (111), and was also confirmed by Marchessault and Rånby (178). The latter have attributed this to an "inductive effect" due to electrophilic substituents, e.g., carboxyl or carbonyl groups, occurring randomly along the molecular chain of the wood cellulose. Thus, when glucose unit B in the following formula contains a carboxyl group, the linkage A—B will be "activated," i.e., it will be more susceptible to hydrolysis, while B—C will be "stabilized":

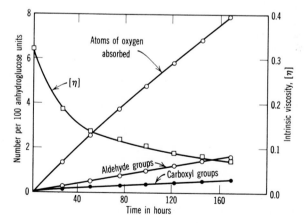

In support of this explanation, Marchessault and Rånby have shown that if the wood pulp is first treated with sodium borohydride, i.e., to reduce any COOH groups to CH₂OH groups, it will subsequently hydrolyze in H_3PO_4 at approximately the same rate as the cotton cellulose.

2. Oxidative Degradation

Cellulose is very sensitive toward oxidizing reagents, the extent of the resulting degradation depending on the nature of the reagent and the conditions under which oxidation occurs.

One of the most important oxidative degradation reactions is the autoxidation of cellulose by molecular oxygen in the presence of alkali. This reaction is of great industrial importance because it is the basis of the "aging" of alkali cellulose through which the molec-

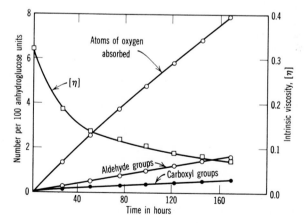

Fig. 42. Functional group development and intrinsic viscosity (in cuprammonium) decrease during autoxidation of alkali cellulose pulp (45).

ular weight of a number of major cellulose products, such as rayon and cellophane, is adjusted to a desired level.

The autoxidation of alkali cellulose is best explained by a hydroperoxide-type, free radical mechanism. The reaction may be catalyzed by transition metals (cobalt, iron, manganese) and retarded by silver and organic antioxidants.

The effect of oxidative degradation on the intrinsic viscosity and on the functional groups in the cellulose chain has been demonstrated by Entwistle and his co-workers (45), and is illustrated in Fig. 42.

Oxidative degradation by a free radical mechanism is also assumed to be the explanation for the decrease in molecular weight and loss of strength observed when cellulose is exposed to ionizing radiation, e.g., high-energy electrons, γ-rays, or neutrons (22,187).

3. Microbiological Degradation

One of the most undesirable forms of degradation, through which billions of dollars are wasted every year, is the decay of wood and other forms of cellulose through enzymes produced by fungi, bacteria, protozoa, plants, and animals.

Enzymatic degradation is actually very similar to hydrolytic degradation except that due to the larger size of the enzyme molecules, as compared to acid molecules, they cannot diffuse readily into the cellulose and their attack is a localized one. This also accounts for the fact that although there is a considerable loss of strength as the degradation continues, this is not accompanied by a large decrease in the degree of polymerization. A comparison of acid and enzymatic degradation is shown in Table XVII (181).

TABLE XVII

Comparison of Acid- and Enzyme-Catalyzed Degradation (181)

Sample	Original DP	Acid hydrolysis		Enzyme hydrolysis	
		Weight loss at level-off (%)	DP after reaction	Weight loss at level-off (%)	DP after reaction
Kiered cotton	4970	4	225	25	4200
Mercerized	5040	6.5	138	35	3040
Decrystallized	4670	7	133	35	3100
Decrystallized	3920	8.9	112	65	1630

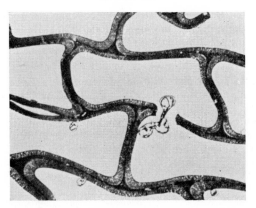

Fig. 43. Cross-section of fir (springwood) degraded for three months by *Merulius domesticus* (2000 ×) (144).

The localization of the attack is also very apparent from photomicrographs of wood fibers such as the one shown in Fig. 43 (144). In order to prevent degradation of wood and other cellulosic materials by fungi and other microorganisms, there is currently much research under way at different laboratories, and it is hoped that eventually a number of satisfactory methods of preservation will be worked out. The approaches vary considerably: some try to prevent contact with microorganisms; others use substances that destroy the microorganism (e.g., fungicides, etc.); still others try to prevent the microorganism from producing the enzyme or enzymes that cause the actual degradation; and, finally, there are many attempts to modify the cellulose chemically to make it resistant against attack. Although the last approach is perhaps intrinsically the most satisfactory, it lends itself, unfortunately, much more readily to the treatment of fibers than to the treatment of wood.

GENERAL REFERENCES

Honeyman, J., ed., *Recent Advances in the Chemistry of Cellulose and Starch*, Interscience, New York, 1959.

Ott, E., H. M. Spurlin, and M. W. Grafflin, eds., *Cellulose and Cellulose Derivatives*, Interscience, New York, 1954.

REFERENCES

1. Alexander, W. J., and R. L. Mitchell, *Anal. Chem.*, **21**, 1497 (1949).
2. Andress, K. R., *Z. physik. Chem.*, **34**, 190 (1929).

3. Ant-Wuorinen, O., *State Inst. Tech. Research, Finland*, Reports No. 96, 118, 131, etc., mostly reprinted in *Paperi ja Puu*, 1953, 1954.
4. Ant-Wuorinen, O., *Paperi ja Puu*, **37**, 335 (1955).
5. Asunmaa, S., *Svensk Papperstidn.*, **58**, 308 (1955).
6. Badger, R. M., and R. H. Blaker, *J. Phys. & Colloid Chem.*, **53**, 1056 (1949).
7. Baker, C. A., and R. J. P. Williams, *J. Chem. Soc. (London)*, **1956**, 2352.
8. Barker, S. A., E. J. Bourne, M. Stacey, and D. M. Whiffen, *J. Chem. Soc.*, **1954**, 171.
9. Battista, O., S. Coppick, J. A. Howsmon, F. F. Morehead, and W. A. Sisson, *Ind. Eng. Chem.*, **48**, 333 (1956).
10. Battista, O. A., and W. A. Sisson, *J. Am. Chem. Soc.*, **68**, 915 (1946).
11. Benoit, H., A. M. Holtzer, and P. Doty, *J. Phys. Chem.*, **58**, 635 (1954).
12. Berglund, O., and B. G. Rånby, Master's Thesis, Upsala University, Sweden, 1955.
13. Berl, E., and R. Klaye, *Z. ges. Schiess- u. Sprengstoffw.-Nitrocellulose*, **2**, 381 (1907).
14. Bock, L. H., *Ind. Eng. Chem.*, **29**, 985 (1937).
15. Brinkman, H. C., *Physica*, **13**, 447 (1947).
16. Brooks, M. C., and R. M. Badger, *J. Am. Chem. Soc.*, **72**, 1705 (1950).
17. Brown, L., P. Holliday, and I. F. Trotter, *J. Chem. Soc.*, **1951**, 1532.
18. Browning, B. L., and L. O. Sell, *Tappi*, **39**, 489 (1956).
19. Browning, B. L., L. O. Sell, and W. Abel, *Tappi*, **37**, 273 (1954).
20. Cassidy, H. G., *Fundamentals of Chromatography*, Interscience, New York, 1957.
21. Cattlett, M. S., R. Giuffria, A. T. Moore, and M. L. Rollins, *Textile Research J.*, **21**, 880 (1951).
22. Charlesby, A., *J. Polymer Sci.*, **15**, 263 (1955).
23. Charlton, W., W. N. Haworth, and S. Peat, *J. Chem. Soc.*, **1926**, 89.
24. Chedin, J., *Chim. & ind. (Paris)*, **61**, 571 (1949).
25. Choudhury, P. K., and H. P. Frank, *J. Polymer Sci.*, **19**, 218 (1956).
26. Claesson, S., *Discussions Faraday Soc.*, **7**, 321 (1949).
27. Cooke, T. F., *Textile Research J.*, **24**, 197 (1954).
28. Coppick, S., O. A. Battista, and M. R. Lytton, *Ind. Eng. Chem.*, **42**, 2533 (1950).
29. Cragg, L. H., and H. Hammerschlag, *Chem. Revs.*, **39**, 79 (1946).
30. Croon, I., *Svensk Papperstidn.*, **62**, 700 (1959).
31. Cross, C. F., and E. J. Bevan, e.g., *J. Chem. Soc.*, **38**, 666 (1880); *Cellulose*, Longmans, Green and Co., London, 1st ed., 1895.
32. Cross, C. F., E. J. Bevan, and C. Beadle, *J. Chem. Soc.*, **63**, 837 (1893).
33. Crum, W., *Ann.*, **62**, 233 (1847); *Phil. Mag.*, **30**, 426 (1847).
34. Davis, W. E., A. J. Barry, F. C. Peterson, and A. J. King, *J. Am. Chem. Soc.*, **65**, 1294 (1943).
35. de Bataafsche Petroleum Maatschappij, N. V., *Brit. Pat.* 679,562 (Sept. 17, 1952); *Chem. Abstracts*, **47**, 7825 (1953).
36. Debye, P., and A. M. Bueche, *J. Chem. Phys.*, **16**, 573 (1948).
37. Denham, W. S., and H. Woodhouse, *J. Chem. Soc.*, **103**, 1735 (1913).
38. Desreux, V., *Rec. trav. chim.*, **68**, 789 (1949).
39. Dobry, A., *Bull. soc. chim.*, (5), **3**, 312 (1936).

40. Doty, P., N. S. Schneider, and A. Holtzer, *J. Am. Chem. Soc.*, **75**, 754 (1953).
41. Duclaux, J., and E. Wollman, *Bull. soc. chim.*, **27**, 414 (1920).
42. Durso, D. F., and J. C. Paulson, *Anal. Chem.*, **30**, 919 (1958).
43. Dymmling, E., H. W. Giertz, and B. G. Rånby, *Svensk Papperstidn.*, **58**, 10 (1955).
44. Ekenstam, A., *Celluloselösungen in Mineralsäuren*, Diss., Lund, Sweden, 1936.
45. Entwistle, D., E. H. Cole, and N. S. Wooding, *Textile Research J.*, **19**, 527 (1949).
46. Erdmann, J., *Ann.*, **5**, supplementary binding, 223 (1867).
47. Findlay, W. P. K., *Decay of Timber and its Prevention*, H. M. Stationery Office, London, 1946.
48. Fischer, E., and G. Zemplén, *Ann.*, **365**, 1 (1909).
49. Fisher, D. G., and J. Mann, *J. Polymer Sci.*, **42**, 189 (1960).
50. Flory, P. J., and T. G. Fox, Jr., *J. Am. Chem. Soc.*, **73**, 1904 (1951).
51. Flory, P. J., O. K. Spurr, and D. K. Carpenter, *J. Polymer Sci.*, **27**, 231 (1958).
52. Forziati, F. H., and J. W. Rowen, *J. Research Nat. Bur. Standards*, **46**, 38 (1951).
53. Forziati, F. H., J. W. Rowen, and E. K. Plyler, *J. Research Nat. Bur. Standards*, **46**, 288 (1951).
54. Fox, T. G., Jr., and P. J. Flory, *J. Phys. & Colloid Chem.*, **53**, 197 (1949).
55. Franchimont, A. P. N., *Ber.*, **12**, 1938 (1879).
56. Franchimont, A. P. N., *Rec. trav. chim.*, **18**, 472 (1899).
57. Fremy, E., *Jahresber. der Chem.*, **1**, 796 (1847–48); *Compt. rend.*, **48**, 275 (1859).
58. Freudenberg, K., *Tannin, Cellulose, Lignin*, J. Springer, Berlin, 1933.
59. Freudenberg, K., and C. Blomqvist, *Ber.*, **68B**, 2070 (1935).
60. Freudenberg, K., and W. Kuhn, *Ber.*, **65B**, 484 (1932).
61. Frey-Wyssling, A., *Science*, **119**, 80 (1954).
62. Frey-Wyssling, A., K. Mühlethaler, and R. W. G. Wyckoff, *Experientia*, **4**, 475 (1948).
63. Frilette, V. J., J. Hanle, and H. Mark, *J. Am. Chem. Soc.*, **70**, 1107 (1948).
64. Gascoigne, J. A., and M. M. Gascoigne, *Biological Degradation of Cellulose*, Butterworths, London, 1960.
65. Geacintov, N., V. T. Stannett, E. W. Abrahamson, and J. J. Hermans, *J. Appl. Polymer Sci.*, **3**, 54 (1960).
66. Gralén, N., *Dissertation*, Uppsala, Sweden, 1944.
67. Gross, S. J., and G. L. Clark, *Z. Krist.*, **A99**, 357 (1938).
68. Gustafsson, C., P. J. Ollinmaa, and J. Saarnio, *Acta Chem. Scand.*, **6**, 1299 (1952).
69. Hart, R., *Ind. chim. belge*, **21**, 1053, 1193, 1309 (1956); **22**, 39 (1957).
70. Haworth, W. N., *Helv. Chim. Acta*, **11**, 534 (1928).
71. Haworth, W. N., *Nature*, **116**, 430 (1925).
72. Haworth, W. N., *The Constitution of Sugars*, Edward Arnold, London, 1929.
73. Haworth, W. N., E. L. Hirst, and E. J. Miller, *J. Chem. Soc.*, **1927**, 2436.
74. Haworth, W. N., C. W. Long, and J. H. G. Plant, *J. Chem. Soc.*, **1927**, 2809.
75. Haworth, W. N., and H. Machemer, *J. Chem. Soc.*, **1932**, 2270.
76. Hengstenberg, J., and H. Mark, *Z. Krist.*, **69**, 271 (1928).

77. Hermans, P. H., *Kolloid-Z.*, **86**, 107 (1939).

78. Hermans, P. H., *Contributions to the Physics of Cellulose*, Elsevier, Amsterdam, 1946, pp. 60, 70.

79. Hermans, P. H., *Physics and Chemistry of Cellulose Fibers*, Elsevier, New York, 1949.

80. Hermans, P. H., *Makromol. Chem.*, **6**, 25 (1951).

81. Hermans, P. H., and A. Weidinger, *J. Appl. Phy.*, **19**, 491 (1948).

82. Hermans, P. H., and A. Weidinger, *J. Polymer Sci.*, **4**, 135 (1949).

83. Herzog, R. O., *Ber.*, **58**, 1256 (1925).

84. Herzog, R. O., *J. Phys. Chem.*, **30**, 457 (1926).

85. Herzog, R. O., and W. Jancke, *Z. Physik*, **3**, 196 (1920).

86. Hess, K., *Die Chemie der Zellulose*, Akad. Verlag., Leipzig, 1928.

87. Heuser, E., and R. Bartunek, *Cellulosechemie*, **6**, 19 (1925).

88. Heyn, A. N. J., *J. Am. Chem. Soc.*, **70**, 2284 (1950).

89. Heyn, A. N. J., *J. Appl. Phy.*, **26**, 519 (1955).

90. Hibbert, H., *Ind. Eng. Chem.*, **13**, 256, 334 (1921).

91. Hiller, L. A., Jr., and E. Pacsu, *Textile Research J.*, **16**, 490 (1946).

92. Hock, C. W., in E. Ott and H. Spurlin, *Cellulose and Cellulose Derivatives*, Interscience, New York, 1954, pp. 347–392.

93. Holtzer, A. M., H. Benoit, and P. Doty, *J. Phys. Chem.*, **58**, 624 (1954).

93a. W. A. Holzer in E. Ott, H. M. Spurlin, and Mildred W. Grafflin, eds., *Cellulose and Cellulose Derivatives*, Part II, Interscience, New York, 1954, p. 515.

94. Honjo, G., and M. Watanbe, *Nature*, **181**, 326 (1958).

95. Howsmon, J. A., *Textile Research J.*, **19**, 152 (1949).

95a. J. A. Howsmon and W. A. Sisson in E. Ott, H. M Spurlin, and Mildred W. Grafflin, eds., *Cellulose and Cellulose Derivatives*, Part I, Interscience, New York, 1954.

96. Huang, R. M. Y., B. Immergut, E. H. Immergut, and W. H. Rapson, *J. Polymer Sci.*, **A1**, 1257 (1963).

97. Hunt, G. M., and G. A. Garratt, *Wood Preservation*, McGraw-Hill, New York, 1938.

98. Immergut, E. H., Dissertation, Polytechnic Institute of Brooklyn, 1953.

99. Immergut, E. H., and F. R. Eirich, *Ind. Eng. Chem.*, **45**, 2500 (1953).

100. Immergut, E. H., and H. Mark, *Makromol. Chem.*, **18/19**, 322 (1956).

101. Immergut, E. H., and B. G. Rånby, *Ind. Eng. Chem.*, **48**, 1183 (1956).

102. Immergut, E. H., B. G. Rånby, and H. Mark, *Ind. Eng. Chem.*, **45**, 2483 (1953).

103. Immergut, E. H., B. G. Rånby, and H. Mark, *La Ricerca Scientifica*, **25**, 308 (1955).

104. Immergut, E. H., S. Rollin, A. Salkind, and H. Mark, *J. Polymer Sci.*, **12**, 439 (1954).

105. Immergut, E. H., J. Schurz, and H. Mark, *Monatsh.*, **84**, 219 (1953).

106. Irvine, J. C., *J. Chem. Soc.*, **123**, 898 (1923).

107. Irvine, J. C., and E. L. Hirst, *J. Chem. Soc.*, **121**, 1585 (1922).

108. Irvine, J. C., and E. L. Hirst, *J. Chem. Soc.*, **123**, 518 (1923).

109. Jolley, L. J., *J. Textile Inst.*, **30**, T4, T22 (1939).

110. Jones, D. W., *J. Polymer Sci.*, **42**, 173 (1960).
111. Jörgensen, L., *Studies on the Partial Hydrolysis of Cellulose*, Oslo, 1950.
112. Jullander, I., Dissertation, University of Uppsala; *Arkiv Kemi Mineral. Geol.*, **21A**, No. 8, 1945.
113. Karrer, P., *Polymere Kohlenhydrate*, Akad. Verlag., Leipzig, 1925.
114. Kinell, P. O., and B. G. Rånby, *Advances in Colloid Science*, Vol. III, Interscience, New York, 1950.
115. Kinsinger, W. G., and C. W. Hock, *Ind. Eng. Chem.*, **40**, 1711 (1948).
116. Kirkwood, J. G., and J. Riseman, *J. Chem. Phys.*, **16**, 565 (1948).
117. Knecht, E., *Ber.*, **37**, 549 (1904).
118. Kraemer, E. O., *Ind. Eng. Chem.*, **30**, 1200 (1938).
119. Krässig, H., *Makromol. Chem.*, **10**, 1 (1953).
120. Krässig, H., and E. Seifert, *Makromol. Chem.*, **14**, 1 (1954).
121. Kratky, O., and G. Porod, *J. Colloid Sci.*, **4**, 35 (1949).
122. Kratky, O., and H. Sembach, *Angew. Chem.*, **67**, 603 (1955).
123. Kuhn, L. P., *Anal. Chem.*, **22**, 276 (1950).
124. Kuhn, W., *Z. physik. Chem.*, **A159**, 368 (1932).
125. Kuhn, W., C. Molster, and K. Freudenberg, *Ber.*, **65B**, 1179 (1932).
126. Landler, Y., *J. Polymer Sci.*, **8**, 63 (1952).
127. Liang, C. Y., and R. H. Marchessault, *J. Polymer Sci.*, **35**, 529 (1959).
128. Liang, C. Y., and R. H. Marchessault, *J. Polymer Sci.*, **37**, 385 (1959).
129. Liang, C. Y., and R. H. Marchessault, *J. Polymer Sci.*, **39**, 269 (1959).
130. Lieser, T., *Kolloid-Z.*, **81**, 234 (1937).
131. Malm, C. J., and L. J. Tanghe, *Ind. Eng. Chem.*, **47**, 995 (1955).
132. Mandelkern, L., and P. J. Flory, *J. Am. Chem. Soc.*, **74**, 2517 (1952).
133. Manley, R. S. J., *Nature*, **189**, 390 (1961).
134. Mann, J., and H. J. Marrinan, *J. Polymer Sci.*, **27**, 595 (1958).
135. Mann, J., and H. J. Marrinan, *J. Polymer Sci.*, **32**, 357 (1958).
136. Marchessault, R. H., and C. Y. Liang, *J. Polymer Sci.*, **43**, 71 (1960).
137. Marrinan, H. J., and J. Mann, *J. Appl. Chem.*, **4**, 204 (1954).
138. Marrinan, H. J., and J. Mann, *J. Polymer Sci.*, **21**, 301 (1956).
139. Marsh, J. T., *Mercerizing*, Chapman & Hall, London, 1941.
140. Marx, M., *Makromol. Chem.*, **16**, 157 (1955).
141. McBurney, L. F., "Degradation of Cellulose," in E. Ott and H. M. Spurlin, *Cellulose and Cellulose Derivatives*, Interscience, New York, 1954.
142. McNally, J. G., and A. P. Godbout, *J. Am. Chem. Soc.*, **51**, 3095 (1929).
143. Meier, H., Dissertation, E. T. H. Zürich, 1955; *Holz Roh- u. Werkstoff*, **13**, 323 (1955).
144. Meier, H., in *Die Chemie der Pflanzenzellwand*, E. Treiber ed., Springer, Berlin (1957).
145. Meier, H., *J. Pure and Applied Chemistry* **5**, 37 (1962).
146. Meyer, K. H., *Z. angew. Chem.*, **41**, 935 (1928).
147. Meyer, K. H., *Natural and Synthetic High Polymers*, Interscience, New York, 1950, p. 299. Table V.
148. Meyer, K. H., and H. Mark, *Ber.*, **61B**, 593 (1928).
149. Meyer, K. H., and H. Mark, *Z. physik. Chem.*, **B2**, 115 (1929).
150. Meyer, K. H., and L. Misch, *Ber.*, **70B**, 266 (1937).

151. Meyer, K. H., and L. Misch, *Helv. Chim. Acta*, **20**, 232 (1937).
152. Meyer, K. H., M. Studer, and A. J. A. van der Wyk, *Monatsh.*, **81**, 151 (1950).
153. Meyerhoff, G., *Makromol. Chem.*, **32**, 249 (1959).
154. Miles, F. D., and M. Milbourn, *J. Phys. Chem.*, **34**, 2598 (1930).
155. Mitchell, R. L., *Ind. Eng. Chem.*, **45**, 2526 (1953).
156. Monier-Williams, G. W., *J. Chem. Soc.*, **119**, 803 (1921).
157. Morehead, F. F., *Textile Research J.*, **22**, 535 (1952).
158. Morey, D. R., and J. W. Tamblyn, *J. Appl. Phy.*, **16**, 419 (1945).
159. Morgan, P. W., *Ind. Eng. Chem.*, *Anal. Ed.*, **18**, 500 (1946).
160. Mosimann, H., *Helv. Chim. Acta*, **26**, 61 (1943).
161. Mühlethaler, K., *Biochim. et Biophys. Acta*, **3**, 15 (1949).
162. Münster, A., *J. Polymer Sci.*, **8**, 633 (1952).
163. Newman, S., and F. Eirich, *J. Colloid Sci.*, **5**, 541 (1950).
164. Newman, S., L. Loeb, and C. M. Conrad, *J. Polymer Sci.*, **10**, 463 (1953).
164a. Nichol, W. D., N. L. Cox, and R. F. Conaway, in *Cellulose and Cellulose Derivatives*, Ott and Spurlin, eds., Interscience, New York, 1954, p. 906.
165. Nishikawa, S., and S. Ono, *Proc. Math.-Phys. Soc. Tokyo*, **7**, 131 (1913).
166. Oberlin, M., and J. Mering, *Compt. rend.*, **238**, 1046 (1954).
167. Ost, L., *Z. angew. Chem.*, **19**, 993 (1906).
168. Oth, A., *Bull. soc. chim. Belges*, **58**, 285 (1949).
169. Outer, P., C. I. Carr, and B. H. Zimm, *J. Chem. Phys.*, **18**, 830 (1950).
170. Payen, A., *Compt. rend.*, **7**, 1052, 1125 (1838).
171. Polanyi, M., *Naturwissenschaften*, **9**, 288 (1921).
172. Porod, G., *Kolloid-Z.*, **124**, 83 (1951); **125**, 51 (1952).
173. Preston, R. D., and W. T. Astbury, *Proc. Roy. Soc. (London)*, **B122**, 76 (1937).
174. Preston, R. D., E. Nicolai, R. Reed, and A. Millard, *Nature*, **162**, 665 (1948).
174a. C. B. Purves in E. Ott, H. M. Spurlin, and Mildred W. Grafflin, eds., *Cellulose and Cellulose Derivatives*, Part I, Interscience, New York, 1954, p. 66.
175. Rånby, B. G., Dissertation, Uppsala, 1952.
176. Rånby, B. G., *Acta Chem. Scand.*, **6**, 128 (1952).
177. Rånby, B. G., *Chem. Eng. News*, **38**, (Nov. 7), 53 (1960).
178. Rånby, B. G., and R. H. Marchessault, *J. Polymer Sci.*, **36**, 561 (1959); R. H. Marchessault and B. G. Rånby, *Svensk Papperstidn.*, **62**, 230 (1959).
179. Rånby, B. G., and A. S. Rydholm, "Cellulose and Cellulose Derivatives," in C. Schildknecht, ed., *Polymer Processes*, Interscience, New York, 1956.
180. Rapson, W. H., and G. K. Morbey, *Tappi*, **42**, 125 (1959).
181. Reese, E. T., L. Segal, and V. W. Tripp, *Textile Research J.*, **27**, 626 (1957).
182. Reinhardt, R. M., J. D. Reid, and G. C. Daul, *Textile Research J.*, **26**, 1 (1956).
183. Richtmyer, N. K., and C. S. Hudson, *J. Am. Chem. Soc.*, **61**, 1834 (1939).
184. Rollins, M. L., *Anal. Chem.*, **26**, 718 (1954).
185. Rollins, M. L., and V. W. Tripp, *Textile Research J.*, **24**, 345 (1954).
186. Sadron, C., and H. Mosimann, *J. phys. radium*, **9**, 384 (1938).
187. Saeman, J. F., M. A. Millett, and E. J. Lawton, *Ind. Eng. Chem.*, **44**, 2848 (1952).
188. Saito, G., *Cellulosechemie*, **18**, 106 (1940).

189. Scherer, P. C., and M. K. Testerman, *J. Polymer Sci.*, **7**, 549 (1951).
190. Schildknecht, C., *Polymer Processes*, Interscience, New York, 1956, p. 364, Figs. 8 and 9.
191. Schulz, G. V., *J. Polymer Sci.*, **3**, 365 (1948).
192. Schulz, G. V., E. Husemann, and H. J. Löhmann, *Z. physik. Chem.*, **B52**, 23 (1942).
193. Schulz, G. V., and M. Marx, *Makromol. Chem.*, **14**, 52 (1955).
194. Schulze, F., *Jahresber. der Chem.*, **10**, 491 (1857); *Chem. Zentr.*, **1857**, 321.
195. Schweizer, E., *J. prakt. Chem.*, **72**, 109 (1857).
196. Sharples, A., *J. Polymer Sci.*, **13**, 393 (1954).
197. Sihtola, H., Proc. Second Cellulose Conference, Syracuse, New York, 1959.
198. Sihtola, H., E. Kaila, and L. Laamanen, *J. Polymer Sci.*, **23**, 809 (1957).
199. Singer, S. J., *J. Polymer Sci.*, **1**, 445 (1946).
200. Sisson, W. A., *Contrib. Boyce Thompson Inst.*, **9**, 239 (1938); **12**, 171 (1941).
201. Sisson, W. A., *Textile Research J.*, **30**, 153 (1960).
202. Siu, R. G. H., *Microbial Decomposition of Cellulose*, Reinhold, New York, 1951.
203. Skraup, L. H., *Monatsh.*, **26**, 1415 (1905).
204. Skraup, L. H., and J. König, *Monatsh.*, **22**, 1011 (1901).
205. Sobue, H., *J. Soc. Chem. Ind., Japan*, **43**, B24 (1940).
206. Sponsler, O. L., *J. Gen. Physiol.*, **9**, 221, 677 (1926).
207. Spurlin, H. M., *J. Am. Chem. Soc.*, **61**, 2222 (1939).
208. Staudinger, H., W. Döhle, and O. Heick, *J. prakt. Chem.*, **161**, 191 (1942).
209. Staudinger, H., and T. Eicher, *Makromol. Chem.*, **10**, 254 (1953).
210. Staudinger, H., and J. Fritschi, *Helv. Chim. Acta*, **5**, 785 (1922).
211. Staudinger, H., K. H. In den Birken, and M. Staudinger, *Makromol. Chem.*, **9**, 148 (1953).
212. Stein, R. S., and P. Doty, *J. Am. Chem. Soc.*, **68**, 159 (1946).
213. Svedberg, T., and K. O. Pedersen, *The Ultracentrifuge*, Clarendon Press, Oxford, 1940.
214. Tamblyn, J. W., D. R. Morey, and R. H. Wagner, *Ind. Eng. Chem.*, **37**, 573 (1945).
215. Technical Association of the Pulp and Paper Industry, *TAPPI Standard* T230 sm 50.
216. Timell, T. E., *Svensk Papperstidn.*, **57**, 777, 844 (1954).
217. Timell, T. E., *Ind. Eng. Chem.*, **47**, 2166 (1955).
218. Timell, T. E., *Pulp Paper Mag. Can.*, **59**, No. 8, 139 (1958).
219. Traube, W., G. Glaubitt, and V. Schenck, *Ber.*, **63**, 2083 (1930).
220. Treiber, E., *Protoplasma*, **40**, 367 (1951).
221. Tripp, V. W., and M. L. Rollins, *Anal. Chem.*, **24**, 172 (1952).
222. Tsuboi, M., *J. Polymer Sci.*, **25**, 159 (1957).
223. Valentine, L., *Fibres*, **16**, 12, 60 (1955).
224. Vink, H., *Arkiv Kemi*, **11**, 29 (1957).
225. Vink, H., *Arkiv Kemi*, **13**, 193 (1958).
226. Waltcher, I., R. Burroughs, Jr., and E. C. Jahn. *Lecture by E. C. Jahn* at International Congress of Pure and Applied Chemistry, Stockholm-Uppsala, 1953.

227. Wardrop, A. B., *Holzforschung*, **8**, 12 (1954).
228. Wardrop, A. B., and R. D. Preston, *Nature*, **160**, 911 (1947).
229. Wellard, H. J., *J. Polymer Sci.*, **13**, 471 (1954).
230. Willstätter, R., and L. Zechmeister, *Ber.*, **62**, 722 (1929).
231. Wolfrom, M. L., and J. C. Dacons, *J. Am. Chem. Soc.*, **74**, 5331 (1952).
232. Woods, H. J., in J. Honeyman, ed., *Recent Advances in the Chemistry of Cellulose and Starch*, Interscience, New York, 1959, p. 138.
233. Wyckoff, R. W. G., *Electron Microscopy*, Interscience, New York, 1949.
234. Zechmeister, L., and G. Tóth, *Ber.*, **64B**, 854 (1931).
235. Zemplén, G., *Ber.*, **59B**, 1254 (1926).
236. Zimm, B. H., *J. Chem. Phys.*, **16**, 1093, 1099 (1948).

CHAPTER 5

The Hemicelluloses

CONRAD SCHUERCH, *State University College of Forestry, Syracuse University, Syracuse, New York*

Addendum

N. S. THOMPSON, *The Institute of Paper Chemistry, Appleton, Wisconsin*

I. Introduction

The cellulose and lignin of plant cell walls are closely interpenetrated by a mixture of polysaccharides called hemicelluloses, most of which are water-insoluble, alkali-soluble substances more readily hydrolyzed by acid than is cellulose. Unlike other plant polysaccharides they form an integral part of the cell wall and presumably fulfill a structural function in the plant. It may be significant in this respect to note that stalk tissues growing under unusual physical strain have abnormal amounts of certain hemicelluloses. Other polysaccharides, which are not considered hemicelluloses, include the hydrophilic gums, which are complex colloids exuded from injured tissues primarily of hardwoods; mucilages, comprised of water extractives of bark, seeds, mosses, and seaweed; pectin, which is a mixture or "triad" of arabinan, galactan, and polygalacturonic acid (primarily characteristic of fruit tissues); and reserve foodstuffs of plants, such as starch.

The hemicelluloses to be described more fully in the following will be those found in the stalk or supporting tissues of woody plants, for these are of most significance to the chemistry of wood. They are primarily modified xylans, glucomannans, and arabinogalactans. The arabinogalactans are soluble in water and are commonly classed among the extractives. They are discussed in this chapter for comparison of composition and structure with those of other nonglucose polysaccharides. There are, in addition, a number of related polysaccharides and complex mixtures found with the hemicelluloses, most of which are usually removed from the tissues under mild conditions of extraction. These are present in small quantity and as yet have been little studied.

In the past chemical investigation of the hemicelluloses has been largely a search for methods of characterization and structure proof, and has involved three problems. The first is the isolation of the polysaccharide from a reasonably homogeneous plant source, since most plant tissues contain a number of cell-types that differ functionally and to some extent chemically (280a). Second is purification, fractionation, and proof of homogeneity, and third is its proof of structure.

Unfortunately the biochemical processes related to the synthesis of these materials, their function in the plant, their distribution within the fiber cell wall, and their possible modification for more practical application (all problems of substantial importance), are by comparison only beginning to attract the interest they deserve. The fate of the hemicelluloses in pulping processes and their present industrial significance have been studied more fully. Each of these topics is discussed below.

II. Isolation and Purification

Individual plant cell walls composed of cellulose and hemicelluloses are bound together by lignin, a highly oxygenated aromatic polymer with a repeating phenylpropane skeleton. On this matrix is deposited a mixture of low molecular weight compounds which may include salts, terpenes, resins, sugars, tannins, and coloring materials, together with some complex water-soluble polysaccharides.

The removal of the low molecular weight impurities from plant tissues is usually relatively simple. Inorganic materials are not often separated, as the extraction of a polysaccharide generally is accomplished by alkali treatment. In most cases, resins, terpenes, and phenolic materials such as the lignans, sterols, tannins, and phlobaphenes can be removed almost completely (280b) by extraction with benzene–alcohol or acetone. Ether, on the other hand, does not always remove even those compounds which are ether-soluble when isolated (280c). Extraction with 70% ethanol or cold water is sometimes used to remove simple sugars, some glycosides, and a few oligosaccharides and complex branched polysaccharides. When necessary, as in annual plants, pre-extraction with oxalates or oxalic acid solutions will dissolve the pectins or polygalacturonic acid, often with considerable specificity (42). Pectins are also found in limited amounts in the bole tissues of a variety of soft- and hardwoods (192). They are usually not removed at this stage, however, because aqueous pre-extractions can also remove the lowest accessible molecular weight fractions of various other polysaccharide systems. Extended hot aqueous extractions tend to remove acetyl groups from the polysaccharides, and the resultant acidity (or that of an oxalic acid extraction) may hydrolyze or degrade the more acid-sensitive polysaccharides. These methods, therefore, should be used with discrimination and with controls.

The residue from the above purification is the raw material from which the hemicelluloses are isolated, usually by extraction with alkaline solutions. The hemicelluloses may be extracted either directly from solvent-extracted plant material, or from its total carbohydrate fraction "holocellulose." Holocellulose may be obtained by oxidative degradation of the lignin with chlorine, followed by extraction with organic solvents, preferably 3% ethanolamine in 95% ethanol (237a,254). Heating wood meal with sodium chlorite solution at pH 3.8 (278,281), or with chlorine dioxide, also removes lignin. The extent of degradation of cellulose and holocellulose caused by these different methods of isolation has been compared and reviewed by several workers (251). Surprisingly, the chlorine method is superior, in this respect, for hardwood and spruce holocellulose, but chlorite is better for cotton (251). The holocellulose produced by the chlorine–

ethanolamine method, however, contains both chlorine and nitrogen, and has suffered some chemical change (64).

Extraction of hemicelluloses from holocellulose is more common than extraction from whole wood because a more complete removal of the hemicelluloses is possible, and in general the hemicellulose obtained is less contaminated with lignin. Nevertheless, this method has some disadvantages; the most soluble carbohydrates may be lost during the holocellulose preparation (65,251). If the holocellulose preparation is not carried out carefully, or if the tissue is completely delignified, carbohydrate degradation and contamination with cellulose fragments result (124). The molecular weights reported for xylan from wheat straw have varied from 45 (27) to 150 (136), and part of these differences may depend on the method of delignification.

A single extraction directly from wood has the advantage of eliminating a rather time consuming process (210), and under optimum conditions most of the hemicellulose from annual plants and hardwoods can be removed. Only those most difficult to extract (55,185, 186) are left behind. However, on a new wood source exploratory experiments should be carried out to determine optimum conditions, for they are not the most drastic conditions of extraction (55,185,186). In general, the two methods are supplementary to one another; one may be advantageous for isolation, with minimum degradation, of the more soluble portions and for control, and the other for isolating the least soluble fractions.

The alkaline extraction itself has certain drawbacks. Ester functions present in the wood are saponified by the treatment, and acetyl groups that are linked to the xylans are lost in the isolation. Whistler (260) has called attention to the danger of a stepwise degradation from the reducing end of the polysaccharide during this process, and if the hemicelluloses in their native state have terminal aldehydic functions, the molecular weights determined on isolated samples are probably somewhat low. The degradation should be least important with the pentosans.

Various pretreatments of wood or holocellulose can affect the yield of hemicellulose under specified conditions by changing their accessibility. Drying of the sample should be avoided, but swelling, with liquid ammonia for example, allows the hemicellulose to be extracted at weaker alkali concentrations (54,177).

Hemicelluloses can be separated rapidly from alkaline solutions by dialysis. This method is often used for experimental preparations

(140), as well as for separation from the steeping liquors of the viscose process. However, they are more commonly isolated by acidification of the alkaline extraction liquors with acetic acid. The fraction which precipitates is traditionally called hemicellulose A (280d). Remaining in solution are the more soluble and more branched polysaccharides (hemicellulose B), which can be precipitated with acidified alcohol or acetone. A portion of the most soluble carbohydrates may even remain in the acetone–water mixture (185). This classical method of isolation thus constitutes a crude fractionation method. The products obtained after precipitation and drying through solvent exchange are usually amorphous and, therefore, much more readily soluble than in their native state. Occasionally "hornification" or irreversible insolubilization has been observed, especially on low molecular weight fractions. This can usually be avoided by the thorough removal of solvent by exchange with miscible nonsolvents.

The classical fractionation method is presently inadequate for serious investigations, and a variety of alternatives are available. Some are modifications of the extraction procedure, whereas others are more suitable for proving the homogeneity of isolated products. Perhaps the most novel of the newer fractional extraction methods is a sequence that first employs dimethylsulfoxide and then water. These solvents, used in this order, remove about half of the xylans of birchwood with their acetyl groups still intact (57,113).

Lithium and sodium hydroxides are generally better solvents for polysaccharides and better swelling agents for cellulose than potassium hydroxide, most probably because their hydrated cations are larger than the hydrated potassium ion (195a). Thus, it is perhaps not surprising that solutions of potassium hydroxide discriminate better between the more readily soluble xylans and the more insoluble glucomannans, and can be used to separate these polymer systems during the extraction process. A glucomannan can be extracted with potassium hydroxide if borates are added as complexing agents (148). It is not certain, however, that potassium hydroxide borate solutions are more effective than one of the other two alkalis without borate. Presumably, sodium hydroxide and borate together should be the most effective mixed solvent of this type.

The extraction of hemicelluloses may also be carried out fractionally by a stepwise increase in alkali concentration (54,95,186). In this way the more soluble and accessible polysaccharides are removed first, and perhaps some insight into their distribution in the fiber may be gained. It should be noted that there is often an optimum alkali concentration for extraction at each temperature. Increasing the concentration beyond this point seems of little value and gives results that are difficult to interpret (55,185,186). An analogous and valuable procedure requires, first, the nitration of the fiber under nonhydrolyzing conditions (12,251) and then extraction of the nitrated fiber by a series of solvent–nonsolvent mixtures in which the proportion of solvent is increased regularly (139,207).

However the polymer sample may be isolated, it is necessary to prove the homogeneity of the product. For this purpose standard fractional precipitation methods with a solvent and nonsolvent have customarily been used. With this technique it is advisable to use two separate systems for the fractionation, though this has not often been done. Typical solvent precipitant combinations are formamide and alcohol, cupriethylenediamine and acid (124), water and ammonium sulfate (18), or water and acetone or alcohol. The last system is reported not to be very satisfactory (178,179). A better procedure is to fractionate derivatives such as the acetate (124,200) or the methyl ether (2). Usually these are dissolved in chloroform and precipitated with petroleum ether.

Although the conventional precipitations outlined above may be applied to any mixture (the solubility of which is only crudely known) and often give good results, they suffer from the disadvantage that different polysaccharides of widely different molecular weight frequently coprecipitate and are only poorly separated (227). This difficulty is especially severe in cases where a microcrystalline precipitate is formed. It will be remembered that molecular weight fractionation of even a single polymer system is highly inefficient when the precipitate is crystalline, rather than separating in a liquid phase.

Mannan and xylan derivatives frequently have a tendency to crystallize and perhaps for this reason are difficult to remove from other polysaccharides by precipitation (227). It is therefore preferable to separate them by making use of known chemical differences. Acidic polysaccharides can often be precipitated from alkaline solutions by copper (91) or cetyl trimethylammonium ion (223). Arabinogalactans, mannans, and other polysaccharides that complex well with borate can next be removed from the residual solution by addition of both borate and cetyl trimethylammonium bromide (34), but the pH should be controlled (58a). Fully substituted derivatives such as the nitrate or acetate of relatively linear polysaccharides (e.g., the glucomannans and xylans bearing only a few uronic acid or arabinose units) are usually insoluble in acetone. More complex products (the arabinoglucuronoxylans and galactoglucomannans of softwood holocellulose) are usually soluble (121). Glucomannans are also scarcely soluble in cuprammonium or potassium hydroxide solutions and are often precipitated with barium. Precipitations with metallic ions have been found to give the most satisfactory results in hemicellulose separations by Meier, and his data are summarized in Table I.

Hemicellulose acetates containing some fractions with carboxyl groups can be dissolved in a water-miscible solvent and poured into a pyridine–water mixture in which neutral acetates are insoluble (204), or they can be converted into chloroform-insoluble salts and the neutrals removed by chloroform extraction of a chloroform–water emulsion (31).

Electrophoresis has been applied frequently to test the heterogeneity of polysaccharides, both in alkali (157) and in borate buffers (58b), usually with a support of glass fiber paper. The technique can be modified to a continuous process for small scale preparative separations (84).

No method of fractionation is generally applicable to all plant products, but those that take advantage of the acidity and linearity of certain of the polysaccharides are preferable to a standard solvent–nonsolvent precipitation procedure. Fractional precipitation following these can then demonstrate that the fractions are of homogeneous chemical composition and differ only in molecular weight. The extent of separation obtained is followed by observing the rotation of the individual fractions, the sugar chromatographic or pentosan analysis, and/or the viscosity.

III. Proof of Structure

Once a polysaccharide has been shown to be homogeneous, the following information is required to establish its structure: the individual sugars present, the number of free hydroxyl groups, the ring size within the individual sugars, the linkage between monomers, the kind of branching and the distribution of branches in the structure, the molecular weight of the polymer, the molecular weight distribution, and the size and shape of the molecule. Only the most important polysaccharide systems have been studied so thoroughly.

TABLE I

Precipitation of Wood Hemicelluloses with Metallic Ions[a]

Polysaccharide	Fehling's solution	Ba(OH)$_2$		Pb(CH$_3$CO$_2$)$_2$	Pb$_2$(CH$_3$CO$_2$)$_3$OH
		$c \leq 0.03M$	$c \leq 0.15M$		
Galactomannan (guaran)	+[b]	+	+	+	+
Glucomannan (coniferous woods)	+	+	+	+	+
Galactan (compression wood)	−	±	+	+	+
Glucuronarabinoxylan (coniferous woods)	−	−	−	−	+
Glucuronoxylan (birch)	+[c]	−	+	+	+
Partially acetylated glucuronoxylan (birch)	+[c]	−	−[c] → +	−	+
Arabinogalactan (larch)	−	−	−	−	−

[a] Unpublished data, courtesy of Dr. Hans Meier, Swedish Forest Products Laboratory, Stockholm.
[b] Plus signs indicate precipitation from solution, minus signs indicate solubility.
[c] Indicates deacetylation by the reagent.

The classes of sugars present in a given polysaccharide can be found by generic tests of some specificity, for example, by fermentations (280c) and by the pentosan (237b) and uronic acid distillation. Individual sugars can be isolated by hydrolysis with formic or mineral acids, or as methylated glycosides by methanolysis of the methylated substrate, then separated and identified quantitatively by chromatography (usually on paper). Uronic acids present in the original polymer usually appear still linked to another sugar as an aldobiouronic acid after hydrolysis. To determine the aldobiouronic acid structures it is advisable to reduce their methylated esters to the corresponding disaccharides which are readily hydrolyzed to simple sugar derivatives (268).

The number of free hydroxyl groups depends only on the kinds of sugars present, and is independent of the degree of branching of the polymer. Therefore, by complete substitution of the polysaccharide by acetylation or methylation one can check the percentage of pentose and hexose in the polymer. Conversely, if the percentage of pentoses and hexoses is known, the completeness of methylation can be calculated. The absence of an hydroxyl peak in the infrared spectrum is also indicative of complete methylation, and the sensitivity of this criterion can be increased by the conversion of hydroxyl to acetyl.

The classical methylation procedure with dimethyl sulfate and potassium hydroxide (122) or methyl iodide and silver oxide, is still a most generally useful tool for structure proof (271a). Because of the difficulty of methylating to completion in an aqueous system it is common practice to acetylate first (124) or to carry out several methylations, finally using organic solvent systems such as dimethylformamide (58a,153) or tetrahydrofuran (92). Hydrolysis or methanolysis of a completely methylated polysaccharide and isolation of the methylated sugars is the standard method for determining nonreducing end groups, branch points, and chain units (Fig. 1) (271b). After complete methylation and hydrolysis, each sugar has a methoxyl-free carbon in the number four or five position which was linked to the oxygen atom of the cyclic acetal in the original polysaccharide. Any other unsubstituted alcoholic hydroxyl must have been protected by acetal linkage to another sugar. Therefore, any sugar with only a single unsubstituted hydroxyl group in the four or five position must have been a nonreducing end group in the original polymer and must have been linked to the polymer chain only through its aldehydic function. A sugar with two unsubstituted hydroxyls was a portion of the polymer chain (or was the reducing end group), and one with three unsubstituted hydroxyls a branch point. These relationships will be made clear by reference to Fig. 1. If the number of branch points does not equal the number of end groups, methylation must have been incomplete (71) or demethyla-

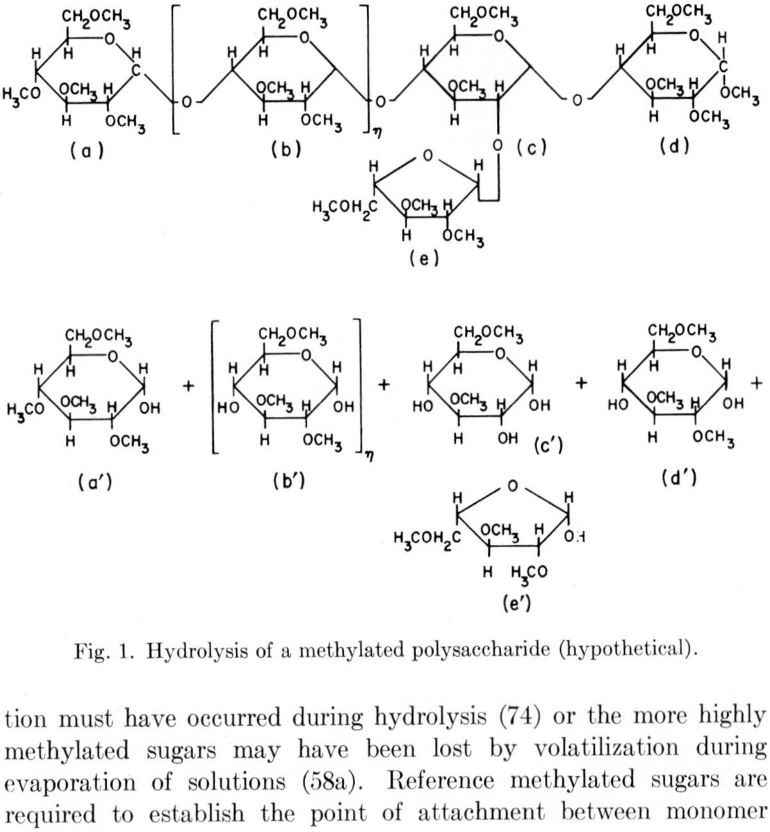

Fig. 1. Hydrolysis of a methylated polysaccharide (hypothetical).

tion must have occurred during hydrolysis (74) or the more highly methylated sugars may have been lost by volatilization during evaporation of solutions (58a). Reference methylated sugars are required to establish the point of attachment between monomer units (11a,39).

If only one hydroxyl on the number four and five carbons is unmethylated, the size of the acetal ring in the undegraded polysaccharide is established unequivocally. However, if both are unsubstituted, either may have been linked to an adjacent sugar or have been a portion of the acetal cycle in the original polymer. Inasmuch as the furanose forms of sugars hydrolyze 50 to 200 times faster than the comparable pyranose structures, a study of the rates of hydrolysis of the polysaccharide will often distinguish between the two possibilities.

A second most important structural tool is the use of specific glycol-cleaving reagents, lead tetraacetate or sodium periodate. For each glycol unit oxidized one atom of oxygen is required; in the latter case one mole of periodate is reduced to iodate (11b,89,194,271c) (Fig. 2).

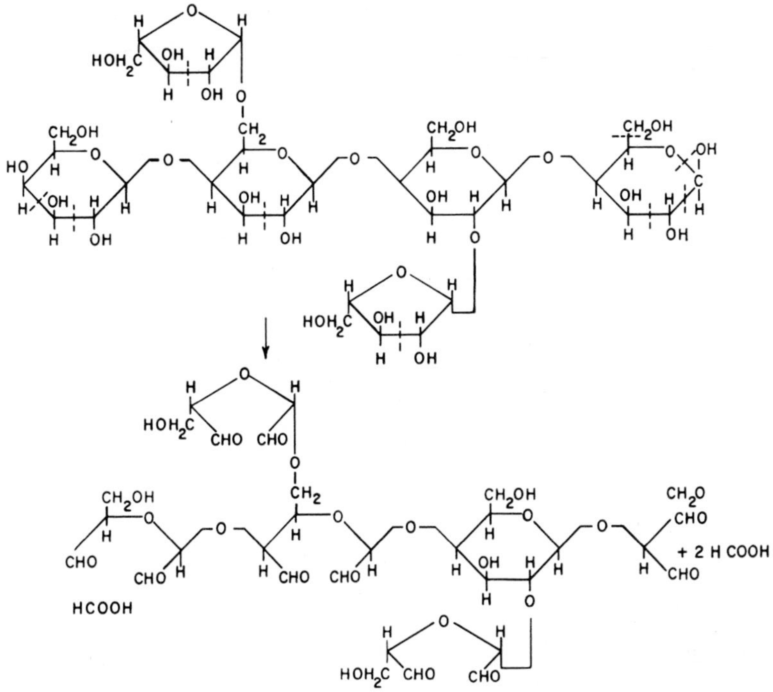

Fig. 2. Periodate oxidation of a branched polysaccharide.

The two adjacent hydroxyl groups appear as free aldehydes. In addition to glycol units, alpha-hydroxyaldehydes, alpha-hydroxyketones and alpha-hydroxyhemiacetals are also oxidized. The acetal linkage, however, is stable to periodate oxidation. Formaldehyde is produced from oxidation of a primary hydroxyl, and formic acid from an aldehyde or a carbinol unit between two other hydroxyl-bearing carbons. By comparison of the amount of periodate consumed and the amount of formic acid and formaldehyde produced, considerable information can be gained regarding the structure of the polysaccharide, the end groups, and the points of linkage between sugar units

(Fig. 2). Special problems in the determination of reducing end groups arise when active methylene groups (135,222,284), malondial-dehyde derivatives (170), or formate esters are present or are formed (133).

There are a number of additional methods that can supplement the above. Tosylation and iodination (99,168,241) or tritylation (165) give reasonably quantitative results for the number of primary hydroxyl groups in polysaccharides. cis-Hydroxyls cause gelation with borate solution. Adjacent free hydroxyl groups cause striking rotations in cuprammonium solutions (11c).

Whether alpha or beta linkages are present between sugar units may be determined most easily by the direction of mutarotation during hydrolysis. The change will be the same as that of a simple glycoside undergoing hydrolysis and mutarotation. However, when many different linkages are present the results become too complex for interpretation. In glucans and galactans, alpha and beta linkages have also been distinguished by infrared spectrophotometry (32).

The formation of dimers, trimers, and higher homologues by acid or enzymic partial hydrolysis is often required to establish unequivocally the structural features of a polysaccharide. Some care must be taken to avoid or identify reversion or repolymerization of the lower homologues, and the formation of artifacts. The amount of lower homologues of a particular size that can be present at any one time in a homogeneous hydrolysis is very small, but this limitation has been overcome in an ingenious fashion by carrying out an enzymic hydrolysis within a semipermeable membrane, through which the intermediate-sized fragments can diffuse before they are further degraded (197). In principle, the method might be extended to hydrolysis by polymeric acids or ion exchange resins.

Although acid hydrolysis is more commonly used, specific enzymes can be especially helpful in determining particular kinds of linkages and in isolating partial degradation products (50,269,272) containing linkages sensitive to acid (43). Sensitive linkages can also be protected chemically against acid hydrolysis if the acetal linkage is on a sugar, bearing a free primary hydroxyl group. Catalytic oxidation of the primary hydroxyl to a carboxylic acid converts the sugar to a uronic acid which is found, after hydrolysis, as the nonreducing unit of an aldobiouronic acid (28).

The oligosaccharides formed by degradations of these types are usually separated by chromatography on Magnesol (172), carbon

(37,267,273), or cellulose (33,132,253). Then, the presence of a homologous series containing identical sugars and linkages is established by hydrolysis of the individual chromatographic bands and by a linear relationship between the rotations and degrees of polymerization of the several oligomers (44,274). (See Fig. 3, from ref. 271f.)

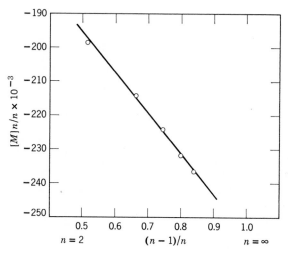

Fig. 3. Relation between degree of polymerization and molecular rotations of β-acetates.

In the presence of alkalis, the reducing end of a polysaccharide undergoes a typical Lobry de Bruyn-Alberda van Ekenstein enolization. When the enolic double bond has migrated to the carbon adjacent to that linked to the polymer chain, the chain is eliminated as an anion. This is the equivalent of an oxidative cleavage of the terminal sugar (now present as a dicarbonyl compound) which rearranges to either meta- or isosaccharinic acid depending on whether the original linkage was 1,3′ or 1,4′. Inasmuch as the second unit in the chain is now exposed, it can be eliminated in the same fashion and the peeling process normally continues throughout the chain. The course of the reaction may be seen in Fig. 4 (75,265), and has been described in detail elsewhere (11f). As mentioned previously, isolated hemicelluloses may be lower in molecular weight than in their native state because of this reaction. The significance of this fact in pulping and refining is discussed later. It is of interest to us at the moment that it has been used as a novel proof of structure

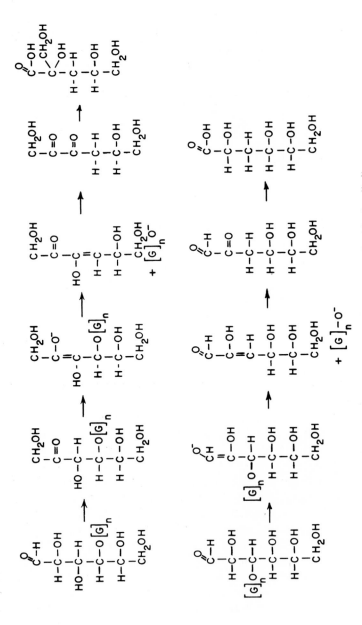

Fig. 4. The peeling reaction of polysaccharides in alkali.

method (75,261,265). The special features of the process are (*1*) that it is apparently the only known stepwise (as opposed to chain) degradation of a polymer from a terminal unit, and (*2*) it constitutes a method of separating a 1,6′ linked side chain from the polymeric backbone. When the side chain is linked to the six position, the oxidized unit and the chain are eliminated, and the side chain remains alkali stable because it lacks a reducing function. A side reaction can occur which prevents the chain degradation from going to completion (166).

It has recently been shown that quantitative immunological methods can be an aid in the determination of chemical structure of various galactans (127). This novel approach requires very small quantities of material, and undoubtedly will be extended to other systems.

When two methods of structure proof are used in conjunction, more information can be obtained than by either method alone. For example, in Fig. 1 we have a linear polysaccharide chain of pyranose units to which is attached a furanose sugar (e). Methylation and complete hydrolysis produce the sugar derivatives shown. If the furanose side chain was first preferentially removed by hydrolysis, and the polysaccharide chain then methylated, the number 2 position of the branch-point sugar (c) would also be methylated, and (c) would appear after complete hydrolysis not as (c′) but as an additional mole of (b′). In such a comparison, the original sugar which was the point of attachment will always appear at different degrees of methylation in the products of the two sequences and thus can be identified.

Consideration of the reactions will show that combining partial preferential hydrolysis with periodate oxidation will give similar, though less complete, information regarding the structure of a polysaccharide. This sequence, which is much simpler experimentally, has been strikingly successful in demonstrating the linear structure of the xylan backbone in wheat flour arabinoxylans (200).

Barry has (35) treated polysaccharides first with periodate and then with phenylhydrazine. The number one and two carbons of oxidized units appear as glyoxalbisphenylhydrazone and the chain is cleaved at that sugar (35,82,190,191) (Fig. 5). If a substantial fraction of the polysaccharide has linkages through the number three carbon of the individual sugars, the degradation is limited and the degraded products can be characterized by further methylations or by successive oxidations of the newly formed nonreducing end groups (Fig. 5). The "Barry degradation" has been of substantial use in structure studies on gums, mucilages and arabinogalactan (24). Other carbonyl reagents do not cause cleavage, but react one mole of reagent per dialdehyde group formed (36).

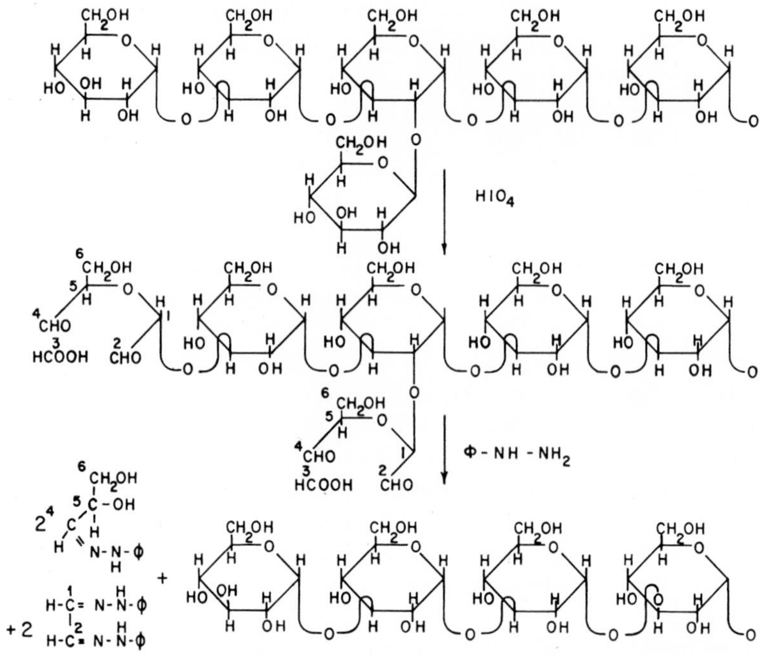

Fig. 5. Barry degradation of a polysaccharide with 1,3' linkages.

Another useful variation on the periodate method is to oxidize the polysaccharide, reduce the new aldehydic functions with sodium borohydride to primary alcohols, and then methylate. The methylated fragments of degraded sugars give direct evidence of the structure of the oxidizable units in the chain (1,149).

Many types of branching have been found among the polysaccharides, and the preceding methods can often distinguish between several possibilities. The number of nonreducing end groups per molecule, found by methylation or periodate oxidation and number-average molecular weight determination, indicates the number of branches in the structure. Whether these branches are present in a multitiered or a feather-type molecule is often apparent from the results of partial hydrolysis in combination with periodate oxidation, methylation, or the isolation of oligomers. The use of two enzymes in sequence has established the multitiered character of starch and glycogen and their average tier length, but little similar work has been done on the hemicelluloses (40,138,154). Very little is known about the regularity of distribution of branches even along the backbone of linear polysaccharides, and structures proposed for branched hemicelluloses represent average values in this respect.

Physical methods such as osmometry, viscometry, electrophoresis, diffusion, ultracentrifugation, isothermal distillation (26), and light scattering are used to supplement the knowledge of the size, shape, and molecular weight distribution of the polysaccharides, derived from the specific methods listed above (11d,104,131,139,207,240,242, 259). However, polysaccharide proof of structure remains largely dominated by organic chemical techniques. As there is still doubt regarding the extent of degradation of the hemicelluloses during isolation and extraction procedures, physical methods at the present time serve mainly to characterize isolated products, to make comparisons, and to set a lower limit on the molecular weight of the native materials. From the few comparative studies carried out, however, it seems probable that the higher values now reported for molecular weights of hemicelluloses are not much too low for them in their native state (250,251).

IV. Distribution of Hemicelluloses in Plant Tissues

By the application of methods such as those outlined above, the structure of the polysaccharides of plant tissues and their distribution in the various tissues is becoming clear. The tissues of dicotyledon gymnosperms (softwoods or conifers), angiosperms (hardwoods), and the monocotyledons (the annual plants, cereal grains, and grasses) have been analyzed for pentosans, uronic acids, and individual sugars. The North American and European softwoods normally contain 5 to 13% pentosans, whereas hardwoods of the same areas have 17 to 32% (95). The annual plants are also rich in pentosans (41,95), but tropical hardwoods generally have lower hemicellulose contents, ranging from 11 to 18% (277).

The weight ratio of the individual sugars in softwoods is found to be the following: D-Glucose, 61–65; D-mannose, 7–16; D-galactose, 6–17; D-xylose, 9–13; and L-arabinose, less than 3.5 (11e). In addition there are minor amounts (1% or less) of L-rhamnose and sometimes L-fucose and 3-O-methyl-L-rhamnose (107). The uronic acids present include 4-O-methyl-D-glucuronic acid and galacturonic acid, the latter from pectin (107).

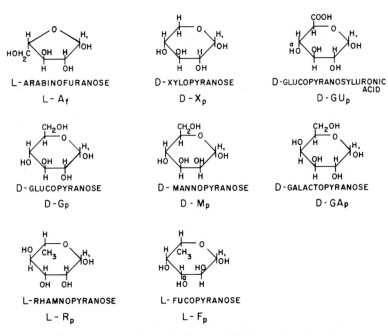

Fig. 6. Common sugars found in the hemicelluloses. (Methoxyl groups frequently found in the positions indicated by a.)

In hardwoods of the temperate zone a similar analysis shows a great preponderance of glucose and xylose: D-glucose, 55–73; D-xylose, 20–39; D-galactose, 1–4; and D-mannose 0.4–4. Minor sugars present include L-rhamnose, L-arabinose, 4-O-methyl-D-glucuronic acid, and sometimes D-glucuronic acid (11e,111,208,243). The same major sugars are found in the monocotyledons.

The above are average values for mature tissues and there are some variations in constitution between the different cell structures found in the stalks of these plants. Variation has been noted between the spring and summerwood of spruce, the heartwood and sapwood of many species, and the compression and normal wood of gymnosperms (14,232,280g). Substantial variation has been observed between normal wood and tension wood in birch (110,151). The commercial fibers ramie and flax are reported to be essentially pure cellulose, whereas the comparable fibers of lower tensile strength from sisal and jute have from 5 to 20% xylan present (271d).

If one compares the variations in sugar content between tissues which differ greatly in function, the comparisons become meaningless since the same sugars appear in widely different polysaccharides which may act as reserve foodstuffs, supporting structures, and exudates.

It appears that there are relatively few basic polysaccharide systems in plant holocelluloses. Modifications of these are elaborated in different plants, and within the same plant in different tissues. Even within a single tissue it is commonly found that the ratio of different sugars within a single polysaccharide system is not constant. In general, those fractions of a single polymer system that are more branched are also more soluble and more accessible. This is understandable, as the more linear structures would be expected to fit more readily into the cellulose crystallites and the branched systems to be in the more amorphous regions of the fiber. It now seems doubtful that there is the sharp distinction between cellulosans and polyuronides suggested two decades ago by Norman (188).

There is a marked similarity in the distribution of the polysaccharides found in a variety of plant fibers. Generally, there is a fraction consisting of heterogeneous branched and soluble polymers which are most readily accessible to extraction. These have not been completely defined as yet. The most soluble and readily extractable fractions can be isolated with cold water and with low concentrations of sodium hydroxide. The actual percentage of product obtained at a given concentration depends on the individual wood or holocellulose sample and its pretreatment, such as swelling, drying, or freezing. In the supporting tissues of softwoods, hardwoods, and annual plants these most soluble hemicelluloses include some portion of all the sugars that are present, and practically the total amount of those minor sugars present in amounts less than 1 or 2%. The less soluble fractions contain hemicellulose systems based primarily on xylose, glucose, and mannose.

Multibranched arabinogalactans have been isolated from the most soluble fractions of a number of softwoods (271e). In western larch this polymer system represents up to 18% of the wood weight, whereas in other species it is only a few per cent of this value (238,255). In some cases uronic acids are reported to be linked to the arabinogalactan structure. The nature of the soluble polysaccharides of softwoods which contain fucose, rhamnose, and 3-O-methylrhamnose is still not clear, although a rhamnose-containing biouronic acid has been obtained by hydrolysis of pine cellulose (213). Glucans, mannans, and a galactoglucomannan (3) are also removed from spruce by warm water (214). The latter at least is found in other softwoods as well.

In hardwoods the most soluble fraction contains, in addition to glucose, xylose, mannose and galactose units, most of the minor sugar units present (rhamnose, fucose (205), and arabinose). These last three sugars have not been found as major components of any polymer system, but rhamnose has been reported to be present in trace amounts in the xylan–uronic acid system (177). Few studies have been reported on the water-soluble fraction of hardwood hemicellulose. In addition to xylans (2,187), the only polysaccharide material isolated has contained a spectrum of sugars (143,250). Some interesting oligosaccharides have also been found (163).

A less soluble polymer system present in softwood is the arabino-glucuronoxylan. Part of this polymer is extracted with arabinogalactan and with the minor sugars, but a substantial portion can be removed only with alkali of higher concentration (214). Xylan predominates in extraction at lower alkali concentrations and the glucomannan at higher. It is difficult to remove the glucomannan completely, and substantial amounts of mannose together with smaller amounts of xylan are found in alpha-cellulose and in purified pulps from softwoods. Curiously enough a highly branched galacto-glucomannan has also been found in pine pulps, although one would expect it to be water-soluble.

Extraction of hardwoods with solutions of increasing alkali concentration next removes relatively pure uronic acid-containing xylans (185) from which acetyl groups have been lost. The later fractions extracted usually contain fewer uronic acids. In hardwoods also, a glucomannan is the polysaccharide most difficult to remove. However, much smaller amounts of mannan are usually found in the residue from alkali extractions of hardwood or hardwood pulps than from such extractions of softwoods (54). Also present in this "resistant hemicellulose" fraction (54) are some xylan and apparently a galactan characteristic of the pectic triad (102). On the basis of his experience and the current literature, Hamilton (121) has listed in a convenient form the polysaccharides found in woods and their approximate proportion (Table II). The dominant hemicellulose in the

TABLE II

Hemicelluloses in Conifers and Deciduous Trees (121)

Polymer	Deciduous[a]	Conifer[a]
4-O-Methylglucuronoxylan	Very large	Small
4-O-Methylglucuronoarabinoxylan	Trace	Medium
Glucomannan	Very small	Large
Galactoglucomannan	Trace, if present	Very small
Arabinogalactan	Trace, if present	Trace to medium
Other galactose-containing polysaccharides	Trace	Trace, if present
Pectin and associated materials	Very small	Very small
Starch	Trace	Trace

[a] The quantities listed correspond approximately to the following percentages of noncellulosic carbohydrates (to convert to a wood basis, use the approximate hemicellulose percentages of 20% softwoods and 25% for hardwoods: very large = 80 to 90%; large = 60 to 70%; medium = 15 to 30%; small = 5 to 15%; very small = 1 to 5%; trace = 0.1 to 1%).

supporting tissues of annual plants is again a xylan modified similarly with arabinose and 4-O-methylglucuronic acid.

Some knowledge has accumulated regarding the distribution of the hemicelluloses within the cell wall of woody plants. The distribution of the xylan–uronic acid system has been measured by allowing cell walls to react with bases that form colored salts (30). The bases react, at least, with the accessible carboxyl groups present and the intensity of the colored salt is measured across the cell wall. It has been found that the carboxyl content is high near the primary wall and decreases approximately linearly across the cell wall to the lumen. Although hemicelluloses are known to exist with varying contents of carboxyl groups, it has been suggested that the carboxyl group is a linear measure of the hemicellulose content across the cell wall (30).

When a woody fiber is subjected to the action of a swelling agent, such as cuprammonium solution, the fiber swells in a characteristic balloon-like fashion. Portions of the outer layers of the fibers, which are insoluble in cuprammonium solution, remain relatively intact and cause restrictions along the length of the fiber. These insoluble collars can be separated in small quantities and have been found by qualitative paper chromatography to consist primarily of mannose with some glucose present. Apparently, therefore, a certain proportion of the mannan in wood is concentrated in a very small fraction of the total fiber (158,279).

A new approach to the problem of polysaccharide distribution within the cell wall has been made by comparing pinewood tracheids at various stages of development (162). Mature cells contained the middle lamella (M), primary wall (P), and the outer, middle, and inner layers of the secondary walls (S_1, S_2, and S_3). Immature tracheids contained M and P; M, P, and S_1; and M, P, S_1, and S_2 layers. Each type was analyzed separately and it was found that arabinan, galactan, and pectic acids were concentrated in M and P (presumably M); S_2 was rich in glucomannan and poor in xylan; and the inner layer S_3 contained more than half the xylan present. This conclusion is based on the assumption that the polysaccharide composition of each layer remains constant once it is formed and does not change on later development of the tracheid. It is perhaps not surprising that these conclusions are at variance with the first work quoted above. They are of sufficient interest to merit expansion and comparison with the results of other investigations. It is known for example that compression wood contains unusual amounts of both lignin and galactan (59,232). If, as this work strongly suggests, galactan, as well as lignin, is primarily a component of the middle lamella, then compression wood differs from normal wood by a greater development of that entire region and not a single chemical component. Polarized infrared spectrometry has been used to identify xylans in crystalline form in native wood slices (158a).

Although the bark of several wood species constitutes a substantial proportion of the wood weight and is of potential economic value, structural investigations of the carbohydrates present have only begun to be reported. In white spruce inner bark (198) starch and polygalacturonic acid represent 5% and 18%, respectively, of the total polysaccharides.

Associated with the pectinic acid is an arabinan and a galactan unlike the usual pectic galactan (i.e., it is highly branched). The hemicellulose fraction contains a glucomannan and a xylan with traces of arabinose but no uronic acids. The polysaccharides can be separated by the customary aqueous and alkaline extractions and copper and cetyltrimethylammonium and borate precipitations.

The inner bark of white birch (176) contains lesser amounts of the pectic triad, and a xylan of relatively high molecular weight, containing 4-*O*-methylglucuronic acid. There is xylan in the amount of 28% of the extractive free bark, and a small amount of a complicated mixture of other polysaccharides. Differences are found in the carbohydrate composition not only of various tree tissues; they have also been

TABLE III

References to Investigations of Some Hemicelluloses

Hemicellulose	References	Hemicellulose	References
Xylans		**Xylans** (*cont'd*)	
		Flax	100
Softwoods		Jute	81,87,233
Hemlock	88,117	Kapok	80
Larch	26a	Milkweed floss	38
Pine	31,61,107,120,146,	Oats	47,92,179
	212,255	Orchard grass	41
Spruce	6,20,86,107,161,214,	Rye	47
	259	Seaweeds	167,199
Hardwoods		Sunflower	42
Apple	101	Timothy hay	95
Aspen	26,145,147,211	Wheat	4,5,10,27,43–47,90,
Beech	2,21,171,256		98,124,164,178,
Birch	54,55,104–106,110,		211
	185,186,216,	**Arabinogalactans**	
	244–247,250,	Fir	238
	251	Larch	7,24,28,43b,56,69,
Cherry	235		129,142,201,
Elm	103,236		271e,276
Eucalyptus	229,230	Pine	31,48,60,61,255
Lemon	15	Spruce	3,59,238
Linden	211	**Glucomannans**	
Locust	16	Aspen	145
Maple	187,248	Birch	247b
Mesquite	217,218	Cedar	119
Oak	11g,193	Hemlock	116,117
Pear	71	Larch	11g
Annual plants		Pine	19,23,49,60,79,146,
Barley	47		156,287
Corn	144,180,181,	Spruce	25,78,85,128,136,
	262–264,266,		175,252
	270,282		
Esparto	22,70,122,126,144,		
	150		

observed in wheat and corn. The xylan of wheat endosperm has variable and high ratios of arabinose to xylose, and the xylans of wheat bran, oat hulls, and corn hulls have much more complex branching than those of wheat leaf and straw (4,5,10,43–47,72,164, 178,179,181,200,262,266).

A number of references to hemicellulose investigations are given in Table III.

V. Detailed Structure of Hemicelluloses

A. XYLANS

The basic skeleton of the xylans found in the tissue of all land plants is a linear backbone of 1,4'-anhydro-D-xylopyranose units linked β. The two seaweeds studied to date are an interesting contrast in that one has both $1 \rightarrow 4$ and $1 \rightarrow 3$ linkages and the other $1 \rightarrow 3$ linkages alone (167,199). The evidence for the 1,4'-β-anhydroxylo-pyranose structure has been gained from methylation and hydrolysis, periodate oxidation, the isolation of homologous oligomers, and other methods. The xylan framework is always found modified in nature.

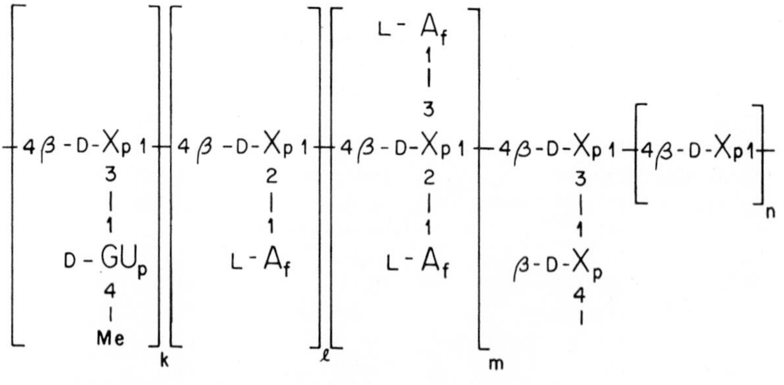

Fig. 7. Typical structural features of xylans in stalk tissues. (These structural features are not all found together in one xylan. The sugars attached to the xylan chain are dispersed randomly. Xylose units linked to two arabinose units are rare, except in arabinoxylans with high arabinose:xylose ratios. The xylose chain may be linear or singly branched; it may be linked to arabinose or 4-O-methyl-D-glucuronic acid, or both together. D-Glucuronic acid may also be present and arabinose may terminate the chain as a nonreducing end.)

The simplest xylan reported, that from esparto grass, contains only a fraction free of any extraneous sugar units, and even it is said to contain a single branch point in a molecule of 75 ± 5 xylose units with the linkage in the three position (259). A similar branching in the structure has been proposed for pear cell wall xylan (190), xylans containing other constituents, from beech (2), loblolly pine (146), barley husks (11g), milkweed floss (38) and wheat straw (44). So far no xylobiose with a 1,2' or 1,3' linkage has been obtained from these plants, although a number of oligomers containing the xylan 1,4' linkage have been isolated. Molecular weights have been studied by end group analysis and by physical methods, and the branched structures suggested at least for pear cell wall, milkweed floss, and esparto grass xylans (DP = ca. 75) are consistent with these data (see Table IV).

Xylan has a high negative rotation, around 100° specific rotation in alkali. On hydrolysis it mutarotates in a positive direction indicating a beta linkage between xylose units. Its rate of hydrolysis is consistent with a pyranose structure. Crystalline xylans can be prepared from several plant sources (47,287) by partial acid hydrolysis under heterogeneous conditions. Presumably the more amorphous portions of the xylan contain uronic acids and are preferentially degraded, leaving behind a more regular fragment of the polymer.

B. ARABINOXYLANS

Arabinoxylans have been found primarily in certain grains and grasses; those from wheat, corn, and esparto grass are perhaps the most thoroughly investigated. They also are formed as artifacts when arabinoglucuronoxylans are subjected to drastic alkaline hydrolysis, and they are reported to be naturally present in applewood (101) and white spruce bark (198).

L-Arabinofuranose units are linked as individual side chains directly to the linear or singly-branched xylan skeleton described above. In the water-soluble arabinoxylan from both esparto grass and wheat flour, the arabinose is linked to the 3 position of the xylose, but in the latter some xylose units are also substituted with arabinose in both the 2 and 3 positions. The ratio of xylose to arabinose varies: esparto 12:5 (22), wheat flour from 2:1 to 1:2.4 (200), apple 7:1 (101). Esparto grass arabinoxylan has not been isolated free of galactose or glucose and may be a more complex polysaccharide. Whether the

TABLE IV

Xylans [β-(1,4')-Anhydroxylopyranose Polymers]

Species	Sugars and position of linkage to xylose	Molecular ratios	Xylan chain	DP	Ref.
Jute	X_p:2α-(4-OMe Gu_p)		Branched		81,87,233
Milkweed floss	X_p:2α-(4-OMe Gu_p)	14:1	One branch	172	38
Kapok	X_p:2α-(4-OMe Gu_p)	8:1	Two branches C_3	200	80
White birch	X_p:2α-(4-OMe Gu_p):3 and 2Ac	11:1:<1	Linear 17% Ac, 75% of Ac on C_2 of Xylose	190–200	57,105
Yellow birch	X_p:2α-(4-OMe Gu_p)	10:1	Linear	192	244
Finnish birch	X_p:2α-(4-OMe Gu_p)	22:1	Linear	22	216
American beech	X_p:2α-(4-OMe Gu_p)	8:1	One branch at C_2	45	2
European beech	X_p:2α-(4-OMe Gu_p)	10:1	Linear	70	21
Sugar maple	X_p:2α-(4-OMe Gu_p)	10:1	Linear	205	248
White elm	X_p:2α-(4-OMe Gu_p)	7:1	Linear	211	103
Trembling aspen	X_p:2α-(4-OMe Gu_p)	9:1	Linear	200	146a
Western hemlock	X_p:2α-(4-OMe Gu_p):3Ar_f	13:3:0.75–4.6–7:1:0		140	88,117
European larch	X_p:2α-(4-OMe Gu_p):3Ar_f	6:1:1	Linear	100	26a
Norwegian spruce	X_p:2α-(4-OMe Gu_p)	5:1	Linear	80–85	20
Sitka spruce	X_p:2α-(4-OMe Gu_p):3Ar				86
Loblolly pine	X_p:Gu_p				31
Southern pine	X_p:2α-(4-OMe Gu_p)	6:1	(Soluble fraction)		31
Spruce	X_p:2α-(4-OMe Gu_p):3Ar	12–18:?:1		>90	120a
(Picea excelsa)	X_p:2α-(4-OMe Gu_p):3Ar	7:1:1	Linear	95 ± 10	214
Scots pine	X_p:2α-(4-OMe Gu_p):3Ar_f	7.5:1.5:1		133	99a
Ginkgo	X_p:2α-(4-OMe Gu_p):3Ar_f	9:0.15:1	Slightly branched	208	176a

linkage of the arabinose is α or β appears not to be established, nor is the distribution of arabinose units along the chain. No xylose end groups have been found in the polymer.

C. GLUCURONOXYLANS

Xylans free of extraneous sugars, but combined with substantial amounts of uronic acids are the most important hemicelluloses of hardwoods, milkweed, jute, and ramie. Rhamnose has sometimes been found as a minor component in these products (100).

The dominant structure of these polymers is a linear or singly branched β-D-(1,4')-xylopyranose backbone. Pyranose forms of D-glucuronic acid or 4-O-methyl-D-glucuronic acid units are attached by an alpha link (47) to the 2 or 3 positions of the xylose. The methylated uronic acid greatly predominates in hardwoods, and usually is linked to the xylose C_2 position. In contrast, the xylan found in sunflower heads contains nonmethylated D-glucuronic acid linked to the C_3 position (42). Xylose to uronic acid ratios vary widely from 3:1 to 20:1, with most average values from 7:1 to 12:1. Acetyl groups are attached to this xylan system, and probably others, but they are saponified during alkaline extraction. They are, however, retained by extraction with dimethyl sulfoxide (57,113), and for the most part are linked to the oxygen of the number 2 carbon of the xylose units and not to uronic acid. No other acyl groups seem to be present (249).

The degree of polymerization reported for the bulk of the xylan–uronic acid system from hardwoods is around 180, with fractions varying from 50 to 300. However, the degree of polymerization of a water-soluble, singly-branched glucuronoxylan obtained from beech wood holocellulose in a yield of 13.4% of the wood weight was 45 (2). Molecular properties of a number of undegraded glucuronoxylans have recently been studied with especial precautions (106a). Several species of hardwood have been reported to have xylans with singly branched structures, but careful physical measurements have not substantiated the claims in some cases.

D. ARABINOGLUCURONOXYLANS

In addition to the pure arabinoxylans and glucuronoxylans a number of xylan fractions have been described containing both arabinose and uronic acids. In the case of wheat straw these have later been fractionated into arabinose-rich and arabinose-free polysaccharides. The separation was not quantitative, however, and present evidence is strong that arabinose and uronic acids are linked to the same xylan chain in softwoods (88), in food crops (249), but probably not in aspen in spite of previous reports (145, cf. 146a). In stalk tissues L-arabinose, and D-glucuronic acid, or more usually 4-*O*-methyl-D-glucuronic acid are all linked directly to a linear xylan chain in the same fashion as in the simpler polymers described above. The presence of the alpha-linked uronic acids results in a much lower negative rotation than that observed in the arabinoxylans.

There has been little economic incentive to investigate the hemicelluloses of the fruits, seeds, or leaves of trees. However, some indication of the variations which may be expected can be gained from the extensive work on corn and wheat plants. The oligosaccharides 2-*O*- and 4-*O*-(α-D-glucopyranosyl uronic acid)-D-xylose (268), α-D-glucopyranosyluronic acid (1,4)-*O*-β-D-xylopyranosyl(1,4)-D-xylose (270) and 2-*O*-(α-D-xylopyranosyl)-L-arabinose (270) have been isolated from corncob hemicellulose B (90,249,268). Therefore, all of the arabinose in this hemicellulose is not terminal. Some of the glucuronic acid must act as the "end unit" in xylan chains (linked 4) rather than as an individual "side chain" (linked 2 or 3). However, sequences of at least seven xylose units are present in corncob hemicellulose A (273,274).

The hemicelluloses from the outer coating or pericarp of cereal grains are markedly different in structure from those found in stalk tissues. That from wheat bran contains both arabinose and xylose singly- and doubly-branched, and as terminal units with more arabinose than xylose in the molecule. D-Glucuronic acid and its 4-*O*-methyl derivative are also present. The degree of polymerization is approximately 300, or 3 to 10 times as great as that reported for the xylan from wheat straw and wheat leaf. Nevertheless, sequences of 7 or 8 xylose units linked in the usual fashion have been found in this polysaccharide.

Similar complex hemicelluloses containing substantial amounts (ca. 10%) of galactose have been found in oat hulls (74,179) and corn hulls (181,262,266). From the "corn fiber gum" there has been isolated the trisaccharide L-galactopyranosyl-(1 → 4)-D-xylopyranosyl-(1 → 2)-L-arabinose (266), and from the oat hull hemicellulose a trisaccharide containing two galactose units and a uronic acid.

E. ARABINOGALACTANS

Arabinogalactans have been found as water-soluble polysaccharides in the species listed previously, and those from both western and European larch have been studied extensively. The physical and chemical properties of these substances vary between species (238) and some contain minor amounts of uronic acid. There has been some question of whether or not the western larch arabinogalactan is contaminated with an arabinose-free galactan (129) as it has not appeared to be homogeneous (201). Ultracentrifugation and electrophoresis have indicated two products of widely different molecular weights (ca. 100,000 and 16,000) (56,271e) in a number of species, but both contain arabinose as well as galactose in slightly varying proportions. As a result the detailed structure is in doubt, but its main features have recently become clear.

The arabinogalactans are highly branched structures. Methylation and hydrolysis of arabinogalactans from western larch by White (276) yielded 2,4-dimethyl-D-galactose, 2,3,4-trimethyl-D-galactose, 2,3,4,6-tetramethyl-D-galactose, and 2,3,5-trimethyl-L-arabinose in a molecular ratio of 3:1:2:1. Recent work has confirmed these as the major products. White has also showed that the 1,6′ linkage between galactose units is of the beta-type, and terminal galactose units are attached in the same fashion to both branched and unbranched galactose units. Although arabinose was originally found linked only in the furanose form to the six position of galactose, and only as a terminal unit, the disaccharide 3-(L-arabinopyranosyl)-arabinose has been isolated in more recent work (24,28,58,142) and it too is linked to the six position of a 1,3′ galactose chain (28).

Careful study of recent publications (24,28,56,58) on this subject is rewarding, for they demonstrate the power of modern methods in discriminating between possible structures of a most complex polysaccharide. By an ingenious and careful application of electrophoresis, and borate-cetyl trimethylammonium precipitations, the degree of heterogeneity has been shown. By means of methylation, hydrolysis, and partial hydrolysis, the Mehltretter-Aspinall sequence of uronic acid formation and hydrolysis (28), Smith's periodate oxidation reduction sequence (1,149), and the Barry degradation (35), certain partial structures have unequivocally been demonstrated to

be important. These are shown in Fig. 8. Other features of the structure, probably of less importance, are still in doubt and under
investigation.

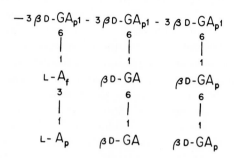

Fig. 8. Typical structural features of arabinogalactans.

The galactan found in compression wood is a different polysaccharide. It is linked β-(1,4′) and contains 13% uronic acids. It is more
closely related to the galactan of pectin (59,271).

F. GLUCOMANNANS

Most of the mannose found in wood is present in the form of a
glucomannan of relatively small molecular weight. The number-
average degrees of polymerization reported vary from 40 to 100.
More recent data suggest the higher value with weight-average
degrees of polymerization about twice this figure. In some cases two
fractions of slightly different molecular weight are found, and sometimes a relatively easily extractable glucomannan is present with
significant amounts of galactose linked to the six position of the mannose units. The less readily soluble fractions probably also have a
few per cent of galactose linked to the molecule. Timell (246a)
proposes that the glucomannans contain variable amounts of galactose, but are probably rarely, if ever, free of this sugar.

The ratio of glucose to mannose in these polysaccharides varies
from 1:1 to 1:4 and the structure is primarily of linear chains of
(1 → 4) linked pyranose units. Di- and trisaccharides containing
two and three glucose units, and two and three mannose units, have
been isolated. The two possible mixed 1 → 4-β-pyranose disaccharides have been found as well. The glucomannans, therefore, seem to

be random copolymers in which the length of sequences of a single sugar depend upon the ratio of the monomers.

As many as three branches per 100 units are found in the gluco-mannans of some species, and the branches are linked to the three position of the glucose unit. The structures, in so far as they are known, have been established by partial hydrolysis, methylation and hydrolysis, periodate oxidations, and physical measurements (see Table V). Meier reports that in certain softwoods, the acetyl groups are attached to the glucomannan system rather than the xylan.

VI. Minor Linkages in Hemicelluloses

Polysaccharides are constructed of monomers that contain two different types of functional groups, each of which reacts only with the other. Their general formula is RAB_n with the single A representing the aldehydic function and the B_n the hydroxyl groups. Structures of this type can lead only to linear, monocyclic, or branched structures (96). If the hemicelluloses form a portion of a network, the formation must therefore be through linkages of a different and unknown type—for example, esters formed between uronic acid and alcoholic hydroxyl groups.

The preceding discussion has outlined the main structural features of the hemicelluloses as if these were completely independent, linear and branched polymers. For a variety of reasons, this is not believed universally. On the contrary, there have been frequent postulates of all the possible kinds of inter- and intrapolymer bonds in wood. Those that have caused the most controversy are lignin-carbohydrate bonds (52,53,160,173,174,185,188,195,196,280h), cellulose-hemicellu-lose linkages (139,207,250) and cellulose crosslinks (112a).

Covalent bonds between hemicellulose and cellulose have been postulated primarily to explain the presence of extraneous sugars in purified cellulose. However, the shortcomings of fractional precipitation methods have now been demonstrated (227) and extraction methods have been improved to the point where wood celluloses containing a fraction of a per cent of extraneous sugars can be prepared (118,139,207,257). The question of covalent bonds between extraneous sugars and the cellulose of wood, therefore, has become less interesting and more remote. The traces found in those cellulose

TABLE V

Glucomannans—Chain Unit $[(1\beta G_p4)_m(1\beta M_p4)_n]$

Species	Sugars	Ratio	Nonreducing ends and linkage to chain	DP	Ref.
White birch	$G_p:M_p$	1:1.1		65	247b
Aspen	G:M:(Gal)	1:2:($\ll$1)			145,147
Western hemlock	G:M	1:4–3	Slightly branched	130	116,117
White spruce	$G_p:M_p$	1:3			252
Sitka spruce	G:M:Gal	1:15:?	Unbranched	40–60	85
Norwegian spruce	G:M	1:3.5–4	Three to four nonreducing ends on 3 position of glucose	68,100	78,161
Norwegian spruce	G:M:Gal	1:7.4:–	(Easily extracted fraction)		172a
Western red-cedar	G:M:Gal	1:2.5:?			119
Scots pine	$G_p:M_p$	1:3	Three nonreducing ends on 3 position of glucose branches, mostly mannose	97	79
Loblolly pine	$G_p:M_p:Gal_p$	7:19:1	One galactan and one mannose terminal; one branch per chain of 30 units		146
Eastern white pine	G:M:Gal	3:1:0.1		95	111a
Ginkgo biloba	G:M:Gal	5:18:1		96	176b
Southern pine kraft pulp	$G_p:M_p:Gal_p$	1:3:1	Five galactan_p end units to 1 mannose end unit; one end unit per 7 chain units; end units linked to 6 positions of chain		120b

products prepared under mild conditions of delignification and extraction (8) are probably no more significant than the traces of extraneous sugars found in cotton.

Of the various phenomena which have been said to point to a hemicellulose-lignin bond, at least one can be rejected. It has been known for many years that hydrolysis of wood under acidic conditions releases hydroxyl groups on lignin and makes them available for methylation (62). As lignin was formerly classified as a nonhydrolyzable polymer, this observation suggested lignin-carbohydrate links. It has now been demonstrated in at least three laboratories (114,220) that phenolic hydroxyls are liberated by this process in carbohydrate-free lignin preparations, so the hypothesis of a lignin-carbohydrate bond is not needed.

Perhaps the most important original justification for the concept of a lignin-carbohydrate bond was that hemicelluloses, cellulose, lignin, and indeed other constituents of woody tissues are much less soluble when in the wood than they are after extraction. However, hemicelluloses interpenetrate the cellulose crystal lattice to some degree, which must impose some physical restraint on their solution. After solution, the crystallinity of the hemicelluloses would be expected to be lost and their ease of solution to be correspondingly increased. Furthermore, lignin has markedly different solubility properties from carbohydrates; it exists in a highly branched form, and probably is, in itself, a network structure (221). It would be expected to impose a physical restraint on the solution of the carbohydrates. The question arises then whether such a physical restraint is sufficient to explain the observed solubility differences between native and isolated polysaccharides. It is now possible to answer this question with a qualified yes. The qualification exists because the extractability of the hemicelluloses varies very greatly between species, even though their structures do not, and the particular experimental technique used gives a convincing answer only in the case of the hardwoods (55,185,186). When white birch wood is extracted with sodium hydroxide, certain observations have been made: more pentosan is extracted with 4% sodium hydroxide at 0° than with 15% sodium hydroxide, and more is extracted at 40° with 6% than with 15% sodium hydroxide. The temperature of extraction does not affect the rate of extraction very much, but does greatly affect the amount of pentosan extracted. None of these observations can be interpreted in terms of a rate-determining step in which covalent bond breaking occurs. Therefore, the pentosan is restrained within the birch wood structure by a physical restraint. This does not demonstrate the absence of a covalent lignin-carbohydrate bond in birch, but does demonstrate that any bonds linking the bulk of the lignin to the bulk of xylan in the wood must be broken quickly by alkali and are not effective in preventing the solution of pentosan. Experiments of the same type on spruce holocellulose suggest the same physical restraints in softwoods, but so little hemicellulose is extracted before delignification that no meaningful data can be obtained on the whole wood (55,185,186). In recent years interest has, therefore, been attracted by other approaches to the same problem, especially ones of more utility in softwood species.

A number of cases have been reported of lignin-carbohydrate complexes (112b). In the past these complexes were usually the result of drastic chemical processes which could easily have produced artifacts, and were not subject to careful fractionations. These are not to be taken seriously. More recently, complexes have been isolated from wood by inert solvents and subjected to careful fractionations. It seems most probable that these fractions represent covalently bound complexes between the most soluble portions of the hemicelluloses and phenolic matter similar to Brauns' native lignin. It is not clear whether they are diagnostic of the structure of the remaining (largely different) hemicelluloses or the insoluble 95% of the lignin that is left.

In contrast to these experiments, Björkman (52) has milled wood to a very fine particle size in nonswelling solvents and isolated lignin-carbohydrate complexes which represent a substantial proportion of the lignin. These are soluble after isolation and can be subjected to solubility and fractionation tests which demonstrate beyond reasonable doubt that they are covalently bonded (160). As it is known that under milling conditions covalent bonds are broken and can be reformed, and since phenolic materials like lignin react readily with free radicals and cations, further evidence seems required to demonstrate that these are not artifacts and preliminary work in that direction has recently been reported (53).

The most complete review of this problem in recent years is that by Merewether (173), who concludes that lignin-carbohydrate bonds are present in wood, but this is still not an entirely general consensus. As Aspinall (11g) states, the present position of the problem is unsatisfactory.

Substantial gains in our knowledge of cellulose and hemicellulose, and lesser gains in our knowledge of lignin structure and behavior have been made without considering the lignin-carbohydrate bond. Clearly, further advance is possible in the same fashion. Nearly all the chemical behavior of wood can be understood and defined in terms of either hypothesis. Ultimately, this relatively minor problem will yield to the same rigorous approach as other structural problems—a concern for the presence of artifacts, and investigation with respect to individual wood species and polysaccharide systems. This is clearly necessary in view of the very great difference in the ease of extraction of quite similar polysaccharides from different woods.

VII. Practical Importance of the Hemicelluloses

The production of paper is by far the largest use for wood cellulose. Here the chemical and physical properties of the hemicelluloses play a profoundly important role.

In the chemical pulping processes, the organophilic lignin is either degraded and dissolved from wood chips as a phenolate salt by hot aqueous alkali, or else is degraded by acid and sulfonated by bisulfite ion for water solubility. The pulping liquors of the alkaline processes are excellent solvents for hemicelluloses and degraded cellulose. The carbohydrate dissolution process has been studied in some detail (11e), as have the kinetics of delignification (112c,112d,155). At the elevated temperatures required for pulping at an economic rate, the polysaccharides are degraded by alkali to compounds of the saccharinic acid type and smaller acidic fragments (109). The kinetics of the degradation are consistent with the mechanism of the "peeling" reaction described previously (73). It is believed that about 50 glucose units are removed by this reaction before the degradation is stopped by oxidation of the reducing function (159). The degradation can proceed again whenever chain cleavage occurs by alkaline hydrolysis of glycosidic linkages (11h). The latter reaction has been shown to occur under alkaline pulping conditions (115), and to be faster for a β-xyloside than a β-glucoside (83). The cleavage of the linkage binding uronic acid to xylan is known to be still faster, perhaps because the 6-carboxylate ion can assist the process by nucleophilic attack on C_1.

The main changes occurring on the polysaccharides during alkaline pulping are therefore reasonably clear. The xylans are dissolved, as macromolecules, relatively early in the process whereas delignification occurs more slowly. While in solution, the most rapid change occurring to the xylans is the elimination of uronic acid residues. This should make them more readily crystallizable and also more susceptible to the "peeling" reaction which occurs as soon as the chain is cleaved by alkaline hydrolysis. Simultaneously, but at a slower rate, the hexosans are degraded by the "peeling" reaction, assisted by some chain breaking reactions (286). The loss in pulp yield which these changes represent, can be controlled to some degree by maintaining a low alkali concentration through a continuous introduction of alkali, but is usually limited only by the protective action of the lignin on the carbohydrate. Whenever the lignin content of the fiber goes below a minimum of 1 or 2%, the solution and degradative attack on both cellulose and hemicellulose becomes too severe for further delignification to be practical.

Most of the alkali consumption in the pulping process is caused by carbohydrate degradation (63,115), and the extent of delignification is controlled by the amount of alkali added at the beginning of the cook. As the alkali is used up, the xylan, which is by now a more crystalline and less soluble polymer, reprecipitates onto the pulp and some penetrates into less accessible portions of the cellulose. A portion of the xylan is thus more resistant to alkaline extraction than that found in holocellulose (11e). The glucuronoxylans and arabinoglucuronoxylans are both found in alkaline pulps with greatly reduced uronic acid contents. It is not clear why a highly branched galactoglucomannan should be found in a kraft pulp, but this is indeed the case.

In the acid sulfite process the rate of delignification depends upon both the hydrogen ion and bisulfite ion concentrations, whereas the hemicellulose (and cellulose) degradation is an acid-catalyzed hydrolysis. Lignin solution, furthermore, is less temperature dependent than carbohydrate hydrolysis. It is, therefore, possible to produce sulfite pulps of low lignin content with very little loss in hemicellulose by pulping with high bisulfite ion concentrations at low temperatures (66–68,77). The rates, however, are far removed from the practical range and, therefore, in this process also it is necessary to sustain losses in the polysaccharide yield (68,112d). The order of appearance of the different sugars in sulfite cooking liquors has been found consistent with their stability toward acid hydrolysis (11e,234), and probably also their accessibility. The simple sugars formed by hydrolysis are not stable in the pulping medium but react further to form aldonic (216a) and probably sulfonic acids (285). Xylans still remaining in sulfite pulp have lost their arabinofuranose side chains as would be expected.

A third method of increasing importance for the production of paper pulps is the semichemical pulping process. This method usually consists of heating wood chips with sulfite solutions nearer the neutral pH range than in the conventional sulfite cook. Although the wood is softened sufficiently to be defibered, acid-catalyzed degradation of both lignin and hemicellulose is suppressed. Xylans dissolved in this process are at least, in part, present in the liquors as polymeric materials, but less are lost than in the chemical processes. The high yield pulp, as it is produced, is useful for many purposes. It can also be bleached with chlorine and extracted with alkali to give some grades of paper pulp in higher yield than can be obtained by the methods mentioned above. Semichemical pulping is apparently especially suitable for hardwoods and agricultural residues rich in hemicelluloses that would be lost more completely in chemical processes, and which are relatively easy to pulp. (See also Chapter 10.)

The operations following pulping and bleaching in papermaking, usually referred to as "beating" or "refining", consist of exposing the fibers (in relatively dilute aqueous suspension) to intensely localized shear fields. The shearing opens up the structure of the individual fibers and produces some fraying and fibrillation. More surface is exposed, swelling is increased, and better bonding can occur in the formation of the ultimate sheet of paper. Simultaneously, the average fiber length is decreased by beating. If not carried too far, this cutting action is not deleterious, but probably allows the fibers to be more readily dispersed and thus to form a more uniform sheet of paper.

It is the usual observation that the presence of significant amounts of hemicellulose material in the pulp increases the rate at which fiber swelling and fibrillation occur, and thus reduces the time and power required for the beating operation. The relative extents to which fiber swelling, fibrillation, and cutting take place during beating appear to be markedly influenced by the kind and amount of hemicelluloses present in the pulp.

Although water is, at best, a mediocre solvent for strongly hydrogen-bonded carbohydrate polymers, it would be expected that a low molecular weight polymer would swell more than one of high molecular weight. This is a reasonable, although probably not complete, explanation of the more rapid beating of high hemicellulose pulps. It has been reported that hemicelluloses rich in uronic acids are especially affective in swelling and softening the fiber (215), perhaps due to the hydrophilic character of their salts.

The actual papermaking process is a complicated operation which, on the conventional fourdrinier type machine, proceeds essentially in the following steps: (1) a filtration operation in which a mat of fibers is formed on the traveling wire of the machine by drainage of the dilute fiber suspension through the wire; (2) a network drainage process in which the still-wet fiber mat is subjected to compacting, while further water is being drained from the pad; (3) a two-phase flow operation in which air strikes through the sheet as still further water is removed, usually by the action of vacuum boxes; (4) after leaving the fourdrinier wire, the sheet undergoes further mechanical extraction of water between a series of press rolls in which two-phase flow of air and water also takes place; and (5) finally the paper is dried in a continuous sheet over a series of heated cylinders and, in the initial stages of this drying operation, further two-phase flow of air and water occurs. It is believed that the hemicellulose content of a pulp influences cellulose-water interaction in all of these steps, and thus affects the ultimate character of the paper obtained.

During the stage of two-phase flow the forces of surface tension act very strongly to produce the ultimate structure of the paper. The greater the extent to which the fibers have been plasticized in the preceding mechanical operation, the better is the bonding derived in the final sheet. It is as an aid to this plasticization that the hemicelluloses apparently play their greatest role in the development of paper strength. So important is this function that even the addition of synthetic resins to pulps or papers with little hemicellulose content usually does not produce papers of adequate strength (94). It is, however, inaccurate to say that hemicelluloses are necessary for strength properties, because reasonably strong papers can be made from cotton cellulose if prolonged beating is employed. Obviously, the desirable physical effects of the hemicelluloses can be obtained in other ways.

Strength properties and other quality criteria of paper are markedly affected by the quantity of hemicellulose present. The results vary widely in detail, depending upon the pulp source, the kind of hemicellulose present, and whether the hemicellulose is added to the pulp suspension and retained by the pulp or is present in the original fiber (134,169,189,231). Nevertheless, certain trends are apparent that follow an explicable pattern.

Since high contents of hemicellulose aid in the bonding of fibers in the papermaking process, paper made of highly beaten pulp of high hemicellulose content becomes very much like a continuous film. Such papers are generally referred to as glassine papers. In general, high hemicellulose pulps produce papers of decreased opacity and increased tensile and bursting strength. Tear resistance is a complicated combination of fiber strength, fiber length, and fiber bonding. If fibers are extremely well-bonded into the sheet, as in the case of high hemicellulose papers, the tear may be quite low. Extremely large amounts of hemicellulose may result in a decrease in tensile and bursting strength properties, not because of the bonding effect, but possibly because the individual fiber strengths may be reduced as a result of the decrease in the number-average molecular weight of the polymer system. An optimum hemicellulose content is, therefore, often found for these properties.

Although the amounts of hemicelluloses that are practical to retain in pulp are beneficial for papermaking, they are invariably a nuisance in the formation of cellulose derivatives or regenerated celluloses. Therefore, cellulose derivatives and regenerated cellulose from wood are for some, though not all (209), purposes inferior to those obtained from cotton. However, developments in wood processing are continually decreasing quality differences between cellulose from the two sources.

If one cellulose sample has a broader molecular weight distribution than another, solutions of the two of the same viscosity and concentration (required for fabrication) will differ in the number-average molecular weight. The sample with the lower number-average molecular weight would, therefore, be expected to have poorer strength (97). Whatever contribution the hemicelluloses make to this shortcoming of wood cellulose, they also appear to have more specific deleterious effects.

The rates of reaction of the hemicelluloses with the reagents used for the formation of derivatives are different from those of cellulose. Their rapid rate of acid-catalyzed hydrolysis tends to contaminate nitrating acids rapidly in cellulose nitrate manufacture. Other hemicellulose derivatives also differ in solubility from the corresponding cellulose derivatives, and they are thus often associated with gel formation and haze (11e). The presence of carboxylic salts in cellulose derivatives causes anomalous viscosity effects in nonpolar solvents (1956) and xylans are rich in uronic acids. In acetone solutions of cellulose acetate, xylan acetate is insoluble and contributes to turbidity but not to viscosity (182).

The use of softwood species for derivative manufacture might be suggested by these facts, but mannans, in which softwood pulps are rich, increase the viscosity of cellulose derivative solutions at high concentrations also (228). If cellulose acetates from different sources (and relatively free of uronic acid salts) are prepared with the same viscosity at 7% concentration their viscosities at 27% concentration are often markedly different. The viscosity ratio, defined as $(\eta_{27\%}/\eta_{7\%}) \times 10^{-2}$, for cotton is reported to be about 11.4, whereas the ratio obtained on various wood pulps ranges from 16 to 46 (228). The logarithm of the viscosity ratio (VR) varies linearly with mannan content of the acetate according to the equation:

$$\log VR = 0.805 + 0.733 \ (\% \text{ mannan})$$

It is possible to decrease the turbidity and false viscosity of cellulose acetates by removing the hemicellulose derivatives by centrifugation or solvent extraction (182), but it is also necessary to use special inefficient pulping methods to obtain dissolving pulps from wood, and only about one-third of the wood weight is left for derivative manufacture.

The pulping sequences most commonly used are (1) acid sulfite pulping, bleaching, alkaline extraction, and (2) prehydrolysis, kraft pulping, bleaching, and alkaline extraction.

The first process is not applicable to certain species, including pines, because some are too resinous and others contain pinosylvin. This extractive interferes with the removal of lignin by the sulfite process. The pinosylvin can be removed by a neutral sulfite pulping stage before acid sulfite pulping, but in this case glucomannans apparently diffuse into the cellulose structure, lose acetyl groups by hydrolysis, and precipitate probably in more crystalline regions and become inaccessible. As a result the quality of the finished pulp is inferior (17). When acid conditions are maintained from the beginning, hemicellulose degradation is sufficiently rapid that this is less of a problem.

The same problem is even more severe in the case of kraft (alkaline) pulping, for both xylan and glucomannan are rendered less accessible by the pulping process. They must, therefore, be first degraded by an acid prehydrolysis in order for the pulps to be satisfactory for manufacture of derivatives.

Prior to viscose preparation, cellulose is steeped in strong alkaline solutions to make a homogeneous alkali cellulose which will react evenly with carbon disulfide. The excess steeping liquors dissolve out residual hemicelluloses and these must be removed by dialysis prior to recycling the alkali in the process (195). A similar cold alkali extraction of acetate pulps is expensive, and instead hot dilute alkali is used to degrade any hemicellulose present. The mechanism of the degradation process is the peeling reaction, and the method is wasteful of cellulose. Various methods of stabilizing the reducing end groups of the carbohydrates have been tried in order to limit the loss in yield. Conflicting reports have been published as to whether hot refining can be effective when reducing groups of the polysaccharides are stabilized against the peeling reaction (29,76,166).

The literature of the technology of these processes is enormous and is outside the scope of this chapter, except in so far as the processes are dictated by the chemistry of these polysaccharides.

The hemicelluloses are not presently used industrially as polymeric materials, but only as a source of furan derivatives by acid distillation of agricultural wastes, and as a substrate (in pulping liquors) for the growth of torula yeast.

The practical application of the hemicelluloses themselves has been hindered by several factors—their molecular weights are low for polymer applications, and their water solubilities are high. In many applications they could, therefore, be expected to compete with plant gums obtainable by water extraction. The optimum practical conditions of extraction have not been well understood, and have not been demonstrated to be commercially attractive. A knowledge of the differences in structure between hemicelluloses from different plant sources has only recently been obtained. Nevertheless, some preliminary research in the direction of practical application has been carried out (271f). Studies on the utility of hemicelluloses as textile sizes (271f) and as beater additives have been reported, but their low retention by the fiber needs to be overcome for the latter application (169,239). The film-forming properties of xylans (226) have been described, and they could have value as alkali-soluble fibers for textile application. A carboxymethyl xylan has been prepared (219) and the use of xylan sulfates as blood anticoagulants has been investigated (137).

VIII. Biochemistry of Hemicelluloses

At the present time, the metabolism of pentose sugars (202) and the synthesis of polysaccharides in higher plants (13,93,108,125,152, 183,184,203,224,225,283) is under investigation. Of the hemicelluloses, most progress has been made in understanding the biosynthesis of xylan.

Of a variety of radioactive sugars tested (including D-xylose), glucose was incorporated into both cellulose and xylan more efficiently than any other. Most of the radioactive carbon in both polysaccharides was in the same position (C_1) as in the original glucose (183,283). Glucose can, therefore, be converted into xylan without rearrangement of the carbon skeleton. Over longer periods of growth more rearrangement was of course observed.

Xylose was incorporated into xylan only after substantial rearrangement of the radioactive C_1 carbon. The xylose apparently readily enters into xylan by first being converted to a compound involved in the hexose monophosphate shunt (i.e., pentose-5-phosphates, glucose-6-phosphates, sedoheptulose-7-phosphate) where it passes through a hexose intermediate before polymerization (183).

The nature of the hexose intermediate is also known with some certainty (13,125). α-D-Glucose-6-phosphate is readily converted to the 1-phosphate. This compound, reacting with uridine triphosphate, through the agency of a pyrophosphorylase, gives uridine diphosphate-α-glucose (UDP-D-glucose). This sugar nucleotide can be oxidized at the C_6 carbon atom to the corresponding uronic acid derivative by diphosphopyridine nucleotide (DPN), and decarboxylated by another enzyme system to UDP-D-xylose, in which the phosphate linkage is still to the C_1 position. This substance acts in a transglycosylation process to add a xylose unit to a suitable acceptor. When the acceptor is a xylose oligomer from xylan with from 2 to 5 xylose units, the product obtained is the corresponding $1 \rightarrow 4'$ beta-linked oligomer with one more xylose unit in the molecule (93). The elucidation of this mechanism shows that there was some element of truth in the old theory that xylan was derived from decarboxylation of glucuronic acid, although the specific sequences previously proposed were fallacious.

It is interesting to note that D-glucuronic acid (13,225) and L-arabinose, in contrast to xylose, can be converted by enzymes directly to their 1-phosphates and UDP derivatives (125). UDP-L-arabinose can be epimerized at C_4 to UDP-D-xylose, and thus be converted to xylan without chain scission or rearrangement (183).

Whereas these developments have been made on plants which are perhaps more amenable to biochemical investigation than forest trees, there can be little doubt that similar processes will be found in the latter. There may be some relation between the fact that of all the pentoses, arabinose is most readily incorporated into the plant's structural elements and is the only free pentose reported in wood (206).

The function of most of the hemicelluloses in plants is undoubtedly primarily structural. However, a portion of the more soluble material has no value for this purpose. It has been observed that in the grape vine there are variations in hemicellulose content of tissues between seasonal periods in which vegetative growth is high, and periods in which the plant is resting. Consequently, the suggestion (152) has been made that hemicellulose acts as a reserve food stuff in this plant. However, the changes which occur in hemicellulose content in the bulk of woody tissue between various seasons must be very slight, as most of the tree trunk consists of dead heartwood. Furthermore, other investigators question both the observation and the conclusion (123,258,275).

Striking decreases in the solubility of xylan have been noted with decrease in the number of arabinose side chains. On the basis of this observation it has been suggested that the plant may take advantage of this difference in solubility in transporting preformed xylan molecules from stationary tissues to rapidly growing centers. The only enzymatic mechanism needed would be one which removed and replaced arabinose side chains on the xylan molecule (200). However, the polysaccharide fraction of maple sap is very largely arabinogalactan and xylan becomes only a minor component in the late spring (9). Perhaps we can conclude that trees find the problems of hydrodynamics more demanding than those of polymer synthesis.

IX. Conclusion

Within the past few years, we have observed a great acceleration of progress in the chemistry of wood hemicelluloses, primarily in the development of elegant new methods for separation and structure proof. The principal polysaccharide systems of stalk tissues are now known with certainty as fairly well-defined methods are available for their separation, and the main features of their structures are clear. Nevertheless, a number of structural problems await solution: a complete picture of the arabinogalactans, a knowledge of the anomeric form of arabinose in arabinoxylans, and the isolation of xylobiose units with other than 1,4' linkages. Comparative molecular weight studies are needed to disclose more completely the conditions of isolation causing degradation. Furthermore, it is surprising that there have not been more investigations of the polysaccharides found in other tissues, and this is another obvious direction for structural studies to follow in the next decade. New approaches to the distribution of the hemicelluloses within the cell wall are producing interesting results and also deserve a quickening of effort.

It has been clear for some time that variations in the structure of xylans—substitution by arabinose, uronic acids, acetyl groups, and branching—are to some extent characteristic of different plant types. A systematic choice of plants is now in order to determine whether these macromolecules can assist or be related more precisely to botanical classifications.

The preliminary studies on the biochemistry and physiology of the hemicelluloses have opened a rich and rewarding field of research, and tools of sufficient power are available to produce results.

Fundamental studies on the structure and chemical properties of these polysaccharides have already defined more precisely the changes occurring during the pulping and purification processes. It remains for future investigators to suggest practical methods to lower the scandalously high waste in the chemical processing of wood.

ACKNOWLEDGMENT

The author gratefully acknowledges his debt to the contributors to the Wood Hemicellulose Symposium, American Chemical Society. Their courtesy in permitting him to read their original contributions and reviews was an aid in including the most recent and timely work.

REFERENCES

1. Abdel-Akher, M., J. K. Hamilton, R. Montgomery, and F. Smith, *J. Am. Chem. Soc.*, **74**, 4970 (1952); F. Smith, *et al.*, *ibid.*, **81**, 2173, 2176, 6252 (1959).

2. Adams, G. A., *Can. J. Chem.*, **35**, 556 (1957).

3. Adams, G. A., (a) *Tappi*, **40**, 1, 721 (1957)   (b) *Can. J. Chem.*, **36**, 755 (1958).

4. Adams, G. A., *Can. J. Chem.*, **32**, 186 (1954).

5. Adams, G. A., *Can. J. Chem.*, **33**, 56 (1956).

6. Adams, G. A., *Can. J. Chem.*, **37**, 29 (1959).

7. Adams, G. A., Paper 2, Wood Hemicellulose Symposium, Division of Cellulose Chemistry, American Chemical Society, September 13–18, 1959, Atlantic City, N. J.

8. Adams, G. A., and C. T. Bishop, *Tappi*, **38**, 672 (1955).

9. Adams, G. A., C. T. Bishop, and I. J. McDonald, *Can. J. Biochem. and Physiol.*, **37**, 507 (1959).

10. (a) Adams, G. A., and A. E. Castagne, *Can. J. Chem.*, **29**, 109 (1951); (b) G. A. Adams, *ibid.*, **30**, 698 (1952).

11. *Advances in Carbohydrate Chemistry*, Academic Press, New York. (a) J. K. N. Jones and F. Smith, **4**, 284 (1949); (b) J. Bobbitt, **11**, 1 (1956); (c) R. E. Reeves, **6**, 108 (1951); (d) C. T. Greenwood, **7**, 290 (1952); (e) W. J. Polglase, **10**, 283 (1955); (f) R. L. Whistler and J. N. BeMiller, **13**, 289 (1958); (g) G. O. Aspinall, **14**, 429 (1959); (h) C. E. Ballou, **9**, 59 (1954).

12. Alexander, W. A., and R. L. Mitchell, *Anal. Chem.*, **31**, 1497 (1949).

13. Altermatt, H. A., and A. C. Neish, *Can. J. Biochem. and Physio'.*, **34**, 405 (1956).

14. Anderson, E., J. Kesselman, and E. C. Bennett, *J. Biol. Chem.*, **140**, 563 (1941).

15. Anderson, E., H. Russell, and W. Seigle, *J. Biol. Chem.*, **113**, 683 (1936).

16. Anderson, E., M. Seeley, W. T. Stewart, J. C. Redd, and D. Westerbeke, *J. Biol. Chem.*, **135**, 189 (1940).

17. Annergren, G. E., and S. A. Rydholm, Paper 22, Wood Hemicellulose Symposium, Division of Cellulose Chemistry, American Chemical Society, Atlantic City, N. J., September 13–18, 1959.

18. *Ann. Repts. on Progr. Chem. (Chem. Soc. London)*, **52**, 260 (1955).

19. Anthis, A. F., *Tappi*, **39**, 401 (1956).

20. Aspinall, G. O., and M. E. Carter, *J. Chem. Soc.*, **1956**, 3744.

21. Aspinall, G. O., E. L. Hirst, and R. S. Mahomed, *J. Chem. Soc.*, **1954**, 1734.

22. Aspinall, G. O., E. L. Hirst, R. W. Moody, and E. G. V. Percival, *J. Chem. Soc.*, **1953**, 1631.

23. Aspinall, G. O., E. L. Hirst, E. G. V. Percival, and I. R. Williamson, *J. Chem. Soc.*, **1953**, 3184.

24. Aspinall, G. O., E. L. Hirst, and E. Ramstad, *J. Chem. Soc.*, **1958**, 593.

25. Aspinall, G. O., R. A. Laidlaw, and R. B. Rashbrook, *J. Chem. Soc.*, **1957**, 4444.

26. (a) Aspinall, G. O., and J. E. McKay, *J. Chem. Soc.*, **1958**, 1059; (b) G. O. Aspinall and P. C. Das Gupta, *J. Chem. Soc.*, **1958**, 3627.

27. Aspinall, G. O., and R. S. Mohamed, *J. Chem. Soc.*, **1954**, 1731.

28. Aspinall, G. O., and A. Nicholson, *J. Chem. Soc.*, **1960**, 2503; G. O. Aspinall, I. M. Cairncross, and A. Nicholson, *Proc. Chem. Soc.*, **1959**, 270.

29. Assarsson, A., L. Stockman and O. Theander, Paper 21, Wood Hemicellulose Symposium, Division of Cellulose Chemistry, American Chemical Society, Atlantic City, N. J., September 13–18, 1959.

30. Asunmaa, S., and P. W. Lange, *Svensk Papperstidn.*, **55**, 217 (1952).
31. Ball, D. H., J. K. N. Jones, W. H. Nicholson, and T. J. Painter, *Tappi*, **39**, 438 (1956); J. K. N. Jones and T. J. Painter, *J. Chem. Soc.*, **1957**, 669.
32. Barker, S. A., E. J. Bourne, M. Stacey, and D. H. Whiffen, *J. Chem. Soc.*, **1954**, 171.
33. Barker, S. A., E. J. Bourne, and O. T. Theander, *J. Chem. Soc.*, **1955**, 4276.
34. Barker, S. A., M. Stacey, and G. Zweifel, *J. Chem. Soc.*, **1957**, 332.
35. Barry, V. C., *Nature*, **152**, 537 (1943).
36. Barry, V. C., J. E. McCormick, and P. W. D. Mitchel, *J. Chem. Soc.*, **1954**, 3692.
37. Barth, F. W., and T. E. Timell, *Can. J. Chem.*, **36**, 1321 (1958).
38. Barth, F. W., and T. E. Timell, *J. Am. Chem. Soc.*, **80**, 6320 (1958).
39. Bates, F. J., *et al.*, *Polarimetry, Saccharimetry and the Sugars*, Circular C440, U.S. Dept. of Commerce, National Bureau of Standards, Washington, D. C., 1942.
40. Beckmann, C. O., *Ann. N.Y. Acad. Sci.*, **57**, 384 (1953).
41. Binger, H. P., J. T. Sullivan, and C. O. Jensen, *J. Agr. Food Chem.*, **2**, 696 (1954).
42. Bishop, C. T., *Can. J. Chem.*, **33**, 1521 (1955).
43. Bishop, C. T., *J. Am. Chem. Soc.*, **78**, 2840 (1956).
44. Bishop, C. T., *Can. J. Chem.*, **33**, 1073 (1955).
45. Bishop, C. T., and G. A. Adams, *Can. J. Research*, **28B**, 753 (1950).
46. Bishop, C. T., *Can. J. Chem.*, **30**, 229 (1952).
47. Bishop, C. T., *Can. J. Chem.*, **31**, 134, 793 (1953).
48. Bishop, C. T., *Can. J. Chem.*, **35**, 1010 (1957).
49. Bishop, C. T., and F. P. Cooper, Paper 15, Wood Hemicellulose Symposium, Division of Cellulose Chemistry, American Chemical Society, Atlantic City, N. J., September 13–18, 1959.
50. Bishop, C. T., and D. R. Whittaker, *Chem. and Ind.*, **1955**, 149.
51. Björkman, A., *Svensk Papperstidn.*, **60**, 243 (1957).
52. Björkman, A., *Svensk Papperstidn.*, **59**, 477 (1956); **60**, 158 (1957).
53. Björkman, A., *idem.*, ref. 51.
54. Björkqvist, K. J., and L. Jörgensen, *Acta Chem. Scand.*, **5**, 978 (1951).
55. Booker, E., and C. Schuerch, *Tappi*, **41**, 650 (1958).
56. Bouveng, H. O., *Acta Chem. Scand.*, **13**, 1869, 1877 (1959).
57. Bouveng, H. O., P. G. Garegg, and B. Lindberg, *Chem. and Ind.*, **1958**, No. 52, 1727.
58. Bouveng, H. O., and B. Lindberg, *Acta Chem. Scand.*, (a) **12**, 1977 (1958); (b) **10**, 1515 (1956).
59. Bouveng, H. O., and H. Meier, *Acta Chem. Scand.*, **13**, 1884 (1959).
60. Brasch, D. J., and J. K. N. Jones, *Can. J. Chem.*, **37**, 1538 (1959).
61. Brasch, D. J., and L. E. Wise, *Tappi*, **39**, 581, 768 (1956).
62. Brauns, F. E., *The Chemistry of Lignin*, Academic Press, New York, 1952.
63. Brauns, F. E., and W. S. Grimes, *Paper Trade J.*, **108**, No. 11, 40 (1939).
64. Browning, B. L., and L. O. Bublitz, *Tappi*, **36**, 452 (1953).
65. Bublitz, W. J., *Tappi*, **31**, 427 (1951).
66. Calhoun, J. M., J. J. R. Cannon, F. H. Yorston, and O. Maass, *Can. J. Research*, **B16**, 242 (1938).

67. Calhoun, J. M., F. H. Yorston, and O. Maass, *Can. J. Research*, **B15**, 457 (1937).

68. Calhoun, J. M., F. H. Yorston, and O. Maass, *Can. J. Research*, **B17**, 121 (1939).

69. Campbell, W. G., E. L. Hirst, and J. K. N. Jones, *J. Chem. Soc.*, **1948**, 774.

70. Chanda, S. K., E. L. Hirst, J. K. N. Jones, and E. G. V. Percival, *J. Chem. Soc.*, **1950**, 1289.

71. Chanda, S. K., E. L. Hirst, and E. G. V. Percival, *J. Chem. Soc.*, **1951**, 1240.

72. Clendenning, K. A., and D. E. Wright, *Can. J. Research*, **28F**, 390 (1950).

73. Collier, R. W., Paper 20, Wood Hemicellulose Symposium, Division of Cellulose Chemistry, American Chemical Society, Atlantic City, N. J., September 13–18, 1959.

74. Connell, J. J., E. L. Hirst, and E. G. V. Percival, *J. Chem. Soc.*, **1950**, 3494.

75. Corbett, W. M., and J. Kenner, *J. Chem. Soc.*, **1955**, 1431.

76. Corbett, W. M., and J. Kidd, *Tappi*, **41**, 137 (1958).

77. Corey, A. J., and O. Maass, *Can. J. Research*, **B14**, 336 (1936).

78. Croon, I., and B. Lindberg, *Acta Chem. Scand.*, **12**, 453 (1958).

79. Croon, I., B. Lindberg, and H. Meier, *Acta Chem. Scand.*, **13**, 1299 (1959).

80. Currie, A. L., and T. E. Timell, *Can. J. Chem.*, **37**, 922 (1959).

81. Das Gupta, P. C., and P. B. Sarkar, *Textile Research J.*, **24**, 705, 1071 (1954).

82. Dillon, T., D. F. O'Ceallachain, and P. O'Colla, *Proc. Royal Irish Acad.*, **55**, B331 (1953); **57B**, 31 (1954).

83. Dryselius, E., B. Lindberg, and O. Theander, *Acta Chem. Scand.*, **11**, 663 (1957); **12**, 340 (1958).

84. Durrum, E. L., *J. Am. Chem. Soc.*, **72**, 2943 (1950).

85. Dutton, G. G. S., and K. Hunt, *J. Am. Chem. Soc.*, **80**, 5697 (1958).

86. Dutton, G. G. S., and K. Hunt, Paper 5, Wood Hemicellulose Symposium, Division of Cellulose Chemistry, American Chemical Society, Atlantic City, N. J., September 13–18, 1958.

87. Dutton, G. G. S., and I. H. Rogers, *J. Am. Chem. Soc.*, **81**, 2413 (1959).

88. Dutton, G. G. S., and F. Smith, *J. Am. Chem. Soc.*, **78**, 2505, 3744 (1956).

89. Dyer, J., in *Methods of Biochemical Analysis*, Vol. 3., D. Glick, ed., Interscience, New York, 1956, p. 111.

90. Ehrenthal, I., R. Montgomery, and F. Smith, *J. Am. Chem. Soc.*, **76**, 5509 (1954).

91. Erskine, A. J., and J. K. N. Jones, *Can. J. Chem.*, **34**, 821 (1956).

92. Falconer, E. L., and G. A. Adams, *Can. J. Chem.*, **34**, 338 (1956).

93. Feingold, D. S., E. F. Neufeld, and W. Z. Hassid, *J. Biol. Chem.*, **234**, 488 (1959).

94. Fineman, M. N., *Tappi*, **35**, 320 (1952).

95. Flanders, C. A., *Arch. Biochem. Biophys.*, **36**, 421, 425 (1952).

96. Flory, P. J., *Principles of Polymer Chemistry*, Cornell University Press, 1953, p. 361.

97. Flory, P. J., *J. Am. Chem. Soc.*, **67**, 2048 (1945).

98. Ford, L. H., and S. Peat, *J. Chem. Soc.*, **1941**, 856.

99. Gardner, T. S., and C. B. Purves, *J. Am. Chem. Soc.*, **64**, 1539 (1942).

99a. Garegg, P. J., and B. Lindberg, *Acta Chem. Scand.*, **14**, 871 (1960).

100. Geerdes, J. D., and F. Smith, *J. Am. Chem. Soc.*, **77**, 3569, 3572 (1955).

101. Gerhardt, F., *Plant Phys.*, **4**, 373 (1929).
102. Gillham, J. K., A. S. Perlin, and T. E. Timell, *Can. J. Chem.*, **36**, 1741 (1958).
103. Gillham, J. K., and T. E. Timell, *Can. J. Chem.*, **36**, 410, 1467 (1958).
104. Glaudemans, C. P. J., and T. E. Timell, *Svensk Papperstidn.*, **61**, 1 (1958).
105. Glaudemans, C. P. J., and T. E. Timell, *J. Am. Chem. Soc.*, **80**, 941, 1209 (1958).
106. Glaudemans, C. P. J., and T. E. Timell, *Svensk Papperstidn.*, **60**, 869 (1957).
106a. Goring, D. A. I., and T. E. Timell, *J. Phys. Chem.*, **64**, 1426 (1960).
107. Gorrod, A. R. N., and J. K. N. Jones, *J. Chem. Soc.*, **1954**, 2522.
108. Greathouse, G. A., *Science*, **117**, 553 (1953).
109. Green, J. W., *Tappi*, **39**, 472 (1956).
110. Gustafsson, C., P. J. Ollinmaa, and J. Saarnio, *Acta Chem. Scand.*, **6**, 1299 (1952).
111. Gustafsson, C., J. Sundman, S. Pettersson, and T. Lindh, *Paper and Timber (Finland)*, **35**, 300 (1951).
111a. Gyaw, M. O., and T. E. Timell, *Can. J. Chem.*, **38**, 1957 (1960).
112. Hägglund, E., *Chemistry of Wood*, 3rd ed., Academic Press, New York, 1951, pp. (a) 48, (b) 297, (c) 476, (d) 414, (e) 498.
113. Hägglund, E., B. Lindberg, and J. McPherson, *Acta Chem. Scand.*, **10**, 1160 (1956).
114. Hägglund, E., and H. Richtzenhain, *Tappi*, **35**, 281 (1952).
115. Häggroth, S., and B. Lindberg, *Svensk Papperstidn.*, **59**, 870 (1956).
116. Hamilton, J. K., and H. W. Kircher, *J. Am. Chem. Soc.*, **80**, 4703 (1958).
117. Hamilton, J. K., H. W. Kircher, and N. S. Thompson, *J. Am. Chem. Soc.*, **78**, 2508 (1956).
118. Hamilton, J. K., and G. R. Quimby, *Tappi*, **40**, 781 (1957).
119. Hamilton, J. K., and E. V. Partlow, *J. Am. Chem. Soc.*, **80**, 4880 (1958).
120. Hamilton, J. K., E. V. Partlow, and N. S. Thompson, (a) *Tappi*, **41**, 811 (1958); (b) *J. Am. Chem. Soc.*, **82**, 451 (1960).
121. Hamilton, J. K., and N. S. Thompson, *Tappi*, **42**, 752 (1959).
122. Hampton, H. A., W. N. Haworth, and E. L. Hirst, *J. Chem Soc.*, **1929**, 1739.
123. Hardwick, N. E., *Australian J. Agr. Research*, **5**, 372 (1954).
124. Harwood, V. D., *Can. J. Chem.*, **29**, 974 (1951).
125. Hassid, W. Z., E. F. Neufeld, and D. S. Feingold, *Proc. Nat. Acad. Sci. U.S.*, **45**, 905 (1959).
126. Haworth, W. N., and E. G. V. Percival, *J. Chem. Soc.*, **1931**, 2850.
127. Heidelberger, M., Z. Dische, W. B. Neely, and M. L. Wolfrom, *J. Am. Chem. Soc.*, **77**, 3511, 4309 (1955).
128. Hess, K., and M. Lüdtke, *Ann.*, **466**, 18 (1928).
129. Hirst, E. L., *J. Chem. Soc.*, **1955**, 2982.
130. Hirst, E. L., and J. K. N. Jones, "The Analysis of Plant Gums and Mucilages," in *Modern Methods of Plant Analysis*, Vol. II, K. Paech and M. V. Tracey, eds., Springer-Verlag, Berlin, 1955, p. 275.
131. Horio, M., R. Imamuru, and H. Inagaki, *Tappi*, **38**, 216 (1955).
132. Hough, L., J. K. N. Jones, and V. H. Wadman, *J. Chem. Soc.*, **1949**, 2511.
133. Hough, L., T. Taylor, G. Thomas, and B. Woods, *J. Chem. Soc.*, **1958**, 1212.
134. Houtz, H. H., and E. F. Kurth, *Paper Trade J.*, **109**, No. 24, 38 (1939).
135. Huebner, C., S. Ames, and E. Bubl, *J. Am. Chem. Soc.*, **68**, 1621 (1946).

136. Husemann, E., *J. prakt. Chem.*, **155**, 13 (1940).
137. Husemann, E., and B. Pfannemüller, *Z. Naturforsch.*, **10B**, 143 (1955).
138. Illingworth, B., J. Larner, and G. T. Cori, *J. Biol. Chem.*, **199**, 631 (1952).
139. Immergut, B., and B. G. Rånby, *Svensk Papperstidn.*, **60**, 573 (1957).
140. *Idem.* ref. 139.
141. Jones, J. K. N., *J. Chem. Soc.*, **1950**, 3292.
142. Jones, J. K. N., *J. Chem. Soc.*, **1953**, 1672.
143. Jones, J. K. N., Paper 16, Wood Hemicellulose Symposium, Division of Cellulose Chemistry, American Chemical Society, Atlantic City, N.J., September 13–16, 1959.
144. Jones, J. K. N., and G. Guzmán, *Anales real. soc. españ. fis. y quim* (*Madrid*) **50B**, 505 (1954); *Chem. Abstracts*, **48**, 12,936 (1954).
145. Jones, J. K. N., E. Merler, and L. E. Wise, *Can. J. Chem.*, **35**, 634 (1957).
146. Jones, J. K. N., and T. J. Painter, *J. Chem. Soc.*, **1959**, 573; **1957**, 669.
146a. Jones, J. K. N., C. B. Purves, and T. E. Timell, *Can. J. Chem.*, **39**, 1059 (1961).
147. Jones, J. K. N., and L. E. Wise, *J. Chem. Soc.*, **1952**, 2750, 3389.
148. Jones, J. K. N., L. E. Wise, and J. P. Jappe, *Tappi*, **39**, 139 (1956).
149. Jayme, G., M. Sätre, and S. Maris, *Naturwissenschaften*, **29**, 768 (1941).
150. Jayme, G., and M. Sätre, *Ber.*, **75**, 1849 (1942); **77**, 242, 248 (1944).
151. Klauditz, W., *Holzforschung*, **11**, 158 (1958).
152. Kostrubin, M. V., *Biokhimiya*, **20**, 360 (1955).
153. Kuhn, R., H. Trischmann, and I. Low, *Angew. Chem.*, **67**, 32 (1955).
154. Larner, J., B. Illingworth, G. T. Cori, and C. F. Cori, *J. Biol. Chem.*, **199**, 641 (1952).
155. Larocque, G. L., and O. Maass, *Can. J. Research*, **19**, 1 (1941).
156. Leech, J. G., *Tappi*, **35**, 249 (1952).
157. Lewis, B. A., and F. Smith, *J. Am. Chem. Soc.*, **79**, 3929 (1957).
158. Lewis, H. F., F. E. Brauns, and M. A. Buchanan, *Paper Trade J.*, **110**, No. 5, 36 (1940).
158a. Liang, C. Y., K. H. Bassett, E. A. McGinnes, and R. H. Marchessault, *Tappi*, **43**, 1017 (1960).
159. Lindberg, B., *Svensk Papperstidn.*, **59**, 531 (1956).
160. Lindgren, B. O., *Acta Chem. Scand.*, **12**, 447 (1958).
161. Lindberg, B., and H. Meier, *Svensk Papperstidn.*, **60**, 785 (1957).
162. Lindberg, B., and H. Meier, Paper 18, Wood Hemicellulose Symposium, Division of Cellulose Chemistry, American Chemical Society, Atlantic City, N. J., September 13–18, 1959).
163. Lindberg, B., and L. Selleby, *Acta Chem. Scand.*, **12**, 1512 (1958).
164. Loska, S. J., and J. A. Shellenberger, *Cereal Chem.*, **26**, 129 (1949).
165. Low, W., and E. V. White, *J. Am. Chem. Soc.*, **65**, 2430 (1944).
166. Machell, G., and G. N. Richards, *Tappi*, **41**, 12 (1958).
167. Mackie, I. M., and E. Percival, *J. Chem. Soc.*, **1959**, 1151.
168. Malm, C. J., L. J. Tanghe, and B. C. Laird, *J. Am. Chem. Soc.*, **70**, 2740 (1948).
169. March, R. E., *Paper Trade J.*, **127**, No. 17, 431 (1948).
170. Marder, H. L., and C. Schuerch, *J. Org. Chem.*, **24**, 1977 (1959).
171. McDonald, I. R. C., *J. Chem. Soc.*, **1952**, 3183.

172. McNeely, W. H., W. W. Binkley, and M. L. Wolfrom, *J. Am. Chem. Soc.*, **67**, 527 (1945).

172a. Meier, H., *Acta Chem. Scand.*, **14**, 749 (1960).

173. Merewether, J. W. T., *Holzforschung*, **11**, 65 (1957).

174. Merewether, J. W. T., *Australian Pulp and Paper Ind.*, *Tech. Assoc. Proc.*, **1951**, 226.

175. Merler, E., and L. E. Wise, *Tappi*, **41**, 80 (1958).

176. Mian, A. J., and T. E. Timell, *Chem. and Ind.*, **1959**, 1552.

176a. Mian, A. J., and T. E. Timell, *Svensk Papperstidn.*, **63**, 769 (1960).

176b. Mian, A. J., and T. E. Timell, *Svensk Papperstidn.*, **63**, 884 (1960).

177. Milks, J. E., and C. B. Purves, *J. Am. Chem. Soc.*, **78**, 3738 (1956).

178. Montgomery, R., and F. Smith, *J. Am. Chem. Soc.*, **77**, 3325, 2834 (1955).

179. Montgomery, R., and F. Smith, *Agr. and Food Chem.*, **4**, 716 (1956).

180. Montgomery, R., and F. Smith, *J. Am. Chem. Soc.*, **79**, 695 (1957).

181. Montgomery, R., F. Smith, and H. C. Srivastava, *J. Am. Chem. Soc.*, **78**, 2837, 6169 (1956).

182. Neal, J., W. Kitchen, A. Schavo, and H. Krässig, Paper 23, Wood Hemicellulose Symposium, Division of Cellulose Chemistry, American Chemical Society, Atlantic City, N. J., September 13–18, 1959.

183. Neish, A. C., *Can. J. Biochem. and Physiol.*, **33**, 658 (1955).

184. Neish, A. C., *Can. J. Biochem. and Physiol.*, **36**, 187 (1958).

185. Nelson, R., and C. Schuerch, *J. Polymer Sci.*, **22**, 435 (1956).

186. Nelson, R., and C. Schuerch, *Tappi*, **40**, 419 (1957).

187. Neubauer, L. G., and C. B. Purves, *Can. J. Chem.*, **35**, 388 (1957).

188. Norman, A. G., *The Biochemistry of Cellulose, The Polyuronides, Lignin, etc.*, Clarendon Press, Oxford, 1937.

189. Obermanns, H. E., *Paper Trade J.*, **103**, No. 7, 83 (1936).

190. O'Colla, P., *Proc. Royal Irish Acad.*, **55B**, 165 (1953).

191. O'Colla, P., *Proc. Royal Irish Acad.*, **55B**, 321 (1953).

192. O'Dwyer, M. H., *Biochem. J.*, **19**, 694 (1925); I. A. Preece, *ibid.*, **25**, 1304 (1931); E. Anderson, *et al.*, *J. Biol. Chem.*, **112**, 531 (1935–36); **121**, 165 (1937); **144**, 767 (1942); **165**, 233 (1946); *J. Am. Chem. Soc.*, **70**, 432 (1948).

193. O'Dwyer, M. H., *Biochem. J.*, **17**, 501 (1923); **20**, 656 (1926); **22**, 381 (1928); **28**, 2116 (1934); **33**, 713 (1939); **34**, 149 (1940).

194. *Organic Reactions*, Vol. II, Wiley, New York, 1944, p. 341.

195. Ott, E., H. M. Spurlin, and M. W. Grafflin, *Cellulose and Cellulose Derivatives*, 2nd ed., Interscience, New York 1954, (a) pp. 847ff.; (b) pp. 466–73; (c) p. 1091.

196. Overbeck, W., and H. F. Müller, *Svensk Papperstidn.*, **45**, 357 (1942).

197. Painter, T. J., *Can. J. Chem.*, **37**, 497 (1959).

198. Painter, T. J., and C. B. Purves, Paper 12, Wood Hemicellulose Symposium, Division of Cellulose Chemistry, American Chemical Society, Atlantic City, N. J., September 13–18, 1959.

199. Percival, E. G. V., and S. K. Chanda, *Nature*, **166**, 787 (1950).

200. Perlin, A. S., *Cereal Chem.*, **28**, 370, 383 (1951).

201. Peterson, F. C., A. J. Barry, H. Unkauf, and L. E. Wise, *J. Am. Chem. Soc.*, **62**, 2361 (1940).

202. Pigman, W., *The Carbohydrates*, Academic Press, New York, 1957.

203. Pubolo, M. H., and B. Axelrod, *Arch. Biochem. and Biophys.*, **36**, 582 (1959).

204. Purves, C. B., *et al.* personal communication.

205. Quick, R. H., *Tappi*, **39**, 357 (1956).

206. Rånby, B. G., *Svensk Kem. Tidskr.*, **66**, 275 (1954).

207. Rånby, B. G., O. W. Waltersdorf, and O. A. Battista, *Svensk Papperstidn.*, **60**, 373 (1957).

208. Rentz, A., *Das Papier*, **10**, 192 (1956).

209. Richter, G. A., *Tappi*, **40**, 429 (1957).

210. Rogers, S. C., R. L. Mitchell, and G. J. Ritter, *Anal. Chem.*, **19**, 1029 (1947).

211. Roudier, A., *Compt. rend.*, **237**, 662, 840 (1953).

212. Roudier, A., Paper 13, Wood Hemicellulose Symposium, Division of Cellulose Chemistry, American Chemical Society, Atlantic City, N. J., September 13–18, 1959.

213. Roudier, A., and L. Eberhard, *Compt. rend.*, **240**, 2012 (1955).

214. Saarnio, J., Ph.D. Thesis, Helsinki University, 1956.

215. Saarnio, J., K. Wathen, and C. Gustafsson, *Paperi ja Puu*, **36**, 209 (1954).

216. Saarnio, J., K. Wathen, and C. Gustafsson, *Acta Chem. Scand.*, **8**, 825 (1954).

216a. Samuelson, O., K. J. Ljungqvist, and C. Parck, *Svensk Papperstidn.*, **61**, 1043 (1958).

217. Sands, L., and W. Y. Gary, *J. Biol. Chem.*, **101**, 563 (1933).

218. Sands, L., and P. Nutter, *J. Biol. Chem.*, **110**, 17 (1935).

219. Schmorak, J., and G. A. Adams, *Tappi*, **40**, 378 (1957).

220. Schuerch, C., *J. Am. Chem. Soc.*, **72**, 3838 (1950); K. Sarkanen and C. Schuerch, *ibid.*, **79**, 4203 (1957).

221. Schuerch, C., *J. Am. Chem. Soc.*, **74**, 5061 (1952).

222. Schwarz, J., *Chem. and Ind.*, **1955**, 1388.

223. Scott, J. E., *Chem. and Ind.*, **1955**, 168.

224. Shafizadeh, F., and M. L. Wolfrom, *J. Am. Chem. Soc.*, **77**, 5182 (1955).

225. Slater, W. G., and H. Beevers, *Plant Physiol.*, **33**, 146 (1958).

226. Smart, C. L., and R. L. Whistler, *Science*, **110**, 713 (1949).

227. Snyder, J. L., and T. E. Timell, *Svensk Papperstidn.*, **58**, 889 (1955).

228. Steinmann, H. W., and B. B. White, *Tappi*, **37**, 225 (1954).

229. Stewart, C. M., *Australian J. Chem.*, **6**, 425 (1953); *Chem. Abstracts*, **48**, 2367 (1954).

230. Stewart, C. M., and D. H. Foster, *Nature*, **171**, 792 (1953).

231. Stitch, D. A., and H. B. Marshall, *Can. J. Research*, **28F**, 376 (1950).

232. Stockman, L., and E. Hägglund, *Svensk Papperstidn.*, **51**, 269 (1948).

233. Srivastava, H. C., and G. A. Adams, *J. Am. Chem. Soc.*, **81**, 2409 (1959).

234. Sundman, J., *Paperi ja Puu*, **32B**, 267 (1950).

235. Tachi, I., and N. Yamamori, *Mokyzai Kenkyu*, No. 4, 11 (1950); *Chem. Abstracts*, **45**, 9856 (1951).

236. Tachi, I., and N. Yamamori, *J. Agr. Chem. Soc. Japan*, **25**, 12 (1952).

237. "Testing Methods, Specifications of the Technical Association of the Pulp and Paper Industry," New York, (a) T-9m-54; (b) T-223m-48.

238. Thompson, J. O., J. J. Becker, and L. E. Wise, *Tappi*, **36**, 319, 541 (1953).

239. Thompson, J. O., J. W. Swanson, and L. E. Wise, *Tappi*, **36**, 534 (1953).

240. Thompson, J. O., and L. E. Wise, *Tappi*, **35**, 331 (1952).
241. Timell, T., *Studies on Cellulose Reactions*, Esselte Akt., Stockholm, 1950.
242. Timell, T. E., *Svensk Papperstidn.*, **60**, 836 (1957).
243. Timell, T. E., *Tappi*, **40**, 568 (1957).
244. Timell, T. E., *J. Am. Chem. Soc.*, **81**, 4989 (1959).
245. Timell, T. E., *Svensk Papperstidn.*, **59**, 1 (1956).
246. Timell, T. E., *Tappi*, **42**, 623 (1959).
246a. Timell, T. E., *Tappi*, **44**, 88 (1961).
247. Timell, T. E., *Chem. and Ind.*, **1959**, (a) 999; (b) 905.
248. Timell, T. E., *Can. J. Chem.*, **37**, 893 (1959).
249. Timell, T. E., *Svensk Papperstidn.*, **60**, 762 (1957).
250. Timell, T. E., C. P. J. Glaudemans, and J. K. Gillham, *Pulp Paper Mag. Can.*, **59**, No. 10, 242 (1958).
251. Timell, T. E., and E. C. Jahn, *Svensk Papperstidn.*, **54**, 831 (1951).
252. Timell, T. E., and A. Tyminski, *Tappi*, **40**, 519 (1957).
253. Tu, C. C., and K. Ward, Jr., *J. Am. Chem. Soc.*, **77**, 4938 (1955).
254. Van Beckum, W. G., and G. J. Ritter, *Paper Trade J.*, **104**, No. 19, 49 (1937); **105**, No. 18, 127 (1937); **108**, No. 7, 27 (1939); **109**, No. 22, 107 (1939).
255. Wadman, W. H., A. B. Anderson, and W. Z. Hassid, *J. Am. Chem. Soc.*, **76**, 4097 (1954).
256. Waldmann, E., V. Prey, and W. Krzandalsky, *Das Papier*, **8**, 84 (1954).
257. Wayman, M., and D. L. Sherk, *Tappi*, **39**, 786 (1956).
258. Wenkler, A. J., and W. O. Williams, *Plant Physiol.*, **13**, 381 (1938).
259. Wethern, J. D., *Tappi*, **35**, 267 (1952).
260. Whistler, R. L., Paper 7, Wood Hemicellulose Symposium, Division of Cellulose Chemistry, American Chemical Society, Atlantic City, N. J., September 13–18, 1958.
261. Whistler, R. L., and J. N. BeMiller, *J. Am. Chem. Soc.*, **82**, 457 (1960).
262. Whistler, R. L., and J. N. BeMiller, *J. Am. Chem. Soc.*, **78**, 1163 (1956).
263. Whistler, R. L., D. R. Bowman, and J. Bachrach, *Arch. Biochem.*, **19**, 25 (1948).
264. Whistler, R. L., H. E. Conrad, and L. Hough, *J. Am. Chem. Soc.*, **76**, 1668 (1954).
265. Whistler, R. L, and W. M. Corbett, *J. Am. Chem. Soc.*, **78**, 1003 (1956).
266. Whistler, R. L., and W. M. Corbett, *J. Am. Chem. Soc.*, **77**, 6328 (1955).
267. Whistler, R. L., and D. F. Durso, *J. Am. Chem. Soc.*, **72**, 677 (1950).
268. Whistler, R. L., and L. Hough, *J. Am. Chem. Soc.*, **75**, 4918 (1953).
269. Whistler, R. L., and E. Masak, Jr., *J. Am. Chem. Soc.*, **77**, 1241 (1955).
270. Whistler, R. L., and D. I. McGilvrary, *J. Am. Chem. Soc.*, **77**, 1884, 2212 (1955).
271. Whistler, R. L., and C. L. Smart, *Polysaccharide Chemistry*, Academic Press, New York, 1953, pp. (a) 29, (b) 52, (c) 45, (d) 135, (e) 203, (f) 269.
272. Whistler, R. L., and C. G. Smith, *J. Am. Chem. Soc.*, **74**, 3795 (1952).
273. Whistler, R. L., and C. C. Tu, *J. Am. Chem. Soc.*, (a) **74**, 3609 (1952); (b) **75**, 645 (1953).
274. Whistler, R. L., and C. C. Tu, *J. Am. Chem. Soc.*, **73**, 1389 (1951).
275. Whistler, R. L., and J. R. Young, *Arch. Biochem. Biophys.*, **89**, 1 (1960).
276. White, E. V., *J. Am. Chem. Soc.*, **63**, 2871 (1941); **64**, 302, 1507, 2838 (1942).

277. Wise, L. E., Paper 2, Wood Hemicellulose Symposium, Division of Cellulose Chemistry, American Chemical Society, Atlantic City, N. J., September 13–18, 1959; also earlier papers, Cf. J. Savard, *Bull. assoc. tech. ind. papetière*, **5**, 271 (1951).

278. Wise, L. E., *Ind. Eng. Chem., Anal. Ed.*, **17**, 63 (1945).

279. Wise, L. E., J. W. Green, and R. Rittenhouse, *Tappi*, **32**, 335 (1949).

280. Wise, L. E., and E. C. Jahn, *Wood Chemistry*, 2nd ed., Reinhold, New York, 1952, pp. (a) 7–72, (b) 1131 ff., (c) 638, (d) 372, (e) 397, (f) 12, (g) 1263, (h) 393.

281. Wise, L. E., M. Murphy, and A. A. D'Addieco, *Paper Trade J.*, **122**, No. 2, 35 (1946).

282. Wolf, M. J., M. M. MacMasters, J. A. Cannon, E. C. Rosewall, and C. E. Rist, *Cereal Chem.*, **30**, 451 (1953).

283. Wolfrom, M. L., J. M. Webber, and F. Shafizadeh, *J. Am. Chem. Soc.*, **81**, 1217 (1959).

284. Wolfrom, M. L., and J. Bobbitt, *J. Am. Chem. Soc.*, **78**, 2489 (1956).

285. Yllner, S., *Acta Chem. Scand.*, **10**, 1251 (1956).

286. Yllner, S., and B. Enström, *Svensk Papperstidn.*, **59**, 229 (1956); **60**, 449 (1957).

287. Yundt, A. P., *Tappi*, **34**, 94 (1951).

Addendum

N. S. Thompson, *The Institute of Paper Chemistry, Appleton, Wisconsin*

Since completion of Chapter 5 *The Hemicelluloses* and final preparation of this volume for publication, the general direction of various hemicellulosic researches appears to be solidifying. Efforts directed toward isolation and characterization of hemicelluloses from wood, as typified by the work of the decade between 1950 and 1960, do not appear to be slackening. Dutton and Murata (12), for example, have studied a glucuronoxylan from applewood, while other workers have prepared and studied glucomannans from jack pine (7), tamarack (*Larix laricina*) (18), and European larch (*Larix decidua*) (6). Several galactoglucomannans have been isolated from eastern hemlock, amabilis fir, Engelmann spruce, white pine, eastern white-cedar, and ginkgo by Timell (40). These have proved to be quite similar to those already isolated from western hemlock, southern pine and redwood (17), and white spruce (1). These galactoglucomannans contained 12 to 20% galactose, depending upon the source. The interesting possibility was raised by Timell (40) that the trace

(1 to 4%) galactose residue present in so-called "glucomannans" isolated from the wood of gymnosperms is actually an integral part of these polysaccharides and that these polymers should be classified as another type of triheteropolymer galactoglucomannan. The detection and isolation of glucomannan acetates from pine holocellu'ose by Meier (21), Koshijima (19), and others (2), and the demonstration that softwood arabinoglucuronoxylan unlike hardwood glucuronoxylan contains little, if any, acetyl groups are of great interest. Other research has been carried out upon the nature of the hemicellulosic constituents of forage plants. Sullivan, Phillips, and Routly (26) have described the composition of the very soluble extracts (predominantly glucuronoxylan) of orchard grass, reed canary grass, tall fescue, timothy, and Kentucky bluegrass. This and other research on alfalfa (25), roselle fiber (11), and cocksfoot grass (5) suggests the similarity between different angiosperm hemicelluloses.

The chemical composition of gymnosperm bark has been studied by Timell. The isolation of six carbohydrate components—pectin, cellulose, glucomannan, arabinoglucuronoxylan, and two galactoglucomannans—has been reported from amabilis fir (39), Engelmann spruce, lodgepole pine, and ginkgo (32). Detailed examinations of the "xylan" (33), glucomannan (34), and cellulose (35) components are found in separate publications. These researches are of botanical significance in that they demonstrate the possible existence of similar carbohydrate synthesis pathways on each side of the cambium layer when cell wall thickening occurs. Additional research on the changes in chemical composition of the cambial cells of hardwoods and softwoods during differentiation into xylem and phloem tissue has been conducted by Thornber and Northcote (31). These investigators were impressed by the similarity of the cambial cell composition of angiosperms and gymnosperms and the lack of similarity of the two phloem and xylem compositions. Other research of biological significance has been carried out by Timell upon the carbohydrate components of ferns (41). The xylan component was found to be quite similar to the corresponding component of softwood (36), as was the galactoglucomannan component of ferns (37). A comparison of the over-all carbohydrate composition of many varieties of ferns suggested that one group resembled angiosperms having low mannose and high xylose compositions while another group of ferns resembled gymnosperms with high mannose contents (38).

The physicochemical properties of the hemicelluloses are being studied in a more vigorous manner than heretofore. Earlier papers on hemicellulose structure contained little physical information apart from limited viscosity studies. More recent publications have made extensive use of some or all physical characterizations such as detailed viscosity studies and molecular weight characterizations using the ultracentrifuge and light scattering techniques. Complex fractionation and electrophoresis techniques are frequently used to verify the homogeneity of preparations. Swenson and co-workers (27) have conducted light scattering and ultracentrifugation studies upon slash pine hemicelluloses, glucomannans, and galactoglucomannans. A careful physical study of the xylan family of hemicelluloses obtained from black spruce pulps by Swenson and Thompson (28) indicated that the molecular properties of these polymers resembled those of the birch glucuronoxylan, reported earlier by Goring and Timell (13). Other studies by Bowering, Marchessault, and Timell (8) and by Thompson and Swenson (29) on glucoxylans and arabinoglucoxylans (derived by reduction of the original "xylans") indicated that the solution properties of these polymers were not influenced by the carboxyl group as much as was expected.

The industrial significance of the hemicellulose components of wood was also the subject of considerable investigation. A detailed survey of their influence in the pulp and paper industry was made recently by Hamilton (14). Research in Europe by McPherson and Öhrn (20), as well as by Pettersson and Rydholm (24), has demonstrated the degree of influence exerted by hemicellulose content upon the paper-making characteristics of pulps. Other workers in Sweden observed that some of the acetyl groups of the glucuronoxylan of hardwoods are retained throughout the sulfite pulping process but are lost rapidly during alkaline processes (2,23). In the case of softwoods, Annergren and Rydholm (3,4) observed that mild alkali pretreatments of sulfite cooks gave pulps of greatly increased yield. This yield was found to have been due to glucomannan retention, and was not observed in the case of hardwood pulps.

Additional research has been devoted to a study of the instability of uronic acids to the hot alkali encountered during the kraft- and soda-cooking processes. Hamilton and Thompson (16) showed the reaction to be typical of many and possibly all uronic acid-containing polymers. Croon and Enström (10) found [as did Hamilton, et al. (15)] that the uronic acid component of hardwood glucuronoxylans was more difficult to remove than the corresponding uronic acid of the softwood arabinoglucuronoxylan. Both groups attributed this to a physical phenomenon related to the structure of the hardwood fiber. Clayton (9), in a semiquantitative study, found that the uronic acid component of isolated glucuronoxylans was removed somewhat more slowly than had been claimed previously (15,16), and was the result of complications introduced by a concomitant methoxyl-cleaving reaction. The dependence of the lability of hemicellulose uronic acid on pH as well as on temperature was demonstrated by Thompson, et al. (30) in a study that characterized the carbohydrate components of full chemical softwood pulps prepared at all pH levels. Meier (22) observed the same phenomenon in the case of birch pulps prepared under similar conditions.

The study of the hemicelluloses appears to be progressing in the directions suggested by Dr. Schuerch earlier in this chapter. Refinements in analysis and technique are leading to the understanding of finer differences and characteristics of the various polymers. The botanical and biological significance of each of the plant components is being pursued with imagination and vigor. The industrial significance of these substances is being revealed at a rate which, it appears, will inevitably compel corresponding technical advances in pulp and paper manufacture.

REFERENCES

1. Adams, G. A., *Tappi*, **40**, 721 (1957).
2. Annergren, G. E., and I. Croon, *Svensk Papperstidn.*, **64**, 618 (1961).
3. Annergren, G. E., I. Croon, B. F. Enström, and S. A. Rydholm, *Svensk Papperstidn.*, **64**, 386 (1961).
4. Annergren, G. E., and S. A. Rydholm, *Svensk Papperstidn.*, **62**, 737 (1959).
5. Aspinall, G. O., and I. M. Cairncross, *J. Chem. Soc.*, **1960**, 3877.
6. Aspinall, G. O., R. Bigbie, and J. E. McKay, *J. Chem. Soc.*, **1962**, 214.
7. Bishop, C. T., and F. P. Cooper, *Can. J. Chem.*, **39**, 793 (1961).
8. Bowering, W. D. S., R. H. Marchessault, and T. E. Timell, *Svensk Papperstidn.*, **64**, 191 (1961).
9. Clayton, D. W., Paper No. 35, Wood Chemistry Symposium, Division of Cellulose Chemistry, American Chemical Society, Washington, D. C., March 26–29, 1962.
10. Croon, I., and B. F. Enström, *Tappi*, **44**, 870 (1961).
11. Das Gupta, P. G., *J. Chem. Soc.*, **1960**, 5262.
12. Dutton, G. G. S., and T. G. Murata, *Can. J. Chem.*, **39**, 1995 (1961).
13. Goring, D. A. I., and T. E. Timell, *J. Phys. Chem.*, **64**, 1426 (1960).
14. Hamilton, J. K., paper presented at the Wood Chemistry Symposium, International Union of Pure and Applied Chemistry, Montreal, P. Q., August 6–12, 1961.

15. Hamilton, J. K., E. V. Partlow, and N. S. Thompson, *Tappi*, **41**, 803 (1958).
16. Hamilton, J. K., and N. S. Thompson, *Pulp Paper Mag. Can.*, **61**, No. 4, T263 (1960).
17. Hamilton, J. K., and N. S. Thompson, *J. Am. Chem. Soc.*, **82**, 451 (1960).
18. Koolman, P., and G. A. Adams, *Can. J. Chem.*, **39**, 889 (1961).
19. Koshijima, T., *J. Jap. Wood Res. Soc.*, **6**, 194 (1960).
20. McPherson, J. A., and O. E. Öhrn, *Svensk Papperstidn.*, **63**, 762 (1960).
21. Meier, H., *Acta. Chem. Scand.*, **15**, 1381 (1961).
22. Meier, H., *Svensk Papperstidn.*, **65**, 299 (1962).
23. Öhrn, O. E., and I. Croon, *Svensk Papperstidn.*, **63**, 601 (1960).
24. Pettersson, S. E., and S. A. Rydholm, *Svensk Papperstidn.*, **64**, 4 (1961).
25. Smith, F., and D. V. Myhre, *J. Agr. Food Chem.*, **8**, 359 (1960).
26. Sullivan, J. T., T. G. Phillips, and D. G. Routly, *J. Agr. Food Chem.*, **8**, 152, 153 (1960).
27. Swenson, H. A., A. J. Morak, and S. Kurath, *J. Polymer Sci.*, **51**, 231 (1961).
28. Swenson, H. A., and N. S. Thompson, Paper No. 34, Wood Chemistry Symposium, Division of Cellulose Chemistry, American Chemical Society, Washington, D. C., March 26–29, 1962.
29. Thompson, N. S., and H. A. Swenson, Paper No. 33, Wood Chemistry Symposium, Division of Cellulose Chemistry, American Chemical Society, Washington, D. C., March 26–29, 1962.
30. Thompson, N. S., J. R. Peckham, and E. F. Thode, paper presented at the Alkaline Pulping Conference, Technical Association of the Pulp and Paper Industry, Houston, Texas, November, 1961; *Tappi*, in press, 1962.
31. Thornber, J. P., and D. H. Northcote, *Biochem. J.*, **82**, 340 (1962); 81, 449, 455 (1961).
32. Timell, T. E., *Svensk Papperstidn.*, **64**, 651 (1961).
33. Timell, T. E., *Svensk Papperstidn.*, **64**, 748 (1961).
34. Timell, T. E., *Svensk Papperstidn.*, **64**, 744 (1961).
35. Timell, T. E., *Svensk Papperstidn.*, **64**, 685 (1961).
36. Timell, T. E., *Svensk Papperstidn.*, **65**, 122 (1962).
37. Timell, T. E., *Svensk Papperstidn.*, **65**, 173 (1962).
38. Timell, T. E., *Svensk Papperstidn.*, **65**, 266 (1962).
39. Timell, T. E., Paper No. 32, Wood Chemistry Symposium, Division of Cellulose Chemistry, American Chemical Society, Washington, D. C., March 26–29, 1962.
40. Timell, T. E., *Tappi*, **44**, 88 (1961).
41. Timell, T. E., *Chem. & Ind.*, **1961**, 474.

CHAPTER 6

Wood Lignins

Kyosti V. Sarkanen, *University of Washington, Seattle, Washington*

Most plant tissues contain, in addition to carbohydrates and extractives, an amorphous polymeric material called lignin (6,23,24,62, 92a,141). In mature wood tissue the amount of lignin varies between 18 and 38%. Lignin is also present in varying amounts in grasses and ferns.

The biological role of lignin in living plants is to form, together with the cellulose and other carbohydrates of the cell walls, a tissue of excellent strength and durability. In a sense, lignified tissues such as wood are comparable to fiber-reinforced plastics in which the lignin represents the plastic binder and the cellulose the reinforcing fibers.

Plant lignin is concentrated mainly in the space between the cells (middle lamella) where it is deposited during the lignification of the plant tissue. The completion of the lignification process usually coincides with stoppage of the living functions of the cells. It is not surprising, therefore, that lignin has been shown to be an irreversible end product of plant metabolism.

The chemical differences that exist between lignin and the other two classes of natural polymers, the carbohydrates and proteins, are quite profound. Wood lignins, for instance, are predominantly aromatic and almost totally insoluble in known solvents, not hydrolyzable to monomeric units, and devoid of the highly regular structure so characteristic of other natural polymers. These properties, connected with the tendency to undergo secondary condensation reactions even as a result of relatively mild treatments, have made structural studies on lignins exceedingly difficult, and at present a detailed knowledge on lignin structure is lacking.

Plant lignins can be divided into three broad classes that are commonly called softwood (gymnosperm), hardwood (angiosperm), and grass lignins. Of these, the softwood lignins form a very homogeneous group, and little if any differences in structure and properties are found between individual species. This group is also that most thoroughly studied. Hardwood and grass lignins, although less completely investigated, appear to show more variance with species.

I. Lignin Preparations

As lignins are insoluble in their native state, the isolation of representative preparations for study presents an important problem in lignin chemistry. For certain purposes, of course, it is not necessary to isolate lignin in pure state because the chemical differences between lignin and carbohydrates often make it possible to use an extractive-free plant material for experimentation. However, when it is necessary to perform a separation of the plant components in order to obtain a carbohydrate-free lignin, difficulties often arise from the chemical changes that may occur in lignin during the process.

Originally cellulose and hemicelluloses were extracted from lignified tissue (with subsequent hydrolysis) by treatment with strong sulfuric acid (111) (*Klason lignin*), or with fuming hydrochloric acid (191) (*Willstätter lignin*). When diluted with water, a brown insoluble substance known as acid lignin remains insoluble. This method is also used for the quantitative determination of lignin (92d) (72% sulfuric acid generally is used), although several uncertainties make the exactness of the method somewhat questionable (143,183).

The determined values are, nevertheless, in good accordance with those calculated on the basis of the holocellulose contents (185). Table I summarizes a number of lignin determinations by the sulfuric acid method on various woods.

TABLE I

Lignin Contents of Various Woods by the Sulfuric Acid Method (32d)

Wood type	Lignin (%)	MeO in lignin
Norway spruce	26.1	15 7
Sitka spruce	27.8	14.9
White spruce	26.5	16.7
Pitch pine	29.2	14.6
Balsam fir	30.1	—
Eastern hemlock	31.5	—
African pencil-cedar	37.7	13.1
Birch	21.0	—
Aspen	17.6	22.9
Maple	23.2	20.2
Beech	23.5	20.4
Ash	24.8	19.9
English oak	22.4	17.4

The drastic conditions used in the preparation of acid lignins cause structural changes in lignin; for instance, the reactivity in sulfonation is decreased (93). Consequently, several efforts have been made to minimize the chemical changes in the preparation of acid lignins. By modifying the original Willstätter procedure, Hägglund and Johnson (94) were able to prepare a hydrochloric acid lignin which could be totally dissolved by sulfonation. Extensive work by Freudenberg (80) and his school has been done on cuproxam lignin. This preparation is isolated by treating extracted sawdust alternately with boiling dilute acid and ammoniacal copper oxide solution, by which means

the cellulose is gradually removed. Differences in the chemical behavior of wood and cuproxam lignins indicate that even this procedure
has not been without effect on the sensitive units in lignin (72).

Only a very small portion of lignin (2 to 3% of softwood and 4 to
7% of hardwood lignin) can be extracted directly by organic solvents.
The isolation of the soluble lignin has been described by Brauns (25).
Ground plant material is exhaustively extracted with alcohol and the
total extracts are precipitated by ether. Ether dissolves the nonlignin
components leaving lignin undissolved in the form of a light cream-
colored powder, generally referred to as "Brauns native lignin"
(BNL).

In most important aspects, BNL is similar to the rest of protolignin.
It shows the same color reactions and similar composition as the
insoluble protolignin; many of the known reactions of the latter, such
as sulfonation, alcoholysis, phenolysis, and reaction with thioglycolic
acid can be carried out on BNL preparations to yield products with
similar compositions and characteristics.

Although BNL is an excellent material for many lignin studies, it
would be incorrect to regard it as identical with the rest of protolignin.
BNL certainly has a lower molecular weight, and has been shown to
contain more phenolic hydroxyl groups (15) than the insoluble
protolignin.

More protolignin can be transformed to a soluble form if wood meal
is first subjected to the action of certain wood-rotting fungi (165).
Such "enzymatically liberated" lignins can represent as much as 21%
of the total lignin. Marked similarity exists between the enzymatically liberated and the corresponding Brauns native lignins, both in
analytical composition and in optical behavior (ultraviolet and infrared spectra).

Through the use of an elaborate grinding procedure, Björkman (22)
has been able to render about 50% of the protolignin in spruce wood
soluble in aqueous dioxane. Analytical data on *Björkman lignin*
demonstrate that the original lignin structure has been more efficiently preserved than in other lignin preparations. Specific conditions are necessary to produce the desired solubility (e.g., the use of a
vibrational ball mill with the wood meal immersed in a nonswelling
medium, such as toluene, during the grinding). It would not appear
impossible, therefore, that some chemical linkages are broken during
the process, although the extent of breakage may be quite small. It
was shown recently that carbon-to-carbon linkages in rubber are in

part split by extensive grinding, with the formation of free radicals (189).

Periodate lignin, isolated by Purves and co-workers (158) by degradation of wood carbohydrates with potassium periodate, probably represents largely unchanged lignin, although some degradation of aromatic nuclei containing free phenolic groups may occur (147). *Dioxane-hydrochloric acid lignin* (62,179) can be extracted in approximately 15% yield of the total lignin with aqueous dioxane containing 2.5% hydrochloric acid. Dioxane does not enter in chemical combination with lignin, but the preparation contains about 1.5 to 2% of chlorine.

Finally, an artificial lignin called *Dehydrogenation polymerizate* (DHP), prepared by Freudenberg (70), should be mentioned. This polymeric substance is formed by enzymatic dehydrogenation of coniferyl alcohol. Its characteristics and significance to lignin synthesis *in vivo* will be discussed in Section V.

II. Structure of Lignin

Lignin probably represents one of the least attractive substances for structural evaluation by the methods of classical organic chemistry. It is generally insoluble in common organic solvents and also undergoes chemical changes under relatively mild conditions. Degradation to simple identifiable compounds always remains incomplete, and often these products are artifacts formed during the degradation, rather than representative of the original structures in lignin. This peculiar behavior explains why progress in the field has remained relatively slow in proportion to the work done.

The absence of rigorous data has led to the proposal of a number of speculative structures for lignin. In testing the validity of various assertions, research on low molecular weight model compounds has often played an important role.

Application of model compounds to the structural problems of lignin is laborious and has its limitations. Clearly, a pronounced dissimilarity in chemical behavior between a model and lignin convincingly invalidates the presence of structures similar to the model in the latter, at least as major components. However, if lignin and a model or a group of models react similarly when subjected to the same conditions, this gives an indication, but never a rigorous proof, that the same structures are operative in both cases. In view of this ambiguity, it is not surprising that differing opinions have existed concerning the significance of model compound research. To many structural problems in lignin chemistry, however, comparative studies between lignin and lignin models appear to represent the only accessible pathway of approach.

A. THE CONCEPT OF LIGNIN AS A PHENYLPROPANE POLYMER

The aromatic nature of lignin *in situ* was convincingly demonstrated by Lange (121) who showed that spruce wood exhibits a characteristic ultraviolet absorption spectrum, similar to those of certain solid guaiacylpropane model compounds. Purves and co-workers (158) calculated the elemental composition of pine and spruce lignins by difference, from the analytical values on extracted wood material and on holocellulose, respectively. The calculated composition (C = 67.5%, H = 6%) is in accordance with an aromatic substance.

The possibility of spruce lignin being composed of phenylpropane units was already recognized by early investigators, namely, Klason (110) and Tiemann and Haarmann (181). Later, Freudenberg (65) demonstrated that the elemental composition of spruce lignin conforms closely to that of a guaiacylpropane polymer. The concept has found valuable support in that a number of phenylpropane derivatives have been isolated from the degradation products of not only spruce, but also of other plant lignins.

Phenylpropane unit

Phillips (152a) was the first to isolate a phenylpropane derivative, dihydroeugenol, (VII), from the degradation products of lignin. This compound was obtained by subjecting alkali corncob lignin to destructive distillation (152a) under reduced pressure. More recently, a large number of various phenylpropane derivatives have been isolated by using improved degradation techniques (Fig. 1).

By high pressure hydrogenation of aspen methanol lignin and by using copper chromite as a catalyst, Harris, D'Ianni, and Adkins (99) were able to isolate the propylcyclohexane derivatives (I), (II), and

(III). The same procedure was later extended by Hibbert and co-workers (85) to the investigation of maple and spruce woods and of maple ethanol lignin. The same products were isolated. When Raney nickel is used as catalyst, the hydrogenation of lignin can be carried out so that the aromatic nuclei remain intact. By applying this technique, Hibbert and co-workers (28) isolated compounds (IV), (V), and (VI) from hydrogenated maple lignin. Shorygina (171) treated spruce wood flour with sodium in liquid ammonia and isolated dihydroeugenol (VII) and 1-guaiacylpropanol-2 (VIII) in good yields

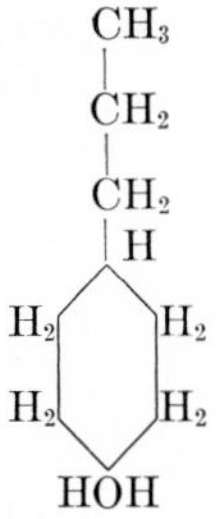

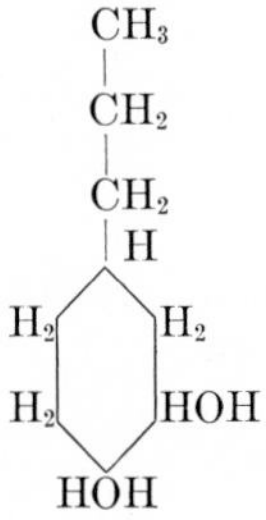

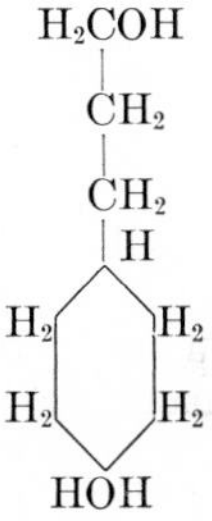

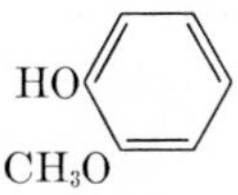

Guaiacyl

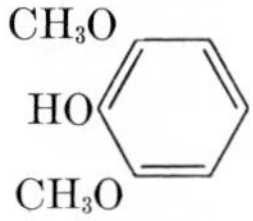

Syringyl

Guaiacyl·CH₂·CH₂·CH₂OH
(IV)

Syringyl·CH₂·CH₂·CH₂OH
(V)

Syringyl·CH₂·CH₂·CH₃
(VI)

Guaiacyl·CH₂·CH₂·CH₃
(VII)

Guaiacyl·CH₂·CHOH·CH₃
(VIII)

Guaiacyl·CO·CH(OC₂H₅)·CH₃
(IX)

Guaiacyl·CH(OC₂H₅)·CO·CH₃
(X)

Guaiacyl·CO·CO·CH₃
(XI)

Guaiacyl·CH₂·CO·CH₃
(XII)

Syringyl·CO·CH(OC₂H₅)·CH₃
(XIII)

Syringyl·CO·CO·CH₃
(XIV)

Syringyl·CH₂·CO·CH₃
(XV)

Fig. 1. Isolated phenylpropane degradation products from lignin.

from the reaction products. Hibbert and co-workers (190) were able to isolate guaiacyl derivatives (IX), (X), (XI), and (XII) from the ethanolysis products of spruce lignin; maple lignin yielded the corresponding syringyl compounds (XIII), (XIV), and (XV) (135) in addition to the guaiacyl derivatives mentioned.

TABLE II

Yields of Phenylpropane Derivatives Isolated from Lignin

Lignin	Method	Phenylpropane derivatives isolated	Estimated yield of phenylpropane derivatives, per cent lignin
Aspen methanol lignin	Hydrogenation	(I), (II), (III)	44
Maple wood	Hydrogenation		25.3
Maple ethanol lignin	Hydrogenation		13.3
Maple wood	Hydrogenation	(IV), (V), (VI)	10 to 15
Spruce cuproxam lignin	Treatment with Na in liquid NH₃	(VII), (VIII)	28
Spruce wood	Ethanolysis	(IX), (X), (XI), (XII)	10
Maple wood	Ethanolysis	(IX) to (XV)	20

Table II gives the yields of isolated phenylpropane derivatives. Hydrogenation and treatment with sodium in liquid ammonia obviously give the highest yields. Still the amounts of identified products generally correspond to less than one-half of the original lignin. Lignin is not degraded completely to monomers, mainly because part of the phenylpropane units are joined by carbon-to-carbon linkages, in a manner to be described later.

On this basis, gymnosperm lignins generally are considered to represent polymers containing exclusively guaiacylpropane units. This view may not be rigorously correct, but should be regarded as a useful approximation that conforms relatively well to the methoxyl contents of various gymnosperm lignin preparations.

Hardwood (angiosperm) lignins contain both guaiacyl- and syringylpropane units. How these units combine to form the lignin molecules poses an interesting question of lignin chemistry. First, hardwood lignin could be a random copolymer of guaiacyl- and syringylpropane monomers. In the extreme opposite case, the monomers could exist in separate molecules forming a mixture of "guaiacyl lignin" and "syringyl lignin." Although the question must be considered unsettled as yet, evidence favoring the latter hypothesis has been presented.

As a minor component, many plant lignins may contain p-hydroxyphenylpropane units. Goldschmid (87) has shown that western hemlock wood, as well as the BNL preparation from the same wood, yield, after hydrolysis, small amounts of p-coumaraldehyde (XVI), besides other identified products.

HO⟨ ⟩—C—C—C	HO⟨ ⟩CH=CHCHO	HO⟨ ⟩CHO
p-Hydroxyphenyl- propane unit	(XVI)	(XVII)

Further support for the existence of p-hydroxyphenylpropane units is afforded by the isolation of small amounts (0.25%) of p-hydroxybenzaldehyde (XVII) (124) from the nitrobenzene oxidation products of spruce wood lignin.

In this connection, certain studies on grass lignins are of interest. These lignins yield substantial amounts of p-hydroxybenzaldehyde on alkaline hydrolysis (40). However, with the exception of p-hydroxycinnamic acid (173) which exists in bagasse lignin in ester-like combination, no p-hydroxyphenylpropane derivatives have been isolated so far. Stone and co-workers (178), who investigated wheat lignin, are of the opinion that p-hydroxybenzaldehyde actually may not be derived from a lignin component. From their studies on living wheat plants containing radioactively labeled lignin, they concluded that components yielding p-hydroxybenzaldehyde in nitrobenzene oxidation participate in plant metabolism, whereas the progenitors of vanillin and syringaldehyde apparently do not (177). This would indicate that lignin, being an irreversible end product of metabolism, is not the source of p-hydroxybenzaldehyde. At least a part of the latter compound could be formed from tyrosine units in wheat protein that were shown to be converted to p-hydroxybenzaldehyde on nitrobenzene oxidation.

Certain aromatic carboxylic acids, present in a number of plant lignins, form a class of their own among the lignin components. By carrying out an alkaline hydrolysis on aspen BNL, Smith (174) was able to isolate p-hydroxybenzoic acid (XVIII) in a yield corresponding to 10% of the preparation. The rate of the hydrolysis process indicated that the acid is linked as an ester to the aliphatic hydroxyl groups of the lignin. Similar ester linkages are present in bagasse BNL which yields 11% of p-hydroxycinnamic acid after alkaline hydrolysis (173). p-Hydroxycinnamic acid is absent in wheat BNL which contains p-hydroxybenzoic, vanillic (XIX), syringic (XX), and ferulic (XXI) acids, present as minor constituents in the bagasse BNL. Only traces of such acids were isolated from Douglas-fir BNL, indicating that the contribution of ester groups to the composition of softwood lignins is of minor significance.

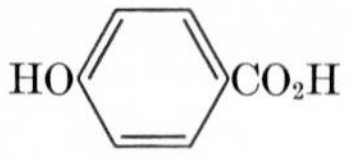

HO⟨   ⟩CO₂H

(XVIII)

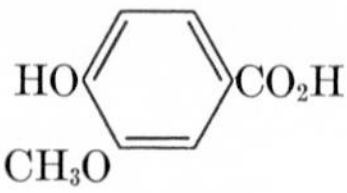

HO⟨   ⟩CO₂H
CH₃O

(XIX)

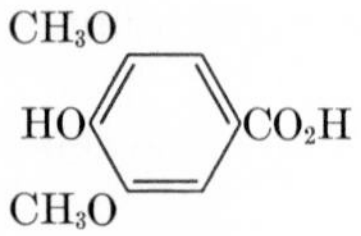

CH₃O
HO⟨   ⟩CO₂H
CH₃O

(XX)

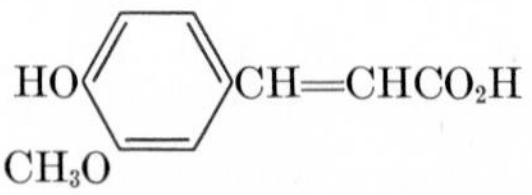

HO⟨   ⟩CH=CHCO₂H
CH₃O

(XXI)

It is interesting to note that p-hydroxybenzoic, vanillic, and syringic acids all contain a C_6C skeleton and, consequently, form an exception to the rule characterizing all lignins as phenylpropane (C_6C_3) polymers. It may be pointed out, however, that the mode of combination of these acids with the lignin molecule is exceptional and, for this reason, they need not be considered lignin monomers in the proper sense. With this provision, the concept of lignins as phenyl-propane polymers appears to be valid without exception.

B. THE MODE OF COMBINATION OF MONOMERIC UNITS IN LIGNIN

In the lignin macromolecule, the monomeric phenylpropane units are linked together both by ether and by carbon-to-carbon linkages. The latter linkages are highly resistant towards chemical degradation and constitute the main factor inhibiting the conversion of lignins to monomeric units in such treatments as hydrogenation, ethanolysis, etc.

Figures 2 and 3 summarize the current views about the nature of intermonomeric linkages in lignin. It should be emphasized that it

Ether Linkages

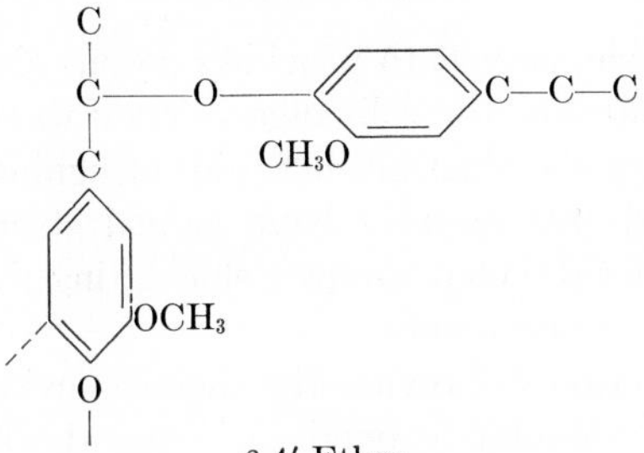

β-4′ Ether

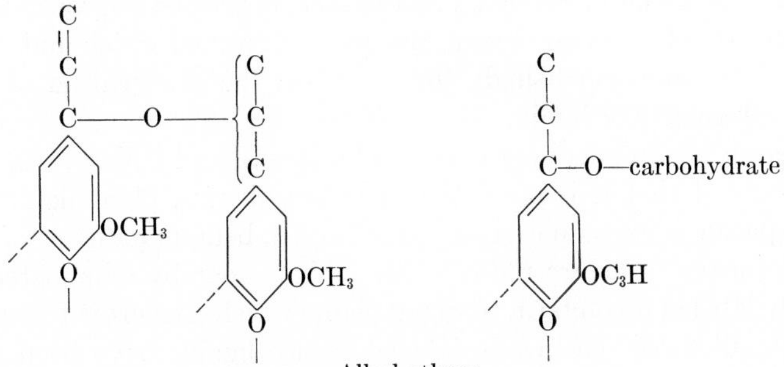

α-Alkyl ethers

Carbon-to-Carbon Linkages

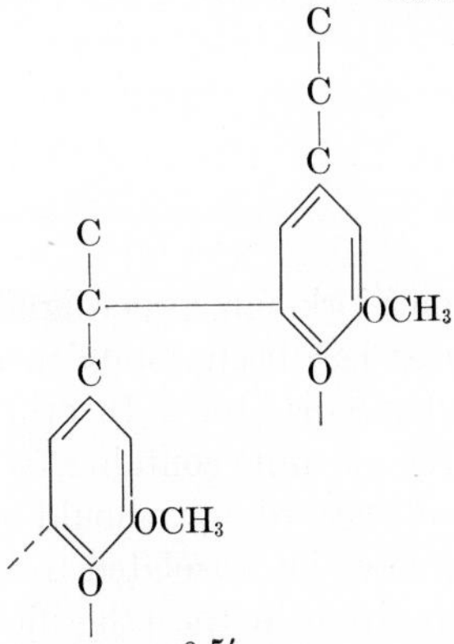

β-5′

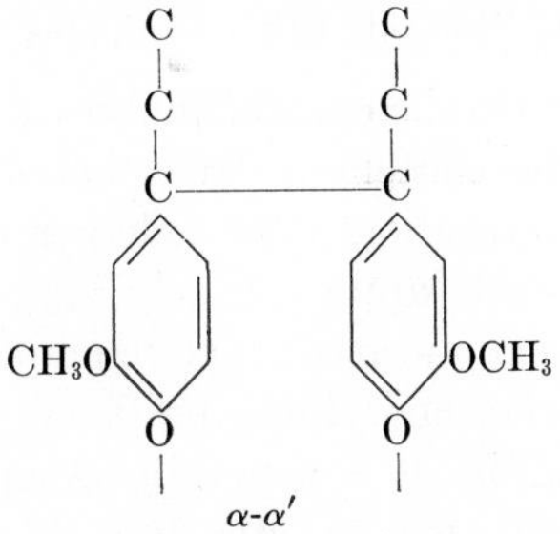

α-α′

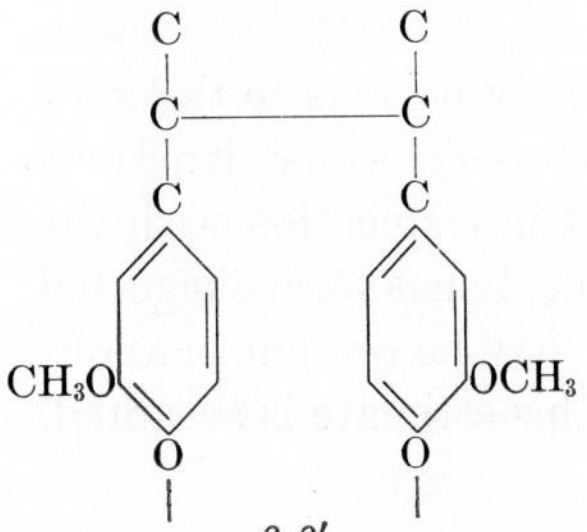

β-β′

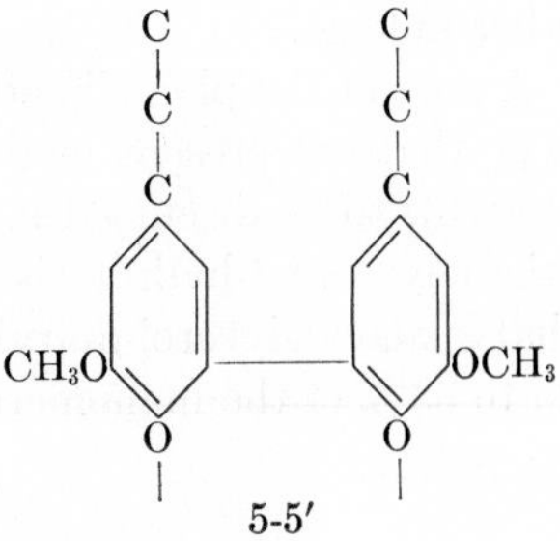

5-5′

Fig 2. Postulated intermonomeric linkages in lignin.

has not been possible, as yet, to provide rigorous chemical proof for the existence of many of these linkages. They were originally proposed to account for the chemical behavior of lignins. These largely speculative propositions recently have gained strong experimental support from studies directed towards elucidating the mechanism of lignin formation in living plants.

The following section will review the chemical evidence supporting the presented intermonomeric bonds, whereas the biochemical evidence will be given in Section V. However, it may be appropriate at this point to refer to one elegant biochemical method which undoubtedly will become increasingly important in the clarification of the structural aspects of lignin.

Research by Freudenberg (64) and by Kratzl and Billek (115) has demonstrated that it is possible to prepare, *in vivo*, plant lignins in which specific side-chain carbon atoms (alpha, beta, or gamma) of the phenylpropane units are radioactive. This is done by administering properly labeled D-coniferin to living plants which convert it to lignin. To date, all three specifically labeled spruce lignins have been prepared. Studies on these radioactive lignins have been invaluable, among other applications, in establishing the nature of carbon-to-carbon linkages in lignin.

1. Ether Linkages

a. Phenolic Ether Linkages

On the basis of analytical determinations on Björkman spruce lignin the content of free phenolic hydroxyl groups has been established to be about 0.30 mole per mole of methoxyl groups (100). In other words, approximately 30% of the guaiacylpropane units contain a free phenolic group; the remaining 70% of the units accordingly should be etherified. Since no diaryl ether derivatives have been isolated from lignin, it is generally assumed that the 4-position in the etherified units is connected to a side-chain carbon of another monomer by an ether linkage.

A part of the phenolic ether linkages probably belongs to the β-4'-type that are present in the guaiacylglycerol-β-aryl ether structures (Fig. 3), to be discussed later in this chapter in connection with the ethanolysis and hydrolysis reactions of lignin. It has been suggested that guaiacylglycerol-β-aryl ether structures may be present in about 25 to 33% of the monomeric units (11). If this estimate is accepted, the β-4' ether linkages may account for up to one-half of the phenolic ether linkages.

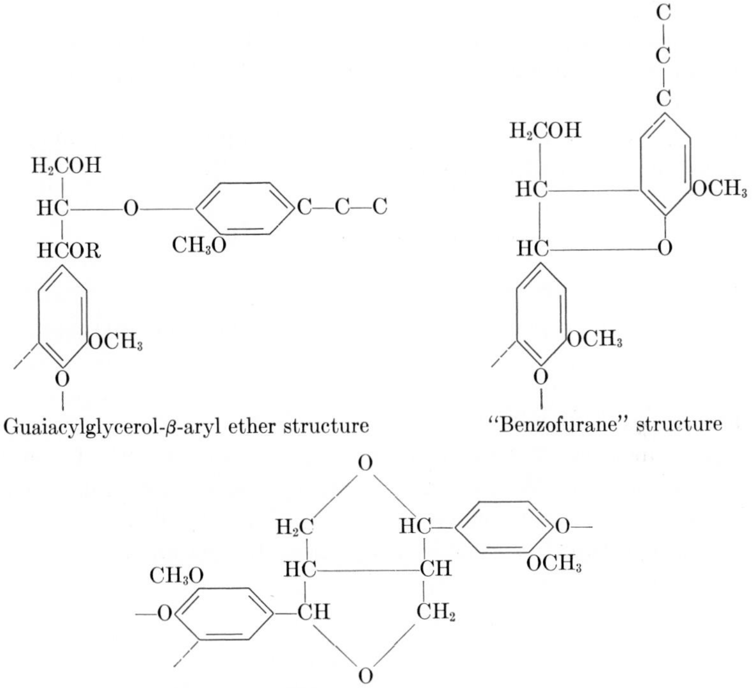

Guaiacylglycerol-β-aryl ether structure   "Benzofurane" structure

Pinoresinol structure

Fig. 3. Special postulated structures in lignin.

Another part of the phenolic ether linkages may belong to the α-4'-type, such as exemplified by the multi-bound benzofurane structure in Fig. 3.

b. Dialkyl Ether Linkages

In addition to phenolic ether linkages, the phenylpropane units in lignin also are connected by ether bonds between the side chains of two monomeric units. Two such bonds, both of the α-γ'-type, exist in the multilinked pinoresinol structure (Fig. 3) whose presence in the lignin structure is postulated mainly on the basis of biogenetic evidence.

The alpha-alkyl ether linkage given in Fig. 2 represents another structure where the ether group alone connects two units ("benzyl-alkyl ether bond"). These structures were originally proposed by Lindgren (128) to account for the hydrolytic solvation of the so-called "solid lignosulfonic acid."

It has been proposed by Freudenberg (64) that the bonds linking lignin to the carbohydrates might be of the alpha-alkyl ether type.

The total amount of dialkyl ether linkages in softwood lignin is not exactly known. Estimations based on lignin preparations amount to about 0.35 per methoxyl, on a molar basis (22).

2. Carbon-to-Carbon Linkages

a. Substituted and Unsubstituted Units

The phenylpropane units containing an intermonomeric carbon-to-carbon linkage at the aromatic nucleus usually are called "substituted" units to differentiate them from the unsubstituted ones which are devoid of such linkages.

Two methods are available for the conversion of both the unsubstituted and substituted units to identifiable low-molecular weight compounds. The principles of these methods are illustrated in the following scheme for the case of an unsubstituted unit:

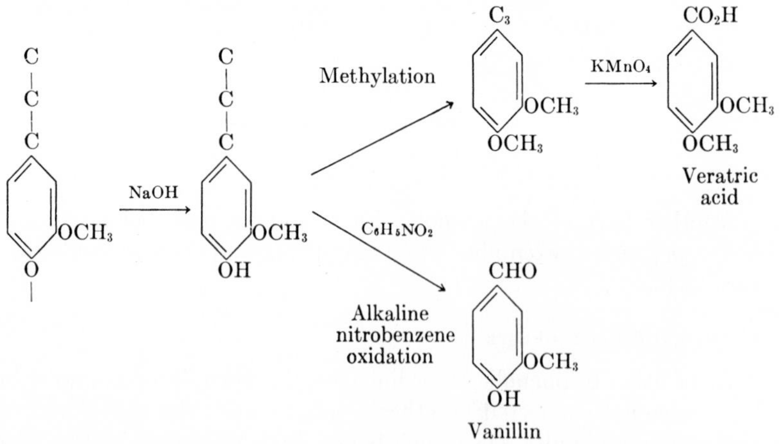

$$
\begin{array}{c}
\text{C} \\ | \\ \text{C} \\ | \\ \text{C} \\ \text{(ring)} \quad \text{OCH}_3 \\ \text{O} \\ |
\end{array}
\xrightarrow{\text{NaOH}}
\begin{array}{c}
\text{C} \\ | \\ \text{C} \\ | \\ \text{C} \\ \text{(ring)} \quad \text{OCH}_3 \\ \text{OH}
\end{array}
$$

Methylation → C$_3$ (ring) OCH$_3$, OCH$_3$ $\xrightarrow{\text{KMnO}_4}$ CO$_2$H (ring) OCH$_3$, OCH$_3$ — Veratric acid

C$_6$H$_5$NO$_2$ ↘ Alkaline nitrobenzene oxidation — CHO (ring) OCH$_3$, OH — Vanillin

The permanganate method was developed by Freudenberg (69) and consists of the hydrolysis of the phenolic ether linkages by alkali at high temperature, followed by a methylation step to protect the phenolic groups thus liberated and by a permanganate oxidation that degrades the side-chains to carboxylic groups (see Fig. 4).

Permanganate oxidation method

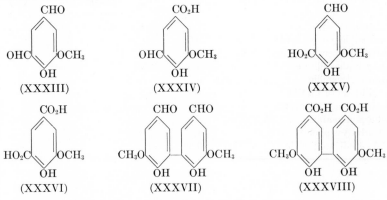

CO$_2$H / OCH$_3$ / OCH$_3$ (XXII)

COCO$_2$H / OCH$_3$ / OCH$_3$ (XXIII)

CO$_2$H / CH$_3$O OCH$_3$ / OCH$_3$ (XXIV)

Nitrobenzene oxidation

CHO / OCH$_3$ / OH (XXV)

CO$_2$H / OCH$_3$ / OH (XXVI)

COCO$_2$H / OCH$_3$ / OH (XXVII)

CHO / CH$_3$O OCH$_3$ / OH (XXVIII)

CO$_2$H / CH$_3$O OCH$_3$ / OH (XXIX)

CHO / OH (XXX)

From Substituted Units

Permanganate oxidation method

CO$_2$H / HO$_2$C OCH$_3$ / OCH$_3$ (XXXI)

CO$_2$H CO$_2$H / CH$_3$O OCH$_3$ / OCH$_3$ OCH$_3$ (XXXII)

Nitrobenzene oxidation

CHO / OHC OCH$_3$ / OH (XXXIII)

CO$_2$H / OHC OCH$_3$ / OH (XXXIV)

CHO / HO$_2$C OCH$_3$ / OH (XXXV)

CO$_2$H / HO$_2$C OCH$_3$ / OH (XXXVI)

CHO CHO / CH$_3$O OCH$_3$ / OH OH (XXXVII)

CO$_2$H CO$_2$H / CH$_3$O OCH$_3$ / OH OH (XXXVIII)

Fig. 4. Oxidation of unsubstituted and substituted phenylpropane units.

The second method, also developed by Freudenberg (73), utilizes a milder oxidant, nitrobenzene, for the degradation of the side chains mainly to aldehydic, and partially to carboxylic, groups. The protection of the free phenol groups is, in this case, unnecessary, and consequently the hydrolysis and oxidation can be carried out in one operation. Higher yields of identified products generally are obtained by the nitrobenzene method, which has therefore been widely used for both structural and taxonomic studies.

In the nitrobenzene oxidation of softwood lignins, 31.9 to 32.3% of the phenylpropane units are isolated in the form of identified compounds (124). Of these, vanillin (XXV) is obtained in highest yields, corresponding to 25 to 28% of Klason lignin (Table IV). Small

TABLE III

Permanganate Oxidation Products of Lignin

Product isolated, per cent lignin	Spruce wood[a] (69)	Spruce wood (156)	Maple wood (74)
Veratric acid (XXII)	7.8	4.9	5.0
Isohemipinic acid (XXXI)	3.4	0.9	1.5
Trimethoxybenzoic acid (XXIV)			7.5

[a] (1) Methylation with diazomethane; (2) treatment with 70% KOH at 170°C; (3) methylation; (4) permanganate oxidation.

TABLE IV

Nitrobenzene Oxidation Products of Lignin

Product isolated, per cent lignin	Spruce wood (124)	Spruce wood (152)	Spruce BNL (152)	Maple (39)	Corn stalks (40)
Vanillin (XXV)	27.5	25.8	25.1	10.5	5.3
Syringaldehyde (XXVIII)	0.06	—	—	34.3	3.2
p-Hydroxybenzaldehyde (XXX)	0.25	—	—	—	1.8
Dehydrodivanillin (XXXVII)	0.80	2.2	2.2	—	—
5-Formyl vanillin (XXXIII)	0.23	—	—	—	—
Vanillic acid (XXVI)	4.8	1.3	1.9	—	—
Syringic acid (XXIX)	(0.02)	—	—	—	—
5-Formyl vanillic acid (XXXIV)	(0.1)	—	—	—	—
5-Carboxyvanillin (XXXV)	1.2	0.6	—	—	—
Dehydrodivanillic acid (XXXVIII)	0.03	—	—	—	—

amounts of *p*-hydroxybenzaldehyde (XXX) and syringaldehyde (XXVIII) among the reaction products may indicate the presence of *p*-hydroxyphenylpropane and syringylpropane units as minor constituents in spruce lignin (Table III) (124). Dicotyledons, including hardwoods, give higher total yields of aldehydes (31 to 51% of the Klason lignin) and the ratio of vanillin to syringaldehyde is usually 1:3 (39). *p*-Hydroxybenzaldehyde has not been isolated (126). The nitrobenzene oxidation products of monocotyledons (e.g. grasses, bamboo, etc.) contain, in addition to vanillin and syringaldehyde (usually isolated in 1:1 molar ratio), substantial amounts of *p*-hydroxybenzaldehyde (40).

By comparing the yields of nitrobenzene oxidation products from lignins to the yields obtained in the oxidation of model compounds, attempts have been made to estimate the amount of unsubstituted guaiacylpropane units in softwood lignins. Since the vanillin yields from model compounds are variable, such estimates can only be approximate. It has been proposed that roughly 50% (123) or possibly more (152), of the monomeric units belong to the unsubstituted type.

The amount of unsubstituted units in hardwood lignins is higher, mainly because the syringylpropane units, which together with the guaiacylpropane units constitute the lignin, appear to exist exclusively in the unsubstituted form. For this reason, hardwood lignins generally give relatively high yields of aldehydes in nitrobenzene oxidation. It should be observed, however, that the vanillin to syringaldehyde ratio (1:3) differs from the ratio of guaiacyl- and syringylpropane units in lignin. On the basis of the methoxyl contents of hardwood lignin preparations (165), these units appear to be present in approximately equal amounts.

The substituted units, which may total up to 50% in softwood lignins, are of two different types. In the majority of substituted units, the 5-position is linked to a side-chain carbon atom of another unit. These units are partially converted to isohemipinic acid (XXXI) by the permanganate oxidation method (Table III) (69) and yield a number of 5-substituted degradation products in the nitrobenzene oxidation (Fig. 4). Recent work by Freudenberg (64,67) on radioactive spruce lignin has proven beyond doubt that the 5-position in these units is connected predominantly with the beta-carbon of another unit. He showed that a spruce lignin and a DHP preparation, both of which were specifically labeled in the beta-position, yielded radioactive isohemipinic acid. The observed radioactivity undoubtedly is due to the 5-carboxyl group in the isolated isohemipinic acid. The isohemipinic acid from a gamma-labeled DHP preparation was inactive, demonstrating the absence of γ-5′ linkages.

In a part of the substituted units a bond probably exists between the 5-positions of two units. Dehydrodiveratric acid (XXXII) and dehydrodivanillin (XXXVII) (Fig. 4) represent degradation products of such structures. Originally regarded to be artifacts formed in the degradation process, these compounds now are believed to originate from 5-5′ bonded structures in lignin (152).

The free phenolic hydroxyl groups, present in approximately 30% of the monomeric units, are distributed between the unsubstituted and substituted units. This was shown by Richtzenhain (156), who methylated spruce wood meal with diazomethane to convert the phenolic hydroxyl groups to methoxyl groups and subsequently oxidized the product with permanganate. Veratric and isohemipinic acids, both derived from originally unetherified units, were isolated in yields corresponding to 4.9 and 0.9%, respectively. However, no traces of dehydrodiveratric acid were found.

b. β-β′ Carbon-to-Carbon Linkages

The naturally occurring lignans, such as pinoresinol, conidendrin, matairesinol, etc., are guaiacyl- or syringylpropane dimers in which the two units are connected by a β-β′ linkage. For this reason, similar structures in lignin are often called "lignan structures."

The only direct chemical evidence for the presence of β-β′ linkages has been afforded by Russian workers (172). They have claimed the isolation of a hydrogenated lignan, 2,3-bis(hexahydrobenzyl)butane, from the products obtained by treating cuproxam lignin with sodium and liquid ammonia.

Lignin often undergoes secondary condensation reactions during the isolation process, especially if acidic conditions are used. As a consequence, anomalous products are sometimes isolated when lignin preparations are degraded oxidatively. As an example, Richtzenhain (156) subjected acid lignins and lignosulfonic acid to methylation and permanganate oxidation, and was able to isolate up to 1.3% of m-hemipinic acid (XXXIX), in addition to the veratric and isohemipinic acids normally obtained. According to Richtzenhain, the formation of m-hemipinic acid may be connected with lignan structures in lignin that could rearrange or condense to isolignan structures under acidic conditions.

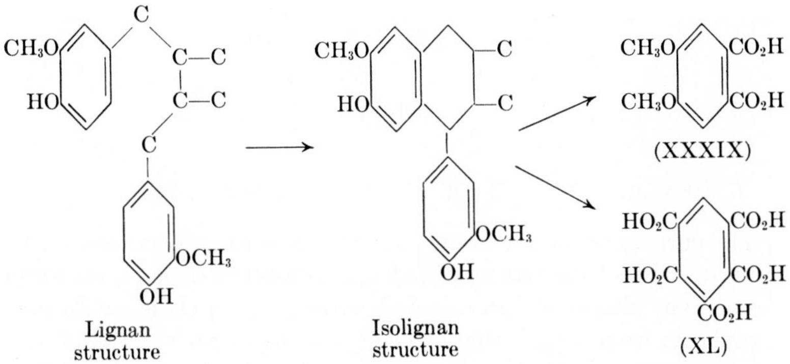

Lignan structure → Isolignan structure →

(XXXIX)

(XL)

Another anomalous degradation product, benzene pentacarboxylic acid (XL), is obtained when isolated lignins are directly oxidized with permanganate (154). The yields from various lignin preparations range from 0.6 to 2.0%, whereas only trace amounts (0.14%) of this acid are obtained from spruce protolignin. The benzene pentacarboxylic acid may very well be an oxidation product of the secondarily formed ring in an isolignan structure.

c. α-α' Carbon-to-Carbon Linkages

The presence of α-α' linkages in lignin was first proposed by Pearl (145) to account for the isolation of the following dimeric products from the cupric oxide oxidation of lignin:

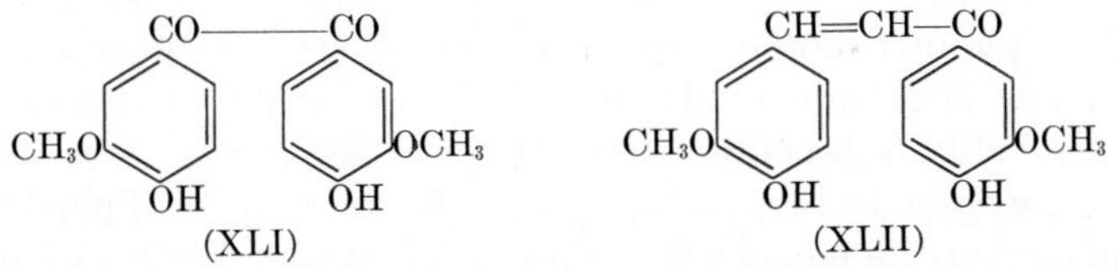

(XLI)　　　　　　　　　(XLII)

Of these, XLI was regarded to be a direct oxidation product of α-α'-linked structure. In structure XLII, the α-β'-linkage was considered to be an artifact, formed in the rearrangement of an originally α-α'-linked structure. These views were supported by model compound experiments.

Vanillil (XLIII), a stilbene derivative, has been isolated both from

the alkaline hydrolysis of spruce lignosulfonic acids (157) and from
the alkaline oxidation products of red pine sawdust (180).

$$HO\langle\rangle CH{=}CH\langle\rangle OH$$
$$CH_3O \qquad\qquad OCH_3$$

(XLIII)

C. GENERAL ASPECTS OF LIGNIN AS A MACROMOLECULE

The purpose of the preceding discussion was to present some of the
current views of the nature of linkages between monomeric units in
lignin. The picture of lignin, as it is unveiled from these still largely
speculative assertions, is that of a complex polymer whose complexity
is owing not to the multitude of monomeric units, but to the variety
of ways in which these units can be linked. This applies, of course,
mainly to spruce and other softwood lignins with which the majority
of experimental data are concerned. The information on hardwood
and grass lignins is still too scanty to justify a discussion, even on
speculative grounds.

The question whether we should expect lignin to be a regularly
built polymer, or whether the structural elements might be combined
in a random fashion, has considerable theoretical interest.

The idea of a well-defined "lignin unit," composed of four guaiacylpropane monomers, was advanced by Brauns (25) and he was also
able to supply certain analytical data to support his view. Later
analyses on different structural elements [such as coniferyl aldehyde
groups (4)] have not been easily compatible with this concept.

Although any rigorous experimental evidence is lacking, a certain
amount of structural randomness in lignin should be considered a
fair possibility, especially if the concept of lignin biogenesis, as proposed by Freudenberg (63), is considered correct. Freudenberg
assumes that the enzymatic action in this process is limited to the
formation of coniferyl alcohol radicals; the subsequent combination
of these radicals to form lignin can scarcely be expected to lead to any
uniform structures, nor to a uniform molecular weight.

The majority of natural, as well as synthetic, polymers is built up
according to the "head-to-tail" principle. The evidence presented in
the previous sections points out that this is not the case with lignin.
If we arbitrarily designate the side chain of a phenylpropane unit as

the "head" of the molecule and the aromatic nucleus as the "tail," the following three categories of linkages between monomeric units are more or less likely to be present in spruce lignin:

1. "Head-to-tail" linkages: (*a*) alkyl-aryl ether linkages between C_4 and a side-chain carbon in another unit; (*b*) carbon-to-carbon linkages between C_5 and a side-chain carbon, probably C_β.

2. "Head-to-head" linkages: (*a*) linkages between β carbon atoms of two monomeric units; (*b*) dialkyl-ether linkages between C_α and a side-chain carbon in another monomer; (*c*) $\alpha\text{-}\alpha'$ carbon linkages (Pearl).

3. "Tail-to-tail" linkages: 5-5' carbon bonds.

Let us first consider such fragments of the lignin molecule that are built up entirely according to the head-to-tail principle. These fragments may exist as chain-like aggregates, or if the heads and/or tails act bifunctionally, also branches might be present. To create a preliminary picture of lignin as a macromolecule, we can presently ignore the latter possibility, keeping in mind that such simplification may not be entirely justified. According to this assumption, fragments connected by head-to-tail linkages would act as "primary chains" of a cross-linked lignin molecule.

The average length of the primary chains can be generally estimated from the amount of end groups. The coniferyl aldehyde groups are probably end groups, but likely to be present only in a fraction of primary chains. It seems reasonable, however, that an unsubstituted guaiacyl unit with a free phenolic hydroxyl group may exist as an end group in every primary chain.

Unsubstituted
guaiacyl unit

A minimum for the free guaiacyl units can be estimated from the yields of veratric acid from diazomethane methylated wood. Richtzenhain's results correspond to about 0.055 free guaiacyl unit per methoxyl (156). From this we may conclude that the average degree of polymerization of primary chains is certainly less than 18.

Gustafsson and Andersen (91) have developed a method for the estimation of unsubstituted guaiacyl units containing a free phenolic group. Such groups react with nitric acid to give dinitro guaiacol.

$$\text{C}_3\text{-[guaiacol: OCH}_3\text{, OH]} \quad \xrightarrow{\text{HNO}_3,\ \text{Et}_2\text{O}} \quad \text{NO}_2\text{-[O}_2\text{N, OCH}_3\text{, OH]}$$

Dinitro guaiacol

The latter compound can be determined quantitatively by paper chromatography. By comparing the yields from wood and model compounds, the authors estimate roughly one free guaiacyl group out of 15 phenylpropane units for spruce lignin; this result corresponds, of course, to an average degree of polymerization of 15 of the primary chains. In view of the estimated contents of phenolic hydroxyl groups ($\sim$0.30 per methoxyl), the figure 15 appears high, although it is not exactly known how the phenolic hydroxyl groups are distributed between end and chain (C_5-substituted) units.

The head-to-head, as well as the tail-to-tail, linkages act as bonds between the primary chains in the lignin molecule and may consequently be properly designated as cross-linkages. Whether a cross-linked polymer exists in the form of molecules of finite size or forms, partially or totally, an infinite network depends largely on the size of the primary chains as well as on the frequency of cross-linked units (61). As far as lignin *in situ* is concerned, our present knowledge of these two characteristics is much too scant to justify any conclusions. Still, as pointed out by Schuerch, the swelling and solubility characteristics of lignin in wood conform with the idea of an infinite network (168). When carbohydrates are removed from wood by periodate, which is probably a method least likely to cause condensation reactions, the lignin is still insoluble and exhibits limited swelling in good lignin solvents. Similarly, Hägglund and Johnson (94) demonstrated that spruce Willstätter lignin, isolated under mild conditions, can be sulfonated in neutral medium to a product which has the characteristics of a cross-linked polyacid and is water-insoluble despite the presence of highly hydrophilic sulfonic acid groups. All the experimental results mentioned are not inconsistent with the concept that a substantial portion of wood lignin exists in the form of a three-dimensionally cross-linked structure that becomes degraded to fragments of finite size by cleaving certain acid-sensitive cross links.

The relatively short primary chain length, indicated by the proportionately high amount of end groups, is in accordance with the low-viscosity values found for isolated lignins (134,176). The viscosity-concentration relationship of isolated ethanol lignins indicates extensive branching (high k'-values) (168); this is in conformity with the idea of ethanol lignins representing branched fragments cleaved from an originally cross-linked polymer.

Some of the molecular weights of lignin preparations recorded in the literature are given in Table V. It may be observed that although

TABLE V

Molecular Weights of Isolated Lignins

Lignin	Molecular weight
Lignosulfonic acids	8600–138,000 (w.a.[a]) (139); 3000–10,000 (w.a.) (148)
Thioglycolic acid lignin	8700–10,400 (w.a.) (89)
Björkman lignin	11,000 (w.a.) (22)
Spruce BNL	860 (n.a.[b]) (108)
Black spruce BNL	4200 (n.a.) (101a)
Ethanol lignins	420 (n.a.) (20); 900–1300 (n.a.) (162); 400 (n.a.) (134)
Acetic acid lignin	13,000–15,000 (w.a.) (89)
H₂S–lignin	1000 (n.a.) (48)

[a] w.a. is the weight-average molecular weight.
[b] n.a. is the number-average molecular weight.

most of the isolated lignins represent oligomeric substances of low molecular weight, the preparations that have suffered little degradation during isolation, such as Björkman lignin or lignosulfonic acids, possess high molecular weights.

The question of the existence of lignin-carbohydrate bonds is still largely problematic. The solubilization of the so-called "solid lignosulfonic acid" in acid hydrolysis was earlier frequently cited as convincing evidence for the presence of such links in wood. Later investigations have revealed, however, that the solubilization is due to the cleavage of internal bonds in lignin itself (94). This result, although substantially decreasing the significance of hypothetical lignin-carbohydrate bonds, does not prove their nonexistence. In fact, the isolation of soluble lignin-carbohydrate complexes has been frequently claimed (cf. 98) and it may be significant that their hydrolysis almost invariably yields hemicellulose sugars. At least linkages between lignin and cellulose seem highly improbable. Electron micrographs of wood show that lignin is mostly packed in between fibrils (103). A chemical bond between these constituents is, therefore, improbable even for topochemical reasons.

D. FUNCTIONAL GROUP ANALYSIS

The characterization of lignins and lignin derivatives by means of quantitative analytical determinations is often difficult because of poor solubility characteristics and a tendency to undergo secondary reactions.

Methoxyl is probably the most characteristic functional group in lignin. The content in softwood protolignin has been estimated to be 15 to 16% (Table I); hardwood lignins, because of the presence of syringyl propane units, show higher methoxyl contents (20.5 to 21.5%) (24a). It has been shown that methoxyl is split from lignin by hydriodic acid only at relatively high temperatures (66). This indicates that all the methoxyl groups in lignin are probably aromatic and not present in acetal or ester groups.

Although positive evidence for the presence of *carboxyl groups* in spruce lignin has not been obtained, the existence of minor amounts of these groups may still be possible. As was mentioned earlier (Section II-A), *ester groups* appear to be present in aspen and grass BNL preparations.

The total amount of *hydroxyl groups* (including both phenolic and aliphatic hydroxyl groups) has been determined by dimethyl sulfate methylation (25,184) and by acetylation (78). The drastic conditions of the former method (concentrated alkali at 60°C.) may cause secondary reactions, such as condensation or partial liberation of phenolic hydroxyl groups (146), and tertiary hydroxyl groups may remain unreacted (79). By acetylation, Freudenberg has estimated the total hydroxyl contents of spruce BNL and cuproxam lignin to be 1.40 and 1.47 per methoxyl, respectively (65).

An extensive amount of work has been done lately on the determination of free phenolic groups in lignin and lignin derivatives. The methods used include potentiometric (50,63) and conductometric titrations (146,161), techniques based on periodate oxidation (8), changes in ultraviolet absorption due to the ionization of free phenolic groups (17,86), reactions with diazomethane (25) or dinitrofluorobenzene, absorption of barium hydroxide by solid lignin, etc. Each of the methods has certain limitations and difficulties may arise from the presence of very weak (e.g., sterically hindered or hydrogen bonded) phenolic hydroxyl groups, the possible existence of carboxylic groups in some preparations, or incomplete solubility of the lignin, etc. Still, the results on Brauns native lignin from spruce by various methods are in good agreement, indicating the presence of 0.5 phenolic hydroxyl group per methoxyl. It is more difficult to estimate the phenolic hydroxyl content of spruce protolignin. For Björkman lignin, the values obtained are 0.3 (100), 0.33 (63), and 0.39 (50). Since sulfonation of lignin probably has little effect on the content of phenolic hydroxyl groups, the determined values for lignosulfonic acids should be close to that of original lignin. Individual determinations have given the following values for softwood lignosulfonic acids: 0.2 to 0.3 (17), 0.39 (50), and 0.32 to 0.43 (63) phenolic hydroxyl group per methoxyl. For organosolv lignins, whose preparation involves some liberation of phenolic hydroxyl groups, the following values have been obtained: 0.36 to 0.39 (spruce ethanol lignin) (162) and 0.41 (dioxane lignin) (63). Thus, although the present results do not allow a precise evaluation of free phenolic groups in spruce protolignin, a general range of 0.30 to 0.35 phenolic group per methoxyl is clearly indicated.

A substantial portion of the aliphatic hydroxyl groups are primary. This is indicated by the isolation of phenylpropane units with primary carbinol groups from hydrogenated lignin [cf. structure (IV), Fig. 1] and by the isolation of methoxyacetic acid from the oxidation products of lignin preparations that have been methylated with dimethyl sulfate (156). Freudenberg has attempted to determine the primary hydroxyls by using the iodine exchange of tosylated lignin as a measure; according to him, most of the aliphatic hydroxyl groups are primary (62).

Of the secondary alcohol groups, those present in position alpha to an unetherified guaiacyl unit have been determined quantitatively. These structures, commonly called "p-hydroxybenzyl alcohol structures" (XLIV), are converted to an indophenol (XLV) by reaction with quinone imide chloride in alkaline solution (82). The indophenol formed may be determined by spectrophotometric methods.

The amount of "p-hydroxybenzyl alcohol structures" in lignin and lignin preparations is relatively small: spruce BNL 0.12 to 0.14, Björkman lignin 0.05 to 0.07, and spruce wood lignin, approximately 0.03, expressed as moles per methoxyl (83).

(XLVI)

p-Hydroxybenzyl alcohols are converted to quinone methides (XLVI) by the successive action of hydrobromic acid and sodium bicarbonate (12). This reaction has been used for the demonstration of the presence of *p*-hydroxybenzyl alcohol structures in lignin, but is not suited for their quantitative determination because of the general instability of quinone methides. Quinone methide structures have recently gained interest as possible intermediates in the biogenesis of lignin (2).

Terminal methyl groups can be determined by the chromic acid oxidation method of Kuhn and l'Orsa (119). Experiments carried out under carefully controlled conditions seem to indicate that lignin contains little or none of these groups (65,136).

The presence of *carbonyl groups* in lignin is indicated by the infrared spectra (107) and by the formation of carbonyl derivatives, such as phenylhydrazones (44,80) and oximes (5). Quantitative determinations based on the oxime formation have given 0.12 and 0.10 carbonyl groups per methoxyl for spruce BNL and lignosulfonic acids, respectively (5). Recent studies have indicated that these values may be too small because of the incompleteness of the reaction. The determinations based on borohydride reduction (84) are probably too high, while improved oximation and infrared methods indicate the content of 0.20 carbonyl groups in Björkman lignin (135a).

A fraction of the carbonyl groups $(0.02/OCH_3)$ exists in the coniferylaldehyde group of spruce lignin (4). Another part $(0.06/OCH_3)$ is located in the alpha position of the side chains in spruce Björkman lignin, and can be evaluated from the change in light absorption caused by sodium borohydride reduction (10). If the higher values for carbonyl contents given in the preceding paragraph are to be considered correct, a substantial number of β-carbonyl groups should exist in lignin. The extent of the participation of such carbonyl groups to various lignin reactions is still unknown.

Trials to determine the amount of *ethylenic linkages*, by halogen addition, by reaction with lead tetraacetate, or by catalytic hydrogenation have failed to provide convincing evidence as to the presence of these groups in lignin (92c). The ultraviolet spectra of lignin derivatives indicate that only small amounts of conjugated double bonds can be present (17).

Accurate data for the elemental compositions of lignins are lacking. This is owing to the fact that lignin preparations isolated under acidic conditions undergo condensation reactions resulting in loss of water and sometimes contain carbohydrate impurities. Other lignin preparations, although less changed, represent only a part of lignin. The difficulty of calculating the original composition from the analytical data on lignosulfonic acids, lignin thioglycolic acids, or alcohol lignins is due to the incomplete knowledge of the reactions involved in the formation of the lignin derivative. As pointed out by Erdtman (57), in the sulfonation of lignin at least two types of reactions, involving either an aliphatic hydroxyl or an ether as the reacting groups, are to be considered.

$$1. \ \text{ROH} + \text{H}_2\text{SO}_3 \rightarrow \text{RSO}_3\text{H} + \text{H}_2\text{O}$$

$$2. \ \text{ROR}' + \text{H}_2\text{SO}_3 \rightarrow \text{RSO}_3\text{H} + \text{R}'\text{OH}$$

To obtain the original composition in the former case, SO_2 should be subtracted from the lignosulfonic acid formula; in the latter, one should subtract H_2SO_3. Both types of reactions probably occur in the sulfonation of lignin; until the extent of these reactions is known, the exact evaluation of the original composition is not possible. Table VI presents some of the compositions of lignin preparations reported in the literature, on a phenylpropane unit basis. In the case of a lignin derivative, such as lignosulfonic acid, the calculation has been based on the arbitrary assumption that only one type of reaction takes place in the formation of the derivative. The detailed formulas for cuproxam, Brauns native, and Björkman lignins are based on approximative determinations and have, therefore, only an orienting significance.

TABLE VI

Average C_9 Formulas of Lignin Preparations

Lignin source	Lignin preparation	C	H	O	OCH₃	Ref.
Spruce	Björkman lignin	9	8.83	2.37	0.96	(22)
Spruce	Brauns native lignin	9	8.7	2.37	0.9	(23a)
Spruce	Cuproxam lignin	9	7.88	2.50	0.92	(65)
Spruce	Dioxane lignin	9	8.7	2.6	0.98	(70)
Spruce	Calculated from the composition of lignosulfonic acid[a]	9	8.2	2.6	0.94	(57)
Spruce	Calculated from the composition of lignin thioglycolic acid[b]	9	8.9	2.85	0.92	(104)
Spruce	Calculated from the composition of ethanol lignin[c]	9	7.6	2.6	0.95	(14)
Birch	Björkman lignin	9	9.03	2.77	1.58	(22)
Beech	Cuproxam lignin	9	7.46	2.72	1.52	(65)

[a] Calculated by subtracting SO_3 from the formula for low-sulfonated lignosulfonic acid.

[b] Thioglycolic acid residues replaced by OH.

[c] Calculated by subtracting C_2H_5OH for every ethoxy group from ethanol lignin, isolated under mild conditions.

Detailed formulas.

Spruce cuproxam lignin: $C_9H_{6.41}O_{0.40}(OCH_3)_{0.92}(OH)_{1.47}(ether\ O)_{0.64}$

Spruce BNL: $C_9H_{6.7}(phenolic\ OH)_{0.5}(aliphatic\ OH)_{0.9}(carbonyl\ O)_{0.15}$
$(aryl\text{-}alkyl\ ether\ O)_{0.5}(dialkyl\ ether\ O)_{0.35}$

Spruce Björkman lignin: $C_9H_{7.68}(OCH_3)_{0.96}(phenolic\ OH)_{0.30}$
$(aliphatic\ OH)_{0.85}(carbonyl\ O)_{0.18}$
$(aryl\text{-}alkyl\ ether\ O)_{0.70}(dialkyl\ ether\ O)_{0.34}$

E. CONIFERYL ALDEHYDE GROUPS

Coniferyl aldehyde (XLVII) (Fig. 5) is only a minor component of lignin, estimated to be present in amounts of 0.020 to 0.025 per methoxyl in spruce lignin and lignosulfonic acids (4). Free coniferyl aldehyde has repeatedly been isolated from acidic hydrolysis products of wood lignin and BNL preparations (5,41,87). It has been convincingly demonstrated that most of the characteristic color reactions, such as reactions with different phenols, aromatic amines, concentrated hydrochloric acid, etc., can be ascribed to these groups (3,112, 151). The colored compound formed by the action of phenols has probably the structure XLIX. Exhaustively diazomethane-methylated lignins do not give color reactions (25); this is due to the formation of pyrazoline derivatives, such as structure L (118). The coniferyl aldehyde group is easily and reversibly sulfonated; the sulfonic acid is reconverted to the original aldehyde by the action of cold alkali (4). By boiling with 0.1N alkali, coniferyl aldehyde groups in wood and in lignosulfonic acids are hydrolyzed to vanillin (LI) and acetaldehyde by reversed aldol condensation (188); both compounds have been isolated from the alkaline hydrolysis products in amounts corresponding to the original contents of coniferyl aldehyde groups (7). If 24% sodium hydroxide (instead of 0.1N alkali) is used in

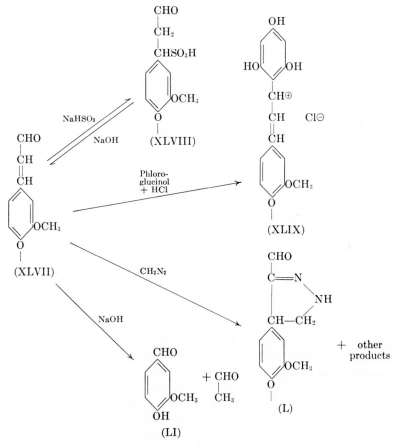

Fig. 5. Reactions of coniferyl aldehyde groups.

hydrolysis, lignosulfonic acids, but not wood lignin, give 3 to 4 times more vanillin and acetaldehyde (0.07 to 0.11 mole/methoxyl) than would be expected on the basis of the determined coniferyl aldehyde groups (7). It has been suggested that lignosulfonic acids may contain structures that are transformed to coniferyl aldehyde groups by the action of strong alkali ("masked coniferyl aldehyde groups".)

III. Physical Properties

In wood, lignin is located chiefly in the middle lamella, the amount gradually diminishing towards the lumina of the cells. According to Bailey (19,20), the middle lamella of Douglas-fir wood consists of roughly 71% of lignin and 14% of pentosans. The high refractive index of lignin in wood, 1.61, as well as the ultraviolet absorption spectrum (121), are consistent with its aromatic nature. The diffuse x-ray diffraction pattern shows that wood lignin is amorphous; still, the self-dichroism exhibited by middle lamellae in ultraviolet light indicates a limited degree of orientation (121). The optical inactivity of lignin is noteworthy in respect to the proposed structural elements that possess asymmetric carbon atoms.

In the ultraviolet absorption spectra of lignin and its derivatives (Fig. 6) the absorptivities of the various structural elements are superimposed on each other. The general similarities of lignin spectra to those of pyrocatechol derivatives and, in the case of hardwood lignins, also of pyrogallol compounds, were recognized at an early date (101). Much valuable comparative work on the spectra of lignin derivatives and of guaiacyl model compounds has been done by Aulin-Erdtman (15,17).

When lignin undergoes a reaction, the changes in molar absorptivities (on a methoxyl basis), plotted against wavelength to form what is called a "difference spectrum," can give important information on the nature and extent of lignin reactions. The ionization of phenolic groups in alkaline solution causes a characteristic change in the ultraviolet spectrum that has been applied in the determination of these groups (17,86). Similarly, carbonyl groups in the alpha-position to the aromatic nuclei in lignosulfonic acids can be evaluated from the change in spectrum caused by the ionization of this group in strong sulfuric acid solution (86). Changes that occur in the contents of alpha-carbonyl or conjugated ethylenic groups, when lignin under-

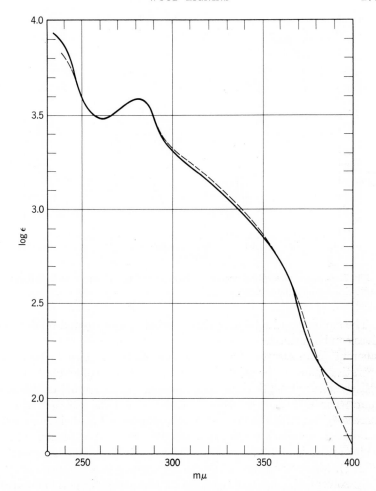

Fig. 6. Ultraviolet absorption spectra of Björkman lignins from *Thuja plicata* (solid line) and *Picea abies* (dotted line) in methyl cellosolve (22a).

goes various reactions, often may be followed by means of difference spectra between reacted and original samples (10,15,16,17,162).

The absorption bands in infrared spectra of lignins (Fig. 7) are considered to be due to the presence of aromatic rings, saturated aliphatic groups, hydroxyl groups, and small amounts of carbonyl groups (107). Infrared spectra have played an important role in establishing structural relationships between lignin preparations.

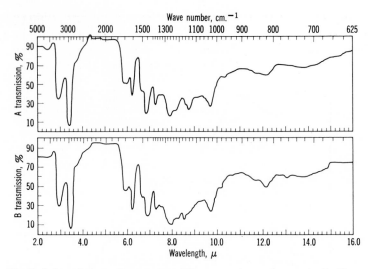

Fig. 7. Infrared absorption spectra of Brauns native and enzymically-liberated white Scots pine lignin (142a).

The swelling and solubility characteristics of lignin and its derivatives can be correlated, as demonstrated by Schuerch (168), with the inherent properties of the solvent system used. Two factors are operative, namely the solubility parameter [after Hildebrand (102)] and the basic strength [hydrogen bonding capacity (88)] of the solvent. The ability of solvents to dissolve or swell isolated lignins increases, first with the basic strength, and second as their solubility parameters approach a value of about 11. This can be illustrated by a plot of the solubility parameter versus hydrogen bonding capacity (Fig. 8), where every solvent system is represented by a single point. Only solvent systems that lie inside a characteristic parabolic area are able to dissolve a given lignin preparation completely. Generally, lower molecular weight lignin fractions are soluble in solvents with a wider range of solubility parameters and hydrogen bonding capacities than are the higher fractions.

As an example of the above rule acetone, dioxane, and pyridine, all known to be good lignin solvents, have δ-values between 10.0 and 10.7 and high hydrogen bonding capacities. High yields of organosolv lignins, when aqueous dioxane (47) or phenol (36) (δ = 11) are used as solvents, are undoubtedly due to the good solvent power of these systems. Methanol and ethanol are not especially good lignin solvents and are unable to dissolve higher molecular weight lignin fragments. Low yields of methanol and ethanol lignins from spruce, unless a good solvent system is used (167), are mainly due to this factor and not as much to condensation reactions, as assumed earlier.

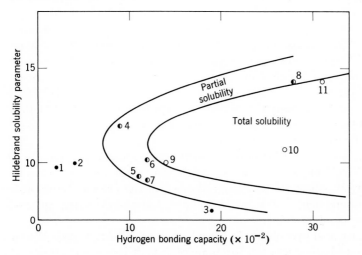

Fig. 8. The effect of the solubility parameter and the hydrogen-bonding capacity of a solvent system on the solubility of kraft lignin (168).

IV. Reactions of Lignin

A. SULFONATION

In the commercially important sulfite pulping process, lignin present in wood chips is converted into soluble lignosulfonic acids by the action of bisulfites and free sulfurous acid at 135 to 140°C. Apart from its technical importance, sulfonation also represents one of the most theoretically interesting lignin reactions.

The evaluation of the mechanism of sulfonation and of the nature of the reactive groups involved has been complicated by the fact that sulfonic acid groups are introduced into a large variety of organic compounds under conditions similar to the sulfite process. As a result, a number of speculative mechanisms have been proposed [for review, see (92b)]. The presentation which follows is limited to a discussion of the sulfonation theory developed by the Swedish school of lignin chemists (*cf.* 130). This theory, while still not rigorously proven in detail, is based on a substantial amount of experimental material and in principle is consistent with the complicated phenomena observed in lignin sulfonation. (See also Chapter 10.)

According to the kinetics of sulfonation in neutral and acidic media, the reacting groups in spruce lignin are divided into three groups, the so-called X-, Z-, and B-groups (54,128,138). The structures assigned to these groups are given in Fig. 9 (21,128). When the sulfonation is carried out in neutral or slightly acidic solution, only X- and Z-groups (collective designation: "A-groups") (54) react to form sulfonic acids (LII) and (LIII) (130), whereas the B-groups remain intact. Both X- and Z-groups are present in approximate amounts of 0.15 per methoxyl; the former reacts very rapidly because of the activating influence of a free phenolic hydroxyl group. The major product, so-called "solid lignosulfonic acid" (95), accordingly contains about 0.3 sulfonic acid group per methoxyl. Since very few linkages between monomeric units were broken in the process, the solid lignosulfonic acid is still in the form of a cross-linked aggregate and is therefore insoluble.

By acid hydrolysis the benzyl ether cross linkages present in group B are broken and the lignin molecule split into soluble fragments; it passes into solution to form what is called "low sulfonated lignosulfonic acids." A convenient way to perform the hydrolysis is to exchange the cations in the solid lignosulfonic acid for hydrogen ions and heat the resulting material in distilled water (120). Simultaneously with the hydrolysis, a reactive group B' (55,125), containing a benzyl alcohol group, is liberated from the originally unreactive structure B (129). Group B' can be further sulfonated (57) both by neutral (125) and acidic sulfite solutions. [Structures (LIII) and (LIV) are identical except for possible differences in the C_2 groups.] Lignosulfonic acids, prepared by this stepwise procedure may contain up to nearly 1 sulfur atom per methoxyl group. However, it has been demonstrated that only 0.6 atom is present in sulfonic acid groups (137,160). Consequently, Mikawa and co-workers (137) have estimated the amount of B-groups to be roughly 0.3 per methoxyl group. The nature of the nonacidic residue, usually called "excess sulfur" (160), is unknown.

In the technical sulfite process, the medium is acidic (pH = 1.5 to 2.0) from the beginning, and all the above-mentioned reactions occur simultaneously. The final sulfonic acid content is usually less (about

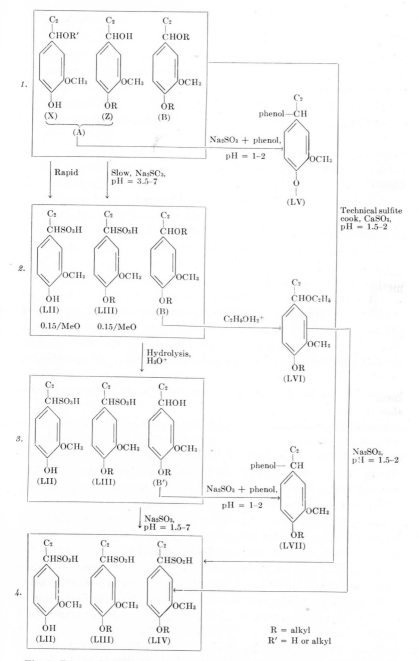

Fig. 9. Proposed mechanism for the sulfonation of softwood lignin: (*1*) reactive structures in wood lignin; (*2*) "solid lignosulfonic acids" (insoluble); (*3*) "low-sulfonated lignosulfonic acids" (soluble); (*4*) lignosulfonic acids.

0.5 per methoxyl) than is obtained in the stepwise procedure; this may, in part, be due to secondary condensation reactions of the reacting groups.

Polyphenols, such as resorcinol, pyrogallol, or phloroglucinol, if present in a normal sulfite cook, retard and even inhibit the dissolution of lignosulfonic acid (54). This is the reason for difficulties found in pulping the heartwood of pine or Douglas-fir; the extracts of the former contain pinosylvin (3,5-dihydroxystilbene) and its mono-methyl ether (54), and those of the latter contain taxifolin (3,5,7,3',4'-pentahydroxyflavanone) (150). If the sulfite cook is carried out in two stages, first with neutral and then with acidic sulfite (Graham process), normal delignification is obtained (54).

To explain the effect of polyphenols, Erdtman assumed that at pH 1.5 to 2 group A reacts more rapidly with phenols than with bisulfite to form an insoluble condensation product; in neutral solution the reactivities are reversed. Much smaller amounts of condensed polyphenols [0.17 mole of resorcinol (54), or 0.07 mole of phloroglucinol (182) per lignin methoxyl] than monofunctional ones [0.5 mole per methoxyl (182)] suffice to inhibit the dissolution of most of the lignin in the sulfite process. Probably, the polyphenols condense with two A groups and cause insolubility by cross-linking rather than by blocking the introduction of the hydrophilic sulfonic acid groups.

If solid lignosulfonic acid is subjected to ethanolysis, it passes into solution and the product contains ethoxyl groups. These are probably formed by the ethanolysis of benzyl ether linkages in group B [B → (LVI)]. The fact that the introduced ethoxyl groups can be replaced by sulfonic acid groups in subsequent acid sulfonation (56) is consistent with the mechanism given in Fig. 9.

Group B' differs from Z by its lower rate of sulfonation. This may be due to differing side-chain structures. It is not impossible that group B' may have a guaiacylglycerol-β-aryl ether structure (9).

Lignin thioglycolic acids bear certain similarities to lignosulfonates. They are formed by the action of thioglycolic and hydrochloric acids (104), probably mainly from the same reactive groups as lignosulfonic acids. In addition, a part of the hydroxyl groups in lignin forms esters with thioglycolic acid.

The evidence for assigning the benzyl alcohol and ether structures, given in Fig. 9, to the relative groups X, Z, and B in lignin, can be shortly summarized as follows:

C
|
C
|
HCOR
⟨benzene ring⟩OCH₃
O
|
(LVIII)

HSCH₂CO₂H →

C
|
C
|
HC—S—CH₂CO₂H
⟨benzene ring⟩OCH₃
O
|
(LIX)

Model compounds to X, Z, B, and B′ groups, such as vanillyl and veratryl alcohols (127) and their ethers (128), guaiacylglycerol derivatives (9,13,130), pinoresinol, (132) etc., show extensive similarities in their reactivities to the groups mentioned. Furthermore, the proposed mechanisms are in accordance with the fact that the sulfonation of lignin proceeds practically without effect on the ultraviolet absorption spectrum (18,122), and that the phenolic content is claimed to remain practically unchanged in sulfonation (15,156) and in the formation of lignin thioglycolic acids (131). Of the postulated X groups, those with unetherified alpha hydroxyls (R = H) have been positively identified in protolignin and their high reactivity in sulfonation has been similarly demonstrated (83). In the further sulfonation of low-sulfonated lignosulfonic acids, the sulfonic acid groups are introduced in equivalent amounts to the loss in total hydroxyl content (57); this is consistent with the benzyl alcohol structure assigned to the B′ groups.

The kinetics of dissolution of lignin in the sulfite process have been the subject of numerous studies. Two separate chemical processes are obviously involved, the introduction of hydrophilic sulfonic acid groups on one hand, and the hydrolytic cleavage of the acid-sensitive linkages on the other. The process which will become rate-determining appears to depend upon the conditions used (97). In the technical sulfite process, the hydrolysis proceeds rapidly owing to the acidity of the medium, and consequently, as demonstrated by Corey and Maass (37), the dissolution rate is mainly controlled by the rate of sulfonation.

The lignosulfonic acids, after being dissolved in the cooking liquor, are hydrolyzed further and the molecular weight is decreased (59). A reduction in the average molecular weight from about 14,000 to 6,000 has been observed (142). During prolonged heating, the molecular weight reaches a minimum after which an increasing trend is observed, probably due to acid-catalyzed condensation reactions (142).

B. ALCOHOLYSIS

Protolignin and various lignin preparations undergo a number of reactions when treated with various alcohols in the presence of mineral acids. Some of these reactions take place even at room temperature. For instance, when spruce Björkman lignin reacted with a mixture of methanol and dioxane containing anhydrous hydrochloric acid ($0.15N$) and the reaction product was recovered by precipitation into petroleum ether, it was found that the methoxyl content had increased by an amount corresponding to 0.57 group per original methoxyl (2).

Three reactions have been considered as possible causes of the observed introductions of alkoxyl groups: (*1*) Acetalization of carbonyl groups (26); (*2*) etherification of enol groups; and (*3*) etherification of alpha-hydroxy or alpha-ether structures (5). Studies on lignin preparations, in which the carbonyl groups were first eliminated by sodium borohydride reduction, indicate the last reaction to be the predominant one accounting for most of the methoxyl groups introduced in cold methanolysis (0.42 or more) (2).

$$R = H \text{ or alkyl}$$

The reaction showing the formation of (LXI) is in accordance with the known behavior of a number of model compounds (2), and is fully consistent with the proposed mechanism for the ethanolysis of the solid lignosulfonic acid, as discussed in the previous section.

Lignin in wood does not become soluble in cold alcoholysis. At an elevated temperature, however, most of the lignin is dissolved, especially if a proper solvent medium is used. This is owing to a solvolytic degradation of the lignin molecule (166) that follows the rapid initial alkoxylation reaction. The increased content of phenolic hydroxyl groups indicates that phenol ether linkages are cleaved in this reaction (162). A part of lignin becomes converted to the monomeric state (190).

In their extensive studies on the ethanolysis of spruce lignin, Hibbert and co-workers were able to isolate and identify the monomeric guaiacyl-derivatives (LXVIII), (LXIX), (LXX), and (LXXI) (Fig. 10), in amounts corresponding to about 10% of the

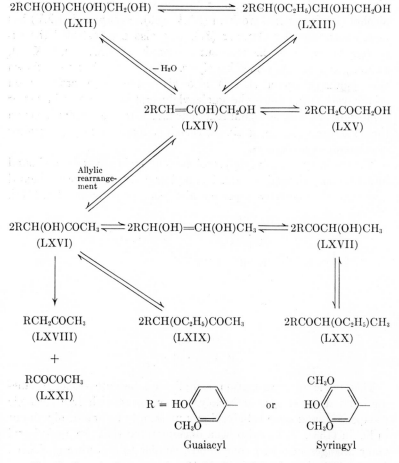

Fig. 10. Genesis of monomeric ethanolysis products from wood lignins.

original lignin (190). Maple lignin gave, in addition to the guaiacyl derivatives, the syringyl derivatives corresponding to (LXIX), (LXX), and (LXXI), and the total yield of monomeric products was higher (20% of original lignin) (29). The same compounds can also be isolated from the ethanolysis products of BNL preparations and of lignosulfonic acids (116).

As convincingly demonstrated by Hibbert, ethanolysis products (LXVIII) to (LXXI) do not represent native side-chain structures in lignin, but are formed by a series of rearrangement reactions from a common progenitor which does not contain a terminal methyl group. He assumed that the progenitor has the structure of β-oxyconiferyl alcohol (LXIV) or its keto form (LXV) (60). Compound (LXV) has been synthesized by Gardner (81), who also demonstrated the expected conversion of this compound to products (LXVIII), (LXIX), (LXX), and (LXXI) on ethanolysis. However, it has been shown that guaiacylglycerol (LXII) also gives the same products on ethanolysis (13). Since the guaiacylglycerol structure is in better conformity with other lignin reactions and with the current ideas on the structure of lignin, it almost certainly represents the progenitor of ethanolysis monomers.

The majority of guaiacylglycerol units in lignin are probably bound bifunctionally through C_4 and C_β-alkyl-aryl ether linkages; a benzyl ether cross-linkage may be present also [e.g., see structure (LXXII)].

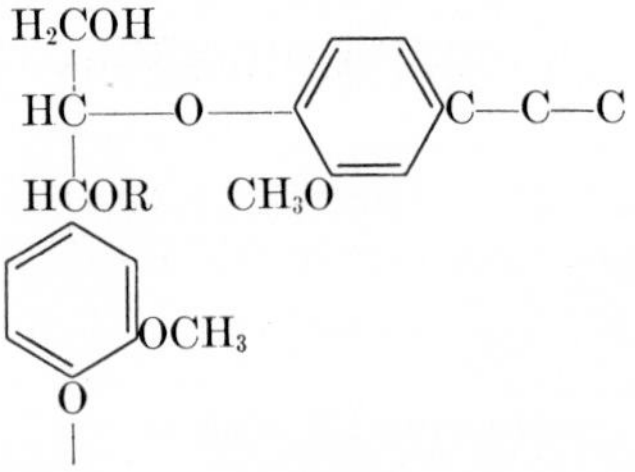

(LXXII)

R = H or alkyl

This mode of combination is indicated because diazomethane-methylated wood gives ethanolysis monomers with free phenolic groups (96), and since 1,2-glycol groups seem to be practically absent in lignin (133). It has also been demonstrated that the β-alkyl-aryl ether linkages in model compounds, similar to structure (LXXII), can be cleaved by ethanolysis (13,130).

Recent evidence points out that guaiacylglycerol-β-ether structures may be present in protolignin in much larger amounts than indicated by the yields of ethanolysis monomers. The reason these groups are not quantitatively transformed to the monomeric state seems to lie in the fact that part of guaiacylglycerol groups are bound by resistant alkyl-aryl ether linkages (162) or by C_5-carbon linkages to other lignin units. Recent results on the re-ethanolysis of ethanol lignins (162), as well as on the methanolysis of Björkman lignin (11), indicate that all phenolic groups liberated during alcoholysis originate from guaiacylglycerol-β-aryl ether structures. On this basis, monomers present in guaiacylglycerol structures may approximate 30% in spruce lignin (11).

The change in ultraviolet spectrum during alcoholysis is mainly due to the formation of conjugated carbonyl groups. Simultaneously with the reactions resulting in the formation of phenolic groups and side-chain rearrangements, condensation reactions take place causing a decrease in oxygen content (162).

C. ACIDIC HYDROLYSIS

When heated in mildly acidic aqueous media, wood lignins undergo a hydrolytic degradation which appears to be analogous to the degradation reaction in alcoholysis. Björkman lignin, hydrolyzed in a dioxane–water mixture with a mineral acid catalyst, yields small amounts of guaiacylacetone (LXVIII), vanilloyl methyl ketone (LXXI), and the ketol (LXVII) (11). Ketones (LXVIII) and (LXXI), together with coniferyl aldehyde, cumaraldehyde, and vanillin, also were isolated, when Douglas-fir wood and the BNL preparations from the same wood were heated in distilled water at 170°C. (87).

Of the compounds isolated, ketones (LXVIII) and (LXXI) are identical with those isolated from the ethanolysis reaction, and (LXVII) corresponds to an intermediate that is converted to its ethyl ether in ethanolysis (cf. Fig. 10). Accordingly, it appears almost certain that the isolated compounds are formed from a guaiacylglycerol-β-aryl ether structure in the original lignin. The analogous course of alcoholysis and hydrolysis reactions is further supported by the fact that in both reactions the end-methyl content of lignin is increased, probably due to the side-chain rearrangement of guaiacylglycerol units (11).

There is, however, an important difference between the two reactions. Whereas substantial amounts of monomeric products are isolated from ethanolysis, the hydrolysis yields only traces of such products. This is probably due to the tendency of alpha hydroxyl groups and of ketol structures to undergo condensation reactions under acidic conditions, especially with the aromatic rings of units containing a free phenolic hydroxyl group. Such condensation reactions are effectively suppressed in the alcoholysis through the etherification of the reactive alpha hydroxyl groups and ketol structures.

The condensation reactions appear, indeed, to predominate under the conditions of acidic hydrolysis, and usually completely overshadow the effects of hydrolytic degradation. Especially sensitive are the p-hydroxybenzyl alcohol groups that are destroyed by a mild acid treatment at room temperature (83). The condensation reactions during the preparation of acid lignins, such as Klason and Willstätter lignins, are reflected in the decreased oxygen contents of these preparations. Heating wood meal in distilled water at temperatures ranging from 100° to 200°C., which may be considered equivalent to a mild acid hydrolysis, progressively decreases the yield of vanillin in nitrobenzene oxidation (117), and the lignin loses its thermoplastic properties as well as the capacity to dissolve in the sulfite process (37). No such changes are observed when wood is heated in the dry state.

Some condensation occurs in the sulfite pulping process, as mentioned earlier in this chapter. The reaction is not extensive because of the blocking action of the sulfonic acid groups. Under abnormal conditions, i.e., when incomplete sulfonation is combined with a high local acidity, condensation reactions can completely inhibit the dissolution of lignin.

The condensing groups in lignin probably include the coniferylaldehyde groups in addition to the alpha hydroxyl groups. Both intra- and intermolecular condensations may occur. Metahemipinic acid that has been isolated from the permanganate oxidation products of acid-treated lignins may be derived from an intramolecularly condensed structure (156). The tendency of lignin to undergo intermolecular condensation reactions perhaps is illustrated best by the fact that it readily condenses with various monomeric phenols (33).

The degradative action of aqueous acids on the carbon-to-carbon linkages of lignin is apparently slight, except when concentrated mineral acids are used. Treatment of lignin with 28% sulfuric acid produces formaldehyde in a yield of 1.5 to 2.0% of the weight of the lignin (75). The formaldehyde isolated from a γ-labeled radioactive lignin has been shown to be radioactive, indicating that the cleavage of a β—γ linkage is involved in its formation (67).

D. ALKALINE HYDROLYSIS

As mentioned earlier, heating of lignin with alkaline solutions causes the splitting of alkyl-aryl ether linkages in the position 4, with the formation of phenolic hydroxyl groups. Such reactions have also been demonstrated with guaiacyl ether model compounds (123). Cleavage reactions occur in lignosulfonic acids even at temperatures below 100°C., with simultaneous decreases in molecular weight (146). To liberate the phenolic groups in lignin, a temperature range between 160 to 170°C. has been used most frequently (74). The ether linkage present in the methoxyl group is more stable and is degraded at temperatures above 250°C.; protocatechuic acid and pyrocatechol have been isolated from such products.

The carbon-to-carbon linkages in lignin also are susceptible to alkaline media. The formation of vanillin and acetaldehyde from coniferyl aldehyde groups already was mentioned. Indications also exist that linkages between β- and γ-carbon atoms of propyl side-chains may likewise become partially degraded. Maple wood lignin, when hydrogenated with Raney nickel catalyst at 160 to 170°C. in a neutral medium, gives products from which monomeric syringyl- and guaiacylpropane derivatives can be isolated (28). When a medium containing 3% of sodium hydroxide is used, only monomeric phenylethane derivatives (LXXIII), (LXXIV), and (LXXV) are isolated (149). It therefore appears probable that the alkaline medium causes a cleavage between the β- and γ-carbon atoms. Furthermore, the existence of both acetoguaiacone (LXXVI) (109) and formaldehyde (113) among the alkaline hydrolysis products of spruce lignosulfonates suggests a cleavage of a β—γ carbon linkage. Cuproxam lignin gives 2 to 3% of formaldehyde by boiling with dilute alkali (75).

A large part of wood lignin becomes alkali-soluble when heated to
160°C. with aqueous alkali, owing to the degradation processes mentioned. The delignification by alkali finds commercial use in the soda
process, a pulping method applicable to hardwood species. The soda
process, as such, is not an effective pulping process for softwoods.
The reason probably lies in the extensive condensation of softwood
lignin under the conditions used.

The condensation reactions in the soda process quite probably are
extensive and cause the formation of new carbon-to-carbon bonds
between monomeric units. Adkins and co-workers (1) were able to
demonstrate convincingly the effect of these reactions on aspen lignin.
They found that aspen soda lignin fails to yield a monomeric fraction
on hydrogenolysis, whereas the methanol lignin from the same wood
is converted to hydrogenated monomers in 44% yield.

E. KRAFT PROCESS

The kraft pulping process is essentially a modification of the soda
process in which a part of the sodium hydroxide base is replaced by
sodium sulfide. Because of its applicability to resinous softwoods,
among other factors, more pulps are presently being manufactured
by the kraft process than by the sulfite pulping process.

In comparison with the soda process, the rate of delignification in
the kraft process is more rapid and the obtained pulps contain less
lignin. Both of these effects are believed to be due to less condensation
in the latter process. It has been proposed that the HS^- ions react
with a part of the condensing groups, thus inhibiting the condensation
reactions (49). This view has gained support from studies on model
compounds (52). These studies indicate that unetherified guaiacylpropane units, containing a hydroxyl or an alkyl ether group in the
alpha-position (LXXVII), may react with hydrosulfide anion,
forming a mercaptan (LXXVIII).

(LXXVII)   (LXXVIII)

According to Enkvist (49) an increasing number of the above structures becomes available for reaction with hydrosulfide ions as the phenolic ether linkages are hydrolyzed by the action of alkali. The protective action of the mercaptan groups appears to be only temporary, retarding rather than inhibiting the condensation reaction.

Kraft lignin, which can be precipitated from the kraft liquors by acidification, is an ill-defined substance containing from 2 to 4% of sulfur. It is of relatively low molecular weight and contains substantial amounts of free phenolic groups. These are formed in the alkaline cleavage of the original phenolic ether bonds, and the cleavage reaction appears to go to completion during the process. In addition, a part of the methoxyl groups is hydrolyzed and converted to methanol and dimethyl sulfide. (See also Chapter 10.)

F. HALOGENATION

The commercial pulping methods generally are based on delignification processes which require relatively high temperatures. There exists, however, a number of chemical agents capable of accomplishing delignification at much lower temperatures. Of these, chlorine in acidic solution converts lignin to a derivative, chlorolignin, which is extractable with aqueous alkali.

The well-known Cross and Bevan (cf. 32b) cellulose determination is one of the applications making use of the delignifying action of chlorine. Moist wood meal, or any other plant material, is treated at room temperature with gaseous chlorine and the chlorinated lignin is extracted with alkali. Repetition of the treatment a few times produces a virtually lignin-free material, with little if any hydrolytic degradation of the cellulosic components.

To a limited degree, chlorination followed by alkali extraction is used as a commercial pulping method to produce straw pulps [Pomilio (153) and deVains (43) processes]. In wood pulp industries, chlorine represents the most important bleaching chemical. The action of chlorine on sulfite and kraft pulps is dependent on the pH of the medium. Acidic chlorine water, which is used in the first stage of the commercial bleaching process, acts as a delignifying agent and converts most of the residual lignin in pulps to a water- and alkali-soluble form. Alkaline hypochlorite, used in the final stage of the bleaching process, is distinctively different from chlorine water in its action and may be properly characterized as a bleaching rather than a deligni-fying agent.

Recent studies (42) on the mechanism of acidic chlorination indi-cate that the following three reactions dominate the early phases of chlorine treatment:

1. Chlorine substitution at the aromatic nucleus, predominantly at position 6 [(LXXIX) → (LXXX)].

2. Electrophilic displacement of the side-chain (LXXXI), facili-tated by the presence of an alpha hydroxyl or alkyl ether group.

3. Chlorine-catalyzed hydrolysis of aromatic ether groups, result-ing in the liberation of methanol and, presumably, in the cleavage of phenol ether linkages (LXXXII).

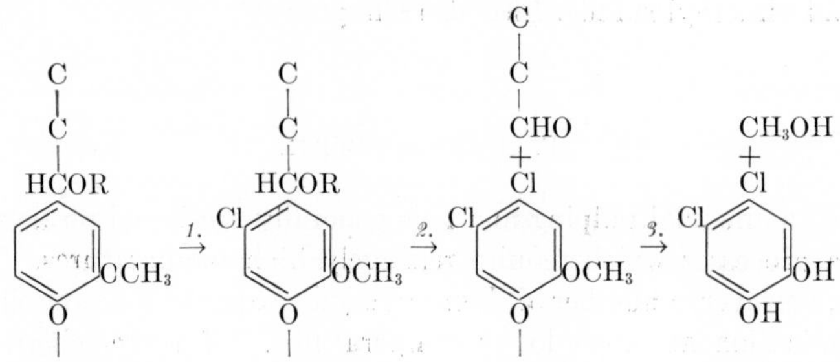

(LXXIX)   (LXXX)   (LXXXI)   (LXXXII)

Of the reactions mentioned, the electrophilic displacement and the hydrolysis of phenol ether bonds effectively reduce the size of the lignin molecule making it more soluble, even if they take place only in a part of the phenylpropane units. The creation of new hydrophilic groups by the hydrolysis reaction makes a further contribution toward increased solubility.

Because of other accompanying reactions, such as further chlorine substitution, oxidation to quinones, etc., the chlorolignins, although of relatively small molecular weight, represent complicated mixtures of various products.

If the chlorination of lignin is carried out in a water-free medium,

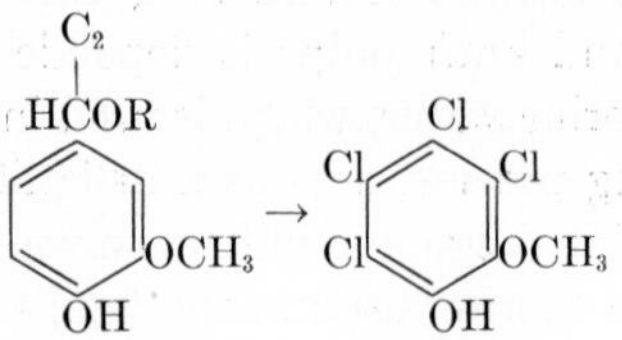

(LXXXIII)   (LXXXIV)

such as glacial acetic acid, the hydrolysis of phenol ethers is inhibited. Tetrachloroguaiacol (LXXXIV) has been isolated from the chlorination of spruce wood lignin in glacial acetic acid (42). It probably is formed from the free guaiacol end groups in lignin.

G. NITRATION

As early as 1849, the French chemist Anselme Payen found that lignin could be removed from plant materials by treating them with concentrated nitric acid and by extracting the nitrated material with alkali and organic solvents (144). Subsequently, nitration of wood meal has sometimes been used as a quantitative method to determine the carbohydrate constituents (32c). To a limited degree, industrial pulps from straw are prepared by the nitration method. Likewise, dissolving pulps from hardwoods can be produced, although the method, as yet, has not proven to be competitive with the more common pulping processes.

The nitration of wood resembles the chlorination reaction in that the lignin is converted to a soluble form under relatively mild conditions which do not appreciably affect the carbohydrate constituents. The analogy may be more than a formal one. Electrophilic side-chain replacement by a nitro group has been shown to occur in the nitration of a number of guaiacyl derivatives (56,91). A product of such a reaction, the 2,4-dinitroguaiacol, has been isolated on nitrating spruce wood meal in ethyl ether, and is apparently derived from a free guaiacyl end group in lignin (91). Furthermore, aromatic methyl ethers generally suffer partial demethylation on nitration. Both a loss in methoxyl content as well as the formation of methanol have been observed on the nitration of lignin (68).

Owing to various reactions a part of the nitric acid becomes reduced to nitrogen oxides, ammonia, and even to hydrogen cyanide (159). Since these reduction products may, in part, react with lignin and its degradation products, the chemical characterization of nitrolignins is a rather difficult task.

H. REACTIONS WITH CHLORINE DIOXIDE AND CHLORITES

The delignifying action of chlorine dioxide was discovered by Schmidt (163) who demonstrated that lignin can be removed from wood meal by treatment with an aqueous chlorine dioxide solution at temperatures as low as room temperature, followed by an extraction with sodium sulfite or a base. Similar action is exerted by a slightly acidified sodium chlorite solution, and the chlorine dioxide generated from the chlorite is probably the principal agent causing the delignification reaction. The carbohydrate components undergo relatively little oxidation or degradation in the process. Consequently, methods based on the use of chlorine dioxide are widely utilized for the isolation or quantitative determination of holocellulose (32a).

In recent times, chlorine dioxide has gained increasing use as a bleaching agent, especially for kraft pulps. Brighter pulps with less cellulose degradation are obtained if chlorine dioxide instead of hypochlorite is used as a final stage of the commercial bleaching process.

The chemistry of delignification and bleaching reactions by chlorine dioxide is incompletely known. In general, chlorine dioxide is a weak oxidant and reacts very sluggishly with saturated aliphatic compounds. It is reactive towards unsaturated compounds, with the exception of α,β-unsaturated carboxylic acids, and reacts very rapidly with phenols, many of which give relatively high yields of oxalic and maleic acids (164). This suggests that the aromatic nuclei of lignin, rather than the side chains, are primarily attacked and degraded by chlorine dioxide.

The isolation of 6-chlorovanillin and 6-chlorovanillic acid from the nitrobenzene oxidation products of chlorite lignin demonstrates the occurrence of chlorine substitution reactions (106). The oxidative degradation may, however, proceed without an intermediate chlorine substitution. This is suggested by the fact that vanillin (XXV), on chlorine dioxide oxidation, is converted in 25% yield to a chlorine-free, crystalline compound (105), later identified as β-formyl muconic acid monomethyl ester (109).

Chlorine dioxide, as well as sodium chlorite, also causes a ring opening in vanillyl alcohol (42b). In addition, various quinone compounds and methanol are formed.

Investigations made on the chlorine dioxide and chlorite oxidations of wood lignin (20b,126b) and lignosulfonates (175) indicate substantial degradation of aromatic nuclei, judging from the disappearance of the characteristic 280 mμ. maximum in the UV-spectrum. However, the data presently available do not allow conclusions as to what degree ring opening and other degradation reactions are involved.

I. VARIOUS ORGANOSOLV LIGNINS

A large variety of so-called organosolv lignins has been prepared by treating plant materials (generally in the presence of small amounts of mineral acid, but also in slightly alkaline or even neutral solutions) with different solvents, such as ethylene glycol (90), dioxane (47), glycol chlorohydrin (169), aqueous butanol (20), phenol (36), thiophenol (27), acetic and formic acids (75,170), ethanolamine (192), etc. The nature of these products as well as the reactions involved in their preparation are incompletely known. Among the organosolv lignins, the phenol lignins have certain interesting characteristics.

Wood, heated with ordinary phenol containing 0.2% of hydrogen chloride at 90 to 100°C., is almost completely delignified in 0.5 to 1 hour (33). The resulting phenol lignin contains a substantial amount of phenol in a condensed form and the analytical composition agrees with the approximate formula

$$C_{42}H_{32}O_6(CH_3O)_5(OH)_4(OC_6H_5) \cdot 3C_6H_5OH.$$

The condensation has been assumed to take place mainly between lignin and the p-position of the phenol. However, at least a partial condensation to the o-position is indicated by the isolation of salicylic acid from the nitrobenzene oxidation products (186).

Condensation between wood lignin and phenols under the action of mineral acids occurs even in the cold; the condensation product, however, does not become soluble. As the condensation proceeds, yields of vanillin in nitrobenzene oxidation are gradually decreased from 26 to 10% of the weight of lignin (140). As mentioned earlier, wood lignin condensed with phenols cannot be dissolved in the sulfite process, probably because the groups reacting in sulfonation may be identical with those condensing with phenols.

V. Biogenesis of Lignin

At an early stage of lignin research, Klason (110), as well as Tiemann and Haarmann (181), expressed the opinion that spruce-wood lignin may be formed in nature from coniferin (LXXXVI), a glucosidic compound present in the cambial sap. Later Erdtman (53) suggested that the biogenesis of lignin may bear similarities to the dehydrogenative dimerization of isoeugenol (LXXXVII) which, by the action of mushroom enzymes, is converted into diisoeugenol (LXXXVIII) (38).

H_2COH CH_3 $HC=CHCH_3$

(LXXXVI)   (LXXXVII)   (LXXXVIII)

In essence, these early views have been confirmed by recent bio-chemical studies, especially by Freudenberg (62–80). It is now generally believed that spruce lignin is formed in nature from coniferin by enzymatic hydrolysis of the glucosidic bond and subsequent dehydrogenative polymerization of the liberated coniferyl alcohol, although the latter process appears to be much more complex than the dimerization of isoeugenol. Freudenberg (67) was the first to demonstrate the effectiveness of radioactively-labeled D-coniferin as the biological precursor of lignin. When this compound is adminis-tered to young spruce buds, the radioactivity can later on be quanti-tatively recovered in the lignin fraction (67,114). The monomers isolated from the ethanolysis products of such lignin proved to be strongly radioactive; see Freudenberg (63) and Kratzl (114). Like-wise, Wacek (187) has demonstrated that phloem cultures do not become lignified unless D-coniferin is added to the culture medium. The D-glucosidase needed for the hydrolysis of D-coniferin has been shown, by Freudenberg (77), to be present in the cambium cells, which are in an active state of lignification, by the blue color that developed when microtome sections of spruce wood were treated

with indican solution. In conjunction with the primary role assigned
to this enzyme is the discovery that radioactive L-coniferin does not
become incorporated in lignin (67).

Apparently the liberated coniferyl alcohol becomes subject to the
dehydrogenative action of an enzyme, laccase, present in the cambial
sap and is converted into an insoluble lignin which is deposited in the
middle lamella and in the cell walls. To study this process in detail,
Freudenberg has performed numerous *in vitro* experiments. Coniferyl
alcohol was subjected to the combined action of air-oxygen and of
either mushroom or cambial sap enzymes in aqueous solution at room
temperature, preferably at a pH range between 5.5 and 6.5. Under
these conditions coniferyl alcohol is slowly converted to a water-
insoluble, light-colored, amorphous polymerizate called "dehydrogenation polymerizate" (dehydrierungspolymerisat, DHP).

DHP shows extensive similarities to spruce protolignin and BNL
preparations (62). The similarities include the elemental composition,
optical inactivity, color reactions, amount of liberated formaldehyde
by the action of mineral acids, formation of isohemipinic acid, amount
and nature of hydroxyl groups, formation and composition of sulfonic
acids, thermoplasticity (in both cases lost by boiling with dilute
mineral acids), infrared spectra of the preparations, as well as their
methylated and sulfonated derivatives, etc. The same monomeric
ethanolysis products can be isolated from DHP as from spruce lignin.
DHP differs from BNL by its somewhat higher methoxyl content
(1.00 instead of 0.92 methoxyl group per guaiacylpropane unit),
higher content of coniferyl aldehyde groups, and by a somewhat
different ultraviolet spectrum. Dehydrogenation polymerizates also

have been prepared from radioactive coniferyl alcohols, labeled both in β- and γ-positions by carbon-14 (67).

From the products formed in the early stages of DHP formation, Freudenberg and co-workers (71) have been able to isolate coniferyl aldehyde (LXXXIX), dehydrodiconiferyl alcohol (XC), D,L-pinoresinol (XCI), guaiacylglycerol-β-coniferyl ether (XCII), and, in addition, some still unidentified products (71). It is especially significant that the same compounds have been found to be present, in small amounts, in the acetone extract of the cambial layer of spruce wood (63). Furthermore, many of the structural elements postulated for spruce protolignin on the basis of chemical evidence are represented in these compounds, such as coniferyl aldehyde (LXXXIX) and guaiacylglycerol-β-aryl ether (XCII) structures, as well as β-5′ (XC) and β-β′ (XCI) carbon linkages and alpha-alkyl ether groups (XCI).

Freudenberg assumes that the enzymatic action in DHP formation, as well as in lignin biosynthesis, is limited to the extraction of a hydrogen atom from the phenolic hydroxyl group in coniferyl alcohol. Such interpretation is consistent with the optical inactivity of lignin. One of the possibilities to be considered for the formation of the above-mentioned dimers is the recombination of the various resonating structures of the coniferyl alcohol radical.

Coniferyl alcohol

(XCIII)   (XCIV)   (XCV)   (XCVI)

For instance, guaiacylglycerol-β-coniferyl ether (XCII) can be visualized as being formed through the radical recombination of resonance structures (XCVI) and (XCIII), followed by the stabilization of the quinone methide group in (XCVII) by addition of water.

In a similar fashion, dehydrodiconiferyl alcohol (XC) could be formed from resonance structures (XCIV) and (XCVI), and D,L-

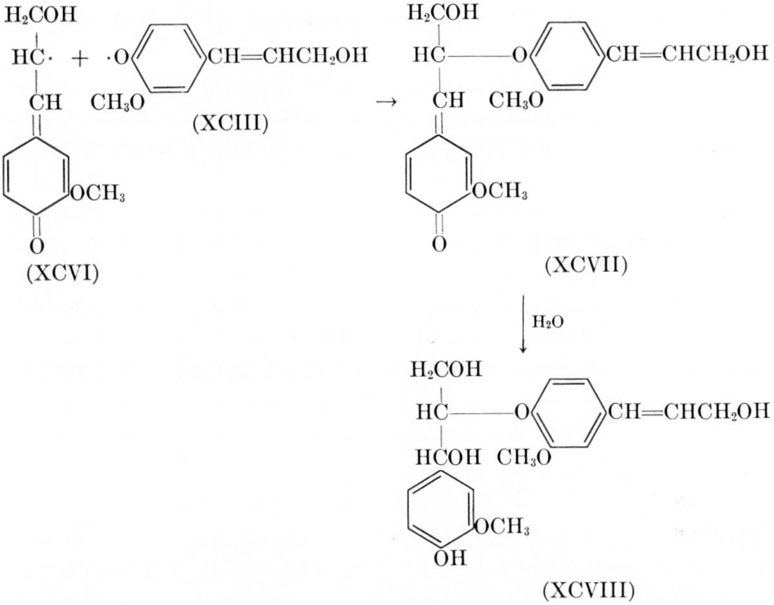

H_2COH

$HC\cdot$ + $\cdot O$⟨benzene ring⟩$CH{=}CHCH_2OH$

CH CH_3O

(XCIII)

⟨quinone methide ring⟩OCH_3

O

(XCVI)

H_2COH

$HC{-}{-}{-}O$⟨benzene ring⟩$CH{=}CHCH_2OH$

CH CH_3O

→

⟨quinone methide ring⟩OCH_3

O

(XCVII)

$\downarrow$ H_2O

H_2COH

$HC{-}{-}{-}O$⟨benzene ring⟩$CH{=}CHCH_2OH$

$HCOH$ CH_3O

⟨benzene ring⟩OCH_3

OH

(XCVIII)

pinoresinol, (XCI), from two molecules of (XCVI). In the former case, the intermediate quinone methide structure would be stabilized by an intramolecular addition of a phenolic hydroxyl group, whereas

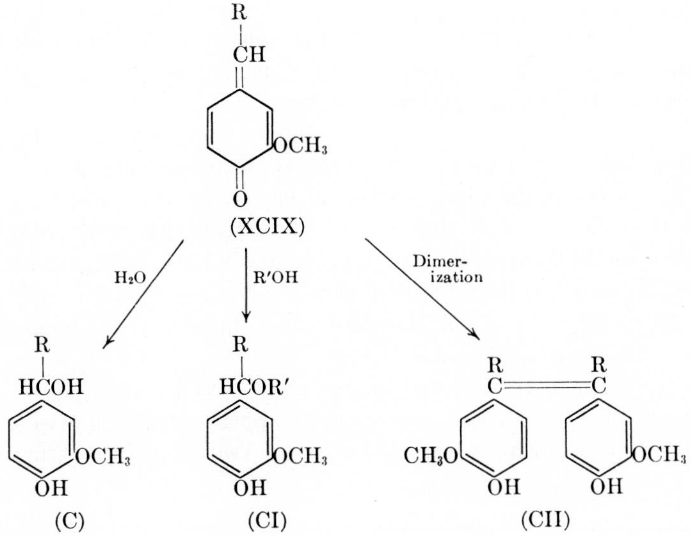

R

CH

⟨quinone methide ring⟩OCH_3

O

(XCIX)

H_2O ↙ $\downarrow$ $R'OH$ $\searrow$ Dimer- ization

R

$HCOH$

⟨benzene ring⟩OCH_3

OH

(C)

R

$HCOR'$

⟨benzene ring⟩OCH_3

OH

(CI)

R R

$C{=}{=}C$

CH_3O⟨ring⟩OH ⟨ring⟩OCH_3 OH

(CII)

in the latter instance two such structures would add gamma-hydroxyl groups.

The suggested addition reactions are consistent with the general behavior of quinone methides (XCIX) which are known to be extremely reactive and easily undergo hydrolysis, alcoholysis, or dimerization (2).

Considering the high reactivity of quinone methides, it seems feasible that the addition reactions leading to the formation of the dimers (XC), (XCI) and (XCII) may not be the only reactions occurring. To illustrate this, let us assume that quinone methide intermediate (XCVII), instead of adding one molecule of water, undergoes reaction with an alcoholic hydroxyl (for instance, with the primary carbinol group of a coniferyl alcohol molecule). In this reaction, an alkyl-ether link would form between two monomeric units (2), e.g., (CIII).

(CIII)

An analogous reaction between the quinone methide and a hydroxyl group belonging to a carbohydrate molecule would result in the formation of a "lignin-carbohydrate bond" (64).

Finally, a reaction between two quinone methides would form a stilbene-like arrangement, and thereby form a carbon-to-carbon linkage between the alpha carbon atoms of two monomeric units.

It thus can be seen that the addition reactions of the dimeric quinone methide intermediates can potentially result in the formation of either one of the three lignin dimers, of a lignin-carbohydrate bond, or a lignin trimer in which the third unit is linked by an alpha-alkyl ether or α-α' carbon-to-carbon bond.

In addition to the isolated dimers (XC), (XCI), and (XCII) the presence of a 5-5' linked dimer (CIV) appears predictable since it would readily form by recombination of two resonance structures (XCIV):

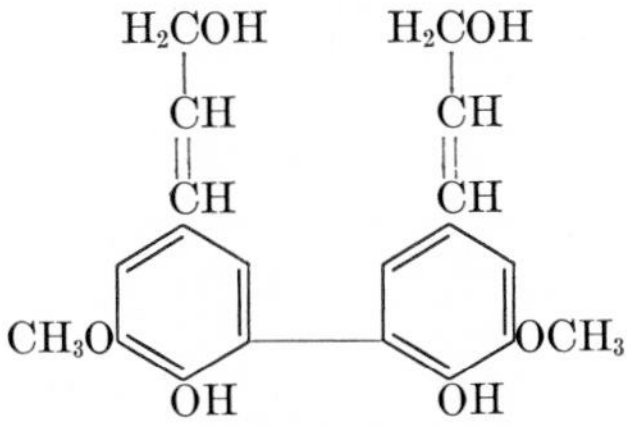

(CIV)

Although it has not been possible, as yet, to demonstrate the presence of dimer (CIV) in the cambial sap of spruce wood, its participation in the polymerization of coniferyl alcohol in the biological formation of lignin appears likely.

It is obvious that continuing dehydrogenation processes, combined with the various radical recombination reactions and additions to the quinone methide intermediates, will result in further polymerization to aggregates of high molecular weight. Consequently, no further assumptions are necessary to describe the polymerization of coniferyl alcohol in spruce wood to high molecular weight lignin. If it is assumed that all the previously discussed radical recombination and addition reactions take place to varying degrees during the polymerization process, the lignin molecule should be a random polymer in which the phenylpropane units are connected by β-4′ and α-alkyl ether linkages, as well as by β-5′, β-β', α-α', and 5-5′ carbon-to-carbon linkages. This is an exactly identical structure with the one arrived at on the basis of chemical evidence, as discussed earlier in this chapter. The agreement of two independent approaches to the same structural problem is indeed remarkable, and adds to the confidence with which the present ideas about the structure of lignin can be accepted. Provision should be made, of course, for possible further modifications and refinements of these concepts which may result from future biogenetic and chemical studies.

As the concept of coniferyl alcohol as the precursor of softwood lignin appears well-established, one would expect coniferyl alcohol, together with the corresponding syringyl derivative (sinapyl alcohol) to play similar roles in the formation of hardwood lignin. Syringin (CV), the glucoside of sinapyl alcohol, has been shown to be present in the bark of many plants, mainly belonging to the family Oleaceae.

However, the biogenesis of hardwood lignin still seems unclear.

$$\text{Glucose} \cdot O \underset{CH_3O}{\overset{CH_3O}{\bigcirc}} CH{=}CH{-}CH_2OH$$

(CV)

Although the lignifying cells of many hardwoods give a blue color with indican solution, indicating the presence of d-glucosidase, the reaction is absent in some species (77). Sinapyl alcohol shows a strong tendency to form syringaresinol, a compound analogous to pinoresinol. By the action of mushroom enzymes, it is transformed to water-soluble dark brown products. If the procedure is applied to a 1:1 mixture of coniferyl and sinapyl alcohols, a light-colored insoluble product, containing both components, is formed; however, the relationship of this polymer to hardwood protolignin has not been clearly established (62).

The position of lignin in general plant metabolism has been the subject of numerous studies based on the administration of radioactive compounds to living plants. Brown and Neish have attempted to locate the position of various potential intermediates in the biological sequence of lignin formation in living plants (30). The dilution of radioactive carbon was taken as the criterion of efficiency. They were able to show that shikimic acid (CVI), an intermediate in the biosynthesis of aromatic amino acids, acts as progenitor of the aromatic nuclei in maple and wheat lignins. Similar results were obtained by Eberhardt and Schubert (46) on sugar cane lignin. They also demonstrated that vanillin, isolated by nitrobenzene oxidation from the radioactive lignin which was prepared by administering active shikimic acid to a living plant, had the same distribution of radioactivity in the ring carbon atoms as the introduced shikimic acid. In the plant, shikimic acid appears to be formed from glucose via phosphorylated sedoheptulose. p-Hydroxyphenylpyruvic acid (CVII) may possibly act as an intermediate between shikimic acid and phenylpropane derivatives.

$$\underset{HOH}{\underset{HOH}{\overset{CO_2H}{\underset{\bigcirc}{\bigcirc}}}}\underset{HOH}{\overset{H_2}{}} \qquad HO{\bigcirc}CH_2COCO_2H \qquad \underset{HO}{\overset{CH_3O}{\bigcirc}}CH{=}CHCO_2H$$

(CVI)   (CVII)   (CVIII)

Brown and Neish (31) determined the radioactivity of vanillin, syringaldehyde, and p-hydroxybenzaldehyde which were isolated by nitrobenzene oxidation after administering different aromatic compounds to living plants. A variety of phenylpropane derivatives, such as phenylalanine, tyrosine, and cinnamic acid, proved to be efficient precursors of lignin. In the case of phenylalanine, the radioactivity of the three isolated aldehydes was on an equal level. Ferulic acid (CVIII) was found to be an especially efficient precursor; the radioactivity was, however, mainly concentrated in vanillin. Freudenberg (63) has subjected lignins formed in a plant, after the incorporation of active phenylalanine and ferulic acid, to degradation by ethanolysis. The monomers isolated proved to be highly radioactive, indicating that the carboxyl groups of the incorporated compounds had been reduced in the biological process. It seems, therefore, plausible that phenylalanine and ferulic acid may represent actual intermediates in the biological pathway between shikimic acid and lignin, as suggested by Brown and Neish.

REFERENCES

1. Adkins, H., R. L. Frank, and E. S. Bloom, *J. Am. Chem. Soc.*, **63**, 549 (1941).
2. Adler, E., *Proceedings of the Fourth International Congress of Biochemistry, Vienna, 1958*, Pergamon Press, 1959, p. 137.
3. Adler, E., K. J. Björkqvist, and S. Häggroth, *Acta Chem. Scand.*, **2**, 839 (1948).
4. Adler, E., and L. Ellmer, *Acta Chem. Scand.*, **2**, 839 (1948).
5. Adler, E., and J. Gierer, *Acta Chem. Scand.*, **9**, 84 (1955).
6. Adler, E., and J. Gierer, in *Die Chemie der Pflanzenzellwand*, by E. Treiber, Springer Verlag, Berlin, 1957, pp. 446–484.
7. Adler, E., and S. Häggroth, *Acta Chem. Scand.*, **3**, 86 (1949).
8. Adler, E., and S. Hernestam, *Acta Chem. Scand.*, **9**, 319 (1955).
9. Adler, E., B. O. Lindgren, and U. Saeden, *Svensk Papperstidn.*, **55**, 245 (1952).
10. Adler, E., and J. Marton, *Acta Chem. Scand.*, **13**, 75 (1959).
11. Adler, E., J. M. Pepper, and E. Eriksoo, *Ind. Eng. Chem.*, **49**, 1391 (1957).
12. Adler, E., and B. Stenemur, *Chem. Ber.*, **89**, 291 (1956).
13. Adler, E., and S. Yllner, *Svensk Papperstidn.*, **57**, 78 (1954).
14. Arlt, H. G., Jr., K. Sarkanen, and C. Schuerch, *J. Am. Chem. Soc.*, **78**, 1904 (1956).
15. Aulin-Erdtman, G., *Tappi*, **32**, 160 (1949).
16. Aulin-Erdtman, G., *Chem. and Ind.*, **74**, 581 (1955).
17. Aulin-Erdtman, G., *Svensk Papperstidn.*, **47**, 91 (1944); **55**, 745 (1952); **56**, 91, 287 (1953); **57**, 745 (1954); **59**, 363 (1956).

18. Aulin-Erdtman, G., A. Björkman, H. Erdtman, and S. E. Hägglund, *Svensk Papperstidn.*, **50**, No. 11B, 81 (1947).

19. Bailey, A. J., *Ind. Eng. Chem., Anal. Ed.*, **8**, 52, 389 (1936).

20. Bailey, A. J., *Paper Trade J.*, **110**, No. 1, 29, No. 2, 29 (1940); **111**, No. 6, 27, No. 9, 86 (1940).

20b. Barton, J. S., *Tappi*, **33**, 496 (1950).

21. Berg, G. A., and B. Holmberg, *Svensk Kem. Tidskr.*, **47**, 257 (1935).

22. Björkman, A., *Svensk Papperstidn.*, **59**, 477 (1956); A. Björkman and B. Persson, *Svensk Papperstidn.*, **60**, 158, 285 (1957).

22a. Björkman, A., and B. Persson, *Svensk Papperstidn.*, **60**, 164 (1957).

23. Brauns, F. E., *Chemistry of Lignin*, Academic Press, New York, 1952, p. 242.

24. Brauns, F. E., (a) in *Wood Chemistry*, L. E. Wise and E. C. Jahn, eds., Vol. I, Reinhold, New York, 1952, pp. 409–539; (b) in *Cellulose*, E. Ott, H. M. Spurlin, and M. Grafflin, eds., Part I, Interscience, New York, 1955, pp. 480–509.

25. Brauns, F. E., *J. Am. Chem. Soc.*, **61**, 2120 (1939); *Paper Trade J.*, **111**, No. 14, 35 (1940).

26. Brauns, F. E., and H. Hibbert, *Can. J. Research*, **13B**, 28 (1935).

27. Brauns, F. E., and W. H. Lane, *Paper Trade J.*, **122**, No. 8, 41 (1946).

28. Brewer, C. P., L. M. Cooke, and H. Hibbert, *J. Am. Chem. Soc.*, **70**, 57 (1948).

29. Brickman, L., W. L. Hawkins, and H. Hibbert, *J. Am. Chem. Soc.*, **65**, 2149 (1940).

30. Brown, S. A., and A. C. Neish, *Nature*, **175**, 688 (1955).

31. Brown, S. A., and A. C. Neish, *Can. J. Biochem. Physiol.*, **33**, 948 (1955).

32. Browning, B. L., in *Wood Chemistry*, L. E. Wise and E. C. Jahn, eds., Reinhold, New York, 1952, (a) p. 1144, (b) p. 1148, (c) p. 1153, (d) p. 1214.

33. Buckland, I. K., F. E. Brauns, and H. Hibbert, *Can. J. Research*, **13B**, 61 (1935).

34. Buckland, I. K., G. H. Tomlinson, and H. Hibbert, *J. Am. Chem. Soc.*, **59**, 597 (1937); *Can. J. Research*, **16B**, 54 (1938).

35. Calhoun, J. M., F. H. Yorston, and O. Maass, *Can. J. Research*, **15B**, 457 (1937).

36. Clark, J. C., and F. E. Brauns, *Paper Trade J.*, **119**, No. 6, 33 (1944).

37. Corey, A. J., and O. Maass, *Can. J. Research*, **13B**, 149 (1935).

38. Cousin, H., and H. Herissey, *Bull. soc. chim. France*, **3**, 1070 (1908).

39. Creighton, R. H. J., R. D. Gibbs, and H. Hibbert, *J. Am. Chem. Soc.*, **66**, 32 (1944).

40. Creighton, R. H. J., and H. Hibbert, *J. Am. Chem. Soc.*, **66**, 37 (1944).

41. Czapek, F., *Biochemie der Pflanzen*, Vol. I, Jena, 1913, p. 689; C. Hoffmeister, *Chem. Ber.*, **60**, 2062 (1927).

42. Dence, C., and K. Sarkanen, *Tappi*, **43**, 87 (1960).

42b. Dence, C. W., M. K. Gupta and K. V. Sarkanen, *Tappi*, **45**, 29 (1962).

43. deVains, A. R., and R. Fournier, *Pulp Paper Mag. Can.*, **22**, 757 (1924).

44. Dorée, C., and L. Hall, *J. Soc. Chem. Ind.*, **43**, 257T (1924).

45. Eberhardt, G., *J. Am. Chem. Soc.*, **78**, 2832 (1956).

46. Eberhardt, G., and W. J. Schubert, *J. Am. Chem. Soc.*, **78**, 2835 (1956).

47. Engel, O., and E. Wedekind, *Ger. Pat.* 581, 806 (1933).

48. Enkvist, T., *Svensk Papperstidn.*, **51**, 225 (1948).

49. Enkvist, T., *Tappi*, **37**, 350 (1954).
50. Enkvist, T., B. Alm, and B. Holm, *Paperi ja Puu*, **38**, 1 (1956); T. Enkvist, B. Alfredsson, and E. Hägglund, *Svensk Papperstidn.*, **55**, 588 (1952); G. Gran and B. Althin, *Acta Chem. Scand.*, **4**, 967 (1950).
51. Enkvist, T., and E. Hägglund, *Festskift tillägnad J. Arvid Hedwall*, **1948**, p. 149.
52. Enkvist, T., M. Moilanen, and B. Alfredsson, *Svensk Papperstidn.*, **52**, 513 (1949).
53. Erdtman, H., *Eiochem. Z.*, **258**, 172 (1933); *Ann.*, **503**, 283 (1933).
54. Erdtman, H., *Svensk Papperstidn.*, **43**, 255 (1940); *Cellulosechemie*, **18**, 83 (1940).
55. Erdtman, H., *Research*, **3**, 83 (1950).
56. Erdtman, H., and J. Gripenberg, *Acta Chem. Scand.*, **1**, 71 (1947).
57. Erdtman, H., B. O. Lindgren, and T. Petterson, *Acta Chem. Scand.*, **4**, 228 (1950).
58. Erdtman, H., and T. Pettersson, *Acta Chem. Scand.*, **4**, 971 (1950).
59. Felicetta, V. F., and J. L. McCarthy, *J. Am. Chem. Soc.*, **79**, 4499 (1957).
60. Fisher, H. E., and H. Hibbert, *J. Am. Chem. Soc.*, **69**, 1208 (1947).
61. Flory, P. J., *Principles of Polymer Chemistry*, Cornell Univ. Press, Ithaca, N.Y., 1953, pp. 358–361.
62. Freudenberg, K., in L. Zechmeister, *Progress in the Chemistry of Organic Natural Products*, **11**, 43 (1954).
63. Freudenberg, K., *Angew. Chem.*, **68**, 84 (1956).
64. Freudenberg, K., *Proceedinys of the Fourth International Congress of Biochemistry, Vienna, 1958*, Pergamon Press, 1959, p. 132.
65. Freudenberg, K., *Das Papier*, **1**, 209 (1947); K. Freudenberg and G. Dietrich, *Ann.*, **563**, 146 (1948).
66. Freudenberg, K., W. Belz, and C. Niemann, *Chem. Ber.*, **62**, 1561 (1929).
67. Freudenberg, K., and F. Bittner, *Chem. Eer.*, **86**, 155 (1953); K. Freudenberg and F. Niederkorn, *ibid.*, **89**, 2168 (1956).
68. Freudenberg, K., and W. Dürr, *Chem. Ber.*, **63**, 2713 (1930).
69. Freudenberg, K., K. Engler, E. Flickinger, A. Sobek, and F. Klink, *Chem. Ber.*, **71**, 1810 (1938); K. Freudenberg, A. Janson, E. Knopf, and A. Haag, *Chem. Ber.*, **69**, 1415 (1936).
70. Freudenberg, K., and W. Heimberger, *Chem. Eer.*, **83**, 519 (1950).
71. Freudenberg, K., and H. Hubner, *Chem. Eer.*, **85**, 1181 (1952); K. Freudenberg and H. Schluter, *ibid.*, **88**, 617 (1955).
72. Freudenberg, K., A. Janson, E. Knopf, and A. Haag, *Chem. Ber.*, **69**, 1415 (1936).
73. Freudenberg, K., W. Lautsch, and K. Engler, *Chem. Ber.*, **73B**, 167 (1940).
74. Freudenberg, K., and H. F. Müller, *Chem. Ber.*, **71**, 1281 (1938).
75. Freudenberg, K., and E. Plankenhorn, *Chem. Ber.*, **75**, 857 (1942); **80**, 149 (1947).
76. Freudenberg, K., and D. Rasenack, *Chem. Ber.*, **86**, 755 (1953).
77. Freudenberg, K., H. Reznik, H. Boesenberg, and D. Rasenack, *Chem. Ber.*, **85**, 641 (1952).
78. Freudenberg, K., F. Sohns, W. Dürr, and C. Niemann, *Cellulosechemie*, **12**, 263 (1931).
79. Freudenberg, K., F. Sohns, and A. Janson, *Ann.*, **518**, 62 (1935).

80. Freudenberg, K., H. Zocher, and W. Dürr, *Chem. Ber.*, **62**, 1814 (1929).
81. Gardner, J. A. F., *Can. J. Chem.*, **32**, 532 (1954).
82. Gierer, J., *Acta Chem. Scand.*, **8**, 1319 (1954).
83. Gierer, J., *Chem. Ber.*, **89**, 257 (1956).
84. Gierer, J., and S. Söderberg, *Acta Chem. Scand.*, **13**, 127 (1959).
85. Godard, H. P., J. L. McCarthy, and H. Hibbert, *J. Am. Chem. Soc.*, **62**, 988 (1940); L. Cooke, J. L. McCarthy, and H. Hibbert, *ibid.*, **63**, 3052, 3056 (1941).
86. Goldschmid, O., *J. Am. Chem. Soc.*, **75**, 3780 (1953); *Anal. Chem.*, **26**, 1421 (1954).
87. Goldschmid, O., *Tappi*, **38**, 728 (1955).
88. Gordy, W., *J. Chem. Phys.*, **9**, 207, 215 (1941).
89. Gralén, N., *J. Colloid Sci.*, **1**, 453 (1946).
90. Gray, K. R., E. G. King, F. E. Brauns, and H. Hibbert, *Can. J. Research*, **13B**, 35 (1935).
91. Gustafsson, C., and L. Andersen, *Paperi ja Puu*, **37**, 1 (1955).
92. Hägglund, E., *Chemistry of Wood*, Academic Press, New York, 1951, (a) pp. 181–332, (b) pp. 196–212, (c) p. 289, (d) p. 326.
93. Hägglund, E., *Acta Acad. Aboensis, Math. et Phys.*, **2**, No. 4, 10 (1922).
94. Hägglund, E., and T. Johnson, *Biochem. Z.*, **202**, 440 (1928).
95. Hägglund, E., and T. Johnson, *Finnish Paper Timber J.*, **16**, 282 (1934); H. Erdtman, *Svensk Papperstidn.*, **48**, 75 (1945).
96. Hägglund, E., and H. Richtzenhain, *Tappi*, **35**, 281 (1952).
97. Häggroth, S., B. O. Lindgren, and U. Saeden, *Svensk Papperstidn.*, **56**, 660 (1953).
98. Harris, E. E., *Tappi*, **36**, 402 (1953).
99. Harris, E. E., J. D'Ianni, and H. Adkins, *J. Am. Chem. Soc.*, **60**, 1467 (1938).
100. Hernestam, S., and E. Adler, *Svensk Kem. Tidskr.*, **67**, 37 (1955).
101. Herzog, R. O., and A. Hillmer, *Chem. Ber.*, **60**, 365 (1927); *Z. Physiol. Chem.*, **168**, 117 (1927); *Chem. Ber.*, **62**, 1600 (1929); **64**, 1288 (1931); *Papier-Fabr.*, **29**, 40 (1931); **30**, 205 (1932).
101a. Hess, C. L., *Tappi*, **35**, 315 (1952).
102. Hildebrand, J. H., and R. L. Scott, *Solubility of Nonelectrolytes*, 3rd ed., Reinhold, New York, 1951.
103. Hodge, H. J., and A. B. Wardrop, *Australian J. Sci. Res.*, **3B**, 265 (1950).
104. Holmberg, B., *Chem. Ber.*, **69**, 115 (1936).
105. Husband, R. M., C. D. Logan, and C. B. Purves, *Can. J. Chem.*, **33**, 81 (1955).
106. Jayne, J. E., *Tappi*, **36**, 571 (1953).
107. Jones, E. J., *J. Am. Chem. Soc.*, **70**, 1984 (1948); *Tappi*, **32**, 311 (1949).
108. Jones, E. J., unpublished results.
109. Kaheki, K., R. A. Murphy, H. White and K. V. Sarkanen, *Tappi*, **45**, 24 (1962).
110. Klason, P., *Svensk Kem. Tidskr.*, **9**, 133 (1897).
111. Klason, P., *Hauptversammlungsber. Ver. Zellstoff u. Papier-Chemiker u. Ingenieure*, **1908**, 52.
112. Kratzl, K., *Monatsh. Chem.*, **78**, 173 (1948); **80**, 437 (1949).
113. Kratzl, K., *Monatsh. Chem.*, **80**, 314 (1949).

114. Kratzl, K., and G. Billek, *Monatsh. Chem.*, **84**, 406 (1953); *Tappi*, **40**, 269 (1957).

115. Kratzl, K., and G. Billek, *Holzforschung*, **10**, 161 (1956); G. Billek, *Proc. of the Fourth International Congress of Biochemistry, Vienna, 1958*, Pergamon Press, 1959, p. 207.

116. Kratzl, K., and E. Klein, *Monatsh. Chem.*, **86**, 847 (1955); K. Kratzl and W. Schweers, *ibid.*, **85**, 1046 (1954).

117. Kratzl, K., and H. Silbernagel, *Monatsh. Chem.*, **83**, 1022 (1952).

118. Kratzl, K., and E. Wittman, *Monatsh. Chem.*, **85**, 7 (1954).

119. Kuhn, R., and F. l'Orsa, *Z. angew. Chem.*, **44**, 847 (1931).

120. Kullgren, C., *Svensk Kem. Tidskr.*, **44**, 15 (1932).

121. Lange, P. W., *Svensk Papperstidn.*, **47**, 262 (1944); **48**, 241 (1945).

122. Lange, P. W., *Svensk Papperstidn.*, **50**, No. 11B, 130 (1947).

123. Leopold, B., *Acta Chem. Scand.*, **4**, 1523 (1950).

124. Leopold, B., *Acta Chem. Scand.*, **6**, 38 (1952).

125. Leopold, B., *Acta Chem. Scand.*, **6**, 57 (1952).

126. Leopold, B., and I. L. Malmström, *Acta Chem. Scand.*, **6**, 49 (1952).

126b. Levitin, N., N. S. Thompson, and C. B. Purves, *Pulp Paper Mag. Can.*, **56**, No. 5, 117 (1955).

127. Lindgren, B. O., *Acta Chem. Scand.*, **1**, 779 (1948); **3**, 1011 (1949).

128. Lindgren, B. O., *Acta Chem. Scand.*, **4**, 1365 (1950); **5**, 603 (1951).

129. Lindgren, B. O., *Acta Chem. Scand.*, **5**, 616 (1951).

130. Lindgren, B. O., *Svensk Papperstidn.*, **55**, 78 (1952); E. Adler and B. O. Lindgren, *Svensk Papperstidn.*, **55**, 563 (1952).

131. Lindgren, B. O., and H. Mikawa, *Acta Chem. Scand.*, **8**, 954 (1954).

132. Lindgren, B. O., and U. Saeden, *Acta Chem. Scand.*, **6**, 91 (1952).

133. Lindgren, B. O., and U. Saeden, *Acta Chem. Scand.*, **6**, 963 (1952).

134. Loughborough, D. L., and A. J. Stamm, *J. Phys. Chem.*, **40**, 1113 (1936); **45**, 1137 (1941).

135. MacInnes, A. S., E. West, J. L. McCarthy, and H. Hibbert, *J. Am. Chem. Soc.*, **62**, 2803 (1940); M. Kulka and H. Hibbert, *ibid.*, **65**, 1180 (1943).

135a. Marton, J., E. Adler, and K. I. Peisson, *Acta Chem. Scand.*, **15**, 384 (1961).

136. McGregor, W. S., T. H. Evans, and H. Hibbert, *J. Am. Chem. Soc.*, **66**, 41 (1944).

137. Mikawa, H., K. Sato, C. Takasaki, and K. Ebisawa, *Bull. Chem. Soc. Japan*, **28**, 649 (1955); **29**, 209 (1956).

138. Mikawa, H., K. Sato, C. Takasaki, and H. Okada, *J. Chem. Soc. Japan, Ind. Chem. Sect.*, **54**, 299 (1951); H. Mikawa, *ibid.*, **54**, 671, 741, 762 (1951).

139. Moacanin, J., W. F. Felicetta, W. Haller, and J. L. McCarthy, *J. Am. Chem. Soc.*, **77**, 3470 (1955).

140. Nakamura, T., T. Kawano, M. Kawasaki, K. Tominaga, T. Awa, and S. Kitaura, *Research Rept., Dept. Chem., Div. Agr., Kyushu Univ.*, No. 12, 43 (1954).

141. Nikitin, N. I., *Die Chemie des Holzes* (translation from Russian), Akademie Verlag, Berlin, 1955, pp. 214–319.

142. Nokihara, E., M. J. Tuttle, V. F. Felicetta, and J. L. McCarthy, *J. Am. Chem. Soc.*, **79**, 4495 (1957).

142a. Nord, F. F., and W. J. Schubert, *Tappi*, **40**, 287 (1957).

143. Norman, A. G., *The Biochemistry of Cellulose, the Polyuronides, and Lignin*, Oxford, 1937, p. 170.

144. Payen, A., *Compt. rend.*, **29**, 493 (1849).

145. Pearl, I. A., *J. Am. Chem. Soc.*, **78**, 5672 (1956); I. A. Pearl and D. L. Beyer, *Tappi*, **39**, 171 (1956).

146. Peniston, Q. P., and J. L. McCarthy, *J. Am. Chem. Soc.*, **70**, 1329 (1948).

147. Pennington, D. E., and D. M. Ritter, *J. Am. Chem. Soc.*, **69**, 187 (1947).

148. Pennington, D., and D. M. Ritter, *J. Am. Chem. Soc.*, **69**, 665 (1947).

149. Pepper, J. M., and H. Hibbert, *J. Am. Chem. Soc.*, **70**, 67 (1948).

150. Pew, J. C., *Tappi*, **36**, 39 (1949).

151. Pew, J. C., *J. Am. Chem Soc.*, **74**, 2850 (1952).

152. Pew, J. C., *J. Am. Chem. Soc.*, **77**, 2831 (1955).

152a. Phillips, M., *J. Am. Chem. Soc.*, **54**, 1518 (1932); M. Phillips and M. J. Goss, *Ind. Eng. Chem.*, **24**, 1436 (1932).

153. Pomilio, U., *Pulp Paper Mag. Can.*, **19**, 1255 (1921).

154. Read, D. E., and C. B. Purves, *J. Am. Chem. Soc.*, **74**, 120 (1952).

155. Reinitzer, F., *Monatsh. Chem.*, **45**, 87 (1924).

156. Richtzenhain, H., *Svensk Papperstidn.*, **53**, 644 (1950).

157. Richtzenhain, H., and C. Hofe, *Chem. Ber.*, **72**, 1890 (1939).

158. Ritchie, P. F., and C. B. Purves, *Pulp Paper Mag. Can.*, **48**, No. 12, 74 (1947); W. J. Wald, P. F. Ritchie, and C. B. Purves, *J. Am. Chem. Soc.*, **69**, 1371 (1947).

159. Routala, O., and J. Sevon, *Cellulosechemie*, **7**, 113 (1926).

160. Samuelson, O., *Svensk Kem. Tidskr.*, **60**, 128 (1948).

161. Sarkanen, K., and C. Schuerch, *Anal. Chem.*, **27**, 1245 (1955).

162. Sarkanen, K., and C. Schuerch, *J. Am. Chem. Soc.*, **79**, 4203 (1957).

163. Schmidt, E., and E. Graumann, *Chem. Ber.*, **54**, 1860 (1921).

164. Schmidt, E., W. Haag, and L. Sperling, *Chem. Ber.*, **58**, 1394 (1925); E. Schmidt and K. Braundsdorf, *Chem. Ber.*, **55**, 1529 (1922).

165. Schubert, W. J., and F. F. Nord, *J. Am. Chem. Soc.*, **72**, 977 (1950); **72**, 3835 (1950).

166. Schuerch, C., *J. Am. Chem. Soc.*, **72**, 3838 (1950).

167. Schuerch, C., *J. Am. Chem. Soc.*, **73**, 2385 (1951).

168. Schuerch, C., *J. Am. Chem. Soc.*, **74**, 5061 (1952); E. C. Jahn, C. V. Holmberg, and C. Schuerch, *Chemistry in Canada, April, 1953*, pp. 35 and 40.

169. Schutz, F., *Cellulosechemie*, **19**, 33 (1941).

170. Schutz, F., and W. Knackstedt, *Cellulosechemie*, **20**, 15 (1942).

171. Shorygina, N. N., *Die Chemie des Holzes* (translation from Russian), Akademie Verlag, Berlin, 1955, pp. 298–300.

172. Shorygina, N. N., T. Y. Kefeli, and A. F. Semechkina, *Zhur. Obshcheĭ Khim.*, **19**, 1558 (1949); through *Chem. Abstracts*, **44**, 3919 (1950).

173. Smith, D. C. C., *Nature*, **176**, 267 (1955).

174. Smith, D. C. C., *J. Chem. Soc.*, **1955**, 2347.

175. Smith, D. M., and C. B. Purves, *Ind. Eng. Chem.*, **49**, 1394 (1957).

176. Staudinger, H., and E. Dreher, *Chem. Ber.*, **75**, 857 (1942).

177. Stone, J. E., *Can. J. Chem.*, **31**, 207 (1953).

178. Stone, J. E., M. J. Blundell, and K. G. Tanner, *Can. J. Chem.*, **29**, 734 (1951).

179. Stumpf, W., and K. Freudenberg, *Angew. Chem.*, **62**, 537 (1950).

180. Tanaka, J., and T. Kondo, *Parapu Kami Kôĝyô Zasshi*, **11**, No. 2, 29 (1957); through *Chem. Abstracts*, **52**, 6784 (1958).

181. Tiemann, F., and W. Haarmann, *Chem. Ber.*, **7**, 606 (1874); **8**, 509 (1875).

182. Ujioka, Y., T. Nakamura, T. Awa, and S. Kitaura, *Research Rept., Dept. Chem., Div. Agr., Kyushu Univ.*, No. 4, 12 (1951).

183. Ungar, E., *Cellulosechemie*, **7**, 73 (1926).

184. Urban, H., *Cellulosechemie*, **7**, 73 (1926).

185. VanBeckum, W. G., and G. J. Ritter, *Paper Trade J.*, **105**, No. 18, 127 (1937).

186. Wacek, A. v., and H. Daubner-Rettenbacher, *Monatsh. Chem.*, **81**, 266 (1950).

187. Wacek, A. v., O. Hartel, and S. Meralla, *Holzforschung*, **8**, 65 (1954).

188. Wacek, A. v., and K. Kratzl, *J. Polymer Sci.*, **3**, 539 (1948)

189. Watson, W. F., *Trans. Inst. Rubber Ind.*, **29**, 32 (1953); L. C. Bateman, *Ind. Eng. Chem.*, **49**, 704 (1957).

190. West, E., A. S. MacInnes, and H. Hibbert, *J. Am. Chem. Soc.*, **65**, 1187 (1943).

191. Willstätter, R., and L. Zechmeister, *Chem. Ber.*, **46**, 2401 (1913).

192. Wise, L. E., F. C. Peterson, and W. M. Harlow, *Ind. Eng. Chem., Anal. Ed.*, **11**, 18 (1939).

CHAPTER 7

Extraneous Components of Wood

M. A. Buchanan, *The Institute of Paper Chemistry, Appleton, Wisconsin*

I. Introduction

All species of wood and other plant tissues contain small amounts, and in some cases quite appreciable quantities, of substances in addition to cellulose, hemicelluloses, and lignin. To distinguish them from the major cell wall components, these additional constituents are known as the extraneous components. Many of these substances are extractable with neutral solvents, and are referred to as extractives. The term extraneous components embraces a wide range of chemical types and includes a very large number of individual compounds. However, no single species contains all the possible compounds or even all the different classes of compounds. The extractives of related species are often similar, and thus there are many family relationships. On the other hand, the exact nature of the extractives often differs distinctly between closely related species, and certain extractives are of value in taxonomy.

There is considerable variation in the distribution of the extractives throughout the wood of a given tree. Sugars and other sap-soluble constituents, and deposited reserve foods such as starch and fats, are found in the sapwood. Phenolic materials, however, are usually deposited in the heartwood. There are variations in the amount of deposited materials throughout the height of the tree and between the main stem and the branches.

There is also variation within the fine structure of the wood. Fats are found in the parenchymatous cells, especially the ray parenchyma, whereas the resin acids are secreted by the epithelial cells and tend to fill the resin ducts. Some materials appear to be deposited in the pores of certain hardwoods. Sap-soluble constituents are present in the sapwood of the living tree, and are deposited within the wood capillaries and on the wood surfaces when the wood is dried.

The extractives often play an important role in the utilization of wood, and influence the physical properties of the wood (141). Colored and volatile constituents provide esthetic values. Certain phenolic compounds lend resistance to fungal and insect attack with resulting durability, and silica imparts resistance to the marine borer. Some extractives are utilized commercially. At present, quebracho extract from the heartwood of the South American tree is one of the chief sources of vegetable tannins; sulfate turpentine and tall oil provide a large proportion of the turpentine, rosin, and fatty acids produced in this country; camphor is an extractive of the camphor tree and is produced synthetically from terpenes obtained from the pines.

Some extractives have negative values in the utilization of the wood. Alkaloids and some other physiologically active materials may present health hazards. The usual calcium base sulfite pulping is inhibited by certain phenols present in pine heartwood, whereas pitch problems and loss of absorbency in wood pulps are due to extractives. Some materials contribute to corrosion (129), and the presence of starch makes wood more susceptible to insect attack.

Extractives occur in other parts of the tree and in other plant tissues, often in higher concentrations than in the wood. Bark and roots are rich sources of extractives, whereas the components of leaves, flowers, and seeds are of great biological importance. Exudates are often produced by sapwood or inner bark especially when the tree is injured. Exudates include polysaccharide gums, water-insoluble resins, and volatile oils. Those comprised of resins and volatile oils are known as oleoresins, and those from the pines are sometimes referred to as "gum". However, the pine exudates are very different from the carbohydrate exudates of some other trees which are the true gums. Latexes secreted by the inner bark are important sources of certain extraneous materials. Although the extractives of wood should be considered in their relationship to the broad field of plant products, this chapter is limited, for the most part, to the materials found in wood.

The extractives have been classified into various groups on the basis of certain structural features, but there is often overlapping because of the polyfunctional nature of some compounds. They may be grouped according to physical properties such as solubility (118), or according to botanical families and genera. Botanical classification is very instructive, but is limited by the fact that many species have not been studied thoroughly.

Several classes of extractives have been reviewed (144), and previous books on wood chemistry have included chapters on extractives (73,188). Wehmer (182) has compiled the older literature according to species, and Karrer (95) has recently listed references for the individual compounds including references to structural studies, as well as to sources of the substances. Reviews have been published on: heartwood extractives of the conifers (46), wood extractives (99), extractives of American pulpwoods (93), the literature for 1957–59 (149), and chromatography in the plant sciences (179). Howes (89,90) has described the sources of the commercial gums and resins and vegetable tannins.

Several articles have discussed the value of infrared spectroscopy in the determination of structure and sterochemistry of the resin acids (26), sterols (38,94), triterpenes (39), and some flavonoids (92).

II. Volatile Oils

Wood often contains appreciable amounts of volatile or essential oils. These, especially the oxygenated constituents, are responsible for the characteristic odors associated with fresh wood. Depending on the species, the volatile constituents consist of terpenes and related substances, paraffin compounds, and even aromatic compounds. These substances, for the most part, have boiling points of over 100°C., but they are characterized by an appreciable vapor pressure at room temperature and by the fact that they distill with steam. In addition to the usual essential oils, steam distillation of wood normally produces some acetic acid owing to the hydrolysis of acetyl groups in the holocellulose; acetic acid, however, should not be considered an extraneous material. At least part of the volatile components are lost when the wood is dried, and thus the usual moisture determination may include substances other than water.

Kurth (119) has compiled data published up to about 1950 on the volatile oils from both oleoresins and wood for species of several families. Most of the substances reported for both softwoods and hardwoods are terpenes or related materials. Mirov (134) has tabulated data on the composition of gum turpentines from the oleoresin from different species of pine. Most of the pines from the southeastern part of the United States and some of the European pines produce turpentines comprised chiefly of α-pinene and β-pinene, the former predominating. The oleoresins from Jeffrey pine and digger pine are unusual in that n-heptane is the major volatile constituent. Small amounts of n-heptane and n-undecane have been found in the turpentines of some other pines (135), and small amounts of octyl, nonyl, and decyl aldehydes are present in some turpentines.

III. Terpenes and Related Materials

Many natural substances have carbon structures which appear to be built-up of isoprene units (2-methylbutadiene, C_5H_8), and these compounds are said to follow the isoprene rule. The term isoprenoid is used to designate the broad class. Although isoprene is not considered a precursor, the isoprene rule has been useful in considering biogenetic relationships (162) and in determining structures. The monoterpenes contain two isoprene units; the sesquiterpenes, three; the diterpenes, four; and the triterpenes have six such units. The C_{40} carotenoids are related materials, but they appear to be rare in wood. The terpenes include both acyclic and cyclic compounds. The apparent addition of each isoprene unit involves the loss of one double bond, and each ring closure results in the loss of an additional double bond. Thus, the acyclic monoterpene ocimene contains three double bonds, whereas the bicyclic pinenes contain only one double bond. The position of the double bonds varies because of isomerization. In addition, the related dihydro- and dehydrocompounds are often found in nature.

Many isoprenoids are alcohols, ketones, or acids which seem to be formed by the addition of water to double bonds and/or oxidation (especially of methyl groups). These include the terpene alcohols, the ketone camphor, and the resin acids. In addition, certain natural products including the tropolones and the sterols appear to be closely related to the terpenes, although they do not follow the isoprene rule.

In a strict sense, the term terpene should refer only to the hydrocarbons, and the oxygenated compounds should be classed as terpenoids. However, terpene is sometimes used in a broad sense to include the oxygen-containing compounds.

The isoprenoids often occur as mixtures of related materials which are difficult to separate. Some of the compounds isomerize readily, and some undergo disproportionation reactions. Asymmetric carbons are present, and as a rule the natural products are optically active. Despite these factors, remarkable progress has been made in the chemistry of these compounds, although our knowledge is far from complete. Owing to difficulties in purification, there are often differences in the physical constants that have been reported.

A. MONOTERPENES

The gum turpentines of most pines are comprised chiefly of mono-terpenes ($C_1 H_{16}$), although paraffin hydrocarbons are the major constituents of the turpentine of a few species. α-Pinene (I) is proba-bly the most important monoterpene. It is the major component of commercial turpentine, and occurs in many other volatile oils. Both the d and l forms are common; the latter occurs in the gum turpentine of slash pine, whereas the former is present in the gum turpentine of longleaf pine. α-Pinene undergoes many chemical reactions (171) and is an important starting material in the synthesis of camphor and other chemicals. The reactions of α-pinene depend, in part, on the presence of a reactive double bond, and in part on a ring system which readily undergoes isomerization.

α-Pinene adds nitrosyl chloride to form a solid derivative, which is useful for identification and purification. In the presence of air, α-pinene undergoes oxidation and polymerization. Apparently, a peroxide, which is responsible for further oxidation to various oxy-genated compounds including sobrerol, verbenol, and verbenone, is formed initially. α-Pinene adds hydrogen chloride with isomerization to form bornyl chloride and some limonene dihydrochloride. Hydra-tion in the presence of mineral acids forms bornyl and fenchyl alcohol. Thermal isomerization produces dipentene, camphene, the acyclic terpene—allo-ocimene, and other products, depending on the heating conditions and the catalyst.

β-Pinene (II), or nopinene, occurs in many essential oils along with α-pinene and is usually present as the l form. β-Pinene does not form a crystalline addition product with nitrosyl chloride, but may be oxidized to the crystalline nopinic acid. It is easily isomerized to α-pinene, and normally is not separated from the latter.

Camphene (III), the only crystalline bicyclic terpene, occurs in a number of essential oils, both in the d and the l forms. As camphene is crystalline it is rather easily obtained in pure form, but the ring structure is unstable and thus, it readily isomerizes. Camphene is an important intermediate in the synthesis of camphor and other chem-icals from the pinenes. α-Pinene can be converted directly into camphene or it may be treated with hydrogen chloride to form bornyl chloride which, on loss of hydrogen chloride, forms camphene. The latter may be oxidized directly to camphor or hydrated to isoborneol which is easily oxidized to camphor. These reactions involve an interesting se·ies of isomerizations involving ring rupture and closure. Chlorination of camphene yields the product known as toxaphene which is used widely as an insecticide. Toxaphene is a mixture of isomeric substances, with a composition approximating $C_{10}H_{10}Cl_8$.

(I)	(II)	(III)
α-Pinene,	β-Pinene,	Camphene,
b.p. 156°C.	b.p. 164°C.	m.p. 51–2°C.,
		b.p. 159°C.

(IV)	(V)	(VI)
Δ³-Carene,	Limonene,	β-Phellandrene,
b.p. 168–9°C./705 mm.	b.p. 177°C.	b.p. 171–2°C.

Δ³-Carene (IV) is the chief constituent of the turpentine from the Indian pine, *Pinus longifolia*. It is also present in European turpentines, and some turpentines from the western part of the United States. It has a sweet penetrating odor, is readily oxidized, and resinifies in the air. It isomerizes to the monocyclic terpene, sylvestrene, which has been obtained from turpentines containing Δ³-carene. On treatment with hydrogen chloride Δ³-carene is converted into a mixture of the hydrochlorides of sylvestrene and dipentene.

Limonene (V), 1,8(9)-*p*-menthadiene, is one of the most important monocyclic terpenes. It is the major constituent of pond pine turpentine, and occurs in other turpentines and essential oils. The inactive form known as dipentene is produced by isomerization of the pinenes, and is present in appreciable amounts in the volatile oils from old pine stumps. Dipentene has a higher boiling point than the pinenes, and is often separated from wood turpentine as an intermediate cut between the pinenes and pine oil. Limonene is a relatively stable terpene, but it does undergo oxidation in the air. In the absence of moisture it forms an optically active hydrochloride, whereas in the presence of moisture dipentene hydrochloride is formed. Limonene can be hydrated to the unsaturated alcohol α-terpineol and the dihydric alcohol, terpin hydrate.

Limonene and some other terpenoids undergo disproportionation reactions in which part of the material is hydrogenated and another part dehydrogenated. Thus, limonene is converted to a mixture of p-cymene and p-menthane when heated in the presence of copper formate (as a catalyst).

β-Phellandrene (VI) is a major constituent of the turpentine from lodgepole pine and from Coulter pine, and occurs in other essential oils including that from Canada balsam. β-Phellandrene is one of the less stable terpenes, and tends to polymerize on distillation at atmospheric pressure.

Other naturally occurring monoterpenes include bicyclic compounds: α-thujene, the chief component of the turpentine from *Boswellia serrata*; Δ⁴-carene, which has been isolated from some European turpentines and from pine needle oil; santene, which is found in East Indian sandalwood oil; monocyclic terpenes: terpinolene and α-terpinene, which are present in wood turpentine as a result of isomerization of the pinenes; acyclic terpenes: ocimene; myrcene, which has been found in loblolly turpentine; and linalool, occurring in the wood of *Ocotea candata*.

B. OXYGENATED MONOTERPENES

Small amounts of oxygen-containing compounds are present in the turpentines from some pines, and considerably larger amounts are present in wood turpentine obtained from aged pine stumps because of changes that occur during the natural aging process. The oxygenated materials have higher boiling points than the corresponding terpenes, and are, therefore, concentrated in the higher boiling fractions. Thus, pine oil from aged stumps consists of 50 to 60% α-terpineol (VII) with smaller amounts of dihydro-α-terpineol, fenchyl alcohol, and other compounds (154,195). Many of these compounds are white crystalline solids with characteristic odors, and for this reason some are known as "camphors." Some are valuable in perfumery.

Terpineol (VII) is formed by the dehydration of terpin hydrate and by the action of sulfuric acid on α-pinene. It is the major constituent of pine oil and is present in camphor oils and some other essential oils. α-Terpineol is easily dehydrated to dipentene and other terpenes depending on the reaction conditions, and it may be hydrated to terpin hydrate. It is a tetrahydro-*p*-cymene alcohol, and thus is related to other compounds discussed in Section III-D.

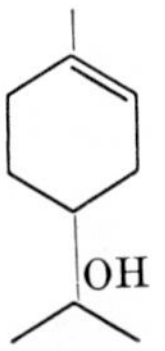

(VII)
α-Terpineol,
m.p. 35°C.,
b.p. 219°C.

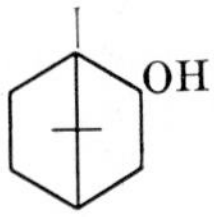

(VIII)
Borneol,
m.p. 208°C.,
b.p. 212°C.

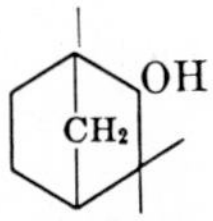

(IX)
Fenchyl alcohol,
b.p. 201°C.

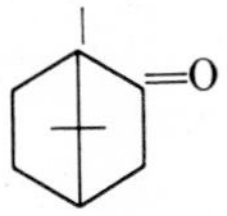

(X)
Camphor,
m.p. 179°C.,
b.p. 209°C.

Borneol (VIII), which has a camphor-like odor, is produced by the hydration of α-pinene and is readily oxidized to camphor. Borneol is a constituent of camphor oil. Bornyl acetate occurs in some essential oils, and seems to be especially common in species of *Abies* (119). Fenchyl alcohol (IX) may be prepared from the pinenes and is found in pine oil. Four optically active isomers of each of these two alcohols are known: *d*- and *l*-borneol, *d*- and *l*-isoborneol, *d*- and *l*-α-fenchyl alcohol, and *d*- and *l*-β-fenchyl alcohol. The α-fenchyl alcohols have melting points of 47 and 48°C., and the β-fenchyl alcohols melt at 5 and 6°C.

Camphor oil obtained from the wood and other parts of the camphor tree, *Cinnamomum camphora* (Lauraceae), contains a large number of terpenes and related materials; however, some of these may be formed during the distillation of the oil from the wood. Camphor (X) is the important constituent and has been an article of commerce for a long time. The *d* form is obtained from the camphor tree, but the *l* and *dl* forms occur in other oils. Since turpentine is a mixture of *d*- and *l*-α-pinene, synthetic camphor is optically inactive, although the active forms may be prepared from active α-pinene. The methylene group adjacent to the carbonyl group is reactive, but otherwise, camphor is a relatively stable compound.

Several additional monoterpene alcohols and carbonyl compounds occur in nature, but acids do not seem to be common in this series. However, chamic and chaminic acids, which have been isolated from the heartwood of *Chamaecyparis nootkatensis*, are C_{10} acids (49).

C. TROPOLONES AND THUJIC ACID

An interesting class of steam volatile compounds is found in the heartwood of western red-cedar and several other species of the cypress family (Cupressaceae). Initially, the compounds were believed to be phenols, but subsequently they were found to be substituted tropolones (47). Tropolone (XI) is cycloheptatrieneolone, and this nucleus is also found in certain mold metabolites and in the alkaloid colchinine.

(XI)
Tropolone

(XII)
Thujic acid,
m.p. 88°C.

The chemistry of the tropolones has been reviewed (142,145). They have aromatic properties, and are somewhat more acidic than are the usual phenols. They form red-colored complexes with ferric salts which change to green with an excess of the ferric salt, and form green-colored complexes with copper acetate and even with metallic copper. This has provided an ingenious method for collecting rather large amounts of tropolones from western red-cedar (62), in which copper bronze screens were placed in commercial dry kilns. After five weeks the deposit of copper complexes which had formed on the screens was dissolved in chloroform, and the free tropolones were liberated with hydrogen sulfide. The tropolones are considered to consist of a highly mobile tautomeric system, having both intramolecular hydrogen bonding and resonance. Because of the rapid tautomeric equilibrium only three monosubstituted products are known, indicating an equivalency for positions 3 and 7, and 4 and 6. Pauson has suggested rules for naming the tropolones (145), but the natural products have been given trivial names.

Substituted tropolones found in wood are listed in Table I. α-, β-,

TABLE I

Tropolones Occurring in the Cupressaceae

Compound	M.p., °C.
α-Thujaplicin (3-isopropyltropolone)	34
β-Thujaplicin (4-isopropyltropolone)	52–3
γ-Thujaplicin (5-isopropyltropolone)	82
β-Thujaplicinol (7-hydroxy-β-thujaplicin)	58
β-Dolabrin (4-isopropenyltropolone)	58–9
Nootkatin [5-(3-methylbutenyl-2)-β-thujaplicin]	95–6
Chamaecin [an ether of thujaplicinol (?)]	
Pygmaein (a methoxythujaplicin)	

and γ-thujaplicin were isolated from western red-cedar (*Thuja plicata*) in which they amount to as much as 1.2% of the heartwood. Concentration is greatest in the outer butt heartwood and gradually decreases to essentially zero in the innermost portion of heartwood (130). β-Thujaplicin was also isolated by Japanese investigators (142), and was known as hinokitol before the identity of the two materials was demonstrated. The crystalline ferric complex was called hinokitin. Subsequently additional tropolones were isolated as follows: nootkatin from *Chamaecyparis nootkatensis* (44), chamaecin from Formosan hinoki (*Chamaecyparis taiwanensis*) (62), β-dolabrin from hiba wood (*Thujopsis dolabrata*) (143), β-thujaplicinol from western red-cedar, and pygmaein from *Cupressus pygmaea* (194). Paper chromatography has indicated additional tropolones which have not, as yet, been characterized (194).

β-Thujaplicin is widely distributed in species of the Cupressaceae and is often the major tropolone in a given species. Nootkatin is common in the genus *Cupressus*, and is the major tropolone in yellow-cedar. The other tropolones appear to be less widely distributed, and in general, amount to less than 0.1% of the woods in which they do occur. Although most of the Cupressaceae species tested contain tropolones, some *Juniperus* species, including *J. virginiana* (eastern red-cedar), apparently do not.

The tropolones have attracted considerable attention because of their significance in taxonomic relationships, and because they contribute to the durability of the heartwood. They are corrosive to steel, but in the presence of free sodium hydroxide they form salts that are not corrosive (129).

In addition to the tropolones, steam distillation of western red-cedar heartwood yields a crystalline acid which was first believed to be dehydroperillic acid because it is easily isomerized to *p*-isopropyl benzoic acid. This acid subsequently was shown to be 4,4-dimethyl-heptatrienecarboxylic acid and was renamed thujic acid (XII) (48). It occurs both in the free form and as the methyl ester.

A second acid named shonanic acid, along with thujic acid, was isolated from an alkaline extract of the wood of *Libocedrus formosana* (127). This acid which was isolated in a yield of 0.2 to 0.4% appears to be a dihydrothujic acid.

D. *p*-CYMENE AND RELATED AROMATIC COMPOUNDS

The aromatic compound *p*-cymene (XIII) is the chief constituent of sulfite turpentine obtained from relief gases in the acid sulfite pulping of spruce and hemlock woods. It occurs in small amounts in some woods, but its presence in sulfite turpentine is due largely to isomerization and dehydrogenation of the monoterpenes present in the original woods. Because of the relatively low yield, sulfite turpentine is not an important commercial product, but some *p*-cymene is synthesized from the pinenes.

(XIII)
p-Cymene,
b.p. 176–7°C.

(XIV)
Carvacrol,
b.p. 237–8°C.

(XV)
p-Methoxythymol,
b.p. 155–6°C./25 mm.

(XVI)
Hydrothymoquinone,
m.p. 142°C.

(XVII)
Libocedrol,
m.p. 87–8°C.

(XVIII)
Methyl chavicol,
b.p. 215–6°C.

Carvacrol (XIV) and thymol are isomeric hydroxy-p-cymenes which occur in several essential oils. The former is found in the volatile oils from some species of the Cupressaceae. Carvacrol, p-methoxythymol (XV), small amounts of p-methoxycarvacrol, hydrothymoquinone (XVI), and thymoquinone are volatile constituents of the heartwood of incense-cedar (193). A dehydrodi-p-methoxythymol, libocedrol (XVII), and heyderiol, 6-(p-methoxycarvacroxy)-p-methoxythymol, have been isolated from the acetone extract of incense-cedar heartwood (192). Libocedrol forms an addition compound with p-methoxythymol, and occurs as such in the wood. A red quinone isolated from the petroleum ether extract is a similar dehydro-compound composed of three p-methoxythymol units, one of which is oxidized to the corresponding quinone (191).

Methyl chavicol or esdragol (XVIII) is present in small amounts in some turpentines and some other volatile oils.

E. SESQUITERPENES

With 15 carbon atoms, a large number of sesquiterpenes are possible, and many have been isolated from vegetable oils (170). Included are cadinene (XIX) and longifolene which are present in some Haploxylon or white pine turpentines, cedrene (XX) and the alcohols cedrenol and cedrol found in cedar wood oil from *Juniperus virginiana*, α- and β-santalene and α- and β-santalol the chief constituents of sandalwood oil, α- and β-gurjunenes from the oleoresin of some *Dipterocarpus* species, lanceol a primary monocyclic alcohol from the wood of *Santalum lanceolatum*, cadinol which is present in West Indian sandalwood oil, guaiol from guaiacum wood oil of *Bulnesia sarmienti*, and the ketones α- and γ-atlantone from the wood of some *Cedrus* species.

(XIX)
Cadinene,
b.p. 134–6°C./11 mm.

(XX)
Cedrene,
b.p. 121°C./12 mm.

Five isomeric cadinenes have been reported which differ in the position of the double bond, and which give the same dihydrochloride (86). The cadinenes and some other sesquiterpenes are bicyclic with a reduced naphthalene structure, while other bicyclic compounds have one ring with less than six carbon atoms. Cedrene, longifolene, and others are tricyclic. Guaiol and some other compounds are partially reduced azulenes, and on dehydrogenation yield blue-colored substituted azulenes. These are responsible for the blue or azulene oils found in some cases. The parent compound, azulene, is isomeric with naphthalene and consists of a 5-membered ring fused to a 7-membered ring. Sesquiterpene lactones with a reduced naphthalene structure have been known for some time in the oils of certain roots and flowers. More recently, lactones have been found which contain a 10-membered ring (175). Cuparene, an aromatic sesquiterpene, and the related cuparenic acid were isolated from *Chamaecyparis thyoides*, and the former occurs in other species of Cupressaceae (45).

F. RESIN ACIDS (DITERPENES)

Several naturally occurring diterpenes and oxygenated derivatives are known (170,181), and of these, the resin acids found in the pine family appear to be the most important in wood chemistry. Camphorene is a hydrocarbon present in camphor oil. The alcohols include phytol, an acyclic compound obtained on saponification of chlorophyll, the phenols ferruginol, and totarol from species of *Podocarpus* and hinokiol from *Chamaecyparis obtusa*. Manoyl oxide and keto-manoyl oxide have been isolated from the wood oil of *Dacrydium colensoi*.

The common resin acids found in pinewood and in pine oleoresin contain a partially reduced phenanthrene ring system and on dehydrogenation yield substituted phenanthrenes. The abietic acid type acids yield retene (1-methyl-7-isopropylphenanthrene) on dehydrogenation, whereas the pimaric acid-type acids give pimanthrene (1,7-dimethylphenanthrene).

(XXI)
Abietic acid,
m.p. 174°C.

(XXII)
Pimaric acid,
m.p. 211 (218)°C.

The abietic acid-type acids include levopimaric, abietic, neoabietic, and palustric acids. They differ from each other in regard to the position of the double bonds. They are relatively unstable and readily undergo isomerization or oxidation. Levopimaric acid is the chief acid in pine oleoresin. It isomerizes to abietic acid when heated, and because of this it is essentially absent in commercial rosins. Abietic acid (XXI) is usually the predominant acid in rosin. It is readily formed from levopimaric acid, and is also formed by prolonged heating of neoabietic and palustric acids. Since abietic acid is formed by isomerization of the other acids, there has been doubt as to whether it was a primary acid occurring in the original oleoresin.

Ultraviolet absorption spectra, however, indicate that abietic acid does exist in oleoresin. The free acid undergoes oxidation, but the quarter sodium salt ($C_{20}H_{29}O_2Na \cdot 3C_{20}H_{30}O_2$) is stable.

Neoabietic and palustric acids occur both in oleoresin and in rosin. Palustric acid, which has been known for only a few years, was isolated first from *Pinus palustris*, and has subsequently been isolated from *P. caribaea*, *P. elliotti*, *P. sylvestris*, and *Picea abies* (28). Thus it appears to be rather commonly distributed in the pines and spruces.

Levopimaric acid reacts with maleic anhydride at room temperature, and abietic, neoabietic, and palustric acids react at elevated temperatures to give the same product. Apparently, the latter three acids when heated are in equilibrium with small amounts of levopimaric acid which forms the adduct. The maleic anhydride reaction is used to separate the reactive acids from the nonreactive acids, and is used commercially in the production of fortified size (177).

The abietic acid-type acids undergo disproportionation when heated and perhaps, to some extent, in nature. Thus, dehydroabietic and dihydroabietic acids are present in oleoresin and in rosin, and tetrahydroabietic acid is often present in rosin. Dehydroabietic acid contains a typical aromatic ring, whereas tetrahydroabietic acid is free of double bonds. The presence of a dihydroabietic acid is indicated in pine oleoresin by the formation of a lactone on treatment with sulfuric acid (54). Since different dihydroabietic acids give the same lactone under these conditions, the exact nature of the dihydroabietic acid in oleoresin and rosin seems uncertain.

Pimaric acid (XXII) and isopimaric acid are pimaric-type acids which differ in configuration and in the location of the nuclear double bond (8a). They do not react with maleic anhydride, do not isomerize readily, and are more stable to oxidation than are the abietic-type acids. These acids were formerly called dextropimaric and isodextropimaric acids, but it has recently been suggested that the shorter names be used because they are not optical isomers of levopimaric acid. Isopimaric acid also occurs in species of the Podocarpaceae and has been called miropinic acid (25).

The structure given for pimaric acid indicates its sterochemistry (19). In this designation, a heavy line indicates the α-configuration, whereas a dotted line indicates the β-configuration. Isopimaric acid has the same configuration at C_1, C_{11}, and C_{12}, but the two acids are epimeric at C_{13} and C_7 (27). The configuration of abietic, and probably neoabietic, acid is the same as that of pimaric acid at C_1, C_{11},

C_{12}, and C_{13}, whereas the configuration of levopimaric acid differs at C_{13} (114).

The resin acids normally occur as the free acids, and they do not esterify readily with alcohols. This fact permits a separation from fatty acids, since the latter are more readily esterified. The resin acids form insoluble salts with certain amines. Thus, cyclohexyl-amine forms acetone-insoluble salts with most of the resin acids, whereas other amines are more or less specific for the precipitation of the individual acids (77). The resin acids develop a red coloration when treated with concentrated sulfuric acid–acetic anhydride, which is the basis of the Liebermann-Storch test for resin acids. However, other natural products including the sterols and some terpene alcohols give colorations with the same reagent.

The resin acids may be partially separated by column chroma-tography (128), but apparently they have not been separated by paper chromatography. Gas chromatography has been used for the separation of the methyl esters, but there is some isomerization at the higher temperatures and some esters were not separated (91).

Published data on the composition of oleoresin and rosins are somewhat variable, owing to an appreciable variation between samples and, to some extent, to different methods of analysis. The acids in the oleoresin from slash and longleaf pines are comprised of

TABLE II

Composition of Rosin Samples[a]

Acid	Gum rosin		Tall oil rosin	
	Lawrence[b]	Genge[c]	Lawrence	Genge
Abietic	20	33	39	37
Palustric	17	5	7	9
Neoabietic	17	14	4	2
Dehydroabietic	5	6	17	23
Isopimaric		18		11
Pimaric		5		3
Dihydroabietic		<1		2
Dihydropalustric		<1		2

[a] All values in per cent.
[b] See ref. 124.
[c] See ref. 65.

20 to 35% levopimaric acid, roughly 10% each of abietic, neoabietic, and palustric acids, and somewhat smaller amounts of pimaric, isopimaric, dehydroabietic, and dihydroabietic acids. Two sets of data from gum rosin and tall oil rosin are given in Table II. These indicate that tall oil rosin contains somewhat more abietic and dehydroabietic acids than does gum rosin. According to Lawrence (124) pinewood contains substances which promote oxidation of levopimaric acid in the wood chips to hydroxy acids which on subsequent processing are dehydrated to form dehydroabietic acid. In addition, tall oil rosin contains less unsaponifiables than does gum rosin.

In addition to the acids listed in Table II, caribeic acid has been reported in the oleoresin of slash pine, but was not indicated in that of longleaf pine (74). Podocarpic acid from *Pterocarpus* species has the phenanthrene ring system, but lacks the three carbon side chain of the usual resin acids (112), and thus is not a diterpene acid. The diterpenoids, cativic, eperuic, vinhaticoic, and voacapenic acids, are found in the oleoresins or in the wood of certain members of the Leguminosae (181). Cativic and eperuic acids are bicyclic compounds, whereas vinhaticoic and voacapenic acids are tetracyclic acids containing a furan ring. The two latter acids were found as methyl esters.

The usual analytical determination of resin acids depends on selective esterification, and includes materials other than resin acids (139). Because of this, results reported for species of birch and aspen may be in error. However, chromatography and color reactions suggest that the wood of white birch and quaking aspen does contain very small amounts of resin acids similar to those found in pine wood (30).

G. STEROLS

A number of natural products from widely different sources are tetracyclic compounds with a reduced cyclopentenophenanthrene ring system, and are known as steroids. The broad class includes sterols, bile acids, sex hormones, adrenal hormones, cardiac glycosides, toad poisons, certain saponins, and some alkaloids (53). Of these, the sterols are most important in wood chemistry. Sterols are secondary alcohols, which on dehydrogenation yield Diels hydrocarbon (XXIII). They usually contain 27 to 29 carbon atoms, and thus are not isoprenoids. However, part of the ring system is that of the common resin acids, and part of the side chain consists of an isopentane or substituted isopentane unit. The naturally occurring sterols have a hydroxyl group at C_3 with the β-configuration, methyl groups attached to C_{10} and C_{13}, and a 6 to 8 carbon side chain attached to C_{17}. Compounds with a double bond are known as stenols, and the fully hydrogenated compounds as stanols.

(XXIII)
Diels hydrocarbon

(XXIV)
β-Sitosterol,
m.p. 140°C.

Sterols are present as minor components in both animal and plant fats, and are present in larger proportions in fats from sources which contain only small amounts of fat. The sterols occur both free and as esters and glycosides. In animal fats, they occur in part as esters of the higher fatty acids, and estimation of both free and combined sterols is a common procedure. Some steroids such as the saponins and the cardiac active materials are glycosides, and recently sterol glycosides have been isolated from the phospholipid fraction of several seed fats. Sterols in wood also occur both free and combined, but the nature of the combined forms has received but little attention in wood chemistry. β-Sitosterol-D-glucoside was isolated from insect-infested wood of *Acer negundo* (116) and from the wood of *Aristotelia serrata* (31), the mixed phthalic acid ester of β-sitosterol and 2-octyl alcohol was obtained from Sitka spruce wood (115), and a sterol glucoside was found in the European aspen *Populus tremula* (150).

Sterols have been isolated from many species of wood, and they seem to be common wood components. β-Sitosterol (XXIV) is the major sterol in the pines, spruces, and larches, and it has been reported in several hardwood species. Smaller amounts of related sterols probably accompany β-sitosterol in these species, and appreciable amounts of dihydrositosterol are present in tall oil pitch. β-Sitosterol has the carbon structure of cholesterol, the common sterol of animal tissues, except that an ethyl group is attached at C_{24}.

Although β-sitosterol is the major sterol constituent of many species of wood, the sterols from some species have not been well-characterized. A sterol from *Betula verrucosa* was originally believed to differ from β-sitosterol (97), but a recent report suggests that the sterol fraction from this species consists of a mixture of β-sitosterol and the corresponding dihydrositosterol (168). The major sterols in *Eucalyptus microcorys* (43) and *Populus tremuloides* (78) apparently are not β-sitosterol.

The sterol from quaking aspen was believed to have the composition $C_{32}H_{56}O$, and was thought to be identical to the sterol isolated previously as the glucoside from the European aspen (150). This compound might be considered a substituted triterpene alcohol, but the Liebermann Burchard color reaction and the changes in molecular rotation on acetylation and benzoylation suggest that it should be classed as a sterol.

Free sterols with a 3-β-configuration react with digitonin (a saponin) to form sparingly soluble complexes consisting of equal molecular proportions of sterol and digitonin. Sterol esters, however, do not form these insoluble complexes. Thus, precipitation with digitonin provides a means of determining free sterols. Total sterols may be determined after saponification. Some nonsterols form complexes with digitonin, but these are somewhat more soluble (53).

The Liebermann-Burchard reaction is a color test for sterols in which the sterol is treated with cold acetic anhydride and sulfuric acid. The color depends on the reaction conditions, but in general β-sitosterol gives a blue coloration which gradually changes to green, and finally fades. The resin acids and at least some triterpene alcohols give a reddish coloration with the same reagent. The presence of a double bond in the ring system seems necessary for this color reaction. Both free sterols and the esters give the reaction, and the procedure has been used for the estimation of total sterols in animal tissues.

G. TRITERPENES

Only a few triterpene hydrocarbons have been found in nature. Squalene, a dihydrotriterpene, occurs in many oils of both vegetable

TABLE III

Some Triterpenes

Compound	M.p., °C.	Source	Refs.
Hydroxyketone			
Hydroxydammarenone-		*Dipterocarpus* species wood	
II (dipterocarpol)	135	and oleoresin	42, 66
Alcohols			
Cycloartenol (muningol)	115	*Pterocarpus angolensis* wood	172
Cycloeucalenol	135–6	Wood of *Eucalyptus microcorys, Erythrophloeum guineense,* and *Swietenia mahogoni*	4, 43
α-Amyrin	186–7	Manila elemi resin	172
β-Amyrin	199–200	Manila elemi resin	172
Ferreol	178–9	*Ferreirea spectabilis* wood	104
Hydroxy acids			
Oleanolic acid[a]	303–4	*Pterocarpus* species wood	3
Arjunolic acid	337–40	*Terminalia arjuna* wood	99
Terminolic acid	347	*Terminalia ivorensis* wood	108
Morolic acid[b]	273	*Mora excelsa* heartwood	12
Betulinic acid	316–8	*Platanus occidentalis* wood	189
Castanogenin[b]	380–2	*Castanospermum australe*	169
Emmolic acid	344–6	*Emmenospermum alphitonioides*	20

[a] Isolated as the acetate, m.p. 258°C.
[b] Occurs in the wood as a saponin.

and animal origin. It has been reported in tall oil (43a), and seems to be present in pine bark (144a). It has been isolated from paper birch wood (28a), and is probably present in many species of wood.

A large number of oxygenated compounds containing 30 carbons have been isolated from a variety of plant sources (172). Most of these follow the isoprene rule and are known as triterpenoids, or simply as triterpenes. Many are alcohols containing 50 hydrogen atoms, and thus correspond to dihydrotriterpenes. Several hydroxy acids and ketones are known. Usually the triterpenes have been obtained from resinous exudates, plant saps, leaves, and bark. To date, they have been isolated from only a few species of wood (see Table III), but it seems likely that future work will indicate a more widespread distribution in wood. The alcohols occur free, as acetates, and as glycosides (saponins). Reference has already been made to steroidal saponins. The term saponin refers to a group of plant glycosides which stabilize aqueous foams. Certain of the saponins cause hemolysis of red blood corpuscles and are toxic to fish. They are subdivided according to the nature of the aglycones obtained on hydrolysis. One group produces steroids, and the other triterpene alcohols or hydroxy acids. The saponins are dispersible with water because of the hydrophilic sugar units, but the free triterpene alcohols are water-repellent substances which tend to prevent loss of water at any exposed surfaces when the plant is injured.

Several triterpenes, including hydroxydammarenone-II, contain a ring structure and side chain similar to that of the sterols (53). Cycloartenol and cycloeucalenol have the same carbon skeleton with the addition of a cyclopropane ring. These compounds have some properties similar to the sterols, and have been designated methyl-sterols. However, their optical rotations and their color reactions suggest that they should be grouped with the triterpenes.

Most of the triterpenes are pentacyclic, and many of these belong to the β-amyrin or oleanane series. The α-amyrin or ursane series has the same ring structure, but the distribution of the methyl groups is different. The lupane series, on the other hand, has a pentacyclic ring system with one 5-membered ring. Oleanolic, arjunolic, terminolic, and morolic acids belong to the β-amyrin or oleanane series.

Many triterpenes contain a double bond in the ring system which is unreactive to the usual addition reagents. The unreactive double bond is usually detected by the color reaction with tetranitromethane. Nearly all of the triterpene alcohols which have been isolated from higher plants are dextrorotatory, and the molecular rotation is increased when the acetate or benzoate is prepared. The changes in molecular rotation are useful in indicating the type of triterpene, and in distinguishing them from the sterols (13). With the Liebermann-Burchard reagent, many triterpenes give a red coloration rather than the blue to green color given by the common sterols.

IV. Fatty Acids

Although fats are normally concentrated in seed tissues, appreciable amounts of higher fatty acids are obtained on saponification of the ether or benzene extracts of the wood of many species. In pine wood, and at least one species of spruce, oleic and linoleic acids are the predominant acids, and small amounts of linolenic acid seem to be present (30,96). These are the common unsaturated C_{18} acids, with one, two, and three double bonds, respectively. Next to oleic and linoleic acids, the C_{16} saturated acid, palmitic acid, is the most abundant fatty acid in the pines. Smaller amounts of the other even-numbered saturated acids from stearic (C_{18}) to lignoceric acid (C_{24}) are also present. Aspen and birch wood contain the above acids, but in these species linoleic acid is the predominant acid and the proportion of oleic acid is much smaller than in the pines.

In addition to the above, small amounts of other acids are present in at least some species of wood. Lauric and myristic acids have been reported by some investigators, and small amounts of saturated acids ranging from C_1 to C_8 (as well as the even-numbered acids from C_{10} to C_{26}) have been reported in European species of aspen and birch (151,168). Palmitoleic (the C_{16} monounsaturated acid), a C_{20} unsaturated acid, $(+)$-4-methylhexadecanoic acid, and n-heptadecanoic acid (41) have been isolated from tall oil. Presumably, these acids were present in the original wood, but some may have been formed during the processing. Gas chromatography has recently indicated the presence of all of the straight chain saturated acids from C_{16} to C_{26} in quaking aspen wood, including the odd-numbered acids (78). At one time, the odd-numbered acids were considered to be absent in the natural fats, but they have recently been isolated from some natural sources, and have been indicated by gas chromatography in others.

Procedures for the identification and estimation of the fatty acids are not always specific. Thus, paper chromatography and the usual methods of analysis do not distinguish between straight and branched-chain acids, or between the isomers of the unsaturated acids. Oxidation studies have suggested that part of the "linoleic acid" in pine wood is actually an isomer (98).

In the sapwood of the living tree and in green wood, most of the fatty acids appear to be present as triglycerides, although small amounts of free acids are normally present in unseasoned wood, and some of the fatty acids may be esterified with higher alcohols such as the sterols. The nature of the glycerides in wood has not been investigated as yet, but based on studies of other fats, it seems likely that the glycerides are chiefly mixed glycerides. In most fats, the saturated acids are often esterified with the primary hydroxyl groups of the glycerol, but otherwise, the distribution tends to be random (190). With the variety of acids found in wood, a very large number of individual glycerides are possible.

At least in some species of hardwoods the fatty materials are concentrated in the ray cells, and the fine fractions of some wood pulps contain up to 25% ether-soluble materials. In European species of alder, aspen, and birch the free acids were in the wood rays for the most part (152), although some were found in the middle lamella of the tracheids and on the walls of the vessels. In Scots pine, the free acids were mainly in the cells of the resin canals, with some in the wood ray cells and in the middle lamella of the tracheids. The location in Norway spruce was similar to that in the pine, except that the concentration was not as high in the resin canals. In *Juniperus communis*, the fatty acids were concentrated in the wood rays and in the middle lamella of the tracheids.

Seasoning apparently results in appreciable hydrolysis of the glycerides to free acids (139), possibly due to enzymatic action. During seasoning, the unsaturated acids are partially oxidized and polymerized. This results in a decrease in petroleum ether solubility on seasoning. Hot alkaline treatment isomerizes the unsaturated acids and, thus, in tall oil part of the linoleic acid has been isomerized to the conjugated isomer. The saturated acids, however, are stable and remain unchanged except for possible hydrolysis of the glycerides.

V. Unsaponifiables

Fats normally contain materials which, after saponification, exist as nonacidic water-insoluble substances, and the proportion of these substances is somewhat higher in fats from sources such as wood which are relatively low in fat content. These unsaponifiables consist of sterols, any triterpene or other higher alcohols that may be present, and hydrocarbons. The sterols, at least, and possibly the other higher alcohols, occur both free and combined in the original fat, and are converted into the free form on complete saponification.

Long chain fatty alcohols and hydrocarbons have been isolated in a few instances, and are probably present in other species which, as yet, have not been fully investigated. Nonvolatile terpene hydrocarbons and very weakly acidic phenolic materials may also be present. The complete nature of the unsaponifiables is still uncertain, and the term "resene" is often used to designate some of the materials of unknown composition. Sterol esters of the fatty acids are difficult to saponify, and some of these may be present in the usual unsaponifiable fraction.

VI. Carbohydrates

Although the major carbohydrate components are nonextractable cell wall constituents, certain soluble substances and some materials which seem to be extraneous components are present in many species of wood. Sugars and glycosides transported by the sap are present in the sapwood and inner bark. Sucrose, glucose, and fructose are common in the sapwood of both softwoods and hardwoods, whereas small amounts of arabinose and glucose are found in the heartwood of several species (173). L-Arabinose is found in both heartwood and sapwood of many conifers including the pines and western red cedar. Its presence may be due to the fact that the arabinans are readily hydrolyzed. L-Arabinonic acid has been isolated as the 1,4-lactone from the heartwood of *Austrocedrus chilensis* (9). Small amounts of raffinose, stachyose, and verbascose were found in European birch wood (125). Phenols and other hydroxy compounds are sometimes present as the more soluble glycosides, but in general the glycosides are more common in the inner bark than in wood.

Starch occurs in the sapwood of many hardwoods, and appears to serve as a reserve food supply. It is not soluble in the usual neutral solvents, but in some cases the granules have been washed out of finely divided wood (32). It is stored in the pith, the wood parenchyma, and in the wood rays. Many of the older methods give questionable results, but the sapwood of some species seems to contain up to about 5% starch.

Polysaccharides, which on hydrolysis yield arabinose and galactose, have been extracted with cold water from the wood of western larch, tamarack, Douglas-fir, black spruce, white spruce, jack pine, Jeffrey pine, and Monterey pine (1,21). A second polysaccharide was isolated from white spruce as an insoluble copper complex, which on hydrolysis gave mannose, galactose, and glucose. Monterey pine also contained small amounts of a glucomannan which formed an insoluble copper complex. The arabinogalactan from western larch ranges from 8 to 18% of the wood, but the soluble polysaccharides occur in the other species in much smaller amounts.

Up to about 0.5% pectic materials have been isolated from the wood of Douglas-fir, loblolly pine, white pine, white spruce, western hemlock, western red-cedar, black locust, lemonwood, and mesquite (6a). These are not extractable with the usual neutral solvents, and they occur within the cell wall in part. However, they are often not considered with the usual cell wall components, and it seems well to mention them here. Pectic substances are galacturonans with associated arabinans and galactans (186). The galacturonic acid residues are largely present as methyl esters.

VII. Polyhydric Alcohols

Some extractives may be considered as derivatives of the sugars in which the carbonyl group is replaced by an alcohol group. These compounds include glycerol, the sugar alcohols, and the cyclitols. Some have the sweet taste and water solubility associated with the simple sugars, but the carbonyl group is absent. Glycerol occurs as fatty acid glycerides in the wood of many species as discussed previously. The alcohols corresponding to the hexoses have not been commonly found in wood, but mannitol is the major constituent of exudates from species of the ash family. Recently, substituted anhydro-sugar alcohol structures have been discovered in bergenin, an extractive of the heartwood of *Shorea leprosula* (82), in vitexin which is obtained on acid hydrolysis of the extract of New Zealand puriri wood *Vitex lucens* (22), and in keyakinin and keyakinol from the heartwood of *Zelkova serrata* (60). Although vitexin has been considered to be an artifact, it seems to occur in the wood both in the free form and as glycosides (167). These compounds, like some glycosides, consist of a phenolic compound combined with a polyhydric chain. However, the linkage is carbon to carbon, and it is not hydrolyzable. Bergenin is the lactone of a substituted gallic acid, whereas vitexin and keyakinin are substituted flavones, and keyakinol is a flavanone.

Polyhydric cyclohexanes known as cyclitols are rather common plant constituents. Those with six hydroxyl groups are known as inositols, whereas those with five hydroxyls are quercitols (7). Pinitol (XXV), a monomethyl ether of *d*-inositol, occurs in the wood of several of the white pines (Haploxylon or five-needled pines), and is especially abundant in the wood of sugar pine. The heartwood of this species also contains *d*-inositol, *myo*-inositol, and sequoyitol (XXVI), a methyl ether of *myo*-inositol (10). Sequoyitol and pinitol have been isolated from the heartwood of the California redwood, and *myo*-inositol has been reported in the wood of European birch (125). In leaves and leafy twigs of the gymnosperms, pinitol was found in several species of the Pinaceae, whereas sequoyitol was found in some species of most families (155).

The cyclitols are extracted by the usual alcohol or acetone extractions because of the presence of some water, but they are insoluble in anhydrous ethanol or acetone. They are rather stable compounds.

(XXV)
Pinitol,
m.p. 186–8°C.

(XXVI)
Sequoyitol,
m.p. 234–7°C.

VIII. Nitrogen Compounds

All samples of wood contain small amounts of nitrogen due to the proteins from the original protoplasm, and several amino acids are present in the xylem sap (18). The woods of a few species contain somewhat larger amounts of nitrogen because of the presence of alkaloids. The term alkaloid is used to designate the natural organic substances which are basic because of the presence of nitrogen. Usually this nitrogen is part of a ring system. Most alkaloids are colorless substances which are concentrated in the living tissues, and which are deposited in the bark or in the seed hulls. Berberine found in barberry wood and liriodenine isolated from yellow poplar heartwood (29,178a) are yellow compounds. Several tropical woods are believed to contain alkaloids. Anibine, 4-methoxy-6-(3'-pyridyl)-pyrone, has recently been isolated from the wood of *Aniba duckei* and *A. rosaeodora* (138), and dictamnine, maculine, and other alkaloids were found in the wood of *Flindersia maculosa* (16). As most alkaloids are physiologically active, their presence is suspected in any woods having poisonous properties. However, some steroids, phenols, and quinones also have toxic properties. Although alkaloids are normally not expected in wood from the temperate zones, tests for basic substances seem worthwhile in any studies of new extracts.

Although the nitro grouping is rare in natural products, 1-nitro-2-phenylethane has been isolated from the wood of *Aniba canelilla* and from *Ocotea pretiosa* (69).

IX. Aromatic Compounds

Certain aromatic compounds have already been mentioned. Many additional aromatic compounds have been isolated from wood, nearly all of which are phenolic compounds. Side chains are often present, and in many instances, a three-carbon side chain is involved in a ring structure. Many phenols are deposited in the heartwood and are responsible for the dark color and durability of the heartwood of several species. Certain phenolic substances are transported in the sap, and small amounts of these are present in the sapwood. Some phenols are extracted with ether or benzene, and thus accompany the fats and resin acids. Others are insoluble in ether, and some ether-soluble materials are not removed by direct ether extraction. Alcohols and acetone give a more complete extraction of the phenolic materials, and the azeotrope of n-propanol and water is especially useful in a Soxhlet-type extraction.

A. ACIDS, SOME ALDEHYDES, AND ALCOHOLS

Esters of phthalic acid have recently been found in the wood of Sitka spruce (115), and tamarack (140) and piperonylic acid has been isolated from the wood of *Ocotea pretiosa* (68). The methylenedioxy group found in piperonylic acid does not seem to be very common in wood extractives, although it occurs in several natural products. Some hardwoods, especially the eucalyptus woods (87), contain gallic and ellagic acids both free and combined as hydrolyzable tannins. Ellagic acid is a lactone of a didehydrogallic acid and is sparingly soluble in most solvents.

p-Hydroxybenzoic acid has been isolated from the alcohol–benzene extract of quaking aspen wood (146), and was obtained by alkaline hydrolysis of the extracts of several species of *Populus* and *Salix* (148). The yield after hydrolysis ranged up to 0.7% in the case of quaking aspen and northern black cottonwood. Smaller amounts of vanillic acid, syringic acid (4-hydroxy-3,5-dimethoxybenzoic acid), vanillin, and syringaldehyde were found in the hydrolysates, and these four substances were found in all of the hydrolysates from the 46 hardwood species which were tested. Ferulic acid (4-hydroxy-3-methoxycinnamic acid) was indicated in most instances. These substances may have been derived from lignin-like materials in the extracts, but the acids were believed to be present, in part, as glucosides (147).

Small amounts of coniferin, syringin, vanillin, and syringaldehyde have been reported in a few species, but these materials appear to be minor extractives in most woods. Coniferin and syringin are the glucosides of coniferyl and sinapyl alcohols, respectively, and are believed to be important lignin precursors (117).

B. LIGNANS

Several dimeric phenylpropane (C_6C_3) compounds, which are linked between the β-carbon atoms, are known as lignans. These occur in roots, heartwood, foliage, fruits, and exudates. Usually the terminal carbon atoms in the side chains are oxygenated, and occur in the form of lactones, alcohols, or ethers. A comprehensive review of the naturally occurring lignans has been published (83), and additional lignans have been discovered since that time (23,56).

Several species contain more than one lignan. Thus in addition to those indicated in Table IV, *Podocarpus spicatus* contains coniden-

TABLE IV

Lignans Found in Two or More Genera

Lignan	M.p., °C.	$[\alpha]_D$	Source
Matairesinol	119	−48.6 (acetone)	*Podocarpus spicatus, Picea excelsa*
Lariciresinol	167–8	+19.7 (acetone)	*Larix decidua, Picea excelsa*
Pinoresinol	130–1	+84.4 (acetone)	*Pinus* and *Picea* species
Conidendrin	255–6	−54.5 (acetone)	*Picea* and *Tsuga* species
Secoisolariciresinol	113	−35.6 (acetone)	*Podocarpus spicatus, Larix decidua*
Lioviol	174	−32.8 (methanol)	*Picea excelsa, Larix decidua*

drin, and *Picea excelsa* contains oxomatairesinol, hydroxymatairesinol, allo-hydroxymatairesinol, and 40 to 50 additional phenols of a similar nature were indicated by paper chromatography (56).

Conidendrin (XXVII) occurs in several spruces and hemlocks, but has not been found in all species of these genera. It dissolves during the sulfite pulping process and at one time was known as sulfite liquor lactone.

Most of the lignans found in wood and wood exudates contain guaicyl units, although dimethoxyisolariciresinol which occurs in alder wood (*Alnus glutinosa*) as a xyloside (59) contains syringyl units, and the lignans eudesmin and gmelinol contain veratryl units, whereas hinokinin contains methylenedioxy groups.

C. STILBENES

Pinosylvin (3,5-dihydroxy-*trans*-stilbene) and its methyl ethers occur in the heartwood of many pines (126). Pinosylvin and the

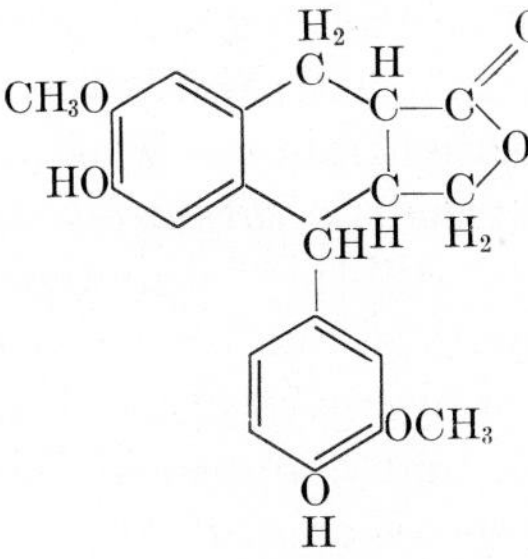

(XXVII)
Conidendrin

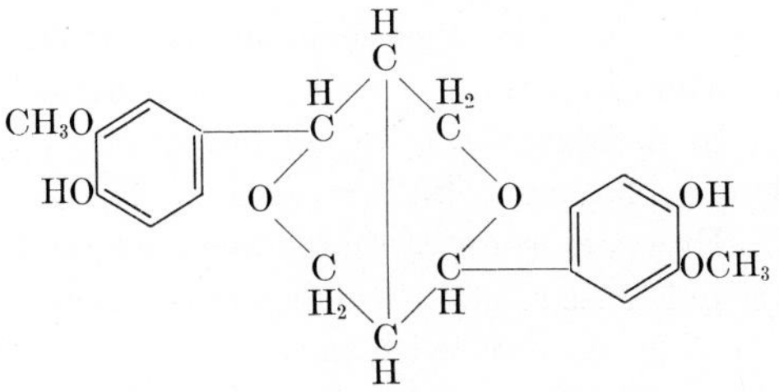

(XXVIII)
Pinoresinol

monomethyl ether form colored compounds with diazotized benzidine, and this reaction provides a convenient color test for pine heartwood. The two substances also condense with lignin in the usual bisulfite pulping process and inhibit the sulfite pulping of pine heartwood. Although the pinosylvins are ether-soluble, they are not extracted from the wood by direct ether extraction. This anomaly has been explained by the hypothesis that the substances occur within impermeable membranes. The "membranes" are soluble in acetone or alcohol, and these solvents extract the stilbenes. The hydroxystilbenes inhibit fungal growth, and thus are responsible for the durability of pine heartwood. They have a strong fluorescence and are readily seen on paper chromatograms under ultraviolet light.

Appreciable amounts of hydroxystilbenes are not found in pine sapwood, and stilbenes other than pinosylvin and its derivatives have not commonly been found in pine heartwood. However, 4-hydroxystilbene and 4-methoxystilbene have been reported in the heartwood of *Pinus griffithii* (132). Other stilbenes appear to be common in the inner bark of the spruces (131). 3,5-Substituted stilbenes with additional substitution in the second ring have been isolated from species of Leguminosae, Moraceae, and Myrtaceae (80). 2,4,3',5'-Tetrahydroxystilbene was isolated from the wood of white mulberry and Osage-orange (123) and from *Artocarpus lakoocha* (137).

For the most part, the stilbenes occur free in wood and are not substituted except by hydroxyl and methoxyl groups. However, the 3-D-glucoside of 3,5,4'-trihydroxystilbene has been isolated from *Eucalyptus wandoo* (80), and a terpenoid side chain is present in chlorophorin from *Chlorophora excelsa* (103).

D. FLAVONOIDS

Several classes of compounds have a common structural feature in that a $C_6C_3C_6$ carbon skeleton is present. The general term flavonoid has been used to designate this broad group of substances which includes chalcones, flavones, anthocyanidins, flavans, and related materials (63). However, some authors have used the term flavonoid in a more restricted sense (75,95). Chalcones are unsaturated ketones which undergo ring closure with an *o*-hydroxyl group to form flavanones or anthocyanidins depending on which ring contains the hydroxyl. Chalcones are colored substances, but they have been reported in only a few species of wood. Okanin (XXIX) and isookanin are *trans* and *cis* isomers from the wood of African greenheart, *Cyclicodiscus gabunensis* (107), and a chalcone named neoplathymenin

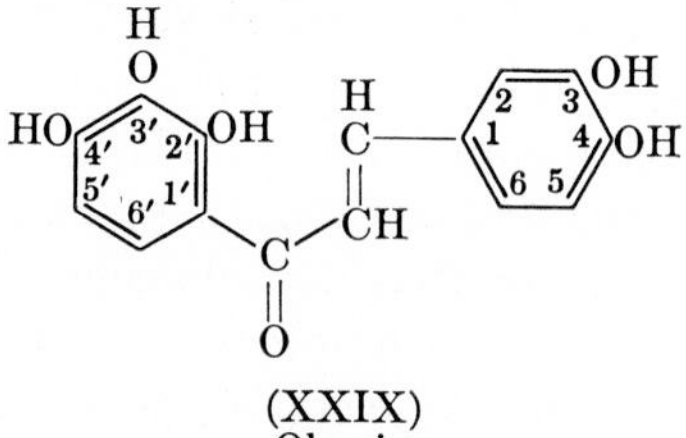

(XXIX)
Okanin
(a chalcone)

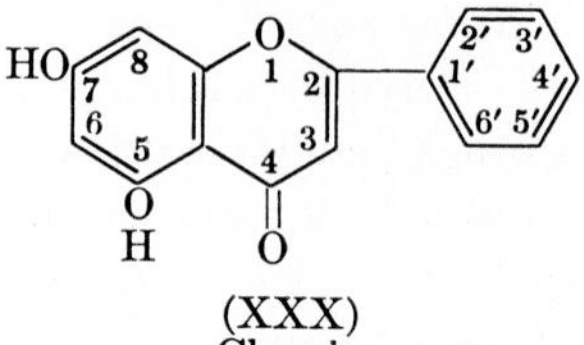

(XXX)
Chrysin
(a flavone)

is the principal crystalline pigment of the wood of *Plathymenia reticulata* (110). Chalcones have been isolated from sodium hydroxide and sodium carbonate soluble fractions of extracts of the wood of *Pinus griffithii* (132) and some *Pterocarpus* species (163). Since chalcones are readily formed from flavanones by ring opening (64), some of the above substances may have been produced during the isolation. The numbering indicated in the structure for okanin is preferred by *Chemical Abstracts*, but many authors use a reversed system which designates okanin as 2,3,4,3′,4′-pentahydroxychalcone. Angolensin from some *Pterocarpus* species (3) is isomeric with a dihydrochalcone.

1. Flavones and Flavanones

Flavones and flavanones (2,3-dihydroflavones) are common wood constituents (see Table V). Flavones are 2-phenylbenzo-γ-pyrones,

TABLE V

Some Naturally Occurring Flavones and Flavanones

Compound	M.p., °C.
Chrysin (5,7-dihydroxyflavone)	275
Morin (3,5,7,2′,4′-pentahydroxyflavone)	290
Fisetin (3,7,3′,4′-tetrahydroxyflavone)	330
Robinetin (3,7,3′,4′,5′-pentahydroxyflavone)	325–30
Quercetin (3,5,7,3′,4′-pentahydroxyflavone)	316–7
Kaempferol (3,5,7,4′-tetrahydroxyflavone)	276–8
Pinocembrin (dihydrochrysin)	194–5
Pinobanksin (3-hydroxydihydrochrysin)	177–8
Naringenin (5,7,4′-trihydroxyflavanone)	251
Taxifolin (dihydroquercetin)	240–2
Aromadendrin (dihydrokaempferol)	237–9
Dihydromorin	226
Dihydrorobinetin	226–8

and those with a hydroxyl in the 3-position are known as flavonols. Flavanones with a 3-hydroxyl group are sometimes called flavanonols. Isomeric compounds in which the phenyl group is attached to the 3-position instead of the 2-position are known as isoflavones and dihydroisoflavones, respectively, but these have not been found in many species of wood. Most of the flavones have been known for a long time, and were constituents of some of the natural dyestuffs. Flavanones have been isolated from many species of wood during the last 12 years, and they seem to be more abundant in wood than the flavones.

Flavones and flavanones found in wood often occur as a mixture of related compounds although the proportion of some constituents may be small. Since the flavanones are rather easily converted to flavones or chalcones, small amounts of these may be produced during the isolation. However, in several cases appreciable amounts of flavone and the corresponding flavanone occur together. Chrysin (XXX) and its 7-methyl ether known as tectochrysin and the corresponding flavanones, pinocembrin and pinostrobin, occur in the heartwood of most of the Haploxylon pines, but the flavones seem to be absent in the Diploxylon group (126). Pinocembrin and the related 3-hydroxy compound, pinobanksin, are found in nearly all species of both groups. Methyl substituted dihydrochrysins (strobopinin, cryptostrobin, and strobobanksin) are found in the heartwood of sugar pine, eastern white pine, and a few other Haploxylon species. The pine heartwood flavonoids have not commonly been found in the wood of other species, but chrysin, tectochrysin, dihydrochrysin (pinocembrin), dihydrotectochrysin, and other flavonoids have been reported in the wood of *Prunus avium* (35,133), pinocembrin has been isolated from South American rosewood, *Aniba rosaeodora* (70), and chrysin and tectochrysin occur in the winter buds of balsam poplar.

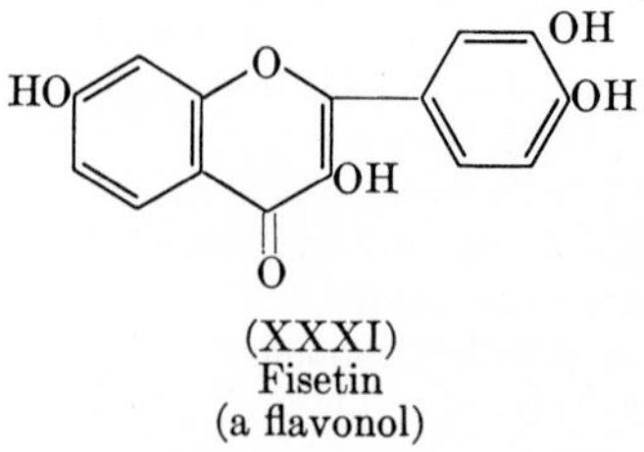

(XXXI)
Fisetin
(a flavonol)

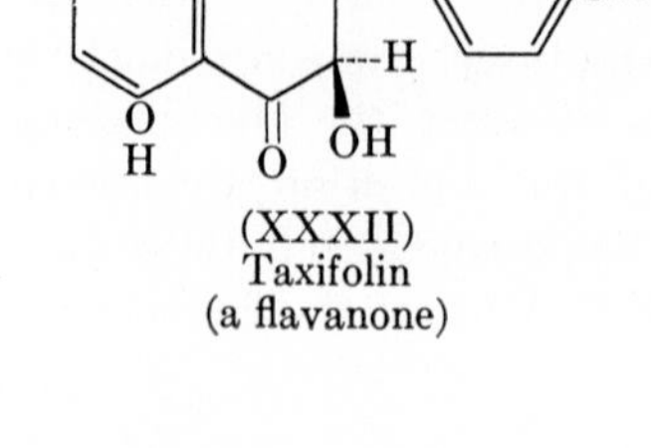

(XXXII)
Taxifolin
(a flavanone)

Taxifolin (XXXII) was isolated originally from Douglas-fir heartwood in a yield of 0.7% (153), and is present in the cork fraction of the inner bark in amounts of up to about 20%. It is a common constituent of species of *Larix*, and has been found in some species of *Prunus*, in *Austrocedrus chilensis* (50), and in *Biota orientalis* (51). It has not generally been found in the pine woods, but has been reported in the heartwood of Maritime pine from the Landes region (34) and in the bark of some pines (84). The 3'-β-glucoside of taxifolin was found in the sapwood and cambium of Douglas-fir, and also in true cedars, larch, and spruce (85). A trace of the 3'-β-glucoside of quercetin was also indicated in the sapwood of Douglas-fir.

Several flavonoids have been found in the woods of various *Prunus* species. Naringenin and aromadendrin and their glycosides are especially common in this genus (79). Naringenin has also been found in the wood of *Ferreirea spectabilis* (104) and of *Nothofagus dombeyi* (153). Aromadendrin occurs in species of *Larix* (59), and together with dihydromorin, it is found in several species of the Moraceae family (123).

Dihydrorobinetin and robinetin were found in the heartwood of black locust to the extent of 5.3 and 2%, respectively (55). Dihydrofisetin (fustin) and fisetin were found in *Gleditsia japonica* (136) and *Rhus* species. Dihydrokaempferol and kaempferol occur in the heartwood of *Afzelia* species (102). In some species flavanones apparently are accompanied by chalcones—liquiritigenin and isoliquiritigenin in *Pterocarpus* species (163), and plathymenin (6,7,3',4'-tetrahydroxyflavanone) and neoplathymenin in *Plathymenia reticulata* (110).

Other flavones found in wood include afzelin, a 3-rhamnoside of kaempferol in the wood of *Afzelia* species (102), and ayanin (3,7,4'-trimethylquercetin) and the related compounds with an additional hydroxyl group, oxyayanin A and oxyayanin B, from the heartwood of *Distemonanthus benthamianus* (111).

Flavones differ from the corresponding flavanones in physical and chemical properties, because of the presence of the conjugated grouping C=C—C=O in the former. In addition, the number and location of the hydroxyl groups influence the properties. The presence of a free hydroxyl in the 3-position is especially important. Flavones are water-insoluble but their glycosides are partially soluble. The flavones fluoresce in ultraviolet light (75), and those with 3-, 3'-, and 4'-hydroxyl groups are strongly colored. The 3-, 4'-, and 7-hydroxyl groups are acidic, whereas the 3-, 5-, and 8-hydroxyl groups form colors with ferric chloride (24). Hydrogen bonding occurs between the 5-hydroxyl and the carbonyl groups. The flavones are rather stable substances, and rather drastic conditions are required to open the pyrone ring.

The flavanones are colorless compounds with little or no fluorescence, and those with several hydroxyl groups are somewhat soluble in water. 3-Hydroxyflavanones form sparingly soluble salts when treated with ammonium hydroxide at pH 6.9 or with sodium acetate, and this permits a separation from catechin, tannins, and other flavonoids which do not form the sparingly soluble salts (121). Flavanones are converted to the corresponding flavones by air oxidation (71,153) or by heating with sodium or ammonium bisulfite solutions (120). The oxygen-containing ring of the flavanones is not as stable as that in the flavones. Flavanones lacking a 3-hydroxyl group may undergo ring opening to form chalcones (64), whereas alkali converts 3-hydroxyflavanones to coumaranones (72).

The flavanones contain two asymmetric centers, and the naturally occurring products are optically active. Inactive flavanones are produced by reducing flavones with sodium hydrosulfite in sodium carbonate solution. Structure XXXII indicates the configuration of taxifolin (36).

Color reactions are of value in distinguishing the various flavanoids. The flavanones and also the 3-hydroxyflavones form orange to magenta colors when treated with magnesium and hydrochloric acid, but only the 3-hydroxyflavanones form similar colors with zinc and hydrochloric acid (153). Treatment with sodium borohydride, followed by exposure to hydrogen chloride, gives reddish colors with flavanones which lack the 3-hydroxyl group (88,161). Isonicotinic acid hydrazide reacts with flavones and flavanones containing free 3-hydroxyl groups to give a strong fluorescence, and a scheme for the quantitative estimation of different classes of flavonoids is based on the use of this reagent (81).

Although not as common as the flavones and flavanones, some members of the isoflavone series have been found in wood. Santal (5,3′,4′-trihydroxy-7-methoxyisoflavone) (93a), occurs in *Pterocarpus santalinus* and *P. osum* (3). Prunetin (XXXIII) has been reported in some *Prunus* species and occurs together with muningin (6,4′-dihydroxy-5,7-dimethoxyisoflavone) in *Pterocarpus angolensis* (106). An isoflavone containing methyxol groups, podospicatin, has been isolated from *Podocarpus spicatus* (23). Ferreirin and homoferreirin are methoxyisoflavanones found in *Ferreirea spectabilis* (113), whereas a 7,2'-dihydroxyisoflavanone from the heartwood of *Sophora japonica* contains a methylenedioxy group (178), and pterocarpin and homopterocarpin found in some *Pterocarpus* species are inner ethers of partially reduced dihydroisoflavones (3).

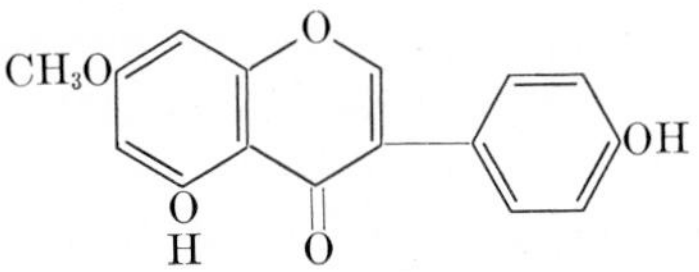

(XXXIII)
Prunetin
(an isoflavone)

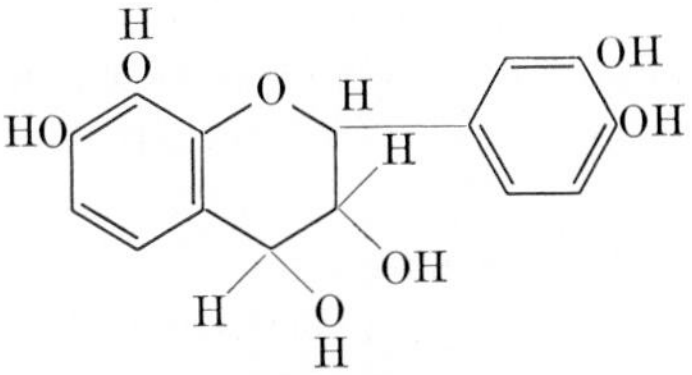

(XXXIV)
Melacacidin
(a flavan-3,4-diol)

2. Leucoanthocyanins

Many species of wood and bark contain colorless materials which on treatment with mineral acids produce red or anthocyanidin-like colors. These substances are known as leucoanthocyanins, or in some cases leucoanthocyanidins. They are difficult to isolate in a pure form, and most of them have not been completely characterized. Some have been shown to be flavan-3,4-diols (100), and some are polymerized tannin-like materials (159). Before discussing these substances, a brief description of the anthocyanidins seems desirable. The latter term designates a class of flavonoid compounds which have sufficient basic properties to form stable salts with mineral acids, and which are usually isolated as the salts. They form red-colored solutions in acid, and some give blue colorations in alkaline solution. In the free base form the anthocyanidins are isomeric with the flavanones, and may be considered as derived from flavones by partial reduction of the carbonyl group to a secondary alcohol. Anthocyanidins often occur as glycosides which are known as anthocyanins.

Both the glycosides and free aglycones are found in some flowers and leaves, but neither seem to be primary constituents of wood. Anthocyanidins may, however, be produced from leucoanthocyanins occurring in wood.

The flavan-3,4-diols which have been characterized include melacacidin (XXXIV) from Australian rosewood *Acacia melanoxylon* (100), leucofisetinidin and a 7,4′-dihydroxyflavan-3,4-diol from the heartwood of *Guibourta* (*Copaifera*) species (158), and a dextrorotatory leucodelphinidin from the kino of *Eucalyptus pilularis* (61). (+)-Mollisacacidin (gleditsin), obtained from the heartwood of *Acacia mollissima* and from *Gleditsia japonica*, and (−)-leucofisetinidin, obtained from quebracho wood, are enantimorphic forms of 7,3′,4′-trihydroxyflavan-3,4-diol (37); the spruce leucoanthocyanidin from the inner bark of black spruce is 5,7,3′,4′-tetrahydroxyflavan-3,4-diol (131). Peltogynol and its steroisomer peltogynol B from the heartwood of *Peltogyne* species are inner ethers of a substituted flavan-3,4-diol (33).

Several suggestions have been made for nomenclature in this area (57,76,166). Originally the term leucoanthocyanin included both glycosides and the free aglycones (157), but recently most authors have used leucoanthocyanidin to designate the aglycones. Some flavan-3,4-diols have been given trivial names, and others have been called leucocyanidin, leucofisetinidin, etc., from the corresponding anthocyanidins. Freudenberg, however, suggests that these should

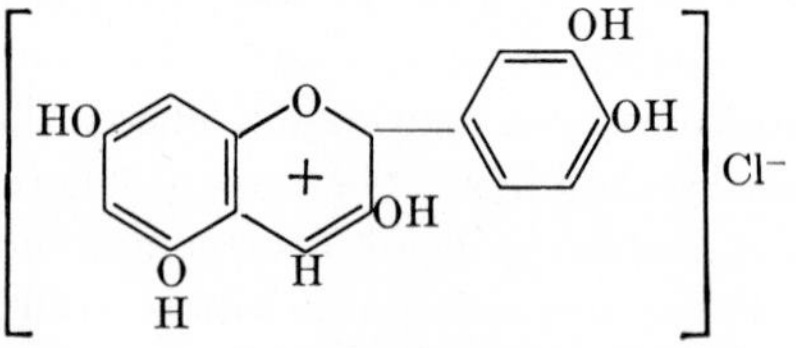

(XXXV)
Cyanidin chloride
(an anthocyanidin)

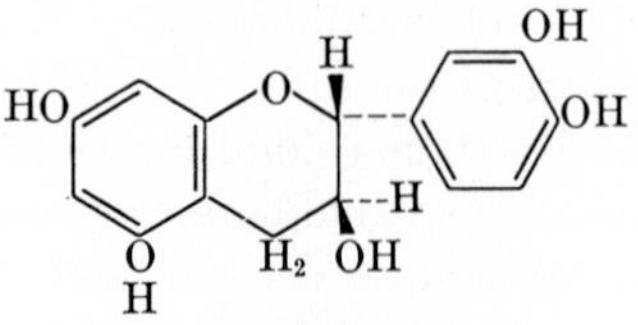

(XXXVI)
(+)-Catechin

be called leucocyanidin hydrate, etc., since water is lost in the conversion to anthocyanidin. The term complex leucoanthocyanin has been used for the polymerized and condensed forms.

Flavan-3,4-diols have been synthesized by reduction of 3-hydroxyflavanones (101). They are somewhat unstable substances which are difficult to purify. The nature of the conversion of leucoanthocyanins to anthocyanidins is uncertain. At least in some instances, the presence of oxygen or external oxidizing agents seems unnecessary. The yield of anthocyanidin is usually low, but is greatest under anhydrous conditions (160). The low yield, coupled with the formation of catechins and phlobaphene materials, has suggested that disproportionation may occur. Recently, a tetramethylflavan-3,4-diol was converted quantitatively into the corresponding anthocyanidin indicating that disproportionation is not necessary in all cases (156). The net changes taking place in the conversion to anthocyanidin salts are the loss of two hydrogen atoms and the elimination of one molecule of water.

3. Flavan-3-ols

The term catechin has been used to name the isomeric 3,5,7,3',4'-pentahydroxyflavans, and also to designate the general class of flavan-3-ols. *Chemical Abstracts* prefers the term catechol because these compounds, upon pyrolysis, yield pyrocatechol. However, the term catechin is still used by many authors. (+)-Catechin (XXXVI) and (−)-epicatechin are the principal naturally occurring catechins, and they are found in many woods and barks (58). These two isomers differ only in the configuration at C_3 (17). Flavan-3-ols with other hydroxylation patterns are known. Thus, (−)-epiafzelechin (3,5,7,4'-tetrahydroxyflavan) has been isolated from the wood of species of *Afzelia* (102).

The catechins are colorless crystalline substances that are somewhat soluble in water. Similar to the flavan-3,4-diols, they are difficult to purify, and undergo condensation and/or polymerization especially in the presence of acids. They have been synthesized from flavan-3,4-diols by hydrogenation (184).

E. TANNINS

Since ancient times, aqueous extracts of certain plants have been used for the conversion of animal skins into leather. The substances responsible for the formation of leather are known as the vegetable tannins. This is a very general term and includes materials of varied chemical composition. Since a blend or mixture of materials is normally required to give the desired leather characteristics, it is often difficult to decide whether or not a given pure substance should be classed as a tannin.

The vegetable tannins are comprised of substances with a high proportion of free phenolic hydroxyl groups and of varying degrees of condensation or polymerization. Usually, only materials of relatively high molecular weight are considered true tannins, but some monomeric materials are fixed by hide powder.

Several classification systems have been proposed for the tannins, some of them quite elaborate. As the exact nature of most tannins is unknown, only the simpler systems seem justified. Freudenberg has divided the tannins into the hydrolyzable class and the condensed tannins or phlopaphene class. The former contain ester and/or glycoside linkages, and on hydrolysis yield acids, sugars, and/or alcohols. Gallic acid, ellagic acid, and glucose are common hydrolysis products (164). Tannins of this class occur in galls and leaves, but are not very common in woods.

The condensed tannins on treatment with acid are polymerized further, rather than being hydrolyzed into simpler substances. Many investigators have attempted to elucidate the structure of the condensed tannins, and many hypotheses have been advanced. Freudenberg suggested, nearly 30 years ago, that the condensed tannins are built up of catechin units, and that the tannins from the different sources differ chiefly in the hydroxylation pattern. Within the last few years, several investigators have recognized the common occurrence of leucoanthocyanin-like materials along with the condensed tannins, and have postulated that the tannins are built up, at least in part, of flavan-3,4-diol units. This is supported by the common occurrence of leucoanthocyanins with tannins (14), and by the discovery of complex leucoanthocyanins in common tannin preparations (159). The complex leucoanthocyanins are polymeric materials that can be converted, in part, into simple anthocyanidins. It seems likely that the condensed tannins are formed in the plant by the condensation and/or polymerization of hydroxyflavans, both leucoanthocyanins and catechins, and perhaps other materials. Since the monomers may differ in the degree of hydroxylation in the aromatic rings, as well as in the pyrane ring, the formation of rather complex molecules is possible.

Tannins are found in many barks, but the wood of most species is relatively free of tannin. However, quebracho wood from South America contains up to 20% tannin, and appreciable amounts are found in chestnut wood, the heartwood of redwood, and several other wood species (188).

The vegetable tannins form blue or green colorations with ferric salts, and these colorations have sometimes been used to classify the materials as pyrogallol tannins and catechol tannins, respectively. Color reactions have been used to detect the presence of tannins in plant tissues, but in some cases the materials present are not considered to be tannins by the tanner. At present, the term polyphenols is often used to designate this general class of materials; this seems to be a desirable usage. The tannins are often accompanied by similar materials, known as phlobaphenes, which are more highly condensed and are not water-soluble.

F. OTHER KETONES AND QUINONES

Several wood constituents, in addition to those mentioned previously, contain carbonyl groups. Maclurin from fustic wood is 2,4,6,3',4'-pentahydroxybenzophenone, and cotoin from *Aniba duckei* is a dihydroxymethoxybenzophenone (70). It is interesting to note that cotoin is similar in physical properties to pinocembrin, which was found in the related species *Aniba rosaeodora*. The two species of *Aniba* also contained two substituted α-pyrones, the alkaloid anibine and 4-methoxy-6-piperonyl-α-pyrone (138). Several substituted benzo-α-pyrones (coumarins) are found in the wood of different species of the Rutaceae (105). Dalbergin, 4-phenyl-6(or 7)-hydroxy-7(or 6)-methoxy coumarin, is found in the wood of *Dalbergia sissoo* (2).

Xanthones are colored substances with a benzene ring fused to the pyrone ring of benzo-γ-pyrone. Euxanthone occurs in the wood of *Platonia insignis* (188), and jacareubin is found in *Calophyllum braziliense* (109).

Compounds with a hydroquinone or pyrocatechol nucleus often are readily oxidized to the corresponding quinone, which in turn may be reduced to the hydroquinone and thus some of the previously described compounds may be oxidized to the quinone form. Several quinones have been found in nature (180), especially in barks and roots and as metabolites of fungi. Quinones have been isolated from the wood of relatively few species, but many dark colored wood extracts have not been thoroughly examined and the quinones may be somewhat more common in wood than present data indicate.

The dyewoods brazilwood and logwood contain brazilin (XXXVII) and a hydroxybrazilin (known as haematoxylin), which on exposure to air are oxidized to the quinoid dyestuffs brazilein and haematin (XXXVIII), respectively.

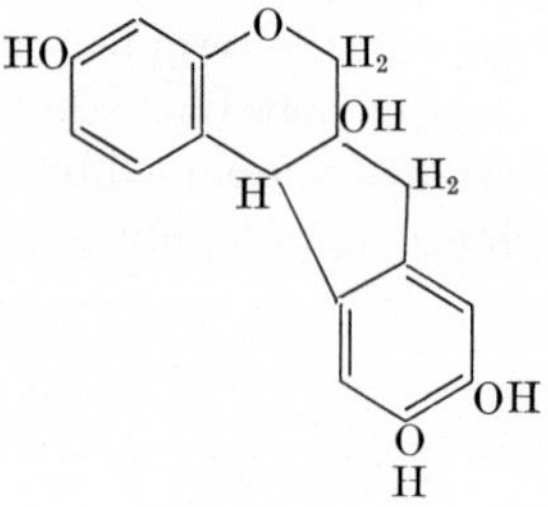

(XXXVII)
Brazilin

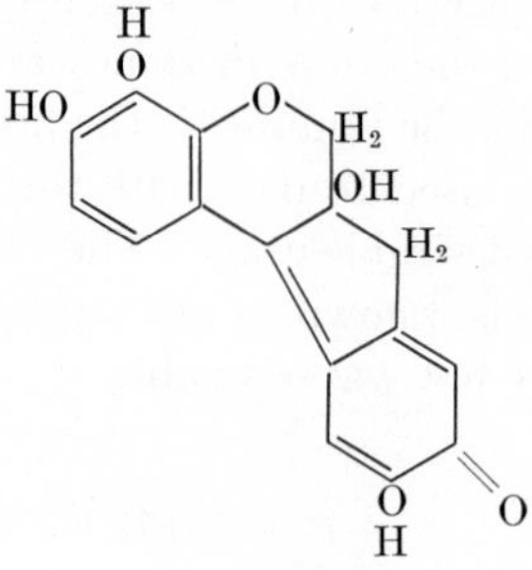

(XXXVIII)
Haematin

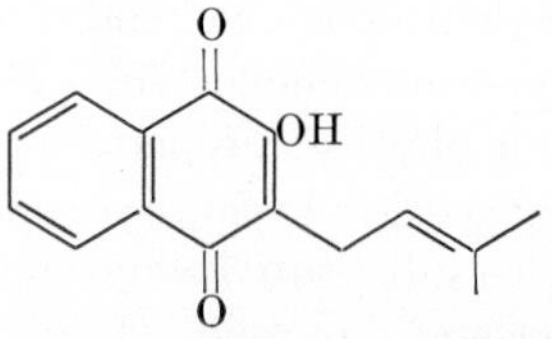

(XXXIX)
Lapachol

Desoxysantalin, occurring in species of *Pterocarpus*, and lapachol (XXXIX), found in several species of the Bignoniaceae, are naphthoquinones. In some species, the yellow-colored lapachol is deposited in the pores, and may easily be seen with a hand lens. The chemistry of lapachol has been studied extensively, and one of the derivatives led to a number of compounds with antimalarial activity (52). Anthraquinones and related materials occur in some species. Chrysarobin, reported in the greenheart woods of South America, is a mixture of anthraquinones and anthrones. Tectoquinone (2-

methylanthraquinone) occurs in teak wood, and 1,8-dihydroxy-3-methyl-9-anthrone has been found in the heartwood of *Ferreira spectablis* and in *Tecoma* species (104).

X. Inorganic Constituents

A number of mineral constituents are necessary for plant growth. These, along with other soluble materials from the soil, are found in mature wood. The composition of the mineral matter in wood depends somewhat on the environmental conditions under which the tree grew, and the location of the mineral within the tree (15). For example, Australian grown *Syncarpia laurifolia* wood contains an average of 0.6% silica, whereas the same species grown in the Hawaiian Islands averages only 0.09% silica (5).

The mineral constituents are comprised chiefly of salts of calcium, potassium, and magnesium, but salts of other elements are present in smaller amounts. The acid radicals are carbonates, phosphates, silicates, sulfates, and in some cases oxalates. In addition, salts are probably formed with the acidic groups of the cell wall components.

Relatively little mineral matter is extractable from wood with water, or other neutral solvents, but most of it is extractable with dilute hydrochloric acid. Crystals of calcium oxalate have been observed in *Juglans*, *Carya*, *Diospyros*, and *Quercus*, especially the live oaks (165). Calcium carbonate is found in the heartwood of species of *Ulmus*, *Celtis*, *Fagus*, and others. Usually, the mineral components are studied by analysis of the ash which remains when the organic matter is burned at high temperatures.

Woods of the temperate zone of the United States usually contain 0.2 to 0.9%, and often less than 0.5%, of ash, whereas some tropical woods contain 4 to 5%. The ash producing constituents are distributed more or less throughout the entire wood structure, as evidenced by the fact that careful ashing of microtome sections gives a pattern of the cell structure. Although the composition of the ash is variable, it is often composed of 40 to 70% calcium oxide, 10 to 30% potassium oxide, 5 to 10% magnesium oxide, and 0.5 to 2.0% ferric oxide. The oxides of manganese, aluminum, and sodium are also present, and spectroscopic analysis indicates the presence of several other metals.

XI. Utilization

In a survey of the chemical treasures of the forest, written nearly 40 years ago, emphasis was placed on the "twilight of the natural dyes", on the collection of oleoresin from the southern pines, and on seed oils (187). A more recent survey of tree extractives indicates that several additional products have become important (6). At present, the extractives of major commercial importance include turpentine, rosin, tall oil fatty acids, and tanning materials. Natural camphor, camphor oil, cedarwood oil, and sandalwood oil are produced, and several resins and gum are utilized. The natural dyestuffs have largely been replaced by synthetic dyes, but logwood extract is still utilized to some extent in the leather and textile industries. Other uses, such as wood ashes for fertilizer and soap making, have nearly disappeared. On the other hand, new uses for extractives will undoubtedly develop. Of potential value are the tall oil sterols, conidendrin, dihydroquercetin, and the thujaplicins.

A. NAVAL STORES AND TALL OIL

Since colonial days, oleoresin has been collected from the southern pines, and has been separated into turpentine and rosin or colophony. These products were useful in the sailing vessels, and their production has long been known as the naval stores industry. In the United States today, oleoresin is collected chiefly from slash and long-leaf pines. The sapwood of the living tree is scarified to permit exudation of the resinous oleoresin. Distillation then separates the volatile turpentine from the nonvolatile rosin. These products are known as gum turpentine and gum rosin, respectively.

Inasmuch as the collection of oleoresin is a laborious process, other means of producing turpentine and rosin have been developed. Destructive distillation of waste pine wood produced some turpentine oils and resins, but currently this is not an important operation. Old pine stumps left from previous lumbering operations proved to be useful for the production of naval stores products. After weathering for several years, the sapwood had rotted away leaving the heartwood stump which was especially rich in resinous material. Steam distillation of the old stumps yielded turpentine and pine oil, or the same constituents and resin acids were removed by solvent extraction. At present, stumps are extracted with a volatile solvent, and the extract is fractionated into turpentine, pine oil, and rosin. The terms wood turpentine and wood rosin are used to distinguish these from the materials produced from the oleoresin. These products depend on a suitable supply of large weathered stumps which, unfortunately, is being depleted.

Within the last few years, the kraft or sulfate pulping industry has become an important source of turpentine, rosin, and fatty acids (11). In the production of southern kraft pulp, pine wood chips are cooked at about 175°C. with an alkaline liquor containing sodium hydroxide and sodium sulfide. In the early stages of the cook, the volatile terpenes distill from the wood and are condensed from the relief gases. The crude turpentine has a disagreeable odor because of the presence of volatile sulfur compounds. However, these can be removed by suitable refining, and the resulting sulfate turpentine is directly competitive with gum turpentine. The yields of sulfate turpentine are variable, but range up to about 0.5%, based on the original wood. The literature, up to about 1945, on sulfate turpentine has been reviewed (40).

In the kraft cook, sodium salts of resin and fatty acids are formed. These remain in the black liquor or aqueous solution of the materials which is separated from the pulp. The black liquor is evaporated and then burned in order to recover the inorganic chemicals and the heat values from dissolved organic matter. When the black liquor is evaporated to about 25% solids, the sodium soaps of the resin and fatty acids separate from the aqueous solution in the form of "skimmings." Acidification yields tall oil which is comprised of the free acids and some neutral materials. Crude tall oil, similar to crude sulfate turpentine, has a poor odor and a dark color attributable to impurities.

Several means have been used to refine tall oil, and at present highly refined products are produced by fractional distillation under vacuum in the presence of steam (1a). The resin acids, as well as the fatty acids, are distilled, and acids with a light color are obtained. The separation is surprisingly good. Tall oil rosin contains only about 1% fatty acids and only small amounts of unsaponifiables, whereas tall oil fatty acids contain as little as 1% impurities. A bibliography of the many references to tall oil has been prepared (183).

Production data for naval stores and tall oil products are given in Table VI (67,174). The production of gum turpentine and gum rosin

TABLE VI

Annual Production in the United States
of Naval Stores and Tall Oil Products

Product	Production	Year
Gum turpentine	120,300[a]	1959
Wood turpentine	172,600[a]	1959
Sulfate turpentine	315,340[a]	1959
Gum rosin	369,350[b]	1959
Wood rosin	1,182,620[b]	1959
Tall oil rosin	305,060[b]	1959
Dipentene	21,400[a]	1959
Pine oil	194,260[a]	1959
Other monocyclic hydrocarbons	108,770[a]	1959
Rosin oil	22,760[a]	1959
Crude tall oil	305,490[c]	1958
Acid refined and distilled tall oil	67,368[c]	1958
Tall oil fatty acids	55,553[c]	1958

[a] 50 Gallon barrels.
[b] 520 Pound drums.
[c] Tons.

has decreased steadily since 1930, whereas that of wood turpentine, rosin, and tall oil products showed marked increases up to about 1957. The data for dipentene and pine oil include both the natural materials from pine stumps and the materials synthesized from turpentine. The other monocyclic hydrocarbons include p-cymene and p-menthane obtained from turpentine. Rosin oil is produced by the destructive distillation of rosin.

Some tall oil is still refined by treatment with 88 to 98% sulfuric acid. The strong acid removes colored materials and other impurities, and causes some dimerization of the resin and fatty acids. The dimerized acids are advantageous in the preparation of some coatings. In recent years, increasing amounts of tall oil have been fractionally distilled under high vacuum in order to produce the more valuable products—rosin and fatty acids.

The largest use for turpentine is reported to be in the production of synthetic pine oil (8), which in turn is used for conversion to terpin hydrate and other chemicals, as a solvent, and in ore flotation. Rather large amounts of turpentine are used in the manufacture of the insecticide toxaphene, and smaller quantities are used in paints and lacquers, and in the manufacture of synthetic resins and camphor.

Rosin is used chiefly for sizing paper. Other uses include the preparation of chemicals, ester gums, and synthetic resins which are utilized in paints and varnishes and in the rubber industry (75a). Alkyd resins, pentaerythritol esters, and cobalt and lead soaps are prepared from the tall oil fatty acids, and these are used in the protective coating and printing ink industries.

B. TANNING EXTRACTS

Extracts of certain barks, woods, and other plant tissues have long been used for converting animal skins into leather and as natural dyes. Although many leathers are now tanned with basic chromium sulfate, the heavy leathers are still tanned with vegetable tannins. At present, most of the natural tannins are produced from the heartwood of quebracho, which grows in South America, and from the bark of wattle trees, cultivated in South Africa. Several other extracts, including the extract of chestnut wood, are used. In the past, eastern hemlock bark and American chestnut wood were major sources of the tannins used in this country. As blight has killed most of the American chestnut trees, this source has largely been depleted, but chestnut extract is being imported from Europe. Eastern hemlock bark was important when the tanner prepared his own extract, but it has not been an important source of commercial extracts.

Recent data are not at hand, but it is estimated that the current annual usage of vegetable tanning materials in the United States approximates 100,000 tons.

The raw materials used for the production of tanning materials are extracted with hot water, and in the case of quebracho wood, pressure vessels are used in order to permit extraction at temperatures slightly above 100°C. The extract is evaporated to a concentrated liquid extract, or is dried to a solid material. The total extract is utilized without removal of the nontannins which are extracted along with the tannin.

Tanning extracts from different sources differ considerably in their tanning action, and the tanner uses a blend of extracts in order to obtain the desired properties in the final leather. Although all of the extracts impart some color to the leather, the tanner desires an extract which does not produce dark colored leathers, and he prefers an extract with a ratio of tannin to total solids of 0.6, or higher.

In addition to their use in leather manufacture, tanning extracts are used to control the viscosity of oil well drilling muds, in water treatment, and in ore flotation. The requirements in these applications differ from those of leather processing, and some extracts which are not suitable for tanning are used in drilling muds.

Several domestic materials have been considered as possible sources of tanning extracts, but several factors tend to limit the practical sources. It is generally considered that the tannin content must be about 6%, or higher, ior a profitable extraction; also, sufficient raw material must be potentially available at one place and at an attractive price. The extract must have a color and other characteristics that are acceptable to the tanner, or it must be of value in some other applications. Western hemlock bark is potentially a source of considerable tannin, but much of the available bark is from logs which have been floated in salt water. The presence of salt is a disadvantage because it tends to precipitate tannins from the tan liquors, and in addition hemlock extract produces leather with a reddish shade. Several oak barks contain tannin, but they have been used to only a limited extent. Most of the pine barks have a relatively low tannin content. The heartwood of the coastal redwood contains some tannin, but this has not proved to be an attractive source. Relatively small amounts of extracts prepared from redwood and western hemlock barks have been used in drilling muds.

C. OTHER UTILIZATIONS

In addition to the pine oleoresins, several other tree exudates are commercially important. Gum arabic is obtained from *Acacia senegal*, the copal resins from species of Leguminosae, the dammar resins from species of Dipterocarpaceae, and the elemi resins from species of Burseraceae. The sources and uses of the natural gums and resins have been reviewed (89). Natural rubber is from the latex of *Hevea brasiliensis*, and quinine is from the bark of *Cinchona officinalis*. Maple syrup and maple sugar are a limited, but interesting, utilization of the early spring sap of *Acer saccharum*.

There are a number of other potential utilizations, but to date they have been of an experimental nature. Vegetable sterols seem to be of therapeutic value in the treatment of arteriosclerosis, and facilities are available for the production of 1000 pounds per day of pharmaceutical grade sterols from tall oil pitch (176). The product consists of a mixture of β-sitosterol and dihydro-β-sitosterol in the ratio of approximately 85:15.

A practical process is available for the isolation of conidendrin from spent pulping liquors (122), and dihydroquercetin can be obtained from Douglas-fir bark (120). Conidendrin can be demethylated to a product known as norconidendrin, which has antioxidant properties. Dihydroquercetin has some antioxidant properties and can easily be converted to quercetin which is a more active antioxidant, and which is of potential value for pharmaceutical purposes. The natural antioxidants are of interest because of their possible use in foods. A glycoside of quercetin, known as rutin, and some citrus flavonoids have found some utilization in the treatment of capillary blood vessel disorders. The thujaplicins, which are good fungicidal agents, can be collected in dry kilns (62) or may be obtained from the spent pulping liquors from western red cedar (185).

REFERENCES

1. Adams, G. A., *Tappi*, **40**, 721 (1957); *Can. J. Chem.*, **38**, 280 (1960).
1a. Agnello, L. A., and E. O. Barnes, *Ind. Eng. Chem.*, **52**, 726 (1960).
2. Ahluwalia, V. K., and T. R. Seshadri, *J. Chem. Soc.*, **1957**, 970.
3. Akisanya, A., C. W. L. Bevan, and J. Hirst, *J. Chem. Soc.*, **1959**, 2679.
4. Amoros-Marin, L., W. I. Torres, and C. F. Asenjo, *J. Org. Chem.*, **24**, 411 (1959).
5. Amos, G. L., and H. E. Dadswell, *J. Council Sci. Ind. Research*, (*Australia*), **21**, No. 3, 190 (1948).
6. Anderson, A. B., *Econ. Botany*, **9**, 108 (1955).
6a. Anderson, E., *J. Biol. Chem.*, **165**, 233 (1946).
7. Angyal, S. J., *Quart. Revs.*, **11**, 212 (1957).
8. Anon., *Chem. Eng. News*, **37**, No. 24, 32 (1959).
8a. Antkowiak, W., J. W. ApSimon, and O. E. Edwards, *J. Org. Chem.*, **27**, 1930 (1962).
9. Assarsson, A., B. Lindberg, and H. Vorbruggen, *Acta Chem. Scand.*, **13**, 1395 (1959).
10. Ballou, C. E., and A. B. Anderson, *J. Am. Chem. Soc.*, **75**, 648 (1953).
11. Barnes, E. O., and M. L. Taylor, *Tappi*, **41**, No. 8, 16A (1958).
12. Barton, D. H. R., and C. J. W. Brooks, *J. Chem. Soc.*, **1951**, 257.
13. Barton, D. H. R., and E. R. H. Jones, *J. Chem. Soc.*, **1944**, 659; D. H. R. Barton, *J. Chem. Soc.*, **1945**, 813; **1946**, 512.
14. Bate-Smith, E. C., and N. H. Lerner, *Biochem. J.*, **58**, 126 (1954).
15. Bergström, H., *Svensk Papperstidn.*, **62**, 160 (1959).
16. Binns, S. V., B. Halpern, G. K. Hughes, and E. Ritchie, *Australian J. Chem.*, **10**, 480 (1957).

17. Birch, A. J., A. V. Robertson, and J. W. Clark-Lewis, *J. Chem. Soc.*, **1957,** 3586.

18. Bollard, E. G. in *The Physiology of Forest Trees*, K. V. Thimann, ed., Ronald Press, New York, 1958.

19. Bose, A. K., and W. A. Struck, *Chem. & Ind.* (*London*), **1959,** 1628.

20. Boyer, J. P., R. A. Eade, H. Locksley, and J. J. H. Simes, *Australian J. Chem.*, **11,** 236 (1958).

21. Brasch, D. J., and J. K. N. Jones, *Can. J. Chem.*, **37,** 1538 (1959).

22. Briggs, L. H., and R. C. Cambie, *Tetrahedron*, **3,** 269 (1958).

23. Briggs, L. H., R. C. Cambie, and J. L. Hoare, *Tetrahedron*, **7,** 262 (1959).

24. Briggs, L. H., and R. H. Locker, *J. Chem. Soc.*, **1951,** 3136.

25. Brossi, A., and O. Jeger, *Helv. Chim. Acta*, **33,** 722 (1950).

26. Bruun, H. H., *Acta Chem. Scand.*, **11,** 907 (1957).

27. Bruun, H. H., I. Fischmeister, and E. Stenhagen, *Acta Chem. Scand.*, **13,** 379 (1959).

28. Bruun, H. H., S. Gåsland, and G. Lundqvist, *Acta Chem. Scand.*, **13,** 1039 (1959).

28a. Buchanan, M. A., S. L. Burson, Jr., and C. H. Springer, *Tappi*, **44,** 576 (1961).

29. Buchanan, M. A., and E. E. Dickey, *J. Org. Chem.*, **25,** 1389 (1960).

30. Buchanan, M. A., R. V. Sinnett, and J. A. Jappe, *Tappi*, **42,** 578 (1959).

31. Cambie, R. C., *New Zealand J. Sci.*, **2,** 257 (1959); through *Chem. Abstracts*, **54,** 3858 (1960).

32. Campbell, W. G., J. L. Frahn, E. L. Hirst, D. F. Packman, and E. G. V. Percival, *J. Chem. Soc.*, **1951,** 3489.

33. Chan, W. R., W. G. C. Forsyth, and C. H. Hassall, *J. Chem. Soc.*, **1958,** 3174.

34. Chopin, J., and G. Grenier, *Chim. & Ind.* (*Paris*), **79,** 605 (1958).

35. Chopin, J., D. Molho, H. Pacheco, C. Mentzer, and G. Grenier, *Bull. soc. chim. France*, **1957,** 192; through *Chem. Abstracts*, **52,** 16,343 (1958).

36. Clark-Lewis, J. W., and W. Korytnyk, *J. Chem. Soc.*, **1958,** 2367.

37. Clark-Lewis, J. W., and D. G. Roux, *J. Chem. Soc.*, **1959,** 1402.

38. Cole, A. R. H., *Fortschr. Chem. Org. Naturstoffe*, **13,** 1 (1956).

39. Cole, A. R. H., and G. T. A. Muller, *J. Chem. Soc.*, **1959,** 1224; see also previous articles in the series.

40. Collins, T. T., Jr., and M. G. Schmitt, *Paper Ind. and Paper World*, **26,** 1136, 1573 (1944–45).

41. Cooke, N. J., and R. P. Hansen, *Chem. & Ind.* (*London*), **1959,** 1516.

42. Cosserat, L., G. Ourisson, and T. Takahashi, *Chem. & Ind.* (*London*), **1956,** 190.

43. Cox, J. S. G., F. E. King, and T. J. King, *J. Chem. Soc.*, **1956,** 1384.

43a. Dickhart, W., *Am. J. Pharm.*, **127,** 359 (1955); through *Chem. Abstracts*, **50,** 7397 (1956).

44. Duff, S. R., H. Erdtman, and W. E. Harvey, *Acta Chem. Scand.*, **8,** 1073 (1954).

45. Enzell, C., and H. Erdtman, *Tetrahedron*, **4,** 361 (1958).

46. Erdtman, H., *Progr. in Org. Chem.*, **1,** 22 (1952).

47. Erdtman, H., and J. Gripenberg, *Acta Chem. Scand.*, **2,** 625 (1948).

48. Erdtman, H., and J. Gripenberg, *Nature*, **164**, 316 (1949).
49. Erdtman, H., W. E. Harvey, and J. G. Topliss, *Acta Chem. Scand.*, **10**, 1381 (1956).
50. Erdtman, H., and Z. Pelchowicz, *Acta Chem. Scand.*, **9**, 1728 (1955).
51. Erdtman, H., and Z. Pelchowicz, *Chem. Ber.*, **89**, 341 (1956).
52. Fieser, L. F., *et al.*, *J. Am. Chem. Soc.*, **70**, 3151 (1948).
53. Fieser, L. F., and M. Fieser, *Steroids*, Reinhold, New York, 1959.
54. Fleck, E. E., and S. Palkin, *J. Am. Chem. Soc.*, **61**, 3197 (1939).
55. Fruedenberg, K., and L. Hartmann, *Ann.*, **587**, 207 (1954).
56. Freudenberg, K., and L. Knof, *Chem. Ber.*, **90**, 2857 (1957).
57. Freudenberg, K., and K. Weinges, *Ann.*, **613**, 61 (1958).
58. Freudenberg, K., and K. Weinges, *Fortschr. Chem. Org. Naturstoffe*, **16**, 1 (1958).
59. Freudenberg, K., and K. Weinges, *Tetrahedron Letters*, No. 17, 19 (1959).
60. Funaoka, K., *Mokuzai Gakkaishi*, **3**, 218 (1957); *Chem. Abstracts*, **52**, 12,395 (1958).
61. Ganguly, A. K., T. R. Seshadri, and P. Subramanian, *Tetrahedron*, **3**, 225 (1958).
62. Gardner, J. A. F., G. M. Barton, and H. MacLean, *Can. J. Chem.*, **35**, 1039 (1957).
63. Geissman, T. A., *J. Chem. Ed.*, **26**, 657 (1949).
64. Geissman, T. A., and R. O. Clinton, *J. Am. Chem. Soc.*, **68**, 697 (1946).
65. Genge, C. A., *Anal. Chem.* **31**, 1750 (1959).
66. Godson, D. H., F. E. King, and T. J. King, *Chem. & Ind.* (*London*), **1956**, 190.
67. Goldfield, E. D., *Statistical Abstract of the United States*, 80th ed., U. S. Government Printing Office, Washington, D. C., 1959.
68. Gottlieb, O. R., and M. T. Magalhaes, *Nature*, **182**, 742 (1958).
69. Gottlieb, O. R., and M. T. Magalhaes, *J. Org. Chem.*, **24**, 2070 (1959).
70. Gottlieb, O. R., and W. B. Mors, *J. Am. Chem. Soc.*, **80**, 2263 (1958).
71. Gregory, A. S., D. L. Brink, L. E. Dowd, and A. S. Ryan, *Forest Prods. J.*, **7**, 135 (1957).
72. Gripenberg, J., *Acta Chem. Scand.*, **7**, 1323 (1953).
73. Hägglund, E., *Chemistry of Wood*, Academic Press, New York, 1951.
74. Hampton, B. L., *J. Org. Chem.*, **21**, 918 (1956).
75. Harborne, J. B., *J. Chromatography*, **2**, 581 (1959).
75a. Harris, G. C. in *Encyclopedia of Chemical Technology*, R. E. Kirk and D. F. Othmer, eds., Vol. 11, Interscience, New York, 1953, p. 779.
76. Harris, G., and R. W. Ricketts, *Chem. & Ind.* (*London*), **1958**, 686.
77. Harris, G. C., and T. F. Sanderson, *J. Am. Chem. Soc.*, **70**, 334 (1948).
78. Harrocks, J. A., *Ph.D. Thesis*, The Institute of Paper Chemistry, Appleton, Wisconsin, June, 1960; I. A. Pearl, and J. A. Harrocks, *J. Org. Chem.*, **26**, 1578 (1961).
79. Hasegawa, M., *Nippon Ringaku Kaishi*, **40**, 111 (1958); *Chem. Abstracts*, **52**, 12,096 (1958).
80. Hathway, D. E., and J. W. T. Seakins, *Biochem. J.*, **72**, 369 (1959).
81. Hawker, C. D., H. W. Margraf, and T. E. Weichselbaum, *Anal. Chem.*, **32**, 122 (1960).

82. Hay, J. E., and L. J. Haynes, *J. Chem. Soc.*, **1958**, 2231.

83. Hearon, W. M., and W. S. MacGregor, *Chem. Revs.*, **55**, 957 (1955).

84. Hergert, H. L., *J. Org. Chem.*, **21**, 534 (1956).

85. Hergert, H. L., and O. Goldschmid, *J. Org. Chem.*, **23**, 700 (1958).

86. Herout, V., and V. Sykora, *Tetrahedron*, **4**, 246 (1958).

87. Hillis, W. E., and A. Carle, *Appita*, **13**, 74 (1959).

88. Horowitz, R. M., *J. Org. Chem.*, **22**, 1733 (1957).

89. Howes, F. N., *Vegetable Gums and Resins*, Chronica Botanica Co., Waltham, Mass., 1949.

90. Howes, F. N., *Vegetable Tanning Materials*, Butterworths, London, 1953.

91. Hudy, J. A., *Anal. Chem.*, **31**, 1754 (1959).

92. Inglett, G. E., *J. Org. Chem.*, **23**, 93 (1958).

93. Isenberg, I. H., M. A. Buchanan, and L. E. Wise, *Paper Ind. and Paper World*, **38**, 945, 1042, (1956–57).

93a. Iyer, R. N., K. H. Shah, and K. Venkataraman, *Proc. Indian Acad. Sci.*, **33A**, 228 (1951); *Chem. Abstracts*, **46**, 10,152 (1952).

94. Jones, R. N., and F. Herling, *J. Org. Chem.*, **19**, 1252 (1954).

95. Karrer, W., *Konstitution und Vorkommen der Organischen Pflanzenstoffe*, Birkhauser, Basel, 1958.

96. Kahila, S. K., *Paperi ja Puu*, **39**, 35, (1957).

97. Kahila, S. K., and A. Y. E. Rinne, *Paperi ja Puu*, **39**, 526 (1957).

98. Kajanne, P., and M. Nieminen, *Paperi ja Puu*, **39**, 471 (1957).

99. King, F. E., *Chem. & Ind. (London)*, **1953**, 1325.

100. King, F. E., and W. Bottomley, *Chem. & Ind. (London)*, **1953**, 1368.

101. King, F. E., and J. W. Clark-Lewis, *J. Chem. Soc.*, **1955**, 3384.

102. King, F. E., J. W. Clark-Lewis, and W. F. Forbes, *J. Chem. Soc.*, **1955**, 2948.

103. King, F. E., and M. F. Grundon, *J. Chem. Soc.*, **1949**, 3348.

104. King, F. E., M. F. Grundon, and K. G. Neill, *J. Chem. Soc.*, **1952**, 4580.

105. King, F. E., J. R. Housley, and T. J. King, *J. Chem. Soc.*, **1954**, 1392.

106. King, F. E., and L. Jurd, *J. Chem. Soc.*, **1952**, 3211.

107. King, F. E., and T. J. King, *J. Chem. Soc.*, **1951**, 569.

108. King, F. E., and T. J. King, *J. Chem. Soc.*, **1956**, 4469.

109. King, F. E., T. J. King, and L. C. Manning, *J. Chem. Soc.*, **1957**, 563.

110. King, F. E., T. J. King, and K. G. Neill, *J. Chem. Soc.*, **1953**, 1055.

111. King, F. E., T. J. King, and P. J. Stokes, *J. Chem. Soc.*, **1954**, 4587.

112. King, F. E., T. J. King, and J. G. Topliss, *Chem. & Ind. (London)*, **1956**, 113.

113. King, F. E., and K. G. Neill, *J. Chem. Soc.*, **1952**, 4752.

114. Klyne, W., *J. Chem. Soc.*, **1953**, 3072.

115. Kohlbrenner, P. J., and C. Schuerch, *J. Org. Chem.*, **24**, 166 (1959).

116. Kondo, T., H. Ito, and M. Suda, *Mokuzai Gakkaishi*, **3**, 151 (1957); *Chem. Abstracts*, **51**, 18,587 (1957).

117. Kremers, R. E., *Tappi*, **40**, 262 (1957).

118. Kurth, E. F., *Ind. Eng. Chem., Anal. Ed.*, **11**, 203 (1939).

119. Kurth, E. F. in *Wood Chemistry*, L. E. Wise and E. C. Jahn, eds., 2nd ed., Vol. I, Reinhold, New York, 1952, pp. 550–563.

120. Kurth, E. F., *Ind. Eng. Chem.*, **45**, 2096 (1953).

121. Kurth, E. F., H. L. Hergert, and J. D. Ross, *J. Am. Chem. Soc.*, **77**, 1621 (1956).

122. Lackey, H. B., W. W. Moyer, and W. M. Hearon, *Tappi*, **32**, 469 (1949).
123. Laidlaw, R. A., and G. A. Smith, *Chem. & Ind. (London)*, **1959**, 1604.
124. Lawrence, R. V., *Tappi*, **42**, 867 (1959).
125. Lindberg, B., and L. Selleby, *Acta Chem. Scand.*, **12**, 1512 (1958).
126. Lindstedt, G., and A. Misiorny, *Acta Chem. Scand.*, **5**, 121 (1951).
127. Lo, T. B., and Y. T. Lin, *J. Chinese Chem. Soc. (Taiwan)*, *Ser. II*, **3**, 30 (1956); *Chem. Abstracts*, **52**, 15,446 (1958).
128. Loeblich, V. M., D. E. Baldwin, and R. V. Lawrence, *J. Am. Chem. Soc.*, **77**, 2823 (1955).
129. MacLean, H., and J. A. F. Gardner, *Pulp Paper Mag. Can.*, **54**, No. 12, 125 (1953).
130. MacLean, H., and J. A. F. Gardner, *Forest Prods. J.*, **6**, 510 (1956).
131. Manson, D. W., *Tappi*, **43**, 59 (1960).
132. Mahesh, V. B., and T. R. Seshadri, *J. Sci. Ind. Research, (India)*, **13B**, 835 (1954); *Chem. Abstracts*, **49**, 11,273 (1955).
133. Mentzer, C., H. Pacheco, and A. Ville, *Bull. soc. chim. biol.*, **36**, 1137 (1954); *Chem. Abstracts*, **49**, 4814 (1955).
134. Mirov, N. T., *J. Forest Products Res. Soc.*, **4**, 1 (1954).
135. Mirov, N. T., *J. Am. Pharm. Assoc., Sci. Ed.*, **47**, 410 (1958).
136. Mitsuno, M., and M. Yoshizaki, *Yakugaku Zasshi*, **77**, 557 (1957); *Chem. Abstracts*, **51**, 14,705 (1957).
137. Mongolsuk, S., A. Robertson, and R. Towers, *J. Chem. Soc.*, **1957**, 2231.
138. Mors, W. B., O. R. Gottlieb, and C. Djerassi, *J. Am. Chem. Soc.*, **79**, 4507 (1957).
139. Mutton, D. B., *Tappi*, **41**, 632 (1958).
140. Nair, G. V., and E. von Rudloff, *Can. J. Chem.*, **37**, 1608 (1959).
141. Narayanamurti, D., *Holz Roh- u. Werkstoff*, **15**, 370 (1957).
142. Nozoe, T., *Fortschr. Chem. Org. Naturstoffe*, **13**, 232 (1956).
143. Nozoe, T., K. Takase, and M. Ogata, *Chem. & Ind. (London)*, **1957**, 1070.
144. Paech, K., and M. V. Tracey, *Modern Methods of Plant Analysis*, Vol. I–IV, Springer, Berlin, 1955–56.
144a. Pajari, K., *Fette u. Seifen*, **50**, 506 (1943); *Chem. Abstracts*, **39**, 207 (1945).
145. Pauson, P. L., *Chem. Revs.*, **55**, 9 (1955).
146. Pearl, I. A., and D. L. Beyer, *Tappi*, **40**, 45 (1957).
147. Pearl, I. A., D. L. Beyer, and D. Laskowski, *J. Org. Chem.*, **24**, 443 (1959).
148. Pearl, I. A., D. L. Beyer, S. S. Lee, and D. Laskowski, *Tappi*, **42**, 61 (1959).
149. Pearl, I. A., and A. S. Gregory, *Forest Prods. J.*, **9**, 85 (1959); Pearl, I. A., and J. W. Rowe, *Forest Prods. J.*, **10**, 91 (1960).
150. Perilä, O., *Suomen Kemistilehti*, **28B**, No. 3, 109 (1955); *Chem. Abstracts*, **49**, 15,233 (1955).
151. Perilä, O., *Ann. Acad. Sci. Fennicae, Ser. A*, **II**, No. 76 (1956).
152. Perilä, O., and P. Manner, *Paperi ja Puu*, **38**, 499 (1956).
153. Pew, J. C., *J. Am. Chem. Soc.*, **70**, 3031 (1948).
154. Pickett, O. A., and J. M. Schantz, *Ind. Eng. Chem.*, **26**, 707 (1934).
155. Plouvier, V., *Compt. rend.*, **245**, 2377 (1957); **247**, 2423 (1958); *Chem. Abstracts*, **52**, 9319 (1958); **53**, 13,295 (1959).
156. Robertson, A. V., *Can. J. Chem.*, **37**, 1946 (1959).
157. Robinson, G. M., and R. Robinson, *J. Chem. Soc.*, **1935**, 744.

366   M. A. BUCHANAN

158. Roux, D. G., *Nature*, **183**, 890 (1959).
159. Roux, D. G., *J. Am. Leather Chemists' Assoc.*, **54**, 614 (1959).
160. Roux, D. G., and M. C. Bill, *Nature*, **183**, 42 (1959).
161. Rowell, K. M., and D. H. Winter, *J. Am. Pharm. Assoc., Sci. Ed.*, **48**, 746 (1959).
162. Ruzicka, L., *Experientia*, **9**, 357 (1953).
163. Sawhney, P. L., and T. R. Seshadri, *J. Sci. Ind. Research, (India)*, **15C**, 154 (1956); *Chem. Abstracts*, **51**, 705 (1957).
164. Schmidt, O. T., *Fortschr. Chem. Org. Naturstoffe*, **13**, 70 (1956).
165. Schorger, A. W., *The Chemistry of Cellulose and Wood*, McGraw Hill, New York, 1926.
166. Seakins, J. W. T., *Nature*, **183**, 1168 (1959).
167. Seikel, M. K., D. J. Holder, and R. Birzgalis, *Arch. Biochem. Biophys.*, **85**, 272 (1959).
168. Selleby, L., *Svensk Papperstidn.*, **63**, 81 (1960).
169. Simes, J. J. H., *J. Chem. Soc.*, **1950**, 2868.
170. Simonsen, J., and D. H. R. Barton, *The Terpenes*, 2nd ed., Vol. III, University Press, Cambridge, 1952.
171. Simonsen, J. L., and L. N. Owen, *The Terpenes*, 2nd ed., Vol. I (1947), Vol. II (1949), University Press, Cambridge.
172. Simonsen, J., and W. C. J. Ross, *The Terpenes*, 2nd ed., Vols. IV and V, University Press, Cambridge, 1957.
173. Smith, L. V., and E. Zavarin, *Tappi*, **43**, 218 (1960).
174. Spitz, R. J., and A. B. Doran, in *Tall Oil*, by J. Weiner, Bibliographic Series No. 133–135, 3rd ed., The Institute of Paper Chemistry, Appleton, Wisconsin, 1959.
175. Steele, J. W., J. B. Stenlake, and W. D. Williams, *J. Chem. Soc.*, **1959**, 3289.
176. Steiner, C. S., and E. Fritz, *J. Am. Oil Chemists' Soc.*, **36**, 354 (1959).
177. Strazdins, E., and E. H. Sheers, *Tappi*, **41**, 658 (1958).
178. Suginome, H., *J. Org. Chem.*, **24**, 1655 (1959).
178a. Taylor, W. I., *Tetrahedron*, **14**, 42 (1961).
179. Thompson, J. F., S. I. Honda, G. E. Hunt, R. M. Krupka, C. J. Morris, L. E. Powell, Jr., O. O. Silberstein, G. H. N. Towers, and R. M. Zacharius, *Botan. Rev.*, **25**, 1 (1959).
180. Thomson, R. H., *Naturally Occurring Quinones*, Academic Press, New York, 1957.
181. Tsutsui, M., and E. A. Tsutsui, *Chem. Revs.*, **59**, 1031 (1959).
182. Wehmer, C., *Die Pflanzenstoffe*, Vol. I (1929), Vol. II (1931), Supplement (1935), Gustav Fischer, Jena.
183. Weiner, J., *Tall Oil*, Bibliographic Series No. 133–135, 3rd ed., The Institute of Paper Chemistry, Appleton, Wisconsin, 1959.
184. Weinges, K., *Ann.*, **615**, 203 (1958).
185. Wethern, J. D., *Forest Prods. J.*, **9**, 308 (1959).
186. Whistler, R. L., and C. L. Smart, *Polysaccharide Chemistry*, Academic Press, New York, 1953.
187. Wise, L. E., *Chemical Treasures of the Forest*, Washington, D. C., The American Forestry Assoc., Reprinted from *American Forests and Forest Life*; *Chem. Abstracts*, **23**, 1266 (1929).

188. Wise, L. E., and E. C. Jahn, *Wood Chemistry*, 2nd ed., Vol. I, Reinhold, New York, 1952.
189. Yagishita, K., and S. Iseda, *Nippon Nogei-kagaku Kaishi*, **29**, 964 (1955); *Chem. Abstracts*, **52**, 20,431 (1958).
190. Young, C. G., *J. Am. Oil Chemists' Soc.*, **36**, 664 (1959).
191. Zavarin, E., *J. Org. Chem.*, **23**, 1198 (1958).
192. Zavarin, E., *J. Org. Chem.*, **23**, 1264 (1958).
193. Zavarin, E., and A. B. Anderson, *J. Org. Chem.*, **20**, 82, 443, 788 (1955).
194. Zavarin, E., R. M. Smith, and A. B. Anderson, *J. Org. Chem.*, **24**, 1318 (1959).
195. Zeitschel, O., and H. Schmidt, *Chem. Ber.*, **60**, 1372 (1927).

Addendum

Recently, books have been published on wood extractives (5) and on the chemistry of the flavonoid compounds (4). Reverse phase glass paper chromatography of the methyl esters of the common resin acids has been reported (3). The major sterol from *Populus tremuloides* heartwood proved to be β-sitosterol (1). Finally, plans to market a water-soluble gum from western larch have been reported (2).

REFERENCES

1. Abramovitch, R. A., R. G. Micetich, and S. J. Smith, *Tappi*, **46**, 37 (1963).
2. Anon., *Chem. Week*, **91**, No. 6, 41 (1962).
3. Daniels, P., and E. Enzell, *Acta Chem. Scand.*, **16**, 1530 (1962).
4. Geissman, T. A., *The Chemistry of Flavonoid Compounds*, Macmillan, New York, 1962.
5. Hillis, W. E., *Wood Extractives and Their Significance to the Pulp and Paper Industry*, Academic Press, New York, 1962.

CHAPTER 8

The Chemistry of Developing Wood

R. E. Kremers, *The Institute of Paper Chemistry, Appleton, Wisconsin*

I. The General Problem

The purpose of this chapter is to appraise, in chemical terms, the biological processes of growth and differentiation as they operate to form wood. Woody tissues are distinguished from nonwoody tissues by the presence of lignin (see Chapter 6), but lignified tissue is not confined to trees and shrubs; for example, wheat and cornstalks are lignified when mature. However, from both the biological and the economic viewpoint wood formation exhibits its maximum and, perhaps, most typical development in tree trunks. The new wood formed each growing season results from the activity of a distinctly different, nonwoody kind of tissue—the cambium. To understand the chemical changes which take place during the development of wood from cambium, we must comprehend something of both the morphological changes (i.e., changes in cell shape and architecture) and the physiological activity (i.e., the interplay of life processes and environment) which embody or influence the chemical developments.

The more obvious morphology of wood formation has been known for a long time. To exist, literally to find their places in the sun, trees develop a gross (visible) differentiation into roots, trunk, and crown. The roots provide anchorage and derive water and minerals from the soil. The trunk provides the strength to support the crown. The smaller branches and twigs display the leaves to the atmosphere and sunshine, so that photosynthesis may occur (Fig. 1). This obvious

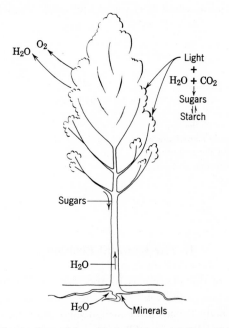

Fig. 1. Cross differentiation of a tree (schematic).

differentiation is paralleled by, and in a sense is the result of, a corresponding internal differentiation of cells and tissues (11). As noted in Chapter 2, the new cells of the cambial zone look very much alike until they undergo morphological and chemical changes, according to the functions which they ultimately perform.

Although the general pattern of differentiation is common to all trees of a species, it is not a rigidly inflexible process. Similar to the physiology of all living organisms, a tree is influenced by its environment—both external and internal (39). Taking trees in the aggregate as woods or forests, the silviculturist knows that a given species exhibits its optimum (or less than optimum) growth, depending upon the local characteristics of site, soil, stand, climate, and other external variables within its geographic range. Internally, the nutrition of a tree is maintained by the general movement of water and minerals upward from the roots to trunk, branches, and leaves, and the movement of sugars, amino acids, and other organic substances downward from the leaves in the sap stream of the inner bark. The ray cells, which lie in a horizontal, radial position, connect individual living cells with the major up and down movements of nutrients. If, for example, a very young fiber cell (fusiform initial) lacks sufficient contact with ray cells, its development will be impaired by a lack of nutrients. Such a cell will either die, remain functional but stunted, or subdivide and change its function by initiating new ray cells. In the latter event, its new function tends to correct the deficiency (3).

Similar to biological studies, chemical experiments with trees can be traced far back into the history of science; many of the earlier investigations, however, stemmed from medical or pharmaceutical interest in finding therapeutically active compounds, such as alkaloids, glucosides, tannins, oleoresins, and other extractable substances. Thus, it came about incidentally that an investigation of black locust as a poisonous plant first called attention to the inner bark as a depot of proteins (19,34) and to the probable biochemical importance of this tissue. On the other hand, the concepts of wood chemistry developed as part of the broader scientific and technical interests in agricultural products and, consequently, have been concerned chiefly with cellulose, the hemicelluloses, lignin, and other categories used by the agricultural chemist (18). It was only rather recently that investigations of bark and wood were combined to provide a sequential analysis of the outer bark, inner bark, cambial zone, sapwood, and heartwood of one tree (2) (see Table I).

Implicit in such unified comparisons is a greater recognition that wood and bark have a common origin, regardless of the apparent physical and chemical differences in the end products. Moreover, these analyses confirmed that there are significant chemical differences between wood and bark, and established that the composition of the cambial zone tissue is radically different from both. Specifically, the cambial tissue resembles young leaves and immature seeds, as it has a very high water content and, on a dry basis, is rich in protein and ash with very little lignin. Such chemical values are characteristic of plant tissues with high metabolic activity, and rationalize the widely observed fact of forest ecology that cambium

TABLE I

Composition of Black Spruce, *Picea mariana* (Mill.) BSP

	Outer bark	Inner bark	Cambial zone	Young sapwood[a]	Sapwood	Heartwood
Ash, %	1.20	3.18	3.57	0.37	0.30	0.28
Protein						
$N \times 6.25$, %	2.05	3.84	7.00	1.66	0.30	0.42
Pentosan, %	11.80	12.03	6.30	8.12	12.05	12.45
Uronic anhydride,						
$CO_2 \times 4.0$, %	8.56	10.00	4.60	3.80	3.72	3.92
Lignin						
(unextracted), %	33.9	6.6	1.83	24.9	26.3	26.1
MeO, %	4.00	2.19	0.72	4.73	4.89	4.75
Tannin, %	1.9	7.6	Neg.	Neg.	Neg.	Neg.

[a] Included last three years of wood.

and inner bark furnish abundant subsistence to many pathogenic microorganisms, insects, rodents, and deer.

Accordingly, the general problem of the chemistry of wood formation is not merely to extend the chemical study of trees, but also to use our knowledge of their morphology and physiology in order to arrive at a better understanding of chemical composition in terms of biological structure and function. In brief, it is to look upon a stick of wood not as something fixed and static, but as something potentially variable with the dynamic forces which produced it.

II. Biochemical Inferences from Chemical Structure

Historically, organic chemists were always interested in the metabolic products of plants and animals. As their knowledge increased, they inevitably speculated on the relations between the reactions which occur in the laboratory and those which occur in a living organism. Laboratory reactions, however, are often very crude in comparison to the mild conditions and high specificity that characterize biological reactions. Consequently, the important contributions of organic chemical speculations have been formal, structural analogies that provide a "comparative anatomy" (5) of plant constituents, but they alone do not establish the existence of a bio-chemical sequence. But the recognition of formal relations and their concomitant reaction mechanisms have, in some cases, preceded by many years the development of confirmatory biochemical evidence. The organic chemistry of wood constituents should, there-fore, be a very useful guide to biochemical studies of wood formation and a criterion for their proper interpretation.

As the organic chemist describes the structures of starch and cellu-lose solely in terms of glucose units, one would infer that these carbohydrates are synthesized by the tree from glucose. Without biological evidence one might be tempted to infer also that these two polysaccharides have similar functions, whereas they are actually quite different. The cellulose is a long, linear-chain polymer with the glucoside linkages in the beta configuration; it is generally a permanent structural unit in the build-up of the plant. Starch, however, consists of both linear and branched polymers, with the glu-coside linkage in the alpha configuration; it functions as a reserve food which is stored or hydrolyzed again for mobilization and metabolic use, depending upon the physiologic needs of the plants.

Similarly, the fact that the hemicelluloses can be hydrolyzed to simple sugars has been taken to indicate that they are synthesized from the sugars. The supposition is that mannans are derived from mannose, the galactans from galactose, the xylans from xylose, and the arabinans from arabinose. More commonly, the hemicelluloses appear to contain two or more kinds of sugar units or sugar deriva-tives. In these instances, the synthetic reactions in the plant cannot follow quite so simple a pattern as when a single sugar is present. Moreover, glucose and xylose, and galactose and arabinose are stereo-chemically related. Accordingly, from the standpoint of structure it is also conceivable that xylans may originate from glucose, and arabinans from galactose, to form the respective pentoses, through an initial loss of the number 6 carbon atom in the hexoses.

The pectic acids are linear macromolecules composed of galac-turonic acid units. In conformity with the preceding inferences, one would assume that the pectic acids are built up by the plant from galacturonic acid molecules. But it is also possible to think that oxidation of the number 6 carbon atoms in a preformed galactan would lead to the same end product. Since the pectins and proto-pectin are more or less completely methylated, they pose the further question of whether the methyl ester groups are formed after the macromolecule has been synthesized, or whether galacturonic acid methyl ester combines to build the macromolecule.

It is noteworthy that with the exception of the hypothetical oxidation of galactan to pectic acid, the inferred syntheses of these macromolecules all depend upon a single type of reaction—intermolecular dehydration. The reverse reaction, hydrolysis, also takes place; for example, the amylases bring about the solubilization of starch. It is thought that the hemicelluloses are hydrolyzed when they serve as reserve food materials, and that the initial breakdown even of cellulose, in decay, is by hydrolytic enzymes. The reaction-type may be expressed as:

$$2(C_6H_{11}O_5)OH \rightleftharpoons (C_6H_{11}O_5)—O—(C_6H_{11}O_5) + H_2O \tag{1}$$

By analogy to laboratory reactions, it seems plausible that the plant synthesis of many esters proceeds basically as a reaction which produces water as a by-product. Significant instances for wood chemistry, in addition to the above pectic (galacturonic) esters, are the fats, the gallotannins, and the esters associated with volatile oils or other extractives. Another especially important dehydration reaction is the synthesis of proteins from the amino acids. As in the dehydration reactions leading to the polysaccharides, all of these reactions are reversible and the degradations are catalyzed by appropriate hydrolytic enzymes.

$$RCOOH + HOR' \rightleftharpoons RCOOR' + H_2O \tag{2}$$

$$RCH(NH_2)COOH + R'CH(NH_2)COOH$$
$$\rightleftharpoons RCH(NH_2)CO \cdot NH \cdot CH(R')COOH + H_2O \tag{3}$$

A very different type of reaction was indicated in the formal deduction that the carbon chains of the fatty acids are synthesized by the condensation of acetic acid molecules or some two-carbon atom equivalent. At the time this inference was first stated, the analogous laboratory synthesis employed sodium ethoxide and absolute alcohol. Obviously, those reaction conditions were very remote from those in a living plant. Nonetheless, it has been established recently that the synthesis of fatty acids proceeds through acetyl-coenzyme-A, which provides the necessary energy of activation in a much less drastic manner than the Claisen condensation. Conversely, the biochemical degradation of the fatty acids does not proceed by hydrolysis, but by oxidation, predominantly at the beta carbon atom. Empirically the reactions are:

$$2CH_3COOH - H_2O \rightarrow CH_3COCH_2COOH \tag{4}$$

$$CH_3COCH_2COOH + 4H \rightarrow CH_3CH_2CH_2COOH + H_2O \tag{5}$$

$$CH_3CH_2CH_2COOH + 2O \rightarrow CH_3COCH_2COOH + H_2O \tag{6}$$

Another structural concept having far-reaching consequences is that the carbon skeleton of the compounds belonging to the terpene series can, with few exceptions, be regarded as being derived from the condensation of isoprene units. This concept has related such apparently diverse compounds as the terpenes, camphors, resin acids, rubber, the carotenoids, and sterols. (For structural formulas see Chapter 7).

On the other hand, the usual methods of organic chemistry failed to elucidate the structure of lignin, and hence have not provided comparable inferences about its synthesis in the plant. Instead, biochemical products formed by the enzymatic oxidation of coniferyl alcohol, eugenol, and other phenols have been used to support speculation about the structure of lignin.

III. Composition of Developing Wood

Logically, one of the first steps to support a biochemical premise derived from structural organic chemistry is to find out whether, in a given species, the trees actually contain the postulated substances. For example, if we assume that cellulose is derived from glucose, we should find out whether or not glucose is present in the cells which are forming cellulose. This thought directs attention to the chemical composition of developing woody tissues. In this context it is convenient, though arbitrary, to regard the constituents of a living cell in three categories: (1) the generally low-molecular weight substances dissolved in the cytoplasm, (2) the higher molecular weight substances which form the cell wall, and (3) the proteins which are present in the nucleus and cytoplasm. To date, very little is known specifically of the proteins in cambial tissues; hence, they will be mentioned only incidentally.

A. METHODS OF COLLECTION

It should be evident that the first problem is to collect material which is botanically authentic. The chemist who is not thoroughly conversant with the identification of trees and tissues should invariably turn to a competent botanist for verification. Particularly, when the chemist does his own collecting, he should take auxiliary materials which will enable a botanist to check authenticity. A tree usually can be identified by its leaves in summer, by its buds and twigs in winter, or by the anatomy of the wood. Such specimens should be taken and properly labeled and preserved at the time each tree is felled or otherwise sampled. Since the growth of a tree is intimately related to its environment, it is usually desirable to record additional biological (or biometric) data such as the place, date, site, soil, height, age, and other pertinent facts. Obtaining satisfactory materials for biochemical studies involves additional considerations, which have led to a variety of procedures which may be grouped into two categories: (1) those which seek to obtain directly only the sap-soluble constituents, and, (2) those which depend first on removing the desired tissue and then on separating the cytoplasmic from the cell wall components.

Plant physiologists, who are concerned with the transport of nutrients and related problems, have often relied on procedures in the first group, whereas chemists have been prone to employ the second.

1. Collection of Sap

Flowing sap. A few woody plants, notably sugar maple, can be tapped before growth starts in the spring to obtain a flow of sap.
Wood sap. The wood (xylem) sap which fills the conducting vessels has been obtained by applying a vacuum to one end of a cut stem (6), or by displacing it with water under pressure (26).
Bark sap. Incisions into the inner bark yield small quantities of the phloem sap. A unique procedure is to decapitate aphids which have been feeding on young twigs and to collect the exudation from the stylets left *in situ* (29).

2. Collection of Tissue

Microdissection. With a microscope and a micromanipulator thin sections of wood can be separated into their component tissues.
Macrodissection. Various procedures have been used to obtain samples of developing wood which permit analysis by established methods. In the following sequence of materials, adapted from Sultze (38), the extent of lignification is taken as a rough index of tissue development:

a. Xylem scrapings (X. Sc.), a watery suspension of tissue fragments; ideally, it would be devoid of lignin.

b. Soft xylem (S. X.), translucent ribbons; about 5% of the total

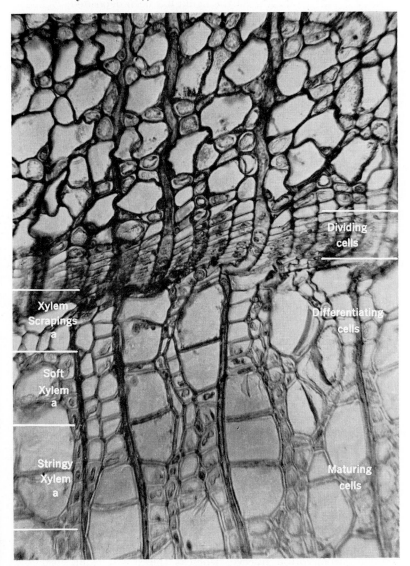

Fig. 2. Active cambium, summer. Cross section. *a*, Approximations only.
Quaking aspen.

lignin has been deposited. (Estimates of lignification are based on analyses of *P. tremuloides* in 1957.)

c. Stringy xylem (Str. X.), semiwoody, tends to break down into stringy fibers; about 20% of the lignin has been deposited.

d. New xylem (e.g., '57X), woody, curls when cut with spoke-shave; about 50% of the lignin has been deposited.

e. Year old xylem (e.g., '56X), woody; fully lignified.

Figure 2 shows the approximate location of these materials, and the changes in their cross-sectional appearance as they develop from the original dividing cells in the cambium into wood.

Satisfactory sequences of materials have been obtained from the aspens (*Populus tremuloides* Michx. and *P. grandidentata* Michx.), sugar maple (*Acer saccharum* Marsh.), jack pine (*Pinus banksiana* Lamb), and balsam fir (*Abies balsamea* [L.] Mill). Soft xylem has been obtained from white and yellow birches (*Betula papyrifera* Marsh., *B. lutea* Michx. f.), and American elm (*Ulmus americana* L.).

B. CYTOPLASMIC CONSTITUENTS

Turning now to the results of chemical investigations of materials collected by such procedures, Table II attempts to indicate the cytoplasmic constituents which have been found in developing woody tissues and the trees from which they were obtained. Although it is very important for the plant physiologist to determine whether or not a given constituent is located in a moving sap stream, because this fact has a bearing on the problem of translocation, the distinction has less significance for the plant chemist. Presumably, the constituent would be available for metabolism in either event. Consequently the table does not indicate the method of collection; but, in each instance, the constituents have been derived from metabolically active outer wood, inner bark, or young twigs. The numerous extractives obtained from whole bark or wood, leaves, and roots have been excluded.

Inspection of Table II shows that sucrose has been found more consistently in the developing wood and inner bark than any other constituent. It is often accompanied by glucose and fructose, but apparently not in the relationship of invert sugar. In the context of general plant physiology, these facts suggest that the sucrose is in enzymatic equilibrium with starch—the sucrose functioning as a soluble carbohydrate reserve, whereas the starch is an insoluble carbohydrate reserve of the tree. Although not usually reported in

TABLE II

Soluble Constituents of Outer Wood and Inner Bark[a]

Compound	Syringa vulgaris	F. quadrangulata	Fraxinus spp.	Eucalyptus	Tilia americana	Acer spp.	Robinia pseudacacia	Malus, Pyrus, Prunus spp.	Ulmus spp.	Quercus spp.	Castanea dentata	Fagus sylvatica	Alnus spp.	Betula spp.	Carpinus betulus	Populus tremuloides	Salix spp.	Bamboo	Picea spp.	Pinus sylvestris
Mannitol			x					x											x	x
Sorbitol																		x	x	x
Arabinose																		x	x	x
Glucose			x													x		x		
Fructose																x		x		
Sucrose			x													x				
Raffinose			x																	
Stachyose																x			x	
Pyrocatechol																				
Vanillin		x		x	x	x	x	x	x	x	x	x		x	x	x				x
Benzoic acid					x			x	x	x		x		x	x	x				
p-OH-Benzoic acid					x			x	x	x		x		x	x	x				
Vanillic acid								x	x							x				
p-Coumaric acid								x	x			x				x				
Ferulic acid																x				
Sinapaldehyde																	x			
Salicin																			x	x
Coniferin	x		x																	x
Syringin																				
Dicarboxylic acid						x												x		
Phenylalanine																x	x			
Tyrosine																x	x			x
Amino acids														x			x			x
Proteins/enzymes						b				x		x		x						
Asparagine								x	x								x			
Glutamine							x	x	x								x			
Citrulline						x		x					x		x					
Allantoic acid												x								
Ash				x																x

[a] After reference 37; see also references 6, 12, 30, 31, and 42.
[b] Sugar maple sap contained NH₃ amides (?), and peptides which hydrolyzed to yield alanine, arginine, aspartic acid, cysteic acid, glutamic acid, glycine, hydroxyproline, leucine, lysine, proline, serine, threonine, and valine (33a).

wood analyses, it is known from microscopy that starch is very commonly found in trees. Equally noteworthy is the absence of the so-called typical wood sugars arabinose, xylose, galactose, and mannose. Likewise, there is no report of either galacturonic or glucuronic acids, which are characteristic of the pectic acids and the aldobiouronic acids of the hemicelluloses, respectively.

The absence of the sugars and uronic acids which structurally make up the hemicelluloses and pectic substances may indicate that present methods of detection have not been perfected sufficiently, or it may have some significance in relation to the biochemical pathways by which these substances are built-up. Although galactose has not been detected as yet in the free state, it is present in combined form in the tri- and tetrasaccharides, raffinose, and stachyose. Each contains the structural equivalent of sucrose, and the third and fourth hexose units are galactose. These oligosaccharides occur in the phloem sap and seem to indicate that the galactose is formed in the leaves and is transported in combined form through the inner bark to the places where it is required.

Not many chemical analyses have been directed to detecting the usual di- or polycarboxylic acids. However, microscopic inspection has revealed calcium oxalate crystals as a widespread deposit in ray cells and the crystalliferous strands. Oxalic acid was formerly regarded as the next to the last stage of oxidation in the metabolism of carbohydrates. Since oxalic acid is a very strong acid, it may be assumed to have a toxic effect if its concentration exceeds a certain minimum; hence, it was inferred that the calcium oxalate crystals, so often seen under the microscope, represented a mechanism for rendering oxalic acid nontoxic. It is equally plausible, however, to assume that the deposition of calcium oxalate removed calcium from the fluids of the tree. Another calcium salt, commonly known as maple sand because it precipitates in the boiling down of maple sap to maple syrup, contains L-malic acid as its major component, together with lesser amounts of citric, fumaric, and succinic acids. These four acids are prominent members of the so-called Krebs or citric acid cycle in respiration. It would be interesting to examine the cambial zone of other species for the occurrence of members of the citric acid cycle. It might also be worthwhile investigating whether the oxalic acid is derived from the keto-acids or this series, for example oxaloacetic acid.

As would be expected of actively growing tissues, nitrogenous compounds in the form of amino acids have been reported. The indications of proteins and enzymes would be limited to exudates or to other materials specifically prepared for the purpose of detecting them. The usual preservative extraction with dehydrating solvents, such as strong alcohol, would insolubilize most proteins and enzymes. The amino acids, phenylalanine, and tyrosine, which have been reported from the willow family, were listed separately because of their importance to current theories of the biogenesis of lignin. Of the so-called amides, asparagine and glutamine have been long known to participate in the storage and transport of nitrogen. Allantoin and allantoic acid apparently have similar functions. Citrulline also seems to be a form in which nitrogen is stored; in addition, it is closely related to the important amino acid, arginine.

As is true of nitrogen, the inorganic ash constituents are important to the metabolism of the plant, but unlike nitrogenous compounds, have received little attention in forest trees.

The remaining compounds, with the exception of benzoic acid, may be looked upon as phenolic substances which are more or less related to current concepts of the biosynthesis of lignin. Only in the case of quaking aspen has any significant number of intermediates been detected, and even when taken in the aggregate they constitute but a very minor percentage of the total soluble solids of lignifying tissues. Perhaps the most that can be said is that at present we have hit only a few of the high spots in the sequence. Even the recorded occurrences of coniferin and syringin are still few in comparison with the known distribution of sucrose, and they may be considered as trivial in relation to the number of tree-forming plant species.

In brief, the soluble constituents of cytoplasm that have been isolated undoubtedly give us important glimpses into the initial stages in the metabolic processes of wood formation. Obviously, more comprehensive and systematic observations must be carried out in order to reveal the continuity of the reactions by which a tree builds its structure out of the primary products of photosynthesis.

C. CELL WALL COMPONENTS

From the standpoint of the pulp and paper industry, interest in the chemistry of wood formation centers primarily on the chemistry of cell wall formation. Although the various pulping operations produce fibers with diverse properties, the pulped fibers retain, more or less intact, the cell walls laid down when the wood was formed. Figures 3 and 4 (23) give the data obtained in efforts to further investigate the development of cell walls in quaking aspen (*Populus tremuloides*). In these figures the progressive or sequential stages of development are arbitrarily spaced along the horizontal axis, the youngest or least lignified stage being first (left) and the fully lignified or year-old xylem being last (right). Each graphic point is the averaged analyt-

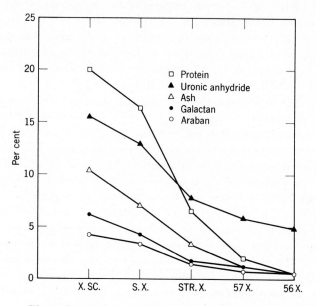

Fig. 3. Quaking aspen, 1957, composition in per cent.

ical result for all samples of each tissue. To obtain these samples 22 trees were felled in the course of 6 collection periods between May 20th and September 5th. Not all stages of wood development were available at each collection period; for example, '57 xylem had not been laid down in sufficient quantity before May 20th, and xylem scrapings could not be collected after June 15th.

It is evident that the percentages of some constituents diminish, whereas others increase, as the cell matures. Particular significance may be attached to the fact that the values for uronic anhydride, galactan, and arabinan decline more or less steadily. These three compounds constitute the pectic complex referred to by both the botanist and the food chemist. According to the botanist, they also constitute the middle lamella, i.e., the material which cements adjacent cell walls and which, possibly, was formed at the time when the first boundary (cell plate) was created between two new cells in the last stages of cell division. At present, the consensus seems to be

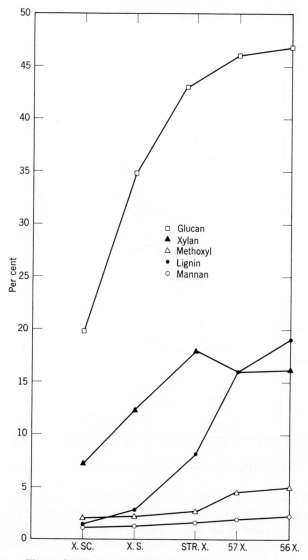

Fig. 4. Quaking aspen, 1957, composition in per cent.

that these pectic materials are not transformed into other substances during the subsequent differentiation of the cells (8,21). If this is so, it can be assumed that the percentage diminution of the pectic constituents is proportional to the weight of other materials deposited in

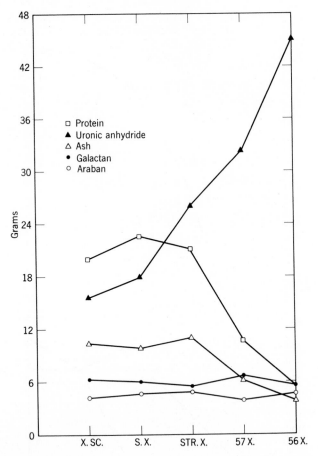

Fig. 5. Quaking aspen, 1957, relative composition in grams.

the cell wall during growth and differentiation. On this premise, the percentage of pectic materials in very young tissue (e.g., xylem scrapings) can be used as an internal index to the subsequent increments in the dry weight of the other constituents (38). Of the three pectic materials, the pectic acid (structurally a polygalacturonic anhydride)

is the most abundant, and hence, would be preferred as a basis for
the internal index calculations. Currently, however, there is no
standard routine analytic method for distinguishing between galacturonic acid derived by hydrolysis from pectic acid and the glucuronic
acid which is associated with the xylan. Accordingly, the calculations
are based on an average of the values for galactan and arabinan in the
xylem scrapings. Figures 5 and 6 (23) show the result of recalculating

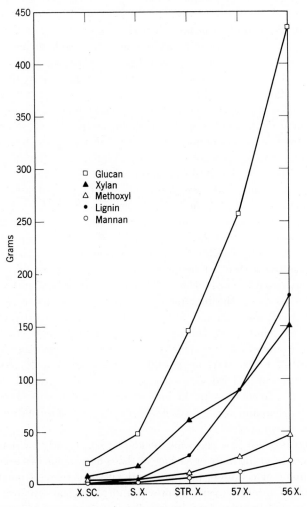

Fig. 6. Quaking aspen, 1957, relative composition in grams.

the percentage composition of each growth stage into gram-weight composition relative to 100 grams of xylem scraping tissue.

In this perspective, the trends in composition were significantly different. Of the 10 components assayed, only protein and ash fell below their original levels. Even so, no significant decline occurred until after the tissue had become sufficiently differentiated to have acquired a definite woody texture. Stated somewhat differently, these components maintained their original level during cell enlargement and the initial stages of differentiation. They declined in the later stages of differentiation when the major synthesis of cellulose, lignin, and hemicelluloses brought about the thickening of the cell walls and their impregnation with lignin. In the aggregate, the net result was a 9- or 10-fold increase in dry weight from the xylem-scraping stage to year-old wood.

A comparison of the relative gram-weight increments of a given component to its total relative weight in mature wood, showed that the amount of glucan deposited increased in each growth increment. Analogous trends were observed for mannan and lignin, and less consistently for xylan and nonlignin methoxyl. Roughly, one-third of the uronic anhydride was deposited in the xylem-scrapings stage, one-fourth in the '57 → '56 xylem stage, and lesser fractions in the intervening stages. By assumption, all of the arabinan and galactan was considered to have been deposited in the xylem scrapings stage. This is not strictly valid; some arabinose is associated with the xylans and galactose with other hemicelluloses. However, the amounts are relatively small in hardwoods. This is not true of conifers.

Comparisons of the increments of each component to the corresponding cell wall increments within the several growth stages indicated that cellulose was always the predominant single component. But it accounted for only 35% of the xylem scrapings stage, whereas it constituted 50 to 60% of the cell wall increments in all subsequent stages (protein and ash-free basis). The uronic anhydride fraction ranked next to cellulose in the first stage; the xylan ranked second in the soft-xylem and stringy-xylem stages; lignin was second in the '57 and '56 xylem stages.

If one assumes that cell wall thickening occurs only by deposition of materials on the interior surface of the cell wall, one can argue that the content of cellulose, mannan, and xylan increases from the exterior to the interior layers. However, morphological evidence clearly indicates that lignin is deposited within the previously formed carbohydrates which constitute the external layers of the cell wall. Hence, at this stage it would be the better part of wisdom to accept statements about cell wall gradients with a degree of reservation.

The chemistry of cell wall development in young tracheid cells from *Pinus sylvestris* has also been studied. Tissues, which represented five stages in a cell wall growth, were discernible in radial, longitudinal sections when viewed through a polarizing microscope, and were separated for microanalysis with a micromanipulator. The results of this work are given in Chapters 5 and 10.

IV. Chemical Reactions in Living Tissue

All of the dry matter in a tree, whether it is in the form of major constituents such as cellulose and lignin or as minor extractives, is derived from the carbon and energy which is made available by photosynthesis. The organic compounds formed by photosynthesis, together with the energy they contain, may enter metabolic pathways directly, or they may be transformed into reserve nutrients, e.g., starch. In either event, transformation of the photosynthetic products will depend upon coupled reactions. The term *coupled reactions* refers to one or more reactions which proceeds with the liberation of energy that is transferred to another reaction, or set of reactions, which absorbs energy. Such reactions are designated as exergonic and endergonic reactions, respectively, and occur more or less simultaneously. In many instances, such coupled reactions proceed in small stages, with many more intermediate compounds than the organic chemist is apt to deal with in the ordinary laboratory synthesis or degradation. The energy changes in a given step of a biochemical reaction are correspondingly small, commensurate with the small structural changes which occur from one intermediate to the next. Table III shows the heat of combustion of typical plant constituents and, to the extent that the heat of combustion exceeds that of a carbohydrate, the difference may be regarded as a measure of the energy which coupled reactions have transferred from carbohydrates into the synthesis of other substances. It is generally recognized that both proteins and fats are richer in energy than carbohydrates, but reference is seldom made to the fact that lignin as well as terpenes, waxes, and some other "extractives" also are energy rich.

Such thermochemical relations, together with inferences from

TABLE III

Heats of Combustion of Typical Plant Constituents

Constituent	Formula	Heat of combustion, kcal. per g.
Glucose	$C_6H_{12}O_6$	3.7
Lignin	$(C_{10}H_{10}O_3)_n$	6.3
	$-C_6H_2\begin{bmatrix} O- \\ O-CH_3 \\ C_3H_5O \end{bmatrix}$	
Cinnamic acid	$C_6H_5-CH=CH-COOH$	7.1
p-Hydroxycinnamic acid	$C_6H_4\begin{bmatrix} OH \\ CH=CH-COOH \end{bmatrix}$	6.0
Tyrosine	$C_6H_4\begin{bmatrix} OH \\ CH_2-CH(NH_2)-COOH \end{bmatrix}$	5.9
Gallic acid	$C_6H_2\begin{bmatrix} (OH)_3 \\ COOH \end{bmatrix}$	4.4

structure and from tissue composition, provide a valuable source of research ideas and criteria. The assertion that a given biochemical reaction actually occurs during wood formation requires substantiation by evidence that can only be derived more directly from living tissues. Over the years very comprehensive pathways of plant metabolism have been proposed and extensively supported by experiment. Except for studies on lignification, very little work of this kind has been done with trees. It has been much more convenient to study much simpler or smaller organisms: bacteria, yeast, molds, or algae. To begin with, scientists hesitated to generalize to higher plants the knowledge gained from microorganisms. However, the viewpoint has become rather generally accepted that many basic mechanisms are similar in plants and animals. Figure 7, which is a greatly oversimplified, schematic diagram, may help the reader to gain an elementary picture of the chemical origins of plant constituents.

The pectic substances, i.e., pectic acid, galactan, and arabinan are prominent components of the middle lamella and primary wall, and

Dry Matter Accumulation
Schematic Pathways

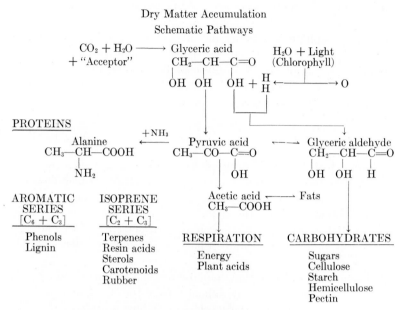

Fig. 7. Chemical origins of plant constituents.

are supposed to originate from D-galacturonic acid, galactose, and arabinose, respectively. As yet there is no direct evidence that these simple carbohydrate compounds exist, as such, in cambial cells. However, small amounts of raffinose and stachyose, which contain galactose, have been detected in the phloem sap of some trees. Apparently very little is known about the precursors of the pectic substances and the biochemical reactions which construct the middle lamella.

Cellulose is quantitatively the dominant cell wall component and is formed at all stages of development. As it is regarded chemically as a pure glucose polysaccharide, and inasmuch as glucose—either free or in the form of sucrose—is commonly present in developing woody tissues, it seems logical that glucose is a direct precursor of cellulose. Actually, glucose marked with C^{14} has been incorporated into the cellulose of cotton hairs (16), *Acetobacter xylinum* (17), and wheat stem (7). Current opinion holds that the enzymatic reaction proceeds through glucose phosphates, e.g., uridine-diphosphoglucose,

$$(C_6H_{11}O_5)O(H_2P_2O_5)O(C_5H_7O_3) \cdot C_4H_2N_2O_2$$

which contain energy necessary for the synthesis of the glucoside linkages of the cellulose chain. A chromatographic indication of organic phosphate was noted in soft xylem extractives of quaking aspen (38), but it was not characterized. An alternate mechanism is cellulose formation by transglycosidation of sucrose. Recently, glucose has been found in a lipid fraction produced by *Acetobacter* and may also be a cellulose precursor in this form.

$$2(C_6H_{11}O_5)O(C_6H_{11}O_5) + H_2O \rightarrow (C_6H_{11}O_5)O(C_6H_{11}O_5) + 2C_6H_{12}O_6 \qquad (7)$$
(Glucose) (Fructose)   (Glucose) (Glucose)   Fructose

Although cellulose is idealized as containing only glucose, it is extremely difficult to prepare even a cotton cellulose which does not yield mannose on hydrolysis. Consequently, it has become a debatable question whether the small amounts of mannose observed represented mannan residues, were an artifact created by the acid hydrolysis, or were structurally a part of the cellulose macromolecule (27).

Although the premise that cellulose originates from glucose in the cell sap does not present any difficulty from the standpoint of structural organic chemistry, the mechanics of how an enzyme, itself a macromolecule, can construct a linear cellulose molecule containing 300 or more glucose units is more difficult to visualize. In developing cotton fibers, x-ray diagrams did not show the characteristics of the native cellulose crystal lattice until about 25 days after flowering. Although cellulose is present in earlier stages, it was not revealed by this property without prior extraction of wax and, in the very immature stages, of other interfering materials with caustic soda (35). In view of the association of wax deposits with cellulose, reference may be made to the occurrence of a "lipid glucoside" in *Acetobacter* cultures (9). On the other hand, some water soluble gums contain cellulose, but whether the apparent solubility of the cellulose is due to colloidal dispersion or to chemical combination with more soluble carbohydrates is unknown. Such observations seem to indicate transitional forms or states of cellulose.

Even more provocative is the fact that mature tobacco pith cells have been induced by proper conditions of tissue cultures to renew their growth without cell division. This enlargement was not merely swelling as a result of water uptake, because there was an increase in the dry weight of the cell wall materials (32) (cf. Table IV). How was the newly formed cellulose laid down? Electron micrographs

TABLE IV

Deposition of Cell Wall Components, Dry Weights (in milligrams)
Tobacco Pith, Growth without Cell Division (32)

Number of days	Additive[a]	Cell wall, d.b.	Polysac-charides[b]	Pectic sub-stances	Lignin	Protein
0		6.5	3.7	1.5	0.9	0.4
6	Sucrose	10.0	5.2	2.3	1.8	0.7
6	Sucrose + indole acetic acid	15.5	9.1	3.5	2.1	0.8

[a] Agar, 0.7%; sucrose, 2%, indole acetic acid, 3.5 mg./l.
[b] Holocellulose less pectic substance and protein.

show that primary layers of cell walls contain a network of microfibrils. Is this structure sufficiently elastic to expand as required? Is the new cellulose laid down as an additional film or lamella of meshed microfibrils on the inner surface of the older cell wall material? Or, are the interfibrillar spaces enlarged by the growth process and new microfibrils created to fill the voids? A recent attempt (36) to sum up the physical, chemical, and biological evidence assumes ". . . that both molecules and microfibrils grow in length at the same time and at the same point, viz., at the top of a microfibril. Here one or more molecules of the cellulose synthesizing enzyme are supposed to be engaged in detaching glucose monomers from some high energy precursor and transferring these monomers to the ends of the (cellulose) molecules . . . The enzyme might be localized . . . with higher plants on the inside of the wall and, in primary walls, probably also in the interior of the wall."

Botanists have sought, for many years, to find a separate and specific structure within the cytoplasm that would account for the synthesis of cellulose in the same way that plastids account for the synthesis of starch. During the 1930's such plastid-like bodies were reported to have been discovered in the large, single-celled algae, *Valonia* and *Halicystis*, and their presence to have been established subsequently in developing cotton hairs (13). According to these observations, the cellulose was synthesized within the plastid, evolving through liquid, jell, and solid states. The plastids eventually ruptured and, depending on the species, liberated the cellulose in the form of either granules or fibrils which were still encumbered with a portion of the plastid matrix. Finally, the cellulosic material was incorporated into the cell wall. These morphological observations were supported by phenomena revealed by polarized light, x-ray diagrams, and chemical treatments. Subsequently, these descriptions and interpretations were criticized and have been largely supplanted by the revelations of the electron microscope. Nonetheless, students of submicroscopic morphology are trying to relate the granular reticulum of the cytoplasm to enzymatic processes. The basic question about the formation of cellulose posed by the earlier botanical investigators is still valid—and is still unanswered.

The deposition of lignin occurs within the existing framework of the cell wall and, accordingly, is regarded as a filling or cementing process. However, lignification and cell wall construction are not mutually exclusive processes in the composite metabolism of a cell. Deposition of lignin in the outer wall may start while the secondary wall is being formed, as is shown very clearly in the accompanying photomicrographs (see Figs. 8 and 9) (41). In the case of the tobacco

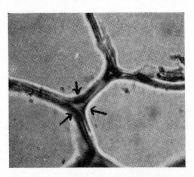

Fig. 8. Initiation of lignification at cell corners, *Pinus radiata*, immature tracheids, according to Wardrop (cross section, ultraviolet light, × 1400).

pith cells mentioned above, the process of enlarging the cell proceeded in spite of the fact that the cell walls had been somewhat lignified. In general, however, lignification must be regarded as a stabilizing process helping to make the woody cell stronger and more durable.

Current concepts of lignification regard coniferyl alcohol as the primary building unit, and state that the processes of dehydrogenation and polymerization transform this monomer into the complex

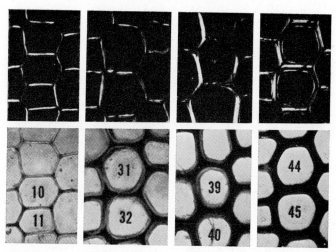

Fig. 9. Comparable photographs taken in ultraviolet light (lower) and between crossed nicols (upper), showing the relation between cell wall formation and the progress of lignification. The numbers refer to the cell number, counted from a point judged to be the cambium. (After Wardrop, × 430.)

polymer. Historically, this idea developed from three facts: the isolation of the glucoside coniferin from some conifers, the similarity in the elementary analyses of coniferyl alcohol and isolated lignin, and the tendency of coniferyl alcohol to resinify. Spruce lignin is thought to conform most nearly to this concept and, consequently, is regarded as the prototype for other lignins. In the case of the hardwood lignins, sinapyl and coumaryl alcohols participate with coniferyl alcohol in the formation of lignin.

In conformity with the principle that lignin must originate with the products of photosynthesis, the biochemical origin of coniferyl alcohol has been related to the simple sugars by analogy to the microbial metabolism of glucose via sedoheptulose, shikimic, and prephenic acids to phenylalanine and tyrosine. Biochemical reactions which would convert tyrosine into coniferyl alcohol via ferulic acid appear analogous to many transformations which occur in respiration and in the synthesis of carbohydrates (Fig. 10). Taken as a whole, this scheme of lignification has much appeal because many steps are consistent with the generalities of plant metabolism (1,33).

Evidence in favor of the proposed pathway has been sought by introducing radioactive C^{14} coniferyl alcohol into trees or other plants.

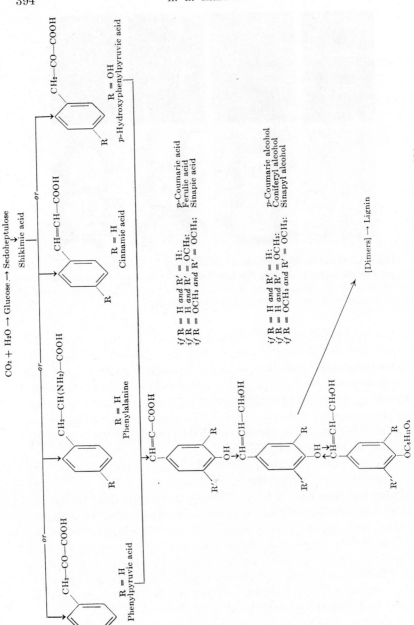

Fig. 10. The general biosynthetic pathway to lignification. (After Faber, reference 12.)

Radioactive precursors of coniferyl alcohol, e.g., shikimic acid, phenylalanine, ferulic acid, and numerous other materials have been similarly tested. Organic chemists have expended a great amount of energy, ingenuity, and time in synthesizing compounds with radioactive carbon atoms in known positions within the molecule, in order to reveal the pathways to lignin. Parallel to the syntheses of the starting materials has been the necessary elaboration of quantitative degradation procedures to recover the radioactivity from the lignin, or more particularly, from the vanillin, the "Hibbert ketones," or other lignin fragments. The radioactive compounds have been administered to the plant in various ways—solid substances have been implanted under the bark, whereas solutions have been injected aseptically or they have been absorbed through the freshly cut ends of stems or tips. Radioautographs have been used to localize the introduced materials, which seem generally not to have been transported any great distance and to have been sequestered by rapidly developing and lignifying cells. Proof that the absorbed radioactivity actually was incorporated into the lignin generally rested upon the assumption that the extraction of the tissue with solvents, such as alcohol, benzene, and water (in which the incorporated materials are soluble under laboratory conditions) removed all materials not converted to lignin. In some instances, whole tissues were subjected to lignin degradation reactions to recover radioactivity. In others, isolated lignins were first prepared by conventional methods.

The resulting data have been regarded not only as proof that coniferyl alcohol participated directly in lignin synthesis, but also as a validation of the sequence starting from glucose. Comparable studies have been made with sinapyl alcohol and parahydroxycinnamyl alcohol to extend the concept to hardwoods. Further affirmation has been found in researches which attempted to simulate lignification *in vitro* by subjecting coniferyl alcohol and related compounds to the action of enzymes or inorganic catalysts (15). Consequently, the proposed pathways as a whole, and the dehydrogenation–polymerization of coniferyl alcohol to spruce lignin in particular, have received very general credence (40).

There still are, however, unanswered questions. As maturing wood tissues carry on a variety of chemical syntheses, introduced radioactive chemicals obviously can enter any of the available pathways of metabolism, some of which do not terminate in lignification. Hence, it has been assumed that the greater the radioactivity recovered in the lignin or its degradation products, the more direct was the relationship between the introduced chemical and lignification. But, the result is still dependent on the nutritional and metabolic balance in the tissues, which has been assumed to be normal.

Another difficulty arises from the fact that lignin cannot be assigned a definite chemical composition or structure. Consequently, it has been assumed, at one extreme, that radioactive material was incorporated into the lignin of the plant if the radioactive material was no longer removable by simple extraction. At the other extreme, it has been proposed that a substance laid down in the plant could not be called lignin unless it qualified with respect to the criteria set forth by eight categories of chemical reactions or physical measurements, each of the many tests being performed preferably with both the original wood and the isolated lignin (22). Many students have held that if the introduced radioactivity was recovered in the form of radioactive vanillin or syringaldehyde, this was cogent evidence that the presumed precursor had truly been built into the lignin. Recently, the argument was advanced that introduced radioactive material had not been incorporated into lignin unless most of the radioactivity was recoverable in the form of "Hibbert ketones." This is an even more restrictive criterion than that of recovering radioactive vanillin or syringaldehyde.

It would seem that the critical problems in connection with the pathways to lignin are the questions of the quantitative relationships and of the reactions in hardwoods. For instance, do trees synthesize enough coniferyl and sinapyl alcohols, respectively coniferin and syringin, to yield the large amount of lignin present in wood? Can the current concepts based on coniferyl alcohol and the "spruce lignin prototype" be extended to hardwood lignins, some of which exhibit a 2.5:1 ratio of syringyl to guaiacyl groups?

It has been relatively easy to follow the deposition and structural distribution of pectic materials, cellulose, and lignin. This is due to the fact that the histologist has one or more distinctive criteria for observing these substances: e.g., the ruthenium red stain for pectic acids, the crystallinity of cellulose, and the phloroglucinol stain for lignin. Unfortunately, no specific criterion is available for the hemicelluloses.

Similar to lignin, hemicelluloses are considered to be cellulose incrusting materials; thus, it is conceivable that representatives of this group might be deposited throughout the cell wall. Of the various efforts directed toward resolving this problem, microdissection and internal index analyses have been mentioned previously. Controlled mechanical attrition has been used to remove outer layers of the cell wall from unbleached, spruce-pulp fibers (20). Analytical comparisons were made between the initial fiber, the S_2 layer, and the $S_1 + P$ layers. And, in still another way, the problem has been studied with the aid of microspectrographic measurements of fibers which had been stained with crystal violet to locate acidic materials (hemicelluloses) (24) or esterified with p-(phenylazo)benzoyl chloride as an index of cellulose or holocellulose (25). In the latter instance, pretreatments with acid or alkali, after delignification, were considered to have removed hemicelluloses.

In brief, these studies have led to a more or less explicitly stated consensus that pectic acid, or its derivatives, are deposited largely in the early stages (i.e., in the outer layers) of cell wall formation. The association of arabinan and galactan with the pectic acid is accepted, too. Beyond this the interpretations are divergent; for pine it was stated that the S_3 layer was strongly acidic, for birch and spruce that it was the least acidic. Other data were thought to indicate a rather uniform distribution of hemicellulose in the wall. Obviously, the problem is far from settled. It appears also that no biochemical studies have been made of the syntheses of hemicelluloses in any tree species. Consequently, statements about biochemical pathways or mechanisms leading to these constituents in wood rest on analogies to what has been observed in other types of plants.

The tertiary wall is the final and innermost structural element of the cell wall. To date, it has not been well characterized by either microscopic or chemical evidence. It seems to be only a small portion of the final cell wall in a wood fiber, and presumably includes the dried out cytoplasmic debris left by the death of the cell (Fig. 11). Too little is known about this layer to warrant further discussion.

Wood formation—the synthesis of cell wall materials—has been considered, so far, in terms of the chemical precursors and their reactions as they are thought to occur in, or close to, a growing, differentiating cell. However, wood formation is responsive to more remote and even external influences. Thus, the more or less favorable fluctuations in the tree's environment are evident in the larger or smaller wood increments (growth rings), and in the lack of symmetry of the growth rings and the cross section of the tree trunk. Specific external situations also can be decisive as to the amount of wood

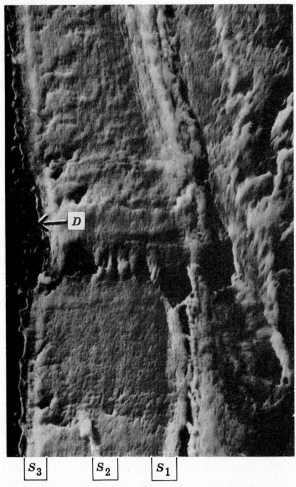

Fig. 11. Electron micrograph of a longitudinal section of a tracheid of *Pinus radiata*, showing the three layers, S_1, S_2, and S_3, of the cell wall. *D*, Cytoplasmic debris. (Wardrop.)

formed; a well-known instance is the limitation imposed by a lack of water in periods of drought. Less obvious in its nature, is the formation of reaction wood in response to mechanical forces whether applied by gravitation, wind pressure, or mechanical loading. In coniferous species reaction wood is formed in the zones of compression and is characterized chemically by a more than average formation of lignin.

In hardwoods, the response occurs in the areas of tension; this wood has a relatively greater amount of cellulose, and there may be other chemical differences. It seems as though there is a certain balance which normally exists between the formation of lignin and cellulose that is shifted one way or the other by the stress or strain to which the wood is subjected. Incidentally, the stone cells of aspen bark which appear to be completely solid exhibit the same percentage of lignin and cellulose as is found in aspen wood.

It was mentioned earlier that in addition to water, the tree obtains its supply of minerals from the soil. The degree to which the roots of the tree can or do absorb the available minerals affects wood formation in various important ways. According to agricultural standards, forest soils, on the whole, are considered poor or even unfit with respect to various essential minerals; they are usually deficient in nitrogen which, together with carbon, hydrogen, and oxygen, is an essential structural element in the proteins, of which nitrogen constitutes about 16%. Phosphorus and sulphur, two other elements which are intimately associated with proteins or protein functions, also tend to be low in forest soils. Perhaps one reason why forest tree species do so well on such soils is that they have mechanisms for conserving these elements more effectively than the usual agricultural plants. Moreover, on areas of virgin timber the plant–soil–biochemical cycle tends to be a closed system; i.e., the minerals taken up by the trees are eventually returned to the soil. This is not so true of areas where forestry is practiced because there the removal of wood and a somewhat greater exposure to erosion results in some transport of minerals away from the soil where they originated.

Magnesium is an essential element in the chlorophyll molecule. Hence, any limitation on its availability to the tree is a potential limitation on the amount of photosynthesis that can take place. The application of magnesium sulfate on certain soils in the Great Lake States has been beneficial to the growth of aspen. Although calcium is chemically related to magnesium, it does not have the same specificity of action. Perhaps its most important function is its association with the pectic materials of the compound middle lamella, where it influences the texture of the cell wall and the movement of metabolic substances into or out of the cell. The so-called trace elements are associated with enzymes and their importance depends on their function as catalysts. Table V is intended to help the reader visualize some of these relations.

TABLE V

Indispensable Elements (15a)

Element	Function (illustrative only)
Nitrogen	Synthesis of amino acids; proteins
Sulfur	Synthesis of amino acids; proteins
Phosphorus	Synthesis of proteins; energy transfer (coupled reactions)
Chlorine	Osmotic and ionic equilibria
Sodium	Osmotic and ionic equilibria
Potassium	Osmotic and ionic equilibria
Calcium	Cell wall stability; Ca oxalate
Magnesium	Chlorophyll synthesis
Iron	Respiration (cytochrome coenzymes)
Copper	Polyphenol oxidase
Manganese	Enzyme activator
Cobalt	Enzyme activator
Zinc	Enzyme activator
Molybdenum	Enzymatic reduction of NO_3

In comparison with orchard practice, the application of fertilizers to forest species occupies a very minor position. Soil deficiencies or other maladjustments have been encountered mostly in seed beds and nurseries where the application of fertilizers is a practical means of correction. On extensive areas the practice has been to plant species that will adapt to the peculiarities of the soil.

V. Wood Quality

Concern for the future wood supply has focused attention on the fact that the problem has two parts: quantity and quality. By quality it is meant those particular attributes of either a small piece of wood or a large quantity of it which make this wood suitable for a particular product or end use. As long as the dominant use of wood was for construction, quality was defined in terms of such physical properties as strength, hardness, softness, freedom from knots, freedom from warp, machinability, grain, and the like. The current practices in the grading of lumber reflect not only these constructional end uses of wood, but also the era when the lumber supply was derived from our fabulous, but now exhausted, virgin forests. Just as the disappearance of the virgin forests made it necessary to devise ways and means of using "inferior" species of trees, so has the variability of reproduction in our second growth forests made it necessary to develop criteria of wood quality which are appropriate both to the newer end uses and to the trees now growing. Older indices of mechanical quality have been refined or extended to include density, growth rate, springwood to summerwood ratio, thickness of the secondary cell wall, and fibril angle. Each of these measurements has been related to one or more properties which make wood suitable, or unsuitable, to use for a given purpose. Moreover, in harmony with the newer utilization practices, these indices are applicable not only to the aggregate wood-yield of a species, but also to the wood derivable from single trees or even parts of a single tree.

The large scale conversion of wood to pulp has resulted in chemical, as well as physical, standards for wood quality. For example, the quantity and the chemical nature of the extractives in a given species of wood may determine which pulping process can be used. Moreover, the chemical composition, as well as the structure, of the pulp fibers has a direct bearing on the kind and quality of the products for which the pulp is suitable.

As was already observed, wood is the net result of the environmental and genetic forces to which a tree is subjected. Silviculture has always taken account of such environmental factors as climate, soil, moisture levels, and plant associations; to a lesser extent, this science has recognized and manipulated genetic forces which are manifested externally, e.g., in tree form, branching and, perhaps, in growth rate. The selection and propagation of slash pine for high yields of oleoresin, of rubber trees for latex, and of cinchona trees for quinine are instances in which genetic means were used for improvements in composition, as determined by measurement of chemical indices. These achievements, however, do not relate directly to the problem of producing more and better wood. From the general pathways of biochemical synthesis, it seems plausible that a definite relationship could be found between the amount or concentration of sugars in the cambial zone and the amount or rate of wood produced. In the case of the sugar maple, a correlation has been established between the sucrose concentration in the sap flow and the growth of the tree, measured as either terminal or radial growth, during the preceding season (4). Sugar concentration in the sap appears to be controlled in part by genetic influences in the sugar maple, but whether it will prove to be a useful chemical index for genetic tree improvement work in other species remains to be seen.

Table VI is an attempt to visualize the relationships between some important indices of wood quality and the intended products or end uses. The reader is cautioned against accepting these expressions too literally, partly because the relationships generally are not as simple as might be inferred from a table, and partly because the subject matter is constantly being elaborated (28, 10).

TABLE VI

Selected Indices of Wood Quality

Index	Use[a]					
	Gross yield, cords	Lumber	Chip-board	Kraft paper[b]	"Soft" paper[c]	Chemical pulp
Specific gravity	X	X	Y	X	X	X
Growth rate	X	Z	X	X	X	X
Springwood				Y	X	
Summerwood	X			X	Y	
Reaction wood		Y				
Fiber length		X		X	X	
Fibril angle		Y				
Cellulose						X

[a] *Symbols:* X = select for values above species average; Y = select for values below species average; Z = correlation established.

[b] For example, bag paper.

[c] That is, papers in which strength is not the predominant quality.

VI. Form

In contrast to the usual treatment of wood chemistry, this chapter has discussed wood as the product of chemical reactions associated with the biological processes of growth and differentiation. Obviously, our current knowledge of this subject is but the merest beginning, and many questions invite further study. To those who may have a continuing interest, the concept of *form* can be a useful guide (41a). *Form* expresses the interrelationships (interdependence) of structure and function. The living tree exhibits many structures ranging in magnitude from the dimensions of the intact forest giant to those of molecules, atoms, and even subatomic particles. For each structure there is a corresponding function, or set of functions—physical, chemical, and biological. The merit of studying the chemical development of wood is that it focuses attention on the step by step creation of the *forms* exhibited by wood. A better understanding of *form* in this context should lead to better practices in both the production and utilization of wood.

REFERENCES

1. Adler, E., *Tappi*, **40,** 294 (1957).
2. Anderson, E. and W. W. Pigman, *Science*, **105,** 601 (1947).
3. Bannon, M. W., *Can. J. Botany*, **35,** 875 (1957).
4. Bickford, E. D., *Seasonal Relationship of Sap Characteristics and the Growth of Sugar Maple*, M. S. Thesis, University of Vermont, Burlington, Vermont, 1959.
5. Birch, A. J., "Biosynthetic Theories in Organic Chemistry," in *Perspectives in Organic Chemistry*, A. Todd, ed., Interscience, New York, 1956, pp. 134–54.
6. Bollard, E. G., "Nitrogenous Compounds in Tree Xylem Sap," in *Physiology of Forest Trees*, K. V. Thimann, ed., Ronald Press, New York, 1958, pp. 83–93.
7. Brown, L. A. and A. C. Neish, *Can. J. Biochem. & Physiol.*, **33,** 658 (1955).
8. Buston, H. W., *Biochem. J.*, **29,** 196 (1935).
9. Colvin, J. R., *Chem. Eng. News*, **38,** 63 (1960).
10. Dadswell, H. E. and A. B. Wardrop, *Appita*, **12,** No. 4, 129 (1959).
11. Esau, K., *Plant Anatomy*, Wiley, New York, 1953.
12. Faber, H. B., Jr., *The Methanol Extractable Aromatic Materials from the Inner Bark of Populus tremuloides*, Thesis, Institute of Paper Chemistry, Appleton, Wisconsin, 1959.
13. Farr, W. H., "Plant Cell Membranes," Chapter VIII in *Growth of Plants*, W. Crocker, ed., Reinhold, New York, 1948.
14. Freudenberg, K., *Angew. Chem.*, **68,** 90 (1956).
15. Freudenberg, K., *Nature*, **183,** 1152 (1959).
15a. Fruton, J. S., and S. Simmonds, *General Biochemistry*, 2nd. ed., Wiley, New York, 1958.
16. Greathouse, G. A., *Science*, **117,** 553 (1953).
17. Greathouse, G. A., *J. Am. Chem. Soc.*, **79,** 4505 (1957).
18. Hawley, L. F. and L. E. Wise, *The Chemistry of Wood*, A.C.S. Monograph, Chemical Catalog Co., New York, 1926; *Cf.* also Schorger, A. W., *The Chemistry of Cellulose and Wood*, McGraw-Hill, New York, 1926.

19. Jones, D. B., C. E. F. Gersdorf, and D. Moeller, *J. Biol. Chem.*, **64**, 655 (1925).

20. Kallmes, O., *Distribution of Constituents Across the Wall of Unbleached Spruce Sulfite Fibers*, Thesis, Institute of Paper Chemistry, Appleton, Wisconsin, 1959.

21. Kertesz, Z. I., *The Pectic Substances*, Interscience, New York, 1951, pp. 273–77.

22. Kratzl, K. and G. Billek, *Tappi*, **40**, 269 (1957).

23. Kremers, R. E. and B. J. Reeder, Institute of Paper Chemistry, Appleton, Wisconsin, unpublished data.

24. Lange, G. and S. Asunmaa, *Svensk Papperstidn.*, **55**, 217 (1952).

25. Lange, G. and S. Asunmaa, *Svensk Papperstidn.*, **57**, 501 (1954).

26. Marvin, J. W. and M. T. Greene, *Plant Physiol.*, **26**, 565 (1951).

27. Matsuzaki, K., K. Ward, Jr., and M. Murray, *Tappi*, **42**, 474 (1959).

28. May, M. N., *Tappi*, **41**, 147 (1958); also other papers presented to TAPPI Forest Biology Committee, *ibid.*, 145–80.

29. Mittler, T. D., "Sieve Tube Sap via Aphid Stylets," in *Physiology of Forest Trees*, K. D. Thimann, ed., Ronald Press, New York, 1958, pp. 401–5.

30. Mugg, J. B., *Methanol Extractable Aromatic Materials in Newly Formed Aspenwood*, Thesis, Institute of Paper Chemistry, Appleton, Wisconsin, 1958.

31. Nelson, E. K., *J. Am. Chem. Soc.*, **50**, 2006, 2028 (1928).

32. Newcomb, E. L., *Ann. Biol.*, **31**, 397 (1955).

33. Nord, F. F. and W. J. Schubert, *Tappi*, **40**, 292 (1957).

34. Power, F. B., *Pharm. J.*, **275** (1901).

35. Rånby, B. G. and J. L. Katzmire, "Formation of the Cellulose Lattice," in *Proceedings First Cellulose Conference*, Syracuse University, Syracuse, New York, 1958, pp. 41–59.

36. Roelofsen, P. A., *The Plant Cell Wall*, Gebr. Borntraeger, Berlin-Nikolassee, 1959, p. 30.

37. Stewart, C. M., *Tappi*, **40**, 244 (1957).

38. Sultze, R. F., Jr., *Tappi*, **40**, 985 (1957).

39. Thimann, K. D., ed., *The Physiology of Forest Trees*, Ronald Press, New York, 1958.

40. Treiber, E., *et al.*, *Die Chemie der Pflanzen Zellwand*, Springer Verlag, Berlin, 1957.

41. Wardrop, A. B., *Tappi*, **40**, 237 (1957).

41a. Whyte, L. L., ed., *Aspects of Form*, Pellegrini and Cudahy, New York, 1951.

42. Zimmermann, M. H., "Translocation of Organic Substances in the Phloem of Trees," in *The Physiology of Forest Trees*, K. D. Thimann, ed., Ronald Press, New York, 1958, pp. 381–99.

CHAPTER 9

CHAPTER 9

The Wood-Water Relationship

B. L. Browning, *The Institute of Paper Chemistry, Appleton, Wisconsin*

The properties of wood and cellulose are profoundly affected by water. In partially-dried materials, changes in the quantity of hygroscopically-bound water induced by variations in the relative humidity of the surrounding atmosphere govern many mechanical and physical properties and the amount of swelling and shrinkage. The effects produced by changes in water content are of great importance in technological applications and processing, and it is of interest to examine the interaction of water with wood and wood components, particularly cellulose (cf. 7,8,14,15,33a,43,49,97).

I. The Sorption of Water Vapor

A. NATURE OF THE SORPTION PROCESS

Dry wood and cellulose absorb water when they are exposed to an atmosphere containing water vapor and, under constant conditions, reach an equilibrium water content which depends on the relative humidity of the atmosphere or the relative vapor pressure of water. The absorption is accompanied by simultaneous swelling. If moist materials are exposed to a dry atmosphere, water is lost and shrinkage takes place. (The relative vapor pressure p/p_o is the ratio of the pressure p of vapor present to the pressure over the pure liquid p_o, at a stated temperature. The relative humidity in per cent equals 100 times the relative vapor pressure.)

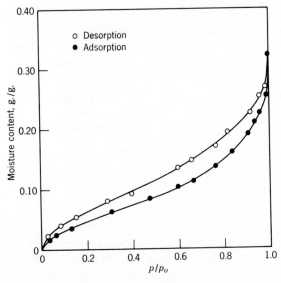

Fig. 1. Sorption of water vapor by klinki pine (data from Ref. 55).

A plot of the water content as a function of the equilibrium relative humidity or the relative vapor pressure yields (at constant temperature) an isotherm of characteristic sigmoid shape (cf. Fig. 1). The partial irreversibility of the absorption process gives rise to a significant hysteresis, and the equilibrium moisture content is higher at a given relative pressure when equilibrium is approached by desorption than when it is approached by absorption.

When desorption and absorption isotherms are determined successively on previously undried wood or cellulose, the original moisture content is not regained as saturation is approached in the region of high relative pressures (88,93,121). The existence of a substantially higher initial desorption isotherm at high relative pressures demonstrates an irreversible loss of hygroscopicity upon initial drying (Fig. 2). A closed hysteresis loop is obtained only when the desorption isotherm is determined after an absorption isotherm.

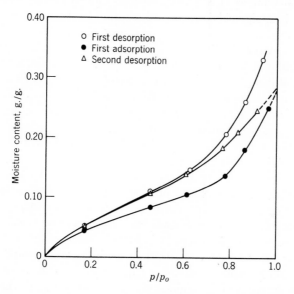

Fig. 2. Sorption isotherms of Santa Maria wood (data from Ref. 93).

Figure 1 illustrates the isotherm obtained when the relative pressure is increased by successive steps from zero to nearly that existing at saturation, and subsequently is decreased to zero in the same way. If an isotherm is determined over only a portion of the relative vapor pressure range and the direction of change in relative pressure is reversed, the isotherm is of similar character but the magnitude of the hysteresis is decreased.

The isotherm is not independent of the size of the successive steps in relative pressure (10,22). In absorption, the values for moisture content of cellulose at a given relative pressure are higher when humidification takes place in one step rather than in several small steps; in desorption, the values are lower when the dehumidification is carried out in one step (26a).

The total absorption and magnitude of the hysteresis are not affected by the presence of air. The same values for absorption of water are found whether they are based on relative humidity in air or on the equivalent relative vapor pressures of water in a system from which air has been removed by evacuation (111,120,122).

The physical interpretation of the absorption process must account for the phenomena of sorption, swelling, and hysteresis, and for the characteristic sigmoid form of the sorption isotherm. The cell wall of wood or of a cellulose fiber behaves toward water as a swelling gel, and the structure is distended as absorption takes place. Only the noncrystalline regions enter into absorption and swelling processes; the crystallites of cellulose are not penetrated by water, and only their surfaces can participate in absorption.

At low and intermediate relative pressures, water appears to be taken up by adsorption on the surfaces (largely the internal surface) of the wood and cellulose structures. It is not supposed that all the internal surface preexists in the dried materials, but rather that swelling occurs with simultaneous enhancement of the available internal surface. As the relative pressure approaches that of saturation, the water enters the fiber structure by a process of condensation.

The sorption gives rise to isotherms which may be looked upon as a composite of three types: (1) surface sorption (Langmuir adsorption); (2) intermediate sorption (multilayer or solid solution); and (3) condensation (surface or capillary). The shape of the isotherm is determined by regions of relative pressure in which these types successively become dominant. Isotherms of sigmoid shape are characteristic of systems in which three requirements are met (14): (1) adsorption is polymolecular; (2) no filling of rigid capillaries is involved; and (3) the heat of adsorption of the vapor is considerably larger than the heat of condensation.

The initial adsorption from the dry state, up to a relative pressure of about 0.2, represents the first rising portion of the isotherm. It is considered that in this region the sorbed water contributes toward formation of a monomolecular layer (monolayer) of water molecules on the accessible surface.

The following, long, nearly linear portion of the isotherm extends from relative pressures of about 0.2 to 0.6. In this region, it is supposed that multimolecular layers (multilayers) of water molecules build up successively on the monolayer first formed. Further swelling, which is nearly proportional to the water content, takes place. The multilayer at a relative pressure of about 0.6 appears to be approximately six molecules in thickness (98). The multilayer formation in this region may represent molecules which are essentially immobilized (71).

At relative pressures above about 0.6, the water content increases further with an increase in relative pressure, and the isotherm rises rapidly as the saturation pressure is approached. In this region of the isotherm, the water is taken up in ways that differ basically from those effective at lower water contents. This has been considered as a region in which water is taken up primarily by a process of condensation. The mechanism has often been attributed to capillary condensation, although it has also been suggested that the water is disposed as a mobile surface layer that differs in character from the underlying immobilized layers (71).

The type of sorption does not change sharply at any given relative pressure. Some multilayer formation may take place before complete formation of the monolayer, and condensation may overlap the region of multilayer formation.

The basic cause for initial adsorption can be assigned to the hydrogen bonding of water molecules to available hydroxyl groups in the noncrystalline regions and on the surfaces of the crystallites. If the major part of the free hydroxyl groups are covered by the formation of derivatives, the hygroscopicity is considerably reduced, although some increase may be noted at very low degrees of substitution (49). In cellulose, energy considerations suggest that the initial strong sorption at low relative pressures results from the linking of one water molecule to two adjacent hydroxyl groups, whereas further sorption leads to combination to single hydroxyl groups and to oxygen atoms (46). Water molecules then condense on surfaces already covered, and the process finally approaches that of condensation in bulk.

As the accessible surface of dry cellulose or wood is only a small fraction of that produced upon adsorption of water, the adsorption in the region of low water contents can occur only by the breaking of hydrogen bonds between the hydroxyl groups of the cellulose with simultaneous surface development. It seems probable that the potential surface of cellulose is largely or completely developed at the water content corresponding to completion of the first monolayer (71). The water content at this point amounts to about 3.2 g. of water per 100 g. of dry cellulose (71).

The explanation of hysteresis must be found in the reversible formation and breaking of hydrogen bonds within the cellulose structure. When cellulose is dried from water, hydrogen bonds are formed between hydroxyl groups on adjacent chains. These bonds will not all be of the same strength because of structural considerations and stresses set up during drying. It has been suggested (120) that the absorbing surface is in a less active condition during adsorption than during desorption. In adsorption the bonding sites available for water are already partially satisfied by hydrogen bonds between the cellulose chains (cf. 126).

The amount of water taken up by adsorption, or lost by desorption, is not determined uniquely by the relative pressure and the temperature, but depends also on the previous history of the sample. It follows that the sorption hysteresis is not constant, and it is found that the adsorption-desorption loop becomes reasonably reproducible only after the material under investigation has been taken through several cycles from dryness to wetness and back again (115,127). This process has been referred to as stabilizing or, perhaps improperly, as "annealing" (92).

The adsorption of water vapor at relative pressures below that corresponding to complete monolayer coverage of the adsorbent has been attributed by some investigators to chemical adsorption or chemisorption (cf. 60). It is not always possible to distinguish sharply between physical and chemical adsorption, although in the latter the chemical nature of the interaction results in enhanced heats of binding. The high initial heat of sorption of water on wood and cellulose indicates that the binding energies are high at low water contents. However, a heat of sorption of 10 to 15 kcal. per mole is commonly accepted as the minimum to place an interaction in the class of chemisorption (131); on this basis, the adsorption of water must be considered essentially physical in nature. The energy involved in initial sorption appears to be that of hydrogen bonding, which is usually in the range of 3 to 8 kcal. per mole.

Many attempts have been made to relate the absorption of water to the formation of hydrates, and suggestions have been made that some definite number of water molecules are associated with each $C_6H_{10}O_5$

unit in cellulose. However, the weight of evidence favors non-stoichiometric binding of water.

The phenomena associated with sorption also can be accounted for by the view that water enters the noncrystalline portion of wood or cellulose to form a solid solution (cf. 7,8). The initial sorption is attributed to surface binding (70,74), and the following second phase then is interpreted as one in which the water molecules enter the structure under physical forces similar to those in a solution.

In the development of the solid solution theory, it has been found necessary to treat the system as a solution with large deviations from ideality. The process of solution of water into the disordered regions deviates from the simple solution theory because of restrictions on the swelling system by the insoluble ordered regions (53,83,91).

In the model proposed by Hailwood and Horrobin (38), the water taken up is assumed to be either combined to form a hydrate or in simple ideal solution. It has been applied to several woods (94), and the relative amounts of water that were surface-bound and capillary-condensed were calculated.

Enderby (32a) has presented a general theory of water adsorption by polymers possessing strongly hydrophilic groups, based on application of statistical mechanics to the polymer-water system. By suitable choice of constants, his general equation for the isotherm takes the form of those derived by Hailwood and Horrobin (solution) (38), Brunauer, Emmett, and Teller (multilayer adsorption, see Section IIB) (16), or Langmuir (monolayer adsorption) (64). However, even the Enderby isotherm does not give reliable extrapolation at very high or very low values of equilibrium moisture content (25a).

The view that capillary condensation may contribute materially to absorption in the region of high relative pressures is based on the observation that the condensation of a vapor to liquid form takes place in capillaries at pressures somewhat below those necessary to liquefy the vapor in bulk. The pressure difference is a function of capillary size and the relationship, for cylindrical capillaries, is expressed by the Kelvin equation:

$$\ln (p/p_o) = 2V\gamma \cos \theta/rRT \tag{1}$$

where p/p_o is the relative vapor pressure, V is the molar volume of the liquid adsorbate, γ is the surface tension of the normal liquid adsorbate, θ is the angle of contact, r is the capillary radius, R is the gas constant, and T is the absolute temperature. It is usually assumed that the cellulose is completely wetted by water, and that cos θ is therefore unity.

When capillary size is deduced by application of the Kelvin equation, the thickness of the water layer sorbed on the surfaces of the capillary must first be deducted. The Kelvin equation fails in application to capillaries of sizes that approach molecular diameters, and it can be applied only with some reservations to capillary diameters below the range of about 50A.

B. THE AMOUNT OF WATER ADSORBED BY WOOD AND ITS COMPONENTS

The adsorption of water vapor by different species of wood and by cellulose from various sources shows considerable variation, although reported isotherms exhibit the same general shape and magnitude of sorption (cf. 45,55,93,94). The water content of wood in the region of a relative pressure of unity approaches 28 to 32% (g. per 100 g. of dry wood). At a relative pressure of 0.5 (50% R.H.) water contents of wood and cellulose are typically in the range of 7.5 to 9.5%.

The ratio of water contents for the adsorption and desorption isotherms, at a given relative pressure, is approximately 0.8 to 0.85 over the range of about 0.1 to 0.9 relative pressure (87,111). This ratio has been called a "hysteresis constant," but it shows considerable variation with the nature of the hygroscopic material. The hysteresis decreases with increases in temperature.

Water is adsorbed only in the noncrystalline regions of cellulose and on the surfaces of the crystallites. Consequently, celluloses of high crystallinity exhibit lower hygroscopicity than those having a structure of lesser order. The moisture regain, i.e., the amount of water vapor adsorbed at a given relative pressure by the dry material (usually expressed as a percentage) is determined as a measure of the accessibility of the cellulose or the proportion of the cellulose existing in a noncrystalline condition. The crystallinity is highest in cotton, somewhat lower in wood cellulose, and least in regenerated cellulose.

Both lignin and hemicelluloses, as well as cellulose, contribute to the hygroscopicity of wood. The adsorption of water vapor by hemicellulose is greater than that by wood, and the adsorption by lignin is less (1,21,84,85). For wood of *Eucalyptus regnans* and its components, the relative sorption capacities found at 25°C. (21) are given in Table I. The calculated fractional contributions of the wood components to the total sorption by the wood are given in the last column of the table. Adsorption isotherms of wood, cellulose, and hemicelluloses show hysteresis of about the same magnitude, whereas the hysteresis is somewhat greater for lignin.

TABLE I

Adsorption of Water by Components of *Eucalyptus regnans*

Components	Sorption capacity relative to wood	Fractional contributions of wood components to the total sorption
Hemicelluloses	1.56	0.37
Holocellulose	1.09	
Wood	1.00	
Wood cellulose	0.94	0.47
Lignin	0.60	0.16
Total		1.00

In studies of sorption and swelling on the lignin isolated from *Eucalyptus regnans* (23), it was found that below a relative pressure of 0.2 most of the water was held by surface adsorption and did not contribute to swelling. Between relative pressures of 0.2 and 0.9 more than half of the water adsorbed entered the lignin structure and caused swelling. At relative pressures above 0.9 the proportion of adsorbed water contributing to swelling decreased rapidly, owing to the increased preponderance of capillary condensation in the void phase (84).

C. EFFECT OF TEMPERATURE ON SORPTION

An increase in temperature results generally in a decrease in the equilibrium moisture content of both wood and cellulose, although at a given relative pressure the amount of moisture retained even at temperatures above 100°C. is a substantial fraction of that held at ordinary temperatures. For example, at 150°C. and a relative pressure of 0.9, cotton may retain 5.2 g. of water per 100 g. of dry material (51b).

When the temperature is increased over the range of 10° to 50°C., there is a decrease in the equilibrium moisture content of cotton at all relative vapor pressures (122). Even at temperatures as high as

150°C., the sorption decreases with an increase in temperature at relative pressures below about 0.8 (130). However, in the temperature range of 60° to 110°C., the moisture content of cotton has been found

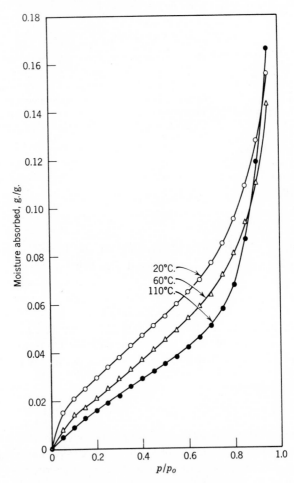

Fig. 3. Effect of temperature on the adsorption of water vapor by soda-boiled cotton (data from Ref. 122).

to increase with an increase in temperature at relative pressures above about 0.8 (122) (cf. Fig. 3). A similar behavior has been noted for paperboard (119). Other measurements on cotton at 120° and 150°C. have not shown this effect, and the moisture content was found to decrease with increase in temperature at all relative pressures (51b).

The increase in moisture adsorption at higher temperatures in the range of high relative pressures is contrary to expected behavior, and it has been attributed to swelling of cellulose under these conditions; it is likely that other factors also are important. In the range of 100° to 150°C., experimental measurements of sorption are complicated by degradation and decomposition of the material. Increased crystallinity promoted by the degradation may contribute to a decrease in adsorption at elevated temperatures.

In drying wood at temperatures up to 100°C. (124a), an increase in temperature has been found to decrease the equilibrium moisture content at all relative pressures used (55,75,105). The sorption of water by wood has been measured at temperatures up to 130°C., but irreversible processes of decomposition begin to take place at the higher temperatures (72).

Investigations of the effect of temperature on hysteresis have been rather limited. At temperatures below 100°C. experimental observations suggest that an increase in temperature results generally in a decrease in hysteresis. At high temperatures experimental difficulties are multiplied and observations usually have been limited to the range of lower moisture contents. From limited data on cotton, it was believed that hysteresis would disappear at about 100°C. (122). From 25° to 40°C. the hysteresis decreased (120), and the decrease was less at low, as compared to high, humidities. However, there appears to be a certain temperature (ca. 30° to 50°C.) above which hysteresis begins to increase at low humidities (127). In the adsorption of water vapor by paper at low humidities, it was found that the hysteresis was retained at temperatures between 100° and 150°C. (48). The hysteresis exhibited by klinki pinewood was found to decrease as the temperature was increased from 10° to 55°C. (55). This action was attributed to a decrease in the number of strong bonding sites with increasing temperature, which affected desorption more than adsorption.

D. FIBER SATURATION POINT

The fiber saturation point expresses the maximum amount of water that can be taken up from the vapor phase at a given temperature by a unit weight of wood or cellulose. Considerable difficulty has been experienced in establishing a rigorous definition. Nevertheless, the concept has proved useful in the study of the many aspects, both theoretical and practical, of the interaction of water with wood and cellulose.

Ideally, the fiber saturation point may be defined as the water content of wood or cellulose when the relative vapor pressure in the surrounding atmosphere is exactly unity. Experimental determinations corresponding to this condition are difficult to obtain, and in the vicinity of saturation extremely close regulation of temperature is necessary to prevent the condensation of water in bulk which occurs with even minute variations in temperature.

The total water present in completely saturated wood is about 2 g. per g. of dry wood, and that in water-swollen cellulose is approximately as great. On the other hand, extrapolation of the adsorption isotherms to a relative pressure of unity appears to lead to values of approximately 0.3 g. of water per g. of dry material (30%). Because adsorption isotherms assume a very high slope as saturation pressure is approached, it is difficult to establish a precise value by extrapolation. [In consequence of the change in sorption with temperature, the fiber saturation point also depends on the temperature (105).]

In water-saturated wood the entire capillary structure, including the pores, is filled with water. The water in the large pores does not contribute materially to the wood properties that are water-dependent, and the viewpoint has been advanced that the water contained in them should not properly be considered a part of the water at the fiber saturation point. For example, extrapolation of values for heat of wetting, adsorption compression of water, electrical conductivity, and several strength properties of Sitka spruce wood lead to fiber saturation points of 25 to 30% (97d).

Inasmuch as water affects these several measurable properties only to the extent that it exists in the fiber wall, the fiber saturation point of wood has been defined (99) as the moisture content which results when the cell walls are saturated, but the microscopically visible capillaries remain free of water. This is shown to occur at relative pressures between 0.99 and 0.999. In order to avoid the difficulty in extrapolation of the isotherm in the region of very high relative pressures, use can be made of the observation that the ratio of water adsorption to volumetric swelling does not vary greatly over a wide range of relative pressures. Hence, if this ratio is multiplied by the swelling in liquid water, a reliable estimate of the fiber saturation point should be found.

The structure of isolated cellulose fibers differs from that of wood in the lack of preexisting large pores and in the lower degree of structural restraints to swelling. In a study of the adsorption of water vapor by cotton, Ashpole (4) reached the conclusion that there is not a unique saturation value obtainable by extrapolation, and that the true equilibrium at saturation pressure corresponds to the moisture held by the water-wet fibers after centrifugation. He believed that the hysteresis loop closes in a desorption-adsorption cycle when the adsorption is continued to the true saturation pressure.

Wood cellulose appears to exhibit similar behavior. When a spruce sulfite pulp that had never been dried was desorbed from the wet condition to equilibrium at a relative pressure of 0.9939, it reached an equilibrium water content of 75.4% (124). This is far in excess of values usually accepted for the fiber saturation point.

If the true fiber saturation point is attained only when the equilibrium partial vapor pressure of water exactly equals the saturation pressure, then in theory adsorption will continue until the surface comprises a plane sheet of water (4). Capillary condensation can take place in capillaries having a wide distribution in size, and true saturation pressure can be reached only after the voids are filled. Calculations of the Kelvin pore diameter show that even surface depressions in fibers may fill at a relative pressure of about 0.999 (4).

At relative pressures approaching saturation, very small energy changes account for large differences in the amount of water taken up. The heat of wetting of cellulose was found to be only 0.3 cal. per g. at a water content of 24.67%, and zero at water contents greater than 28.43% (71). In the range of relative pressures from about 0.999 to unity the energy change associated with sorption so nearly equals that of condensation that the differences are too small to be measured experimentally.

It appears that a theoretically defined fiber saturation point is neither physically meaningful nor amenable to exact experimental determination. On the other hand, a fiber saturation point corresponding to a condition in which only the small pores and capillaries are filled with water and the large ones are not fails to provide a precise definition. It was suggested many years ago that it may be more appropriate to speak of a *fiber saturation region* to describe the border zone in which adsorption changes from the intermicellar to the capillary type (86).

II. Surface Areas of Wood and Cellulose

A. EXTENT OF SURFACE AREA

Wood is a porous material and possesses a considerable volume of voids which include pores and capillaries of diverse sizes and shapes. Most of the large pores are associated with the lumens in the fiber tracheids and other cells, but the small pores and capillaries are of submicroscopic size. The microscopically visible capillary surface of wood with a density of 0.4 amounts to 0.2 m.^{2} per g. (97a); the internal surface of wood swollen by water or other polar liquids is, however, very much larger than this value.

As cellulose fibers are small in size (about 15 to 40 μ in diameter) they possess a considerable external specific surface. For unbeaten wood pulp fibers, values (in m.^{2} per g.) of 0.67 to 1.59 have been found by microscopic measurements (36), 0.64 to 1.57 by the surface catalytic (silvering) method (13,24), 0.93 by the air permeability method (12), and 0.76 to 1.62 by the water permeability (hydrodynamic specific surface) method (20,51,67,117).

The internal surface area of cellulose fibers is related to the capillary-porous structure and depends upon previous treatment. When fibers are subjected to the action of water and other polar molecules, a swollen structure of very large internal surface results; however, when a fiber is dried from water, the cell wall collapses and shrinks, partly because surface tension forces are effective in bringing together neighboring surfaces which are then hydrogen-bonded (18,19). Accessible pores of appreciable size do not remain, and measurement by gas adsorption (40,113) of the total accessible surface, both external and internal, of fibers dried from water amounts to scarcely more than the external surface alone. The large internal surface of the swollen structure can be retained only by replacement of water by less polar liquids, before drying.

The physical and surface properties of wood are related to the changes in internal surface and internal volume which take place when polar gases and liquids enter the wood structure. The properties of cellulose fibers are influenced to an even greater extent; the manufacture of paper, the processing of cellulose textiles, and the reactivity of cellulose in chemical reactions illustrate the significance of the internal structure of the fiber. A knowledge of surface area, particularly the internal surface, is basic to an understanding of the behavior of cellulosic materials.

B. MEASUREMENT OF SURFACE AREA

Gases and vapors are adsorbed generally on the surfaces of solids, under appropriate conditions of temperature and pressure. A number of relatively nonpolar gases are adsorbed on the surfaces of porous materials such as wood and cellulose without concomitant swelling. It is presumed that the adsorption takes place, at first, in a layer one molecule thick to form a monolayer, and that subsequent adsorption results in the formation of multilayers.

If the amount of gas required to form a monolayer can be found and the area of each adsorbed molecule is known, it is possible to arrive at a figure for the total surface on which adsorption has taken place. The physical adsorption of nonswelling gases near their boiling point forms the basis for one of the most reliable methods for the determination of total accessible surface areas of porous adsorbents.

Nitrogen gas at $-195°C$. is commonly employed, although argon, neon, hydrogen, butane, and other gases, at appropriate temperatures, also are applicable (31). The use of krypton at $-195°C$. is advantageous because the pressure change occurring during adsorption is large as compared to the maximum measured pressure, and measurements can be made with good accuracy (31,81).

Langmuir (64) derived an equation that can be applied to adsorption data for calculation of the amount of gas required to form a monolayer. Brunauer, Emmett, and Teller (16) extended the theoretical treatment to multilayer adsorption and developed an equation, based on a kinetic interpretation, which effectively describes sorption isotherms of many types. They interpreted the beginning of the long linear portion of the isotherm as completion of the monolayer and the start of formation of multilayers, and related the experimentally determined isotherm with the amount of adsorbate necessary for monolayer coverage of the surface of the adsorbent; Cassie (20a) derived a formally identical equation by statistical mechanics.

The most useful form of the Brunauer, Emmett, and Teller (BET) equation is:

$$p/V(p_o - p) = (1/V_mC) + [(C - 1)/V_mC](p/p_o) \qquad (2)$$

where V is the volume (at STP) of vapor adsorbed at the relative vapor pressure p/p_o, V_m is the volume (at STP) of vapor adsorbed when the entire adsorbent surface is covered with a complete monolayer of adsorbate, and C is a constant. The value of C is related to the heat of adsorption in the first adsorbed monolayer (E_l) and the heat of condensation of the vapor (E_L) by:

$$C = K \exp\left[(E_l - E_L)/RT\right] \tag{3}$$

where R is the gas constant, T the absolute temperature, and K is a factor which is approximately unity from the region of partial adsorption up to the quantity of adsorption required to complete the first monolayer.

A plot of $p/V(p_o - p)$ against p/p_o usually gives a straight line for relative pressures p/p_o between 0.05 and 0.30. From the slope $(C - 1)/V_mC$ and intercept $1/V_mC$ of this plot the monolayer volume can be found and, with the known cross-sectional area of each molecule of the adsorbate, the area of solid adsorbent accessible to the gas can be calculated.

A method of deriving surface areas from adsorption data, in which a value for the area occupied by each adsorbed molecule is not necessary, has been devised (39), and areas so found are generally in agreement with those found by application of the BET theory (31,40,71).

The surface areas of several cellulose preparations and of wood have been determined by application of the BET equation to nitrogen adsorption data (32,40,41,50,69,82,118). As the adsorption of nitrogen is not accompanied by swelling to a significant extent, the method can be applied to the determination of surface areas after swelling by polar molecules, if collapse of the structure during removal of the swelling agent is avoided.

The expanded capillary structure of water-swollen fibers can be largely retained if the water is replaced with a water-miscible organic liquid such as methanol, which in turn is replaced by a methanol-soluble, nonpolar liquid such as benzene (5,59,112). Fibers from which water has been removed by solvent exchange have large surface areas, as measured by gas adsorption (34), and the specific surface may reach 100 to 300 m.^{2} per g. (106).

The nature of the final replacement liquid has a relatively large effect on the surface area. The total surface area of spruce wood pulp was found to increase from 44 to 130 m.^{2} per g. when n-pentane was used instead of benzene as the final exchange solvent, and to 196 m.^{2} per g. when the fibers were finally dried from n-hexane at 101°C.

(69). The effect of the solvent-type has been related to the surface tension (69), or to the cohesive energy density (116).

The surface areas of cellulosic materials that have been swollen by the adsorption of water vapor can be determined by application of the BET equation to the water sorption isotherm. Surface areas of 139 to 236 m.² per g. have been calculated in this manner (98). The areas found by nitrogen adsorption on a water-swollen material, dried by solvent exchange, are about 30% smaller than those derived by application of the BET equation to the water adsorption data. It is evident that the expanded structure is largely retained by the solvent exchange procedure, and that the total area of the swollen material may be as much as 100-fold greater than the area that results after drying from water.

It is believed that some shrinkage of the structure takes place upon drying of the material after solvent exchange because of the presence of a monomolecular layer of alcohol which has not been replaced by the nonpolar liquid (98,104). The tenacious retention of polar solvents has been observed by several investigators (19,112). Even nonpolar solvents are sometimes retained by a process thought to be physical "inclusion."

C. PORE SIZE AND PORE SIZE DISTRIBUTION

The pore size and pore size distribution of porous adsorbents can be calculated from the reduction of relative pressure in pores of different sizes by application of the Kelvin equation (9,76,90). Nitrogen sorption isotherms of the type shown in Fig. 4 have formed the basis for most calculations. The lack of hysteresis at relative pressures below approximately 0.4 to 0.5 is attributed to the absence of swelling; at higher relative pressures the adsorption and desorption isotherms differ because of condensation and evaporation processes in preexisting capillaries. It is customary to base pore size calculations on the desorption branch. The lower limit of relative pressure at which the adsorption and desorption curves join (Fig. 4) corresponds to a value of r of not less than two molecular diameters, by the Kelvin equation.

It is necessary to make assumptions concerning the shape of the pores, and to correct for the thickness of the multilayer film remaining on the walls after the inner capillary volume is emptied at a given relative pressure. The calculations are not believed to be reliable for capillary radii smaller than about 25A. (76). Structure curves may be drawn by plotting the volume adsorbed against the pore radius calculated from the relative pressures by the Kelvin equation. A pore–size distribution curve is obtained by differentiating the structure plot.

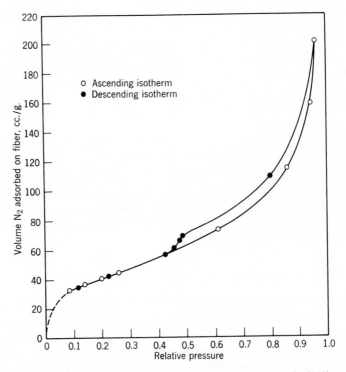

Fig. 4. Sorption of nitrogen by western hemlock sulfite pulp (118).

The pore sizes of cellulosic materials swollen by water and solvent exchanged to retain the swollen structure have been found from nitrogen adsorption data. Chlorite holocellulose from spruce wood was found to have pore diameters of 10 to 120A., with a maximum in the distribution curve at 38A. (40). The most common pore size in the fibers of western hemlock sulfite pulp was found to be 44A. (118). Pore sizes of approximately 40A. were thought to be characteristic of the fine structure of wood cellulose fibers, and possibly to be related to the arrangement of the basic structural units (118).

III. The Thermodynamics of Sorption

Physical adsorption always occurs with the evolution of heat and a decrease in free energy of the system. The thermodynamics of the sorption process is concerned with changes in enthalpy, free energy, and entropy which take place upon addition or removal of water, and during the course of swelling which occurs in the presence of water.

The total heat of adsorption of water from the vapor state is larger than the heat produced by addition of an equal quantity of liquid water to an adsorbent. The difference is the latent heat of condensation of the water vapor. That is, for a given amount of water:

$$H_v = H_l + L \qquad (4)$$

where H_v is the heat resulting from adsorption of water vapor and L is the latent heat of condensation. The quantity H_l has been called the "heat of swelling" (129), although it is the adsorption of water rather than swelling that is responsible for the evolution of heat (77b).

The integral heat of adsorption ΔH is the total heat evolved, in calories per gram of dry adsorbent, in passing from the dry state to any specified water content or regain, c. As the latent heat of condensation is not included, ΔH is the *integral net heat of adsorption*.

It is difficult to measure integral values directly for intermediate water contents. The most reliable values are found by calorimetric determinations of the heat of wetting by liquid water on wood or cellulose, previously equilibrated with various amounts of adsorbed water. If the heat of wetting of 1 g. of dry adsorbent is H_o, and that of partially saturated adsorbent containing c grams of water is H_c, then $H_o - H_c$ is the integral heat of adsorption ΔH of c grams of water *from the liquid* on 1 g. of dry adsorbent (125). From a series of determinations, the integral net heat of adsorption from dryness to any desired water content can be estimated.

The differential heat of adsorption $\overline{\Delta H}$ is the heat evolved on addition of a unit quantity of water to an infinite quantity of adsorbent at a specified water content. Like the integral heat of adsorption, it is taken above the heat of condensation and is designated the *differential net heat of adsorption*. This value cannot be determined directly, but can be found from the slope of the curve of calorimetric heat of wetting versus moisture content by graphical differentiation at the required value of moisture content (30), or by differentiation of the equation of the curve in the vicinity of the desired value. The determination of $\overline{\Delta H}$ at low moisture contents may be aided by the observation that the logarithm of the heat of wetting is linear with the regain c in this region (26).

The differential heat of adsorption can also be calculated from the variation of the vapor pressure of the partially saturated adsorbent with temperature, at fixed adsorbate concentrations. The calculation must be derived from the sorption isosteres, which express the relation between the partial vapor pressure and the temperature at constant moisture contents. The sorption isosteres are found by suitable replotting of the isotherm data obtained at different temper-

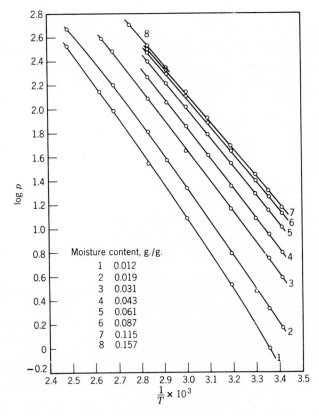

Fig. 5. Isosteres for adsorption of water vapor on soda-boiled cotton (data from Ref. 122).

atures, and are virtually linear over limited temperature ranges. Illustrative isosteres for cotton are shown in Fig. 5.

The isosteric differential net heat of adsorption from the liquid $-\overline{\Delta H}$ in cal. per g. of water may be calculated (127) from the sorption isotherms at two reasonably close temperatures T_1 and T_2 (in °K.) by means of the integrated form of the Clausius-Clapeyron equation:

$$\log (p/p_o)_1 - \log (p/p_o)_2 = (-\overline{\Delta H})(M/2.303R)[(1/T_2) - (1/T_1)] \quad (5)$$

where $(p/p_o)_1$ and $(p/p_o)_2$ are the equilibrium relative pressures corresponding to the stated moisture contents at absolute temperatures T_1 and T_2, M is the molecular weight of water, and R is the gas constant.

The determination of differential heats of adsorption from calorimetric data based on heats of wetting are considered more accurate than calculation from the sorption isotherms (77a), although the values found by the two methods are in approximate agreement. At very low moisture contents, it is difficult to find an expression for the isostere that adequately fits experimental data (25a).

The heat of sorption is by no means independent of temperature. At low moisture contents the effect is small, but it increases with increasing moisture content. The total heat of wetting of a stabilized cellulose (in cal. per g.) was found to decrease from 12.55 at 0.9°C. to 11.0 at 20.3°C., and to 10.0 at 45.1°C. (126). For cotton cellulose, the temperature coefficient of enthalpy is $+0.06$ cal./g. degree from 25 to 50°C. (30a). The integral heat of sorption on *Araucaria klinkii* wood was found to decrease with increasing temperature at all water contents greater than 0.12 g. per g. (58). As the effect of temperature is not significant at low moisture contents, it was concluded that the energy of binding of the strongly bound water is relatively unaffected by temperature.

The heat of wetting of cellulose as a function of temperature has shown a discontinuity at about 23°C. (126b). Above and below this temperature the relationship is linear, with the effect of temperature on heat of wetting being greater on the low temperature side. A similar discontinuity was found in the relationship of apparent specific volume and temperature (126a). The apparent transition temperature in both properties is attributed to a change in structure of the cellulose in the amorphous region.

The integral heat of sorption at first increases rapidly with increase in moisture content, and then approaches a plateau as the relative pressure in the neighborhood of saturation is reached. The total integral net heat of sorption at the saturation pressure, which is equivalent to the heat of wetting, is about 10 to 13 cal. per g. of dry cellulose and about 18 to 20 cal. per g. of dry wood. The initial differential net heat of sorption is about 270 to 330 cal. per g. of water for sorption on cellulose and values for sorption on wood are in the same range (2,6,37,42,47,55,58,71,75,77a,105,125).

The initial differential net heat of sorption of water is high because of the strong binding of water at very low moisture contents. The differential heat falls rapidly with increase in water content and then approaches zero when the water content reaches about 0.3 g. of water per g. of dry adsorbent (30% on a dry basis). This relationship lends weight to the selection of a value in this range as a practical "fiber saturation point."

The change in differential free energy $\overline{\Delta F}$ when 1 mole of water is adsorbed on an infinite mass of adsorbent in equilibrium with pressure p at absolute temperature T can be found at any specified water content from the adsorption isotherm data by:

$$\overline{\Delta F} = RT \ln (p/p_o) \quad \text{cal. per mole} \tag{6}$$

The integral free energy ΔF required to transfer water molecules from the vapor state to the solid surface is expressed by (29,30):

$$\Delta F = -RT \int_0^1 n\mathrm{d}\ [\ln (p/p_o)] + nRT \ln (p/p_o) \tag{7}$$

where the process is:

absorbent (dry at $p = 0$) $+ n\mathrm{H_2O}$ (at p_o)
$$\rightarrow \text{absorbent (with } n\mathrm{H_2O} \text{ at } p)$$

The integral free energy can be found by a graphical method (11,29).

The integral and differential net entropies of sorption are found from the corresponding integral and differential enthalpies and free energies by the equations connecting these three thermodynamic functions:

$$\Delta S = (\Delta H - \Delta F)/T \text{ and}$$
$$\overline{\Delta S} = (\overline{\Delta H} - \overline{\Delta F})/T \tag{8}$$

The free energy of sorption and entropy changes have been reported for cellulose and for wood (51a,58,71,105). The integral and differential free energy changes show the same trend with water content as the integral and differential heats of sorption.

The entropy curve for cellulose shows an intermediate maximum at a moisture content of about 5.4% (71). A similar break in the entropy curve for wood was found at 8 to 9% moisture (58). The discontinuity is attributed to the relative contributions, in different ranges of moisture content, of the negative entropy inherent in the ordering process of adsorption, and of the disorganization of the cellulose gel structure during adsorption of water. There is no hysteresis in the enthalpies of adsorption and desorption of water vapor on cellulose. Since the sorption curves determine the free energy function, it is concluded that the hysteresis in these systems is an entropy phenomenon (71).

Values for the thermodynamic quantities for sorption of water on cellulose selected from the data of Morrison and Dzieciuch (71) are given in Table II. The specimen of cotton had never been heated

TABLE II

Calculated Thermodynamic Quantities of the Cellulose–Water System[a] (71)

n[b]	p/p_o	$-\Delta H$[c]	$-\Delta F$[c]	$-\Delta S$[d]	$-\overline{\Delta H}$[e]	$-\overline{\Delta F}$[e]	$-\overline{\Delta S}$[f]
0	0	0	0	0	7600		
0.05	0.021	297	148	0.50	4640	2300	7.86
0.1	0.071	498	247	0.84	3350	1570	5.98
0.15	0.156	640	313	1.10	2230	1095	3.81
0.2	0.265	740	358	1 28	1720	785	3.14
0.4	0.656	1005	448	1.87	860	250	2.05
0.6	0.853	1122	481	2.16	330	94	0.79
0.8	0.932	1176	493	2.29	180	38	0.48
1.0	0.984	1204	497	2.37	75	13	0.21
1.2	0.995	1218	497.5	2.42	30		
1.4	0.9995	1230					

[a] The three values, $-\overline{\Delta H}$, $-\overline{\Delta F}$, and $-\overline{\Delta S}$, are the differential quantities. The temperature is 24.6°C.

[b] Expressed in moles of water per 100 g. of cellulose.

[c] Expressed in calories per 100 g. of cellulose.

[d] Expressed in entropy units per 100 g. of cellulose.

[e] Expressed in calories per mole of water.

[f] Expressed in entropy units per mole of water.

above room temperature, and the initial differential heat of sorption (422 cal. per g. of water) was considerably higher than values previously reported.

The integral net heats of sorption up to a relative pressure of 0.8, and water contents found at this pressure for *Eucalyptus regnans* wood and its components, are given in Table III (58). Because the

TABLE III

Heats of Sorption of Wood Components

Component	Sorbed water m, g./g.	$-\Delta H$ cal./g.	$-\Delta H/m$
Wood	0.149	15.6	105
Holocellulose	0.163	17.5	105
Wood cellulose	0.137	14.5	106
Hemicelluloses	0.270	29.8	110
Lignin	0.124	12.9	104

values for $-\Delta H/m$ are about the same, it was concluded that the sorbed water must be held in a similar manner by the wood components, and that the difference in integral heats of sorption must result from differences in total number of adsorption sites rendered available in each. Studies of differential heats of sorption on wood and cellulose have indicated that in general the distribution of binding energies is similar. Slight variations in structure can well account for the minor differences that have been found (3,56).

From the effective molecular contact area obtained by application of the BET equation to water adsorption data, it is possible to calculate the heat of adsorption, i.e., $E_l - E_L$, at the point corresponding to completion of the first monolayer (98). For wood and cellulose, values of 81.7 to 91.7 cal. per g. were found in this way. Directly determined values of differential heat of adsorption at the point corresponding to monolayer coverage are comparable and only slightly higher (57,124).

By applying a relationship presented by Jura and Harkins (52) to data for an adsorption isotherm, the free energy of adsorption of water vapor per unit area of absorbing surface can be calculated (98). For wood and cellulose the free energy change $-\Delta F$ (in ergs per cm.^{2}) at 20°C. was found to increase from about 18 at a relative pressure of 0.05 to about 124 at a relative pressure of 0.95. There is a considerable temperature coefficient for free energy of adsorption, because the effective area of molecular contact in swelling systems increases with temperature.

IV. Swelling and Shrinkage

A. SWELLING IN WATER AND OTHER LIQUIDS

Little or no swelling of wood or cellulose takes place in relatively nonpolar liquids such as benzene, whereas more polar solvents produce significant swelling. Attempts to relate the degree of swelling to the dielectric constant (28,61), the dipole moment (110), and the surface tension of the liquid (63,110) have been only partially successful, although good correlations are often found within classes of compounds. The tendency for hydrogen bonding appears to be important (110). The swelling is related inversely to the molecular weight of the swelling liquid in a homologous series (54,63). The degree of swelling increases with the density of the wood, but the relationship is not an exact one (54,63,66). The volumetric swelling of several woods in water and organic liquids is given in Table IV.

TABLE IV

Percentage Volumetric Swelling of Woods (63)

Solvent	Umbrella tree	Poplar	Birch	Beech	Pine
Water	9.0	15.3	14.7	21.1	
Methyl alcohol	7.1	11.3	12.1	14.0	14.5
Ethyl alcohol	6.0	12.3	13.4	16.1	14.2
Propyl alcohol	5.0	10.0	10.9	13.4	6.9
Butyl alcohol	4.5	7.3	6.2	8.4	
Formic acid	10.4	17.8	19.1	29.6	20.4
Acetic acid		14.0	13.3	23.0	19.4
Propionic acid	8.0	12.0	11.5	17.1	
Butyric acid	11.0		13.2	22.4	12.2
Pyridine	10.6	19.6	21.1	25.2	16.8

The use of swelling data in determining the fiber saturation point for water has already been mentioned. The fiber saturation point has also been calculated (63) from swelling data and wood density according to:

$$U_f = \alpha_V/r_o \qquad (12)$$

where α_V is the volumetric swelling and r_o is the oven-dry density of the wood. Of the five woods investigated the fiber saturation points ranged from 31.0 to 43.8% for water and from 18.7 to 36.8% for methanol. It is to be expected that the fiber saturation point will depend upon the kind of liquid (or vapor).

Swelling in organic liquids such as alcohols, carboxylic acids, glycerol, and pyridine, as well as in water, leads to a decrease in strength properties (62), and the relationship expressed by equation (13) has been proposed.

$$\sigma = [A/(v^2 \cdot \epsilon)] + B \tag{13}$$

where σ is the strength property, v is the volumetric swelling, ϵ is the dielectric constant of the liquid, and A and B are constants.

The volumetric swelling of cellulose fibers is difficult to measure. Microscopic methods have been used for both wood and cotton fibers (25,80,128). The swelling of cotton hairs, as deduced from microscopic measurements of the diameter, was found to manifest a hysteresis similar to the moisture regain curve (25).

Although dilatometric measurements are not free from objection, they furnish an approximate measure of swelling. Such determinations have shown greater swelling in polar than in nonpolar solvents (61,78). Measurements on an eucalypt alpha-cellulose pulp, in various solvents, showed the following volumetric swelling—acetone: 28%, ethanol: 42%, water: 118%, dimethylformamide: 120%, pyridine: 120%, formamide: 133%, monoethanolamine: 212%, and ethylenediamine: 222% (68).

The reagents that produce significant swelling are those which should be capable of forming hydrogen-bonded complexes with the cellulose molecule (47,68). This is to be expected, as hydrogen bonds must be ruptured before swelling can occur. Action of mild swelling agents is confined to the amorphous portion of the fiber. Liquids such as the alkyl amines are capable of entering the crystalline regions and reducing the amount of crystalline cellulose.

The swelling of cellulose in organic liquids has been related to the Hildebrand solubility parameter, or cohesive energy density of the liquid (116). For nonpolar liquids the relation given in equation (14) holds approximately.

$$\ln Q = a - k(\delta_p - \delta_o) \tag{14}$$

Q is the degree of swelling, δ_p and δ_o are the solubility parameters of polymer and solvent, respectively, and a and k are constants. The value of δ_p for cellulose is not known, but it is substantially larger than δ_o for nonpolar solvents. For polar liquids (116) the swelling of cellulose can be related only empirically with an apparent solubility parameter (17).

B. MEASUREMENT OF DENSITY

The density of wood substance or of cellulose is most commonly determined by a displacement procedure. If there were no interaction between solid and fluid, the kind of fluid should be without effect (95). Experimentally, it is noted that the density found depends to a large extent on the kind of fluid, particularly when liquids are used for displacement.

For example, apparent densities found at 25°C. for Alaska cedar heartwood were 1.474 in carbon disulfide and carbon tetrachloride, 1.476 in benzene, 1.478 in chloroform, 1.537 in ethanol, and 1.548 in water (95). The density found with helium gas was 1.536. Cotton cellulose had an apparent density of 1.598 with water as the displacement liquid, and 1.574 when benzene was used.

Davidson (27) found that the density of cellulose was greatest when water was used as a displacement medium and least when nonswelling liquids such as benzene were used. Intermediate values were obtained with helium gas. The lower values of density were thought to result from incomplete penetration of the porous structure by the larger benzene molecules. The higher value in water was attributed to attractive forces between cellulose and water which lead to compression of the sorbed water. The calculated density of the first part of the adsorbed water can be as high as 1.4 (1a), falling progressively to a density of unity as the fiber saturation point is reached.

Very high compressive forces have been calculated for water adsorbed on cellulose and wood when the correct density of the adsorbent was assumed to be that found by displacement of helium or of benzene (27,33,95,104,107). Determinations of the density of cellulose in helium or in benzene that has replaced a swelling medium lead to values which approach that calculated from x-ray data (96). These fluids penetrate voids in the noncrystalline zones, whereas the values obtained when water is used for displacement suggest that the forces of hydrogen bonding lead to a contraction of the water.

The concept of high compression and high density of adsorbed water has been rejected by some investigators (43,44).

Hermans (43) has pointed out that the concept of density applicable to macroscopic systems may not be valid when extrapolated to the molecular scale. The measurement of intermolecular voids by penetration of units whose dimensions are of the same order of magnitude can hardly be expected to lead to a unique value of density independent of the displacement liquid used (54). However, if water molecules are attached to the cellulose surface by hydrogen bonds in such a way that the energy is greater than in liquid water, a volume contraction is to be expected (6).

The interaction between the liquid and cellulose may be expected to play an important role in the displacement process. Hydrogen bonding undoubtedly is a factor, together with other attractive forces, which probably causes orientation of the sorbed molecule (96). The extent of interaction is evidenced by maximum swelling produced by the liquid, and the swelling would be expected to show correlation with the measured true density of the wood. Indeed, it has been found (95) that liquids that cause wood to swell appreciably give higher values for density. This is shown by the data in Table V which gives

TABLE V

Density of Wood and Swelling in Displacement Liquids (54)

Liquid	Density of wood substance, g./ml. at 23.3°C.	Areal swelling (tangential and radial), %
Methanol	1.567	13.1
Acetic acid	1.555	13.6
Pyridine	1.554	16.1
Ethanol	1.548	11.1
Formamide	1.541	16.1
Methyl acetate	1.538	8.1
Water	1.535	14.1
Propanol	1.480	0.7
Butanol	1.466	0.6
Benzene	1.450	0.6

density and swelling values of *Pinus radiata* wood. Moreover, it is to be expected that swelling will open up the fine structure, and thus give greater penetration of the displacement liquid, and that for liquids of the same swelling power the observed density would be greatest in the liquid having the smallest molecules (54).

C. SHRINKAGE AND DRYING

In green wood the cell walls are largely, or completely, saturated with water, but many of the larger voids remain empty. The presence of free water in the larger capillaries does not affect the gross external volume, but removal of water from the cell walls results in shrinkage of the wood. During drying, the free water evaporates first, and water in the cell walls is not removed until the fiber saturation point is reached.

The external shrinkage of wood from green to oven-dry dimensions varies from about 4 to 14% tangentially, 2 to 8% radially, and 0.1 to 0.2% longitudinally. The volumetric shrinkage varies from about 7 to 21%. Shrinkage at intermediate moisture contents is proportional to the amount of moisture removed below the fiber saturation point. Swelling of dry wood by moisture absorption is related to moisture content in a similar manner. Dimensional changes on swelling and shrinkage do not show the hysteresis characteristic of the amount of water adsorbed. The swelling and shrinkage increase with increases in the wood density.

Green wood, as sawed from the log, may have a moisture content ranging from 40% to as high as 200%, on a dry basis. The large amount of water renders the lumber unfit for most commercial purposes, and the excess water must be removed by seasoning, curing, or conditioning. The shrinkage of unseasoned wood during use may result in the appearance of defects such as warping, checking, and splitting. By drying to a moisture content approximating that encountered in use, the amount of further change is reduced. Lumber is generally cured by either air-seasoning or kiln-drying.

Air-seasoning is carried out at ordinary temperature by piling lumber so that free access of air is permitted. Drying must be slow to permit the wood to dry uniformly and to prevent checking and warping. Drying is continued until the moisture content reaches approximately 15 to 20% and several weeks may be required, the amount of time depending on the location and the season.

In kiln-drying, lumber generally enters the kiln in an air-dried or partially dried condition, although some West Coast softwoods are dried green from the saw. The dry bulb temperature in the kiln is usually not above 200°F., and then only at the end of the drying schedule. In the initial stages, the relative humidity is maintained at a high level to control moisture gradients in the wood and to prevent checking and splitting. A drying schedule must be followed, and this depends on the species of wood, the size of the pieces, the kiln conditions, the original moisture, and the final moisture desired. Kilns are commonly steam-heated, but furnace-type kilns using gas or oil for fuel are also used. Improper drying conditions lead to uneven shrinkage and the defect known as case-hardening, in which the surface dries too quickly and the stresses set up cause splitting and warping when the wood is dressed or sawed.

The movement of water toward the surface of the wood during drying is caused by differences in vapor pressure and by diffusion of the liquid. The movement is most rapid toward the end surfaces, and is more rapid toward the tangential (flat-grained) surfaces then toward the radial (edge-grained) surfaces. The rate of drying is controlled by the relative humidity, the temperature, and the circulation of the air in contact with the wood.

D. DIMENSIONAL STABILIZATION

Reduction of the swelling and shrinkage of wood and cellulose products caused by variations in water content is of great importance in many technical uses. Many methods for dimensional stabilization have been proposed (101a), but usage so far has been limited because of cost or of deterioration associated with the treatment.

Protective coatings such as paints and pore sealers, and impregnants such as waxes, are effective in reducing the rate of water gain or loss, but they are without influence on the final moisture equilibrium. Mild heat treatment and pressing as in the "Staypak" process also do not change the final equilibrium value (123).

Two types of treatments have shown some success in stabilizing wood (and in some instances paper) toward moisture-induced dimensional changes. The first is the introduction of bulking agents which prevent the collapse of structure during the removal of water. Salt and sugar, applied as solutions, act as bulking agents and reduce shrinkage, but they have the disadvantage of being soluble in water (97b). Polyethylene glycol, which also can be applied from water solution, is effective (101), and much use has been made of phenolic resins as bulking agents (35,97c,108). Other treatments are based on esterification [e.g., acetylation (2a,79,109)] and etherification [e.g., cyanoethylation with acrylonitrile (35,79)]. β-Propiolactone reacts, without need for a catalyst, to produce polyester side chains on the cellulose and can reduce swelling from 60 to 70%.

The second important type of treatment produces cross-linking. Heating the wood in the presence of formaldehyde is very effective (100,114), and as little as 0.5% of formaldehyde may reduce swelling and shrinking by as much as 60%. An acid catalyst, e.g., zinc chloride, is needed to accelerate the reaction, and some reduction in strength properties takes place. Other aldehydes such as glyoxal and furfural possess no advantages over formaldehyde. Acrolein and polyacrylamide also are capable of increasing dimensional stability by cross-linking (123).

Heat treatments at temperatures above those normally used in kiln-drying impart permanent dimensional stability to wood, but loss of strength and embrittlement of the wood may occur (89,102). The effect of heating is ascribed to polymerization of the hemicelluloses rather than to cross-linking (100).

REFERENCES

1. Algar, W. H., H. W. Giertz, and A. -M. Gustafsson, *Svensk Papperstidn.*, **54**, 335 (1951).
1a. Alinče, B., *Svensk Papperstidn.*, **65**, 216 (1962).
2. Argue, G. H., and O. Maass, *Can. J. Research*, **12**, 564 (1935).
2a. Arni, P. C., J. D. Gray, and R. K. Scougall, *J. Appl. Chem.*, **11**, 163 (1961).
3. Ashpole, D. K., *Nature*, **169**, 37 (1952).
4. Ashpole, D. K., *Proc. Roy. Soc. (London)*, **A212**, 112 (1952).
5. Assaf, A. G., R. H. Haas, and C. B. Purves, *J. Am. Chem. Soc.*, **66**, 59 (1944).
6. Babbitt, J. D., *Can. J. Research*, **A20**, 143 (1942).
7. Barkas, W. W., *The Swelling of Wood under Stress*, H. M. S. O., London, 1949.
8. Barkas, W. W., "The Mechanical Properties of Wood and Their Relation to Moisture," in *Mechanical Properties of Wood and Paper*, R. Meredith, ed., Interscience, New York, 1953.
9. Barrett, E. P., L. G. Joyner, and P. P. Halenda, *J. Am. Chem. Soc.*, **73**, 373 (1951).
10. Beever, D. K., and L. Valentine, *J. Polymer Sci.*, **32**, 521 (1958).
11. Boyd, G. E., and H. K. Livingston, *J. Am. Chem. Soc.*, **64**, 2383 (1942).
12. Brown, J. C., *Tappi*, **33**, 130 (1950).
13. Browning, B. L., and P. S. Baker, *Tappi*, **33**, 99 (1950).
14. Brunauer, S., *The Adsorption of Gases and Vapors*, Vol. I, Princeton University Press, Princeton, 1943.
15. Brunauer, S., and L. E. Copeland, "*Surface Tension, Adsorption*," in *Handbook of Physics*, E. U. Condon and H. Odishaw, eds., McGraw-Hill, New York, 1958.

16. Brunauer, S., P. H. Emmett, and E. Teller, *J. Am. Chem. Soc.*, **60**, 309 (1938).

17. Burrell, H., *Interchem. Rev.*, **14**, No. 1, 3 (1955).

18. Campbell, W. B., *Ind. Eng. Chem.*, **26**, 218 (1934).

19. Campbell, W. B., *The Cellulose-Water Relationship in Papermaking*, Canada, Dept. of the Interior, Forest Service, Bull. 84, Ottawa, 1933.

20. Campbell, W. B., *Tappi*, **32**, 265 (1949).

20a. Cassie, A. B. D., *Trans. Faraday Soc.*, **41**, 450 (1945).

21. Christensen, G. N., and K. E. Kelsey, *Australian J. Appl. Sci.*, **9**, 265 (1958).

22. Christensen, G. N., and K. E. Kelsey, *Holz Roh- u. Werkstoff*, **17**, 178 (1959).

23. Christensen, G. N., and K. E. Kelsey, *Australian J. Appl. Sci.*, **10**, 284 (1959).

24. Clark, J. d'A, *Tech. Assoc. Papers*, **25**, 568 (1942).

25. Collins, G. E., *J. Textile Inst.*, **21**, T311 (1930).

25a. Cooper, D. N. E., *J. Textile Inst.*, **52**, T433 (1961).

26. Cooper, D. N. E., and D. K. Ashpole, *J. Textile Inst.*, **50**, T223 (1959).

26a. Daruwalla, E. H., and R. T. Shet, *Textile Research J.*, **32**, 165 (1962).

27. Davidson, G. F., *J. Textile Inst.*, **18**, T175 (1927).

28. deBruyne, N. A., *Nature*, **142**, 570 (1938).

29. Dole, M., and A. D. McLaren, *J. Am. Chem. Soc.*, **69**, 651 (1947).

30. Dunford, H. B., and J. L. Morrison, *Can. J. Chem.*, **33**, 904 (1955).

30a. Dymarchuk, N. P., and K. P. Mishchenko, *Trudy Leningrad. Tekhnol. Inst.*, No. 7, 115 (1959); through *Chem. Abstracts*, **56**, 4163 (1962).

31. Emmett, P. H., *Catalysis*, Vol. I, Reinhold, New York, 1954.

32. Emmett, P. H., and T. DeWitt, *Ind. Eng. Chem., Anal. Ed.*, **13**, 28 (1941).

32a. Enderby, J. A., *Trans. Faraday Soc.*, **51**, 106 (1955).

33. Filby, E., and O. Maass, *Can. J. Research*, **7**, 162 (1932).

33a. Forshee, B. W., *Bibliography on the Interaction of Cellulose and Moisture*, Natl. Bur. Standards Report No. 7064, U.S. Department of Commerce, Washington, D.C., 1961.

34. Forziati, F. H., R. M. Brownell, and C. M. Hunt, *J. Research Natl. Bur. Standards*, **50**, 139 (1953).

35. Goldstein, I. S., W. A. Dreher, E. B. Jeroski, J. F. Nielson, W. J. Oberley, and J. W. Weaver, *Ind. Eng. Chem.*, **51**, 1313 (1959).

36. Graff, J. H., M. A. Schlosser, and E. K. Nihlen, *Tech. Assoc. Papers*, **24**, 529 (1941).

37. Guthrie, J. C., *J. Textile Inst.*, **40**, T489 (1949).

38. Hailwood, A. J., and S. Horrobin, *Trans. Faraday Soc.*, **42B**, 84 (1946).

39. Harkins, W. D., and G. Jura, *J. Am. Chem. Soc.*, **66**, 1366 (1944).

40. Haselton, W. R., *Tappi*, **37**, 404 (1954); **38**, 716 (1955).

41. Haywood, G., *Tappi*, **33**, 370 (1950).

42. Hearmon, R. F. S., and J. N. Burcham, *Nature*, **176**, 978 (1955); *Chem. & Ind.*, **1956**, 807.

43. Hermans, P. H., *Contributions to the Physics of Cellulose Fibers*, Elsevier, New York, 1946.

44. Heertjes, P. M., *Rec. trav. chim.*, **61**, 751 (1942); through reference 43.

45. Higgins, N. C., *Forest Prods. J.*, **7**, 371 (1957).

46. Honeyman, J., *Recent Advances in the Chemistry of Cellulose and Starch*, Heywood and Co., London, (1959).

47. Horiike, K., and S. Kato, *J. Japan Wood Research Soc.*, **5**, 181 (1959).

48. Houtz, C. C., and D. A. McLean, *J. Phys. Chem.*, **43**, 309 (1939).

49. Howsmon, J. A., "Structure-Sorption Relationships," in *Cellulose and Cellulose Derivatives*, E. Ott, H. M. Spurlin, and M. W. Grafflin, eds., Part I, 2nd. ed., Interscience, New York, 1954.

50. Hunt, C. M., R. L. Blaine, and J. W. Rowen, *J. Research Natl. Bur. Standards*, **43**, 546 (1949).

51. Ingmanson, W. L., and B. D. Andrews, *Tappi*, **42**, 29 (1959).

51a. Inoyatov, N. S., I. K. Khakimov, and K. U. Usmanov, *Uzbek. Khim. Zhur.*, No. 6, 16 (1960); through *Chem. Abstracts*, **56**, 2607 (1962).

51b. Jeffries, R., *J. Textile Inst.*, **51**, T339, T399, T441 (1960).

52. Jura, G., and W. D. Harkins, *J. Am. Chem. Soc.*, **66**, 1356 (1944).

53. Kawai, T., *J. Polymer Sci.*, **37**, 181 (1959).

54. Kelsey, K. E., *Australian J. Appl. Sci.*, **6**, 190 (1955).

55. Kelsey, K. E., *Australian J. Appl. Sci.*, **8**, 42 (1957).

56. Kelsey, K. E., and G. N. Christensen, *Australian J. Appl. Sci.*, **10**, 269 (1959).

57. Kelsey, K., and L. N. Clarke, *Nature*, **176**, 83 (1955).

58. Kelsey, K. E., and L. N. Clarke, *Australian J. Appl. Sci.*, **7**, 160 (1956).

59. Kistler, S. S., *J. Phys. Chem.*, **36**, 52 (1932).

60. Kollmann, F., *Holz Roh- u. Werkstoff*, **17**, 165 (1959).

61. Kress, O., and H. Bialkowsky, *Paper Trade J.*, **93**, No. 20, 35 (1931).

62. Kumar, V. B., *Holz Roh- u. Werkstoff*, **15**, 423 (1957).

63. Kumar, V. B., *Norsk Skogsind.*, **11**, 259 (1957); **12**, 337 (1958).

64. Langmuir, I., *J. Am. Chem. Soc.*, **38**, 2221 (1916).

65. Malmquist, L., *Holz Roh- u. Werkstoff*, **17**, 171 (1959).

66. Mariaux, A., *Holzforschung*, **12**, 51 (1958).

67. Mason, S. G., *Pulp Paper Mag. Can.*, **48**, No. 10, 76 (1947); A. A. Robertson and S. G. Mason, *ibid.*, **50**, No. 13, 103 (1949).

68. McKenzie, A. W., *Australian J. Appl. Sci.*, **8**, 35 (1957).

69. Merchant, M. V., *Tappi*, **40**, 771 (1957).

70. Meredith, R., *J. Textile Inst.*, **48**, T163 (1957).

71. Morrison, J. L., and M. A. Dzieciuch, *Can. J. Chem.*, **37**, 1379 (1959).

72. Noack, D., *Holz Roh- u. Werkstoff*, **17**, 205 (1959).

73. Odincovs, P., *Trudy Inst. Lesokhoz. Problem, Akad. Nauk Latv. S. S. R.*, **12**, 45 (1957); through *Chem. Abstracts*, **52**, 21,073 (1958).

74. Peirce, F. T., *J. Textile Inst.*, **20**, T133 (1929).

75. Pidgeon, L. M., and O. Maass, *J. Am. Chem. Soc.*, **52**, 1053 (1930).

76. Pierce, C., *J. Phys. Chem.*, **57**, 149 (1953).

77. Rees, W. H., (a) *J. Textile Inst.*, **39**, T351 (1948); (b) W. H. Rees, in *Moisture in Textiles*, J. W. S. Hearle and R. H. Peters, eds., Interscience, New York, 1960.

78. Richter, G. A., L. E. Herdle, and W. E. Wahtera, *Ind. Eng. Chem.*, **49**, 907 (1957).

79. Risi, J. and D. F. Arseneau, *Forest Prods. J.*, **7**, 210, 245, 261, 293 (1957).

80. Rollins, M. L., *Textile Research J.*, **17**, 19 (1947).

81. Rosenberg, A. J., *J. Am. Chem. Soc.*, **78**, 2929 (1956).

82. Rowen, J. W., and R. L. Blaine, *Ind. Eng. Chem.*, **39**, 1659 (1947).

83. Rowen, J. W., and R. Simha, *J. Phys. Colloid Chem.*, **53**, 921 (1949).

84. Runkel, R. O. H., and M. Lüthgens, *Holz Roh- u. Werkstoff*, **14**, 424 (1956).

85. Sadoh, T., and S. Kajita, *Mokuzai Gakkaishi*, **2**, 237 (1956); **3**, 100 (1957); *Chem. Abstracts*, **51**, 9152, 18,587 (1957).

86. Saechtling, H., and H. Zoker, *Kolloid-Beih.*, **40**, 413 (1934).

87. Seborg, C. O., *Ind. Eng. Chem.*, **29**, 169 (1937).

88. Seborg, C. O., F. A. Simmonds, and P. K. Baird, *Paper Trade J.*, **107**, No. 19, 45 (1938).

89. Seborg, R. M., H. Tarkow, and A. J. Stamm, *J. Forest Prods. Research Soc.*, **3**, No. 3, 59 (1953).

90. Shull, C. G., *J. Am. Chem. Soc.*, **70**, 1405 (1948).

91. Simha, R., and J. W. Rowen, *J. Am. Chem. Soc.*, **70**, 1633 (1948).

92. Simril, V. L., and S. Smith, *Ind. Eng. Chem.*, **34**, 226 (1942).

93. Spalt, H. A., *Forest Prods. J.*, **7**, 331 (1957).

94. Spalt, H. A., *Forest Prods. J.*, **8**, 288 (1958).

95. Stamm, A. J., *J. Phys. Chem.*, **33**, 398 (1929).

96. Stamm, A. J., *Textile Research J.*, **20**, 631 (1950).

97. Stamm, A. J., "Surface Properties of Cellulosic Materials," in *Wood Chemistry*, L. E. Wise and E. C. Jahn, eds., Reinhold, New York, 1952, (a) p. 691; (b) p. 745; (c) p. 746; (d) p. 776.

98. Stamm, A. J., *Tappi*, **40**, 761, 765 (1957).

99. Stamm, A. J., *Holz Roh- u. Werkstoff*, **17**, 203 (1959).

100. Stamm, A. J., *Tappi*, **42**, 39 (1959).

101. Stamm, A. J., *Forest Prods. J.*, **9**, 375 (1959).

101a. Stamm, A. J., *Forest Prods. J.*, **12**, 158 (1962).

102. Stamm, A. J., H. K. Burr, and A. A. Kline, *Ind. Eng. Chem.*, **38**, 630 (1946).

103. Stamm, A. J., and L. A. Hansen, *Ind. Eng. Chem.*, **27**, 1480 (1935).

104. Stamm, A. J., and L. A. Hansen, *J. Phys. Chem.*, **41**, 1007 (1937).

105. Stamm, A. J., and W. K. Loughborough, *J. Phys. Chem.*, **39**, 121 (1935).

106. Stamm, A. J., and M. A. Millett, *J. Phys. Chem.*, **45**, 43 (1941).

107. Stamm, A. J., and R. M. Seborg, *J. Phys. Chem.*, **39**, 133 (1935).

108. Stamm, A. J., and R. M. Seborg, *Ind. Eng. Chem.*, **31**, 897 (1939).

109. Stamm, A. J., and H. Tarkow, *J. Phys. Colloid Chem.*, **51**, 493 (1947).

110. Stamm, A. J., and H. Tarkow, *J. Phys. Colloid Chem.*, **54**, 745 (1950).

111. Stamm, A. J., and W. A. Woodruff, *Ind. Eng. Chem.*, *Anal. Ed.*, **13**, 836 (1941).

112. Staudinger, H., and W. Döhle, *J. prakt. Chem.*, **161**, 219 (1942).

113. Swanson, J. W., and A. J. Steber, *Tappi*, **42**, 986 (1959).

114. Tarkow, H., and A. J. Stamm, *J. Forest Prods. Research Soc.*, **3**, No. 2, 33 (1953).

115. Taylor, J. B., *J. Textile Inst.*, **43**, T489 (1952); **45**, T642 (1954).

116. Thode, E. F., and R. G. Guide, *Tappi*, **42**, 35 (1959).

117. Thode, E. F., and W. L. Ingmanson, *Tappi*, **42**, 74 (1959).

118. Thode, E. F., J. W. Swanson, and J. J. Becher, *J. Phys. Chem.*, **62**, 1036 (1958).

119. Ulm, R. W. K., *Tech. Assoc. Papers*, **21**, 157 (1938).

120. Urquhart, A. R., *J. Textile Inst.*, **20**, T125 (1929).

121. Urquhart, A. R., and N. Eckersall, *J. Textile Inst.*, **21**, T499 (1930).

122. Urquhart, A. R., and A. M. Williams, *J. Textile Inst.*, **15**, T433, T559 (1924).

123. U.S. Department of Agriculture, Forest Service, Forest Prods. Lab., *Report of Dimensional Stabilization Seminar*, News Note No. 2145, 1959.

124. Van den Akker, J. A., W. A. Wink, and F. C. Bobb, *Tappi*, **42**, 340 (1959).

124a. Villiere, A., *Holzforschung*, **14**, 146 (1960).

125. Wahba, M., *J. Phys. Colloid Chem.*, **52**, 1197 (1948); **54**, 1148 (1950).

126. Wahba, M., and K. Aziz, *J. Textile Inst.*, **50**, T558 (1959).

126a. Wahba, M., and K. Aziz, *J. Textile Inst.*, **53**, T291 (1962).

126b. Wahba, M., K. Aziz, and A. N. Apostolides, *J. Textile Inst.*, **53**, T318 (1962).

127. Wahba, M., and S. Nashed, *J. Textile Inst.*, **48**, T1 (1957).

128. Weidner, J. P., *Tech. Assoc. Papers*, **22**, 564 (1939).

129. White, H. J., and H. Eyring, *Textile Research J.*, **17**, 523 (1947).

130. Wiegerink, J. G., *J. Research Natl. Bur. Standards*, **24**, 645 (1940).

131. Zettlemoyer, A. C., *Chem. Revs.*, **59**, 937 (1959).

CHAPTER 10

Manufacture of Wood Pulp

N. Sanyer and G. H. Chidester, *Forest Products Laboratory,* Forest Service, United States Department of Agriculture, Madison, Wisconsin*

* Maintained at Madison in cooperation with the University of Wisconsin.

I. Introduction

Wood is converted to pulp for the manufacture of paper and paperboard, and for the production of regenerated cellulose and cellulose derivatives. The separation of the fibers in the wood may be accomplished by purely mechanical means, by treatment with chemicals to dissolve the lignin that cements the fibers together, or by a combination of mechanical and chemical treatments. For many purposes the resulting pulps are subjected to bleaching and purification treatments. The choice of process depends on the requirements for color, purity, strength, and other properties of the pulp that are, in turn, determined by the kind of paper in which they are to be used. The basic technology of the manufacture of pulp is described in several books and other publications (48,289). In this chapter, it is the purpose to discuss primarily the chemistry involved in the preparation of pulp from wood.

A. HISTORY

The use of wood for making pulp came about because of an increasing need for writing and printing papers. Rags became scarce and high in price. Modern papermaking, to supply the requirements for printing, publishing, and all the varied uses for paper to which we are accustomed, did not develop until low-cost wood pulp became available. Therefore, the history and development of wood pulping parallels that of papermaking and printing. Dard Hunter brilliantly described the early developments in this field in *Papermaking Through Eighteen Centuries* (133).

The soda process, patented by Watt and Burgess in 1853 (312), was the first commercial chemical pulping process in which a solution of caustic soda was used to cook wood chips under pressure at elevated temperatures. About the same time, the mechanical pulping process was developed in Germany, after a machine for making groundwood was designed by Keller of Saxony in 1840 (219) and the practicability of using large quantities of low-cost groundwood in printing papers was demonstrated in the 1850s. Tilghman invented the sulfite process in 1866 (300), whereby an acid solution of calcium bisulfite and sulfur dioxide was used to cook chips under pressure. The sulfite pulping process, about 15 years after its invention, was applied commercially in Sweden and in Germany to produce a light-colored pulp in contrast to the brown pulp obtained by the soda process.

Eaton, in the United States (70), patented the use of sodium sulfate as a replacement for soda losses during chemical recovery in the alkaline process, but Dahl in Danzig (60) was responsible for the commercial application of the same idea independently. The sodium sulfate was added to spent liquor but it was reduced to sodium sulfide in the recovery furnace. The sulfate process produced a much stronger pulp in greater yield than the soda process and, for this reason, it was also called the kraft process (from the German *Kraft*, strength). It remains the most versatile process for making pulps from all kinds of wood species. The strong brown pulp used for wrapping or bag papers and board is produced from coniferous woods, especially from southern pines, by the sulfate process. It is also used to make the strong bleached pulps, used in many grades of white papers.

Although hardwoods were utilized conventionally to make the soda pulp used in printing papers, an increase in the use of hardwoods for pulp, especially in making paperboards, was started about 1925 with the development of high-yield pulps produced with a neutral sulfite solution that contains sodium sulfite and either sodium bicarbonate or caustic soda. Since the wood chips were only partially delignified and reduced to pulp at the end of cooking by mechanical treatment in the disk mill, it was called the neutral sulfite semichemical process (253). Neutral sulfite semichemical pulps from hardwoods are widely used for the manufacture of corrugating medium.

Among the newer commerical processes is the "Chemigroundwood" process (177) in which bolts of wood that have been treated with neutral sulfite liquor at elevated temperature and pressure are used for grinding. This mild chemical cooking softens dense hardwoods that cannot be ground with satisfactory results otherwise.

Another new pulping process introduced during the past decade is the cold soda process. In this method, chips are treated with caustic soda at room temperature and are reduced to pulp by disk milling (41,42). This process is assuming importance for the production of bulky groundwood-type pulps from dense hardwoods in very high yields. Similar chemimechanical pulps of high yield are produced from coniferous woods by disk milling chips that have been treated in hot sulfite liquors of pH 5–8 (51).

The steaming and exploding of wood chips before disk milling to produce high-yield pulps has become of great commercial interest in the production of hardboard, insulating board, and other structural material. Among these processes are the Asplund and Masonite processes (27,12). Disk mills are also employed to reduce softwood chips to groundwood pulps that are suitable for most of the products in which the conventional pulp made with grindstones is used.

B. CLASSIFICATION OF PULPING PROCEDURES

The descriptions of present and potential pulping processes are summarized below in four different classes.

1. Chemical pulping. Sulfate (kraft), soda, sulfite pulping and, in fact, any process that accomplishes delignification by chemical treatment may be included in chemical pulping. Digested chips are reduced to pulp upon blowing from the digester, and no mechanical fiberization other than mild agitation is required. The lignin is extensively modified, and from 60 to 90% of it is removed from the wood. The pulp yield varies from 45 to 60% of the wood.

2. Semichemical pulping. Neutral sulfite semichemical, high-yield kraft, high-yield sulfite, and other pulping methods fall into the category of semichemical pulping. In this process the wood chips, after cooking, require moderate milling. The lignin is partially modified, and a varying proportion is removed. The pulp yield varies from 55 to 80%.

3. Chemimechanical pulping. Cold soda, chemigroundwood, and hot sulfite (neutral or acid) pulping, high-pressure steam treatment, and other mild chemical treatments are classed as chemimechanical pulping. The treated chips require extensive milling or grinding. The lignin is slightly modified and only a small amount is removed. Pulp yield from these processes varies from 80 to 95%. These processes are especially suited for pulping dense hardwoods.

4. Groundwood or mechanical pulping. Groundwood pulping is accomplished by the grinding of bolts of wood with a grindstone or by the disk milling of chipped wood. Fiberization takes place entirely by mechanical means. The lighter-colored and lower-density woods are desired. A very small amount of chemical aids may be used for the improvement of brightness. Lignin modification and removal is negligible. The yield of pulp is about 95%.

II. Structure and Chemistry of Wood

A. CHEMISTRY OF CELL WALL

In order to have a clear understanding of delignification processes, it is helpful to briefly review the physical and chemical composition of the cell wall and the distribution and degree of association of lignin with other cell wall components (see also Chapters 2 and 4).

Although pulping processes are chiefly concerned with the removal of lignin, there is a substantial loss of wood hemicelluloses, which may be unavoidable rather than intentional, except in the production of dissolving pulp. Some hemicellulose removal during pulping, however, may be desirable in order to obtain better quality paper pulps. Better controlled and more selective removal of lignin and hemicellulose, individually, is therefore desirable for specific control of pulp quality and for more effective utilization of all chemical components of the cell wall. The behavior of wood hemicelluloses during delignification is also influenced by their location in the cell wall and their state of association with lignin and cellulose.

1. Lignin

Since the behavior of lignin is a major concern of all pulping processes, its distribution in the cell wall is important. Microanalysis and micro-optical measurements have shown that lignin is distributed in decreasing concentration from the intercellular layers toward the lumen (15,164,163). The largest concentration is in the corners of the cells in the middle lamella which, with the primary wall of neighboring cells, form a single layer: the compound middle lamella. The first layer (S_1) of the secondary wall is closely associated with the primary wall, and is a border area where the dominant lignin phase of the compound middle lamella terminates. In the compound middle lamella and, probably, in the S_1 layer of the secondary wall, lignin is the dominant component, constituting 60 to 90% of the dry material in this area. Across the second layer (S_2) of the secondary wall, the proportion of lignin continuously decreases and, in the tertiary wall, its presence is hardly detectable. The penetration and distribution of lignin within the S_2 layer varies, however, probably constituting 20 to 30% of the total lignin, depending on the wood species, climatic conditions, growth rate, cell wall thickness, and abnormal growth because of natural causes.

The lignin polymer in coniferous woods is built primarily of guaiacyl units and, in hardwoods, of almost equal quantities of guaiacyl and syringyl units. In addition to these major units, both types of wood also contain small quantities of parahydroxy phenylpropane units (173). It is postulated that the precursor or the monomer of lignin, probably coniferyl alcohol for coniferous woods, polymerizes by enzymatic dehydrogenation and oxidation (85,161) as the lignification progresses. If the lignin, isolated by Björkman (23,24) from finely divided wood with neutral solvents, is assumed to represent the protolignin, the following functional groups may be present in spruce lignin: phenolic hydroxyl, dialkyl ether, aliphatic hydroxyl, carboxyl, parahydroxy benzyl alcohol, and arylalkyl ether.

The mechanism of chemical degradation of lignin during pulping will depend on the type of ether bonds between the guaiacyl-propane monomers. Among these linkages, the dialkyl ethers involve α-carbon atoms of the propane group, hence a benzyl ether type, and arylalkyl ethers involve β- and, to a lesser extent, γ-carbon atoms. In addition to these ether linkages, the presence of several types of carbon-to-carbon linkages has been postulated. These bonds result in condensed lignin units, and they do not generally involve delignification reactions. The most important carbon-to-carbon linkage is between the ortho position to the phenyl group and one of the carbon atoms of the propane group involving about 30 to 40% of the guaiacyl units (4), and one half of these could be phenylcoumaran type. The presence of a few biphenyl linkages has also been postulated (14,221, 222), and more recently the presence of a substantial number of these linkages has been indicated (223a).

2. Wood Carbohydrates

The kind and quantities of the major carbohydrates in the cell wall vary between deciduous and coniferous woods, and some minor variations also are present between the species of each class (see Chapter 5, Hemicelluloses). The carbohydrates occurring in each class of wood are listed in Table I according to decreasing quantity or importance.

TABLE I

Deciduous woods	Coniferous woods
Cellulose (40–45)[a]	Cellulose (39–41)
4-O-Methylglucuronoxylan (20–30)	Glucomannan (15–18)
Glucomannan (2–3)	4-O-Methylglucuronoarabinoxylan (8–10)
Arabinogalactan (trace)	4-O-Methylglucuronoxylan (1–2)
Galactoglucomannan (trace)	Arabinogalactan (2–3)
Pectic materials (1)	Galactoglucomannan (1–4)
Starch (trace)	Pectic materials (1)
	Starch (trace)

[a] The numbers in parentheses are the approximate percentages.

The first three polysaccharides are the major constituents which concern pulping, and their behavior and reactions will be discussed under each delignification process.

Meier (198,200) isolated tracheids and fibers in different stages of maturation by micromanipulation and quantitatively determined the sugar in the acid hydrolyzates from these cell fractions. The approximate distribution of various polysaccharides in different layers of cell wall were estimated as shown in Table II. In estimating

TABLE II

Per Cent Distribution of Polysaccharides in the Different Layers
of the Fiber Wall (200)

Polysaccharide	$M + P^a$	S_1	S_2 outer part	S_2 inner part $+ S_3$	$M + P + S_1 + S_2 + S_3$
Birch					
Galactan	16.9	1.2	0.7	0.0	1.1
Cellulose	41.4	49.8	48.0	60.0	53.7
Glucomannan	3.1	2.8	2.1	5.1	3.6
Arabinan	13.4	1.9	1.5	0.0	0.7
Glucuronoxylan	25.2	44.1	47.7	35.1	40.9
Spruce					
Galactan	16.4	8.0	0.0	0.0	1.8
Cellulose	33.4	55.2	64.3	63.6	61.7
Glucomannan	7.9	18.1	24.4	23.7	22.5
Arabinan	29.3	1.1	0.8	0.0	0.8
Glucurono-arabinoxylan	13.0	17.6	10.7	12.7	13.2
Pine					
Galactan	20.1	5.2	1.6	3.2	3.1
Cellulose	35.5	61.5	66.5	47.5	56.2
Glucomannan	7.7	16.9	24.6	27.2	24.8
Arabinan	29.4	0.6	0.0	2.4	1.8
Glucurono-arabinoxylan	7.3	15.7	7.4	19.4	14.1

[a] Contains also a high percentage of pectic acid.

these compositions from the sugar analysis, it was assumed that no new deposition of carbohydrate would take place during, or after, the completion of the maturing of the cells in the cell wall layer already formed.

Acetyl groups are important constituents of the cell wall, especially in regard to pulping hardwoods. Acetyl content in hardwoods varies from 3 to 5% and, in coniferous woods, from 1 to 2%. In hardwoods, these groups are attached to xylan units (109) but, in coniferous woods, they are also attached to glucomannan (200).

The structure of xylan-containing hemicelluloses has been shown to contain branches of single units of uronic acid or uronic acid and arabinose attached to a xylan polymer (301,114,115). Glucomannans are found to be essentially linear polymers with some indication of branching (58). It has not been fully established whether galacto-glucomannans are true chemical entities or mixtures of glucomannan and galactomannan (199,301a).

The other minor carbohydrates and pectic substances are of little interest to chemical pulping processes, since they are generally dissolved and destroyed under mild cooking conditions.

3. Lignin—Carbohydrate Linkages

The chemical and physical structure of the compound middle lamella is extremely important to the fiberization of wood. Its properties are influenced by the type and degree of association of lignin and hemicelluloses. Because of their heteropolymeric and branched nature, the hemicelluloses and pectic substances are in a highly swollen state and easily permeable to lignin precursors (or monomers). Therefore, the possibility exists that some primary bonds may form between the lignin polymer and hemicelluloses, in addition to secondary bonds involving hydrogen bonding. The complete drying of wood could bring an irreversible change in the rheological properties of this layer, which cannot be restored to a biologically fresh state.

The association of lignin with the polysaccharides in other regions of the cell wall is, again, governed by the accessibility of the polysaccharides to the lignin precursors during lignification. Since hemicellulose does not enter the crystalline and ordered areas of cellulose but is deposited on the surface of cellulose fibrils and microfibrils in an amorphous state (209), it is permeated by lignin monomers, possibly forming a solid solution with the final lignin polymer formed. Again, during this process, the formation of primary bonds in addition to hydrogen bonding between these two amorphous colloids is a good possibility.

The nature and extent of these linkages have been of theoretical and technical interest (184,203). The close association of these wood components affects the delignification processes because it retards the lignin solubility and causes loss of carbohydrates. All the direct evidence cited for the presence of these linkages is based on the preparation of lignin-carbohydrate complex compounds by various methods. Among these are the complex fraction obtained from finely divided wood by neutral solvents (23,24) or by enzymatic hydrolysis (223), the complex dissolved in cuprammonium hydroxide from sulfonated wood (246), and one obtained from chlorinated wood by extraction with alcoholic caustic solution (304). These complexes probably contain chemically bound carbohydrates that are rich in xylose and other hemicellulosic sugars. It is, however, still open to debate whether the strong association of lignin and hemicellulose in these complexes is mostly due to hydrogen bonding (181). Although the alkali solubility of hemicellulose of finely divided woods varies with species, the major portion of these can be extracted from many deciduous woods under relatively mild conditions, 20 to 80°C. (28, 212). This suggests that not all of the hemicelluloses are linked to lignin or that these linkages are sensitive to mild treatment with alkali.

The type of these linkages has not been established, but the presence of β-phenyl-glycosidic bonds is favored most (83). The sensitivity of these bonds to alkali and acid treatments and their abundance in plants provide good argument for their presence. The presence of benzyl ether (5) or an ether with β carbon of the propyl group with hemicelluloses, however, are also possibilities (4).

4. Minor Constituents of Wood

Some of the extraneous components of wood are important in pulping. Among these are the resins. In pulping, the resins are converted to products such as tall oil, rosin, and paracymene, and are therefore economically important. They can, however, also be a problem in pulp purification, especially the unsaturated fatty acids that create the pitch problem in pulps made from resinous woods.

The extraneous material containing reactive phenolic nuclei, such as tannins, hydroxystilbenes, and flavanones, are important in acid pulping processes because of their condensation with lignin, thereby retarding the delignification of some species.

Some natural dyestuffs that are present, especially in the heart-wood of many species, may cause a bleaching problem with mechanical and chemimechanical pulps. The quantities of these materials, however, are small, and they are generally destroyed in chemical pulping processes. The stains caused by microbiological attack behave somewhat similarly to natural dyes.

B. ANATOMY AND PERMEABILITY OF WOODS

The structure of wood is of primary importance in pulping processes, where the physical distribution of cell wall components and their surface area and porosity govern the rate of heterogeneous reactions involved. The morphology of wood fibers, in regard to kind, size, and distribution, influences the over-all pulping rate as well as the properties of the final product. The influence on pulping of anatomical differences in woods, however, stems primarily from the initial rate of penetration of the liquor, and the actual rate of delignification is only slightly affected by wood structure.

The anatomical differences between coniferous and deciduous woods are most striking. The thin-walled vessel elements are the main routes of liquid penetration into deciduous woods. In the heartwood of many deciduous woods, however, these vessels are plugged with tyloses, which prevent liquid flow. Liquid flow into deciduous woods, whether they are ring porous or diffuse porous, does not take place as uniformly as that in coniferous woods, and the liquor reaches the middle lamella of the tracheids or fibers by two distinct mechanisms (296). The first step is the uniform capillary penetration through the open vessels, similar to penetration in coniferous woods, and its rate is proportional to the pressure gradient. The second step is the diffusion of ions in water into the areas between the vessels where the rate is controlled by the concentration gradient and is slow in comparison with capillary flow. The diffusion medium is mostly the submicroscopic capillary water in the cell wall.

The capillary penetration in coniferous woods takes place by flow through the tracheids that is restricted by the openings of bordered pit pairs of adjacent cells. In case of hardwood fibers, the pits are fewer and smaller in diameter and are of very low porosity, consequently they greatly restrict the capillary flow. From these observations, it was concluded that appreciable capillary flow in the cross-fiber direction can take place in coniferous woods (178) but only to a limited extent in hardwoods (310a).

The permeability of woods toward flow of water (150) or air

(285,293) under a pressure gradient, or the measurement of sinkage time of wood blocks (217,269,324), are used to determine the rate of capillary flow of liquids in different woods. It has been shown that the capillary flow rate varies between species. It is higher for coniferous woods than for deciduous woods. Sapwood has a higher capillary flow than heartwood. It is relatively unaffected by the density of the wood or the composition of the liquor. Capillary flow is generally effective in the grain direction and, to a limited extent, in the cross-grain direction in coniferous woods.

The diffusion through wood is measured by ionic diffusion rate measurements under a concentration gradient (188) or by electrical conductivity measurements (284,286,294). It increases with the moisture content of the wood and is 4 to 10 times more effective in the fiber direction than in the cross-fiber direction. Moreover, diffusion varies with wood density and is strongly affected by liquor composition. The strongly alkaline solutions, above pH 13, diffuse at nearly equal rates in longitudinal, radial, and tangential directions (294). Diffusion rate can also be accelerated by purging the wood with steam at atmospheric or superatmospheric pressure (188). Apparently, some physicochemical changes take place in the cell wall structure when wood is exposed to alkali, or heat, in case of steaming, resulting in increased effective capillary cross-sectional area.

III. Processing Aspects of Pulping

A. WOOD PREPARATION

The source of wood for pulping is not only standing trees but also residues from saw log-cutting operations, lumber mills, veneer plants, and other woodworking mills. The amount of residual material used for pulping is now between 16 and 18% of the total volume, and is expected to rise considerably higher as the demand for pulpwood increases.

The wood has to be freed of bark for most chemical pulping when cleanliness of the final product is desired. Several types of barkers varying in mechanical design, are used. Chemical debarking is also used, to a limited extent, to kill hardwood trees by application of a chemical during the season in which the cambium is active.

The wood is reduced to chips before cooking or similar treatments by chippers, which cut the wood to a desired size, varying from $\frac{3}{8}$ to $\frac{7}{8}$ inch long, from $\frac{1}{6}$ to $\frac{1}{16}$ inch thick, and from $\frac{1}{2}$ to 1 inch wide. The chips are screened to remove undersize and oversize material. The oversize chips are generally reduced in size by chip crushers or rechippers.

Since a small proportion of the wood fibers are cut during chipping, the average fiber length of the pulp tends to be lower than that in wood. Above a certain minimum chip length (about $\frac{1}{2}$ inch), however, the increase in chip length does not significantly affect the pulp properties. The chip size is kept to a minimum for uniform liquor penetration and cooking, especially in acid processes. The actual damage to the fiber by cutting during chipping is apparently small in comparison with compression failure along the length of the fibers caused by a crushing action of the chipper knives. These fissures are the chief cause of loss of pulp strength during acid cooking, which results in increased accessibility and localized degradation of cellulose by acid hydrolysis (17,93,93a,122).

B. COOKING

Either batch type or continuous digesters are used to cook wood, and they are constructed of appropriate material and design to resist corrosion and withstand the desired cycles of temperature and pressure. The batch digesters for long cycle sulfite cooks range from about 4,000 to 12,000 cubic feet, which is two or three times larger than those used in relatively short cycle kraft pulping. Continuous digesters are suitable for kraft and semichemical pulping and produce more uniform pulp than batch systems.

1. Liquor Penetration

Since the size of the wood chips used in pulping is fairly large, the penetration of cooking liquor is not instantaneous, and a concentration gradient of cooking chemicals exists inside the chips during the early part of the process. Consequently, the reactions proceed in a somewhat topochemical fashion, and the delignification is not entirely uniform. To accomplish uniform penetration of chemicals into the chips, a sufficient length of time is allowed for heating up in all pulping processes. Depending on the type of liquor and wood species used, this period varies from 1 to 4 hours.

A great deal of interest in rapid impregnation of chips with cooking chemicals has developed, especially in connection with continuous pulping. The reduction of chip size to match sticks in a secondary operation was used with limited success in alkaline and semichemical pulping (215), producing similar results from relatively thin chips made with the present chippers. In pulping with acid liquors, for which the heating-up time is longest, the chips cannot be subjected to a secondary mechanical treatment for size reduction because of the increased acid susceptibility of mechanically damaged wood.

The purging of air from chips by steaming at, or above, atmospheric pressure and applying hydrostatic pressure after submerging the chips in cooking liquor has been found to be the most efficient method of impregnation. This method is successfully used in reducing the heating-up period in sulfite pulping from 3 to 4 hours to less than 1 hour (190,324,302,291,65,117).

2. Digestion

The chemical concentration in the cooking liquors and the temperature and duration of digestion are dictated by the efficiency and selectivity of delignification process and the economic factors involved. The chemical kinetics require the use of a high concentration of the pulping agents, but chemicals too much in excess are either wasted by decomposition or are harmful to the carbohydrate components of wood, resulting in a degraded or lower yield of pulp. Liquor-to-wood ratio influences the liquor strength and, to a limited extent, the total chemical. Temperature is the other major variable which, again, is determined for each process and wood species to achieve optimum pulp yield and strength, as well as optimum cooking time. At the end of cooking, the contents of the digester are blown out. In chemical pulping, this results in complete fiberization of wood. For semichemical and high-yield pulps, the cooked chips are fiberized in a disk mill.

C. WASHING AND CLEANING

The pulp is washed using vacuum- or diffuser-type washers to free it from residual cooking liquor and, then, is screened to eliminate shives and fiber bundles. If further shive and dirt elimination is necessary, it is passed through centrifugal cleaners. The spent liquor is evaporated and burned for recovery of chemicals, or disposed to the streams in mill effluent.

IV. Sulfite Process

Up to a few years ago, the sulfite process was understood only as an acid sulfite digestion, whereby cooking acid was composed of water, sulfur dioxide, and calcium bisulfite. In order to achieve efficient chemical recovery, magnesium, sodium, and ammonia bases have been used. With calcium base, the pH of the cooking acid at room temperature varies between 1.5 to 2.3, above which calcium sulfite precipitates. Magnesium base can be employed at a higher pH, up to 4.5, without the formation of insoluble magnesium sulfite. The sodium and ammonium bases do not impose any limitation on the pH of the sulfite process, and can be used in acid as well as in alkaline cooking conditions.

There are no great differences between the bases employed other than the slightly lower ionic mobility of the bivalent bases. Consequently, the sodium and ammonium base sulfite cooks are only slightly faster than calcium and magnesium base cooks. The use of sodium and magnesium bases has introduced several new variations of sulfite processes, and the following classification of these variations will be referred to in this chapter.

Acid sulfite:	1.5 to 2.5 pH
Bisulfite:	2.5 to 5.5 pH
Neutral sulfite:	5.5 to 8.5 pH
Multistage sulfite:	
1st stage	5.0 to 7.5 or 1.5 to 4.5 pH
2nd stage	1.5 to 3.0 or 7.5 to 9.0 pH
	and any other combination of the single stages

Bisulfite and multistage digestions are especially useful in pulping of resinous and acid-sensitive wood species and in the production of stronger or higher yields of pulps.

A. COOKING VARIABLES

The technical cooking acid containing 0.7 to 1.4% calcium oxide (or other equivalent base) and 5 to 10% sulfur dioxide is prepared by absorbing sulfur dioxide, formed from the burning of sulfur, in a milk of lime or in a tower containing wet limestone. During the cooking process, the penetration of acid sulfite liquor into the chips is slow and determines the rate of heating. The cooking temperature is increased by increasing the amount of base or the ratios of combined to total sulfur dioxide. This ratio varies between 1:4 to 1:7. At the start of the cook, an excess of total sulfur dioxide is maintained to increase the rate of penetration and the sulfonation of the lignin and, as the temperature is raised, part of the sulfur dioxide gas is relieved and used in the fortification of fresh cooking acid. Raising the temperature too fast results in a "burnt" cook because of condensation of lignin in the presence of free sulfur dioxide and in the absence of bisulfite or cations. The time to maximum temperature varies from 3 to 5 hours, and about the same length of time is used at the top temperature. The digester is further relieved during the blow-down period toward the end of the cook to recover excess sulfur dioxide and to prevent the acidity of the cooking liquor from further increase.

In the production of rayon grade pulps, high free sulfur dioxide and relatively high cooking temperatures are used. Therefore, in comparison with the conditions used in paper grade pulp digestions, the acidity of the cooking liquor reaches a higher level earlier during the cook, which results in the hydrolysis of hemicelluloses as intended.

B. RATE AND MECHANISM OF DELIGNIFICATION

The rate of delignification has been studied much more in the sulfite pulping process than in any other method. Miller and co-workers (206,207) in the United States, Maass and his associates in Canada (46,328), and Hägglund and co-workers in Sweden and Finland (97,98,107) have contributed to this field and stimulated the more fruitful research of the past decade. (See also Chapter 6.)

The rate of delignification is proportional to the excess sulfur dioxide of the cooking liquor (207,256,328), and the rate approximately doubles with each 10°C. rise in temperature. It was postulated that the concentration of hydrogen and bisulfite ions is the most important variable of sulfite pulping (328). The absolute rate values found in these studies, however, cannot be applied with assurance because of the uncertainty in the methods of lignin analysis used. The Klason lignin does not represent the total residual lignin in the pulps because part of the sulfonated lignin dissolves in sulfuric acid used in lignin determination. Since the test result varies also with the degree of sulfonation, the delignification rates reported are

generally too high. Measurement of the delignification rate is further
complicated by the heterogeneous nature of the reactions taking
place. The activity of ionic species found in the cooking liquor, even
if kept constant, would not be expected to appear the same in the
solid lignin phase. Therefore, any proportionality of delignification
with the strength of the cooking liquor in respect to one or the other
ionic species can be approximate only.

Hägglund (110) postulated that delignification in the sulfite
process takes place in two stages: in the first, lignin is sulfonated in
the solid phase, producing a solid lignosulfonic acid; this is followed,
in the second stage, by acid hydrolysis of this acid to a water soluble
form. The hydrolysis was considered to be the slower and, therefore,
the rate-determining reaction. On the other hand, Maass and co-
workers (46) suggested that the sulfonation is the rate-governing step.
Although it has long been recognized that lignin is sulfonated and
depolymerized before dissolution in sulfite liquor, until recently no
plausible mechanism could be suggested for these reactions.

From sulfonation studies on lignin, it has been shown that lignin
contains at least two types of groups, A and B (75,182,183) (Fig. 1).

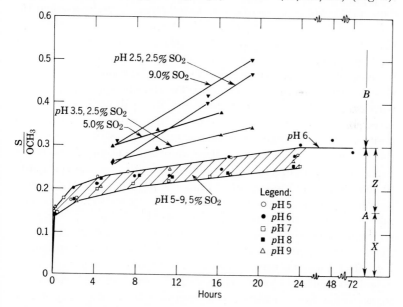

Fig. 1. The sulfonation rate of spruce wood at 135° in sulfite solutions of
different pH's [Lindgren (183)].

The A group can be sulfonated with neutral sulfite solution which, in turn, contains two groups of different rates of reactivity, X and Z (183,204). Group X sulfonates rapidly and probably consists of benzyl alcohol and ethers containing a free p-hydroxy group. Group Z sulfonates slowly in neutral sulfite solution and probably contains benzyl alcohols with a blocked p-hydroxy group. Group A reacts more quickly with phenols than with bisulfite at pH 1.5 to 2, but reacts more rapidly with bisulfite than with phenols at a pH above 3.5. The B group can be sulfonated in acid sulfite liquors but not in weakly acidic or neutral sulfite solutions. These groups do not easily condense with phenols, and they are probably benzyl alkyl ethers with blocked p-hydroxy groups. Group B can be hydrolyzed to B' groups, which then can be sulfonated in neutral (174) or acid sulfite liquors. The B' groups are probably the same as X groups. (See also Chapter 6.)

These somewhat simplified types of structural groups of lignin that involve the α-carbon atom of the side chain are chiefly responsible for most of the sulfonation, hydrolysis, and condensation reactions. In pulping with acid sulfite liquors and using excess total sulfur dioxide, it is not possible to determine whether the sulfonation or the acid hydrolysis is the rate-determining step. It is obvious, however, that the acid hydrolysis will be the rate-determining step when the cooking-liquor pH is too high for hydrolysis and subsequent sulfonation of B groups. Häggroth, Lindgren, and Saedén (112) proved this by comparing the loss in methoxyl content of wood meals cooked with sulfite liquors of varying strength and pH with those of the corresponding residues subjected to an acid hydrolysis with dilute hydrochloric acid. The latter values, termed so as to correspond to the sulfonated lignin, indicate the rate of sulfonation. As shown in Fig. 2, at a pH 2.4 or above, the sulfonation rate is very fast compared to actual delignification rate—which is governed by the rate of hydrolysis—and the total sulfur dioxide concentration does not influence the lignin dissolution. At pH 1.3, however, the liquor strength influences the rate of delignification where at high sulfur dioxide concentration hydrolysis is the rate-determining reaction. At low sulfur dioxide concentration, both hydrolysis and sulfonation are rate-determining reactions. However, in a sense, all these cooks were made with excess chemical charge because of the high liquor ratio (100–400:1) used.

By applying the same technique, Rydholm and Lagergren (256)

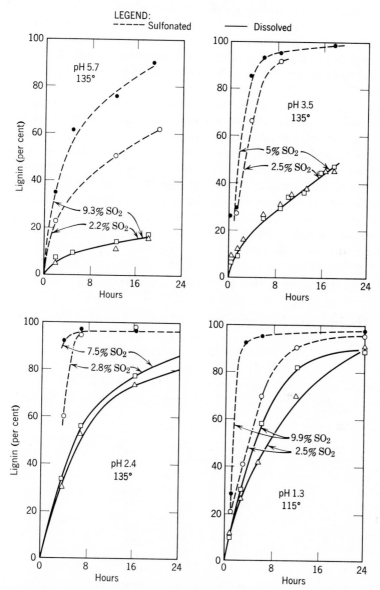

Fig. 2. The influence of pH and total SO₂ on the rate of sulfonation and hydrolysis of lignin [Häggroth, Lindgren, and Saedén (112)]. - - -, sulfonated; —, dissolved.

studied the rate of technical sulfite cooks and came to the conclusion that the delignification involves concurrent sulfonation and dissolution by hydrolysis. It was shown also that the lignin dissolved during technical sulfite cooking or subsequent acid hydrolysis had a sulfur-to-methoxyl ratio of 0.5 to 0.7 or 0.3 to 0.5, respectively (256,176,78), while the corresponding value for the lignin remaining in the pulp was 0.2 to 0.3. Further, it was found that when excess chemical was used during the cooking, the delignification rate as well as the sulfonation rate was increased. From these observations, Rydholm and Lagergren proposed a "sulfitolysis" mechanism for the sulfonation and concurrent depolymerization of lignin, involving some of the B groups besides hydrolysis and the subsequent sulfonation mechanism cited above. Consequently, the rate of dissolution of partially sulfonated lignin should then be proportional to the acidity alone in the case of hydrolysis and to both acidity and bisulfite ion concentration in the case of sulfitolysis.

C. HYDROGEN AND BISULFITE ION CONCENTRATIONS, DONNAN EFFECT

The hydrogen ion concentration of sulfite liquors during cooking has been a subject of many studies of theoretical and technical interest. It has been known that the acidity of sulfite liquor at the cooking temperature is much lower than that measured at room temperature. The concentration of hydrogen and bisulfite ions was estimated by extrapolating the values obtained from conductivity and

TABLE III

Temperature Dependence of the Apparent Dissociation Constant
of Sulfurous Acids (255)

Temperature	Dissociation constant
25	0.0172
70	0.0046
100	0.0024
110	0.0016
120	0.0011
130	0.0008
140	0.0005
150	0.0003

partial pressure of sulfur dioxide above the cooking liquors up to 90°C. (18,91). The hydrogen ion concentration also was measured experimentally from the hydrolysis rate of starch at the cooking temperature (105). More recently, Ingruber (135,136) was able to measure the hydrogen ion concentration by direct pH measurement on aqueous sulfur dioxide solutions at temperatures up to 150°C. and also during sulfite cooking. Rydholm (255), using direct and indirect data obtained by other workers, calculated the approximate dissociation constant of sulfurous acid that is shown in Table III.

Rydholm (255,254) was able to estimate the concentration of hydrogen and bisulfite ions during cooking, using these constants and the pH values of the cooking liquors determined at room temperature and, by applying corrections for additional amounts of acid, mainly sulfurous and α-hydroxysulfonic acids formed during cooling of the sample. A brief summary of the results obtained in three different sulfite cooks is shown in Table IV. At the beginning of the digestion,

TABLE IV

Change in Liquor Composition During Sulfite Digestion (255)

Time (hr.:min.)	Temperature (°C.)	Total SO_2 (mM per 1)	$[H^+]$ (mEq. per 1)	$[HSO_3^-]$ (mEq. per 1)
Rayon pulp (ratio of total to combined $SO_2 = 7:1$)				
0 00	80	1,170	11.6	289
3 35	122	574	4.1	156
8 15	150	164	1.7	24
10 15	150	62	27.8	1
11 30	135	8	20.2	0.2
Strong paper pulp (ratio of total to combined $SO_2 = 5:1$)				
0 00	64	880	15.0	241
4 00	115	696	4.1	168
8 00	135	313	2.3	73
10 00	135	222	2.6	47
11 00	128	66	5.4	9
Greaseproof paper pulp (ratio of total to combined $SO_2 = 5:1$)				
0 00	75	950	8.5	315
5 00	110	706	4.5	185
7 00	121	667	3.6	161
11 30	122	375	2.2	123
13 45	111	349	5.8	75

the acidity decreases because the dissociation constant of sulfurous acid diminishes with increasing temperature and also because of the relief of sulfur dioxide. Later, during the cook, the acidity rises as the result of formation of new acids. Among these, the carboxylic acids are probably dissociated to a very limited extent and can be disregarded. The lignosulfonic, α-hydroxysulfonic, and sulfuric acids would affect the acidity and, therefore, the rate of formation of these acids and the amount of base or combined sulfur dioxide used in the liquor will determine the pH. In a sense, these acids are formed at the expense of bisulfite ions. Therefore, when the concentration of strong acids exceeds that of the base, the acidity of the liquor begins to increase; first governed by the dissociation constant of sulfurous acid, then by that the new strong acids formed.

During the cook, bisulfite ions continuously decrease as they are used up in the sulfonation of lignin and wood sugars or are converted to other sulfur acids. If there is no base or only a small amount in the cooking liquor, the concentration of bisulfite ions will be very small, especially at high temperatures where the dissociation constant of sulfurous acid is very low. Therefore, pulping with the solution of sulfur dioxide is possible only with very high total sulfur dioxide and at low temperatures (121a,244,291,225). In the absence of base, the hydrogen ion concentration in the solid lignin phase starts increasing at the beginning of the cook as the strong sulfonic acid groups are formed. Therefore, the use of high digestion temperatures results in the condensation of lignin before the sulfonation has progressed far enough. Soldium sulfate, however, can be used as buffer in pulping with sulfur dioxide solution (242). This is possible since, because of the low dissociation constant of bisulfate ion at the cooking temperature, nearly one half of the base is available for the formation of combined sulfur dioxide or bisulfite ions.

Although the foregoing describes the change in the acidity of cooking liquors, the acidity of the solid lignin phase will be different and governed by the Donnan equilibrium (96). Partially sulfonated lignin behaves like a cation exchange resin: the concentration of salt and the type of cations involved affect the equilibrium and, consequently, the acidity of the solid phase. It was shown in cooking presulfonated and cation exchanged wood with SO_2-water that the monovalent cations, Na^+ and NH_4^+, caused more rapid delignification than the divalent cations, Ca^{2+}, Ba^{2+}, and Mg^{2+}, and the delignification was slowest with the trivalent aluminum ion (250,256). When sodium base was used, the amount of cation taken up by the wood was equivalent to only 5 to 10% of the sulfonic acid groups but, in the case of calcium base cooks, nearly all of the sulfonic acid groups were neutralized (256). Therefore, the acidity of the solid phase is higher when monovalent bases are used and the hydrolysis and dissolution of lignin takes place at a higher rate. This indicates that when polyvalent bases are used, the combined sulfur dioxide or amount of base should be kept at a minimum. However, the technical acid sulfite cook with soda base is, if any, only slightly faster than calcium, probably because of the low acidity of the solid phase resulting from the large excess base used in these liquors. Therefore, not the acidity of the lignin phase but rather that of the liquor might control the hydrolysis of lignin where the sulfonated lignin, possessing a large surface area, provides a reaction zone at the liquid-solid interface. Otherwise, one would conclude that hydrolysis is not in any way a rate-governing reaction in delignification.

The addition of sodium chloride or calcium chloride retarded the delignification rate of presulfonated wood with sulfite liquors of corre-

TABLE V

Change in Molecular Weight of Lignosulfonic Acids During
Acid Sulfite Delignification (214)

Reaction time (hrs.)	Yield (%)	Degree of delignification (from CH_3O) (%)	Estimated molecular weight of lignin in liquor
Hemlock			
0.5	86.5	20.3	3,000
1.0	76.7	30.8	4,000
3.0	56.0	75.2	11,000
6.0	45.8	95.7	10,000
9.0	44.2	98.1	9,000
12.0	41.9	99.1	5,500
Sugar maple			
0.5	—	16.5	800
1.0	—	26.5	1,300
2.0	—	50.5	1,600
4.0	—	76.0	2,100
6.0	—	87.0	1,300
8.0	—	98.0	1,700

sponding bases, probably as a result of lowered acidity in the solid lignin phase. The salting-out effect or some reactions involving chloride ions, however, may also cause the retarding of the delignification (137).

The average molecular weight of lignosulfonic acids dissolved in the course of sulfite digestion was estimated from diffusion measurements (214,81). The molecular weight of lignosulfonic acids from maple was found to be about one fifth as large as that from hemlock and spruce, Table V. This indicates that the molecular weight of the native lignin of hardwoods is also considerably lower than that of softwoods. It was also shown that low molecular-weight fractions are dissolved first and, as the digestion proceeds, the molecular weight of lignosulfonic acids passes through a maximum. With prolonged heating, the molecular weight of the dissolved acids slowly decreases because of continuous hydrolytic degradation of lignosulfonic acids. Similarly, during partial delignification with liquors of low acidity, only a low molecular-weight fraction of lignin goes into solution. Upon further digestion of these spent liquors, after adjusting the acidity down to acid sulfite cooking level, the molecular weight of the lignosulfonic acids were all decreased, Table VI.

TABLE VI

Molecular Weight of Lignosulfonic Acids from Incremental Delignification[a] of Hemlock (81)

Sulfite liquor (pH)	Yield (%)	Degree of delignification (from CH_3O) (%)	Lignin molecular weight	
			Before hydrolysis	After hydrolysis[b]
4.8	—	26.7	3,400	1,900
4.8	82.1	36.3	6,600	4,800
3.4	72.9	55.6	14,500	7,200
2.5	61.1	81.3	30,000	10,500
2.1	51.5	95.5	20,500	13,000

[a] Fifteen hours at 130°C.
[b] Fifteen hours additional digestion in acid sulfite liquor at 130°C.

From these observations, it may be concluded that like other natural polymers the lignin is a polymolecular compound, and the rate of delignification in any pulping process must be influenced by the degree of polymolecularity of the protolignin and cannot be expected to fit a simple rate function. The lignosulfonic acids dissolved in the cooking liquor are slowly hydrolyzed and further sulfonated for the duration of the digestion.

D. BEHAVIOR OF WOOD POLYSACCHARIDES DURING SULFITE PULPING

The hydrolytic degradation of wood polysaccharides lowers the yield of carbohydrates and also the pulp strength. The hydrolysis of hemicelluloses by sulfite liquor proceeds faster than that of cellulose because of their amorphous nature and higher accessibility, and the nature of glycosidic bonds involved. As the delignification nears completion, however, the hydrolysis of cellulose is accelerated because of the elimination of protective lignosulfonates and increased exposure of cellulose to base-depleted cooking liquor of increased acidity. Although partial hydrolysis of wood polysaccharides causes recrystallization and a decrease in accessiblility, or debranching and readsorption of hemicellulosic species, it does not entirely counter the progress of the degradation.

Along the cracks and compression failures in the cell wall formed by natural causes or during chipping of wood, the accessibility of cellulose to cooking acid increases causing localized severe hydrolytic attack and further weakening of fiber. This partly accounts for the low strength properties of sulfite pulps. Apparently by shortening the length of acid-cooking period and using a neutral or slightly alkaline sulfite stage in the latter part of the delignification, this localized degradation of the cellulose can be held to a minimum. However, because of the highly crystalline nature and low over-all accessibility of cellulose, the loss of yield and degradation of this polysaccharide due to hydrolytic attack is relatively small.

The behavior of noncellulosic polysaccharides during pulping has been the subject of many recent studies, as the improved methods of partition chromatography and other new techniques in carbohydrate fractionation became available (114). Hamilton and Thompson (116) followed the course of hemicellulose degradation by examining the residual species of noncellulosic carbohydrates left in the pulp. During acid sulfite pulping, the minor polymers, such as arabinogalactan, galactoglucomannan, pectin, and starch, are completely hydrolyzed. The 4-O-methylglucuronoarabinoxylan of softwoods is converted to 4-O-methylglucuronoxylan, losing the acid-labile terminal units of arabinofuranose. The new polymers, as an artifact in softwoods and as the original polymer in the hardwoods, are further degraded by hydrolytic cleavage of the xylose-xylose glycosidic bonds into molecules of shorter chain length, and largely dissolve in the cooking liquor. The glycosidic bonds, which are closer to the uronic acid branch, are more resistant to acid hydrolysis and may persist into the sulfite spent liquor.

The glucomannans of both softwoods and hardwoods exhibit moderate stability. The glucomannan is the major hemicellulose in softwoods. It has been found that the acetyl groups are attached to this polymer in softwoods (160a,200c), and Rydholm and his coworkers (8,8b) demonstrated that the acetyl groups split off by neutral or slightly alkaline sulfite liquirs more easily than in acid sulfite liquors. This latter phenomenon has been cited as the cause of better adsorption or retention of mannan and of increased yield in the two-stage sulfite process of Graham (92). Binger and Norman (21) found that alkaline sulfite pretreatment of hardwoods results in an increase in the amount of xylan resistant to acid hydrolysis. Since the acetyl groups in the hardwoods are mostly associated with xylan, the mechanism of xylan retention must be also governed by the ability of recrystallization and better adsorption of the deacetylated polymer. On the other hand, the acetyl groups in birch were shown to survive the acid sulfite digestion, which may not be favorable to the retention of xylan, such as encountered in neutral sulfite and kraft pulping (8b,216).

The neutral sulfite semichemical pulping does not cause the preferential cleavage of any one sugar residue from xylose containing hemicelluloses where the original polymer compositions survive onto the pulps with little change (114).

E. NEW DEVELOPMENTS

1. Bisulfite Process

The solution of sodium or magnesium bisulfite can be used as a cooking liquor at a pH of 2.5 to 4.5 containing little or no excess sulfur dioxide (302,65,66,118,158). For an optimum delignification rate, however, high cooking temperature (155 to 170°C.) and high chemical concentration have to be used. Because of the low acidity of the cooking liquor, the heating-up time can be shortened when the chips are purged of air and preimpregnated. The method is especially useful in the production of relatively high-yield pulp of the semi-chemical type.

The bisulfite process is particularly suitable for the pulping of acid-sensitive woods, such as pine and Douglas fir whose heartwood contains phenolic extractives. Erdtman (77) and Lindstedt (185) have isolated a number of flavones and flavanones from the heartwood of pine species, and Pew (220) has isolated taxifolin from the heartwood of Douglas fir, flavanones that inhibit the acid sulfite pulping of the heartwood of these species. The use of liquor with relatively low acidity prevents the condensation of these resins with lignin as explained under the mechanism of sulfonation. The process is also better suited than the acid sulfite process for the pulping of dense hardwoods in which the uniform penetration of the liquor is a critical factor. Neither of these acid processes are well suited for pulping hardwoods on account of the low yield and strength of the pulps. A desirable pulp, however, can be obtained from the hardwoods by partial delignification with a slightly acidic (5 to 6 pH) or a neutral sulfite liquor, which will be described later.

2. Two-Stage Sulfite Processes

Although these processes were primarily developed for pulping of pine in which sulfite liquors of varying pH were used in two consecutive stages, they resulted in significant improvements in pulp yield or strength over the conventional acid sulfite pulping.

A two-stage sulfite process, invented by Graham in 1882, has been found suitable for pulping of pine heartwood; the first stage is a sodium sulfite treatment, which is then followed with a calcium base acid sulfite digestion (92). From the chemical recovery consideration, the use of sodium base in both stages was found to be most practical and resulted in large-scale industrial application of the method (281). Also, Graham's technique provided a suitable way to pulp wood that became resistant to acid sulfite pulping because of the penetration of phenolic bark extractives into the surfaces of logs during water transportation (307). The attendant yield gain of about 5% over the bisulfite process is an attractive feature of this technique. The use of a liquor pH of 5.5 to 8.0 in the first stage prevents the condensation of group A in lignin with phenolic extractives as described earlier under sulfonation of lignin and, during subsequent acid sulfite stage, delignification takes place without difficulty. The yield gain in this process was found to result from a more effective retention of gluco-mannans (7,266) presumably because of extensive deacetylation of this polysaccharide during the first stage (8,8a).

In a two-stage process, the use of a bisulfite liquor pH 3.5 to 4.0 in the first stage permits the use of relatively high temperature, 160 to 170°C., and a short cooking period, 1.5 to 2.0 hours, to effect the sulfonation of the lignin of resinous woods. In the second stage, the hydrolysis is performed by injecting sulfur dioxide and adjusting the pH of the liquor to 1.5 to 2.0, and heating at 120 to 140°C. for 1.5 to 2.0 hours. The bleachable sulfite pulps of moderate yield and strength similar to bisulfite pulps are obtained in relatively short time and with the use of a less amount of base (113).

To alleviate the pitch problem, especially in the production of dissolving pulp from pine, Sivola (279) developed a process consisting of an acid sulfite or bisulfite cooking stage that is followed by a slightly alkaline sulfite digestion at a pH of 8 to 9. The use of a high excess of sulfur dioxide in the first stage produces a dissolving pulp, while use of a bisulfite in the first stage gives a strong paper pulp of the kraft type but light in color (266,218). In any of these multistage sulfite processes, when cooking in near neutral or alkaline liquor is contem-plated, only the use of the soluble bases is possible. Therefore, there have been several chemical recovery systems developed for the soda-base sulfite spent liquor in conjunction with these multistage processes.

3. Neutral Sulfite Process

The use of sodium sulfite solution as cooking liquor has long been of interest (31). Without the addition of a buffering agent, however, the liquor pH decreases well below 7 because of the formation of wood acids during digestion. At the U.S. Forest Products Laboratory, it was found that the addition of sodium carbonate or bicarbonate to the sodium sulfite solution gave a cooking liquor with a pH more nearly constant at 7 to 8 during digestion. This liquor was effective in partial delignification of hardwoods (253). This process is called neutral sulfite semichemical (NSSC) pulping. It is used in producing high-yield pulps (70 to 80%) from hardwoods for the manufacture of corrugating board. At somewhat lower yield, 60 to 70%, the pulps can be bleached, producing pulps of highest yield and strength that can be obtained from hardwoods. Fully cooked pulps made by the neutral sulfite process do not have any great yield and strength advantages over the kraft process.

The neutral sulfite method is not practical in pulping coniferous woods because it requires the use of too much chemical and too long a cooking time. This is somewhat overcome by the use of alkaline sulfite liquor containing sodium sulfide instead of carbonate as buffer (52,156,195a). In this way, fully cooked pulps can be made from pine that is equal to kraft pulp in quality and yield. The high content of lignin in coniferous woods and its slow solubilization characteristics and the resistance of the resins of these woods toward dissolution in neutral sulfite liquor are the chief obstacles for the use of this process with coniferous woods.

The studies on the mechanism of neutral sulfite delignification of aspen indicate that lignin is only partially sulfonated with a sulfur to methoxyl ratio of about 0.07, and is depolymerized (267). After a fast initial rate, the delignification slows down, and the main portion of lignin does not dissolve in the cooking liquor; only after mechanical fiberization of the chips at the end of digestion is it dispersed in hot water during washing. The heterogeneous nature and generally lower molecular weight of native lignins in hardwoods partly explains their suitability for pulping by this process.

During neutral sulfite semichemical pulping of aspen, the hemicelluloses of increasing molecular weight are dissolved and continuously degraded in the cooking liquor (167,227). At a 75% pulp yield, about one fourth of the hemicelluloses removed from the wood can be recovered from the spent liquor. No simple sugars and di- or trisaccharides are found in the cooking liquor, indicating that the low molecular weight oligosaccharides are easily degraded to aldonic and other sulfocarboxylic acids in the presence of high bisulfite ion concentration. The neutral sulfite semichemical pulps from hardwoods, however, contain the largest quantities of hemicellulose of any pulp.

F. SIDE REACTIONS DURING SULFITE COOKING

All of the sulfur consumed during sulfite processes is not used for the sulfonation of lignins. Depending on the cooking conditions and wood species used, a great portion of sulfur dioxide is decomposed or bound to dissolved wood degradation products of lignin or carbohydrate origin. The lignosulfonic acids dissolved in the cooking liquor are slowly hydrolyzed and further sulfonated, continuously, for the rest of the cooking period. In a sense, the sulfur used for these side reactions is wasted.

The decomposition reactions are the most important side reactions of sulfite liquor. Decomposition takes place by the disproportionation of sulfur dioxide to a higher and lower state of oxidation at elevated temperatures, forming thiosulfate and sulfate (159,306). Thiosulfate, in turn, becomes an autocatalyst for the subsequent decomposition, which is faster than the initial rate of disproportionation that takes place during the induction period. After the thiosulfate concentration reaches a particular level, the precipitation of sulfur takes place, and the acidity of the liquor rapidly rises. In sulfite liquor, because of the presence of various active organic compounds during cooking, the mechanism of the decomposition of cooking acid becomes highly complex. There are several such decomposition reactions that involve organic compounds. Wood sugars, formed during sulfite cooking, are involved in the decomposition of bisulfite ions in which sugars are oxidized to aldonic acids and bisulfite ions are reduced to thiosulfate (108) according to following mechanism:

$$2CH_2OH(CHOH)_4CHO + 2HSO_3^- \rightarrow 2CH_2OH(CHOH)_4COOH$$
$$+ S_2O_3^{-2} + H_2O$$

In a similar manner, terpenes are converted to p-cymene (252) and formic acid to carbon dioxide (290) by the sulfite liquor with the simultaneous formation of thiosulfate. The problem of liquor decomposition becomes very acute when large quantities of spent liquor are used for makeup due to the presence of a large amount of sugars and other hydroxyaldehydes (292). Although many side reactions occur which might result in the formation of these compounds, only small quantities of thiosulfate or polythionates are found in the spent liquor. This has been attributed to the possible reaction of these compounds or of their decomposition product, the hydrogen sulfide, with lignin, forming organic sulfur compounds other than sulfonic acid type (264,237). Hoge (130) also found that the polyphenolic extractive, dihydroquercetin, which inhibits the sulfite pulping of douglas-fir heartwood, promotes the bisulfite decomposition in the absence of wood but not in the presence of wood. Apparently wood, or its reaction products, removes thiosulfate from the liquor during the early portions of the cooking cycle and retards the bisulfite decomposition. Because of the slow delignification rate, however, douglas fir requires long digestion and, during the latter part of the cooking cycle as thiosulfate accumulates, the liquor decomposes by autocatalysis.

The simple sugars or oligosaccharides of low-degree polymerization, dissolved in the cooking liquor, are continuously transformed by oxidation to aldonic acid according to a reaction mechanism already mentioned, or by the formation of true sulfonic acids that can be reducing- as well as nonreducing-type sulfocarboxylic acids (176,123). The oxidation of aldoses to aldonic acid is increased with increasing base concentration in sulfite liquor because of the presence of large bisulfite ion concentration (104). Because of higher digestion temperature used, the concentration of thiosulfate formed in cooking with bisulfite liquors reaches the critical levels earlier than that of acid sulfite digestion, which results in autocatalytic decomposition of cooking acid with the precipitation of sulfur and formation of sulfuric acid. Once triggered, this reaction takes place in a few minutes, as indicated by the dark color and sharp increase in the acidity of the cooking liquor (157). Therefore, in bisulfite processes, the delignification cannot be carried out to the same extent as in the acid sulfite process without encountering the decomposition of cooking liquors toward the end of the digestion period.

G. BY-PRODUCTS FROM SULFITE PULPING

1. Volatile Products

The sulfite spent liquor is known to contain organic acids, methyl alcohol, methyl glyoxal, formaldehyde, and furfural. The aldehydes are generally the cause of loosely bound sulfur dioxide in spent liquors and create an analytical problem. The volatile organic acids are chiefly acetic (originating from the esters of carbohydrates and primarily acetates of xylan and glucomannan) and a trace amount of formic acid. The quantity of volatile acid in the spent liquor, depending on the species, varies from 2 to 10 g./l. Methyl alcohol also originates from wood hemicelluloses and appears in small quantities.

Spent liquor from neutral sulfite semichemical pulping of hardwoods contains up to 12 to 13 g./l. of acetic acid and 1.0 to 1.5 g./l. of formic acid. A commercial process has been developed (54) for the separation of these acids, whereby the concentrated and acidified neutral sulfite semichemical liquor is extracted with aqueous methyl-ethyl ketone and, after evaporation of the solvent, the acids are stripped out with steam. Formic acid is separated from acetic acid by aziotropic distillation with ethylene dichloride, and the acetic acid is further purified by a final distillation.

The condensed relief gases from the sulfite process produce a crude oil that contains p-cymene, terpenes, sesquiterpenes, and fatty and resin acids.

2. Fermentation Products

The sugars of spent liquor are converted to ethyl alcohol, baker's yeast, fodder yeast, or organic acids and alcohols, depending on the fermentation process used. The production of ethyl alcohol in sulfite mills is common in the Scandinavian countries and in Germany.

The amount and kind of wood sugars present in the spent liquors depend on the wood and the process employed. Mannose is the major constituent in waste liquors from coniferous woods, but xylose is the principal sugar from deciduous woods. Only a very small amount of glucose is found in waste liquors and, in alcoholic fermentation only, the hexose sugars are involved.

The commercial yeasts have to be acclimatized to the sulfurous acid present in small quantities in the sulfite liquors ready for alcoholic fermentation. To keep the quantity of sulfur dioxide at a minimum and to adjust the pH to a level suitable for the yeast cell, which is about 5, chalk or lime is added to the spent liquor at 80 to 90°C. Free and loosely bound sulfur dioxide, involving organic compounds containing carbonyl groups, is precipitated and removed as calcium sulfite because it will otherwise lower the alcohol yield by tying up acetaldehyde, the intermediate fermentation product. The loosely bound sulfur dioxide, occurring chiefly as formaldehyde and methylglyoxal bisulfite compounds, is in much less quantity in liquors from dissolving pulp manufacture than in spent liquors from paper pulp manufacture (2,3). Most of it, however, is decomposed at or about pH 6, and a small amount left in the liquor does not interfere with the fermentation except to reduce the yield by a few per cent or to cause a small amount of impurity, such as acetaldehyde.

Complete elimination of sulfur dioxide can be accomplished by making liquor slightly alkaline, which results in acetone-free ethyl alcohol (3). The crude spirit contains 3 to 5% methyl alcohol and a small amount fusel oil. The larger part of methyl alcohol is already present in the spent liquor, and a smaller portion is formed during fermentation of methylated sugars (100). The fusel oil contains isobutyl, isoamyl, amyl, n-hexyl alcohol, and the terpene alcohols including l-borneol and d,l-fenchyl alcohol (160). The sulfite spirit is freed of these impurities by rectification.

The production of baker's yeast (Saccharomyces cerevisiae) from sulfite spent liquor is also a fairly common practice. A most promising development, however, came about by the use of wild yeasts for the production of fodder. Among these, torula was most successful; not only hexoses but also pentose sugars in the sulfite liquors were utilized. The dry yeast yield is about 50% on the sugar, and the protein content of the yeast is 50 to 55% (259).

Clostridium butylicum ferments 70 to 80% of the reducing sugars to a mixture containing 75% butanol, 20% acetone, and 5% ethanol (319). Lactobacillus pentosus ferments the sulfite liquor, producing 285 pounds lactic and 75 pounds acetic acid per ton of pulp (171). Clostridium polyfermenticum converts about one-half of the reducing sugar into butyric acid (61).

3. Lignin and Vanillin

The lignosulfonic acids from sulfite liquor can be precipitated with excess lime, and a process is developed on this principle by Howard (132). In the first stage, enough lime is added to bring the pH to 10.5, precipitating the calcium sulfite, which is filtered out. Upon adjusting the pH to 12, by further addition of lime, calcium salt of lignosulfonic acid settles out as flocculent precipitate, which is separated from liquor by decantation and filtering.

By treating with sodium hydroxide, carbonation, and ion-exchange techniques, the appropriate pure salts of lignosulfonic acid are prepared, such as sodium, magnesium, or ammonium lignosulfonate. These lignin products found uses in tanning, asphalt cements, rubber, and boiler-water treatment industries, and in soil stabilization, oil well drilling fluids, and as a solid dispersing agent in clay slips and other similar industries and in textile dying and fixing.

Another well known use of lignosulfonic acids has been in the production of vanillin through alkaline oxidation (265). The yield is about 4% on lignin. Vanillin is extracted with butanol and further purified by forming its bisulfite addition compound. Vanillin is, of course, produced more simply by heating the sulfite liquors directly with sodium hydroxide at elevated temperature and pressure. Then the acidified liquor is extracted with benzene, and the vanillin is removed from the benzene as sodium bisulfite addition compound (127).

H. CHEMICAL RECOVERY IN SULFITE PROCESSES

The economic incentive and the desire of the elimination of stream pollution are the major reasons for the development of recovery systems. The calcium-base sulfite spent liquor can be evaporated and burned for the recovery of heat only. There are several practical chemical recovery systems for the soda-base sulfite liquors and one for magnesia-base liquors, which have found industrial application.

The recovery of magnesia-base sulfite liquors is the simplest. The inorganic salt separates into magnesium oxide and sulfur dioxide upon evaporation and burning of the liquor to recover the process heat (303). Magnesium oxide is separated from the flue gases in cyclone dust collectors and, after it is slaked, the magnesium hydroxide slurry is used in a series of venturi tubes to absorb sulfur dioxide from the cooled flue gases. After the addition of make-up sulfur dioxide and magnesium oxide for the losses, the cooking liquor pH is adjusted for bisulfite or acid sulfite cooking as desired.

The sodium-base sulfite recovery system has greater technical importance because it is also useful in multistage pulping, using near neutral or alkaline liquors and in the neutral sulfite semichemical process. In principle, five established industrial processes differ only in the manner in which the sulfur dioxide is generated from hydrogen sulfide fixed as sodium sulfide in the smelt obtained upon burning evaporated spent liquor. In one process, the sodium carbonate is separated by fractional crystallization, and sodium sulfide is recirculated to the furnace. The hydrogen sulfide generated is burned to sulfur dioxide (30). In the second process, the hydrogen sulfide that is stripped from green liquor with flue gases in a carbonation tower is returned to the furnace and oxidized to sulfur dioxide (271). In the third process, hydrogen sulfide, stripped from green liquor with pure carbon dioxide, is converted to sulfur dioxide in a special burner (279). In the fourth process, hydrogen sulfide, stripped from green liquor with carbon dioxide, is converted to sulfur in Claus reactors and, then, it is burned to sulfur dioxide (49). In the fifth process, the hydrogen sulfide, generated by direct sulfitation of the green liquor with sulfur dioxide or sodium bisulfite, is burned in a sulfur burner to sulfur dioxide (317).

V. Alkaline Pulping Processes

A. GENERAL

Although Watt and Burgess invented the soda process in 1853, the widespread industrial application of the process was hampered by the technical difficulties encountered in chemical recovery and digestion systems.

Eaton in the United States and Dahl in Danzig discovered independently the use of sodium sulfate for replacing the alkali lost during pulping and chemical recovery. The sulfate was reduced to sulfide in the recovery furnace, which in turn accelerated the delignification rate, resulting in higher yield and pulp strength. This became the most popular pulping method, and was called the sulfate or kraft process. It is suitable for making strong pulps from any species of wood. The method of replacing soda and sulfur losses with salt cake is still the most common and economical practice.

The prehydrolysis kraft process produces one of the highest quality dissolving pulps used to make rayon filament for tire cord. With the modernization of the recovery system, the economics of the process became more favorable. Despite all these advantages, sulfate process mills bring a serious air pollution problem to the surrounding communities. Perhaps a practical way of eliminating the malodorous gases—methyl mercaptan, dimethyl sulfide, or disulfide and hydrogen sulfide—emanating from the digesters and recovery furnaces may someday be found.

The soda process produces a weak, soft pulp. No expansion in mill capacity for making soda pulp has taken place for many years. Only a few soda pulpmills are left, mostly producing pulps from hardwoods that are suitable for use in printing papers.

In contrast to the bright color of sulfite pulps, the pulps from alkaline processes are brown in color. This characteristic color is due to modified residual lignin and the lignin degradation products readsorbed by the pulp (226,276). Although the alkaline pulps are more difficult to bleach and the bleaching cost is higher than for sulfite pulps, kraft pulp can be bleached to a desirable brightness level.

B. VARIABLES AND RATE OF ALKALINE PULPING

1. Soda Process

The rate of delignification in the soda process is slower than in kraft pulping and, generally, 5 to 6% more sodium hydroxide is required to produce the same degree of delignification. Most woods can be pulped by the soda process, using 25 to 27% caustic soda and from 2 to 4% of sodium carbonate based on wood, a liquor-to-wood ratio of 4 to 1, and heating 90 to 120 min. at 170 to 173°C. A reduction of the residual lignin to below 10%, however, results in great losses in carbohydrate yield and pulp strength in pulping coniferous woods.

2. Kraft Process

In the kraft process, the *active alkali* is calculated as the sum of the per cent of NaOH and Na$_2$S on wood expressed as equivalent Na$_2$O. In addition to these chemicals, the cooking liquor contains, as in the soda process, from 10 to 12% sodium carbonate based on the total chemicals used. This is primarily imposed by the efficiency of the causticizing operation during the chemical recovery. The sodium sulfide fraction of active alkali is called *sulfidity*, and is as follows:

$$\text{Sulfidity} = 100 \times \frac{\text{Na}_2\text{S (as Na}_2\text{O)}}{\text{NaOH (as Na}_2\text{O)} + \text{Na}_2\text{S (as Na}_2\text{O)}}$$

The cooking cycle in the sulfate process requires about 3 to 4 hours, using 14 to 18% active alkali, 20 to 30% sulfidity, and heating for 90 to 120 min. at 170 to 173°C.

The rate of delignification increases with increasing temperature and alkali concentration, but above certain levels pulp yield and strength are adversely affected. Above 180°C., for example, the alkaline delignification becomes less specific and degradation of wood polysaccharides is accelerated, resulting in loss of yield and pulp strength. The effect of an excess of alkali is critical, especially toward the end of the cook after removal of the major portion of lignin where the degradation and loss of carbohydrates proceeds at a faster rate. Therefore, the optimum chemical charge can best be determined from the concentration of residual active alkali left in the black liquor at the end of the cook. Depending on the wood species, the cooking conditions used, and the degree of delignification desired, this residual may vary between 10 to 15 g./i.

Bray, Martin, and Schwartz (36) studied the effect of increasing the amount of chemical from 15 to 25% in the sulfate pulping of longleaf pine, where the delignification rate and chemical consumption increases with increasing chemical. Further increase in the amount of chemical above 25% of wood weight, however, results i.1 loss of carbohydrate yield (277).

It was shown by Bixler (22) that alkaline liquors selectively attack the middle lamella before taking any noticeable action on the lignin of the secondary wall. The microscopic observations were made during the microdigestion of spruce wood sections of a 20-μ thickness. In contrast, the sulfite liquor attacks the lignin of the middle lamella and secondary wall simultaneously and, assumably, results in the weakening of the fiber.

Laroque and Maass (165), among others, were able to show that the rate of alkaline delignification closely approximates that of monomolecular reaction. However, it has been found that the rate constants calculated for monomolecular reaction continuously drift downward, especially during removai of the first one third or one half of the lignin (103). These rate constants, however, are only approximate because of the unreliability of the method used in the analysis of residual lignin in the pulps. Moreover, this trend in rate constant during cooking may be expected when the heterogeneous nature of the reaction and the polymolecularity of the lignin are considered.

Since alkaline liquors easily penetrate into wood, the chip size is not very critical, and a large variation in size does not have any measurable effect on pulp quality; nor are chipper-damaged chips susceptible to deleterious action by the alkaline cooking liquor (93, 122). Therefore, kraft pulping can easily be adapted to a continuous processing, whereby the heating-up time or impregnation period can be eliminated by using thin chips and a retention time of only 1.0 to 2.0 hours. Continuous digesters are used in several of the new kraft mills, although the retention time is somewhat similar to batch operation.

3. Effect of Sulfidity

The rate of delignification increases with increasing sulfidity of the cooking liquor up to a point and, then levels off. Above 25% sulfidity, the rate remains practically unchanged. However, when the cooking liquors of higher sulfidity are used, the active alkali charge has to be increased to keep the effective alkali constant. The effective alkali is defined as the sum of sodium hydroxide and one half of the sodium sulfide, both expressed as per cent of sodium oxide based on the wood.

Hägglund and Hedlund (103) studied the dissolution of lignin from spruce wood at 160° at various sulfidities, which is illustrated in Fig. 3. The efficiency of lignin removal increases with increasing

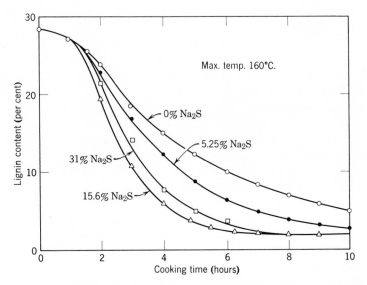

Fig. 3. Delignification rate of spruce wood with liquors of varying sulfidity, active alkali 24.2% NaOH [Hägglund and Hedlund (103)].

sulfidity, as was found by Bray, Martin, and Schwartz in kraft pulping of douglas fir (37). The latter authors assumed that sodium sulfide in the cooking liquor hydrolyzes according to the following equation:

$$Na_2S + H_2O \rightleftharpoons NaOH + NaHS$$

and sodium hydroxide is the only active delignification reagent. Accordingly, they defined the effective alkali in kraft pulping that is described above. They found that, with effective alkali constant, the rate of delignification and pulp strength increased by increasing the sulfidity from 0 to 20%. Beyond this point, the improvement was negligible.

By the kraft process, the hardwoods are pulped more easily, require less active alkali but about the same sulfidity, and produce higher yields of pulp that contain less lignin than coniferous woods (34,147). Hardwoods contain 20 to 30% less lignin than coniferous woods, which accounts for the ease of delignification of these species without considering the lower molecular weight or chemical properties of hardwood lignin. Legg and Hart (169,168) studied the effect of sulfidity in kraft pulping of jack pine, douglas fir, aspen, and birch, and came to the conclusion that the optimum delignification rate, carbohydrate yield, and pulp strength are attained at 30% sulfidity. However, relative increase in yield and pulp quality with increasing sulfidity from 15 to 30% was apparently small.

During kraft pulping, only about one half of the original sodium

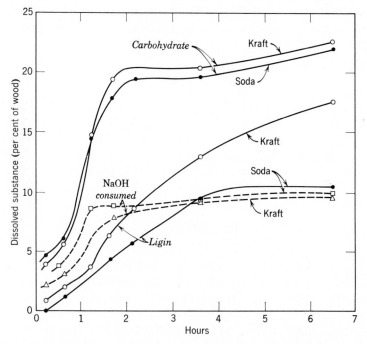

Fig. 4. Kraft and soda digestion of spruce wood at 140°C., 105 minutes heating to maximum temperature [Enkvist (74)].

sulfide and two thirds of the active alkali are consumed (29). The rates of dissolution of carbohydrates during soda and kraft cooking of spruce wood are about the same when compared at equal alkali consumption or when equal amounts of active alkali are used (74), Fig. 4. The delignification in kraft digestion proceeds at a faster rate than in soda. The lignin dissolution in the soda process slows down rapidly after about one third of the lignin is dissolved. During alkaline cooks, lignin does not dissolve until toward the end of the heating-up period, and the lignin dissolution is most rapid at the end of the temperature rise after 30 to 40% of the wood is dissolved (33,146).

In kraft pulping, a lower alkali concentration or lower cooking temperature and shorter cooking time are used. Consequently the carbohydrates, being subjected to less severe treatment, produce a stronger pulp, in a better yield. There is no protective action of sodium sulfide against the alkaline degradation of wood polysaccharides, since degradation in kraft and soda liquors of equal alkali strength is about the same under the same cooking conditions (56, 295).

C. DELIGNIFICATION MECHANISM

Basically, the reactions of kraft process are postulated to involve the same groups and reaction site of lignin that are known to take part in sulfite delignification. There are two active ionic species, bisulfide and hydroxyl ions, in the kraft liquor that determine the course of delignification. The concentration of bisulfide ion is governed by the concentration of hydroxyl ion and the equilibrium constants of the following hydrolysis reactions:

$$S^{-2} + H_2O \rightleftharpoons SH^- + OH^- \qquad K_1$$
$$SH^- + H_2O \rightleftharpoons H_2S + OH^- \qquad K_2$$

It has been estimated (238) that in a $0.1M$ solution of sodium sulfide at room temperature, the S^{-2} ions predominate above pH 13, the SH^- ions between pH 7 and 13 and, below pH 7, H_2S is predominant. The equilibrium constants of these hydrolysis reactions at the cooking temperature are not known, but it may be assumed that the above pH limits will be higher. Since the actual pH of the kraft liquor is about 14 at the beginning and 11 and 12 at the end of the cook, it is expected that the S^{-2} ions are nearly completely hydrolyzed to HS⁻, as postulated by Bray, Martin, and Schwartz (37). This is especially true for the liquor inside the chips for which the pH would be well below 14 because of the buffering effect of wood acids.

The reaction of hydrosulfide ion with lignin involves p-hydroxybenzyl alcohol or benzyl alkyl ether groups and carbonyl groups (5,6,205). These reactions take place under relatively mild conditions and probably are completed well before the maximum temperature is reached during kraft cooking. The lignin isolated from spruce wood by digesting with kraft liquor at 100°C. contains 1.3% mercaptan and 0.6% disulfide sulfur (73). The concentration of sodium sulfide in the cooking liquor decreases rapidly at the start, and it then remains practically constant for the rest of the cooking period (193). The kraft lignin precipitated from black liquor by acidification contains only 1 to 2% sulfur, and it has not been possible to correctly identify the sulfur organic linkages in thiolignin. There does not appear to be any thiol or thiocarbonyl group, nor any disulfide, polysulfide, or dialkyl sulfide linkages, and only the presence of an aryl alkyl sulfide or a sulfur linkage involving a heterocyclic compound has been speculated (73,82). Apparently some of the sulfur linkage introduced into lignin at the beginning of digestion is split off under the influence of hydroxyl ion, forming new hydrosulfide or thiosulfate ions to start a new reaction cycle. In the course of these reactions, a limited number of sulfur linkages are formed that are stable against the influence of alkali.

The base-catalyzed reactions of lignin during the kraft process are by far the most important ones. The phenyl alkyl ether groups are hydrolyzed by alkali at elevated temperature, resulting in the activation of new benzyl alcohol or benzyl alkyl ether groups for subsequent reaction with hydrosulfide ions (172). The extensive hydrolysis of the ether linkages results in the fragmentation and dissolution of lignin. The molecular weight of kraft lignin from coniferous woods is about 2,000 (82,95), which is considerably lower than that of sulfite lignin. The kraft lignin contains a phenolic hydroxyl group in almost every phenylpropane unit.

When the wood is digested with hydrogen sulfide or sodium hydrosulfide at a pH from 7 to 8.5 and 100°C., a large amount of organic sulfur, 7 to 21%, is introduced into the lignin (71,99). The thiolignin can be extracted from the wood residue with sodium hydroxide solution at room temperature. Upon heating it in sodium hydroxide solution at 160°C., the thiolignin loses hydrogen sulfide, and its sulfur content decreases from 9 to between 2 and 4%, becoming similar to common kraft lignin (72). More recently it has been claimed, however, that most of the sulfur found in thiolignin from commercial black liquor or from the wood digested in the solution of sodium hydrosulfide is largely physically entrapped elemental sulfur and not organically bound (328a).

The sulfidation reaction of lignin is strongly retarded when the carbonyl groups are eliminated by reduction with borohydride (86). Therefore, the carbonyl groups of lignin play an important role in kraft pulping of wood, although it is not the only site, as it was once generally assumed, involved in the formation of sulfur linkages.

Most of the lignin dissolved in a kraft digestion precipitates upon acidification of black liquor. About one fourth of the dissolved lignin, however, remains soluble in acidified black liquor, and the methoxyl content of this soluble lignin is about one half of that of precipitated alkali lignin or of the original lignin in the wood (276). These degradation products are formed by the demethylation of lignin, which also results in the formation of methyl alcohol, methyl mercaptan, and dimethyl sulfide as by-products during kraft pulping. When the wood is treated with a solution of sodium hydrosulfide at elevated temperature, the lignin is converted to water-soluble degradation products, primarily a phenolic and carboxylic type (40). This would indicate that the excess hydrosulfide ions catalyze the depolymerization of lignin and stabilize the active groups formed, thereby blocking the recondensation of the scission products. In the presence of excess alkali, as in kraft liquor, the deactivating effect of bisulfide ions may not be effective enough to prevent the condensation of the degradation product. The ortho position to the new phenolic hydroxyls formed by alkaline hydrolysis of alkoxyaryl ether linkages is the primary site for such condensation.

From these observations, it can be summarized that during the early stages of kraft pulping the reactive groups of lignin are blocked, and some of the alkoxybenzyl ether linkages are split by the hydrosulfide ions. Alkaline hydrolysis of alkoxyphenyl ether groups becomes effective at elevated temperature where new phenolic hydroxyl groups are formed and alkali soluble low molecular weight degradation products begin to dissolve in the cooking liquor. Newly activated benzyl alcohol and alkoxybenzyl ether groups, as a result of the formation of a free hydroxyl group in the para position, are again blocked and stabilized by hydrosulfide ions. The over-all delignification, however, is governed by the alkaline hydrolysis of the basic linkages of lignin polymer.

D. BEHAVIOR OF WOOD POLYSACCHARIDES DURING ALKALINE PULPING

During alkaline digestion, the carbohydrates are subjected to at least two different types of degradation: one is the peeling off of the monomers at the reducing end by oxidative degradation (55), and the other is the scission of glucosidic linkages by alkaline hydrolysis. Samuelson and Wennerblom (263) have estimated that during alkaline digestion of cellulose about 50 glucose units are oxidized to isosaccharinic acid and peeled off consecutively, each time exposing a new reducing end group in each chain before an alkali stable metasaccharinic acid is formed that remains attached to the polymer. At elevated temperatures, new reducing end groups are formed by the alkaline cleavage of glycosidic bonds feeding the peeling-off reactions.

The mechanism of the predominant end-group degradation and stopping reaction has been elucidated (191,192). The gluco-isosaccharinic acid dissolved in alkaline liquor undergoes further fragmentation, forming lower molecular weight acids, that is, β,γ-dihydroxy butyric, glycollic, lactic, acetic, and formic acid (56). The mechanism of alkaline hydrolysis of glycosidic bonds is not completely clear, although some variable in regard to type of sugar and glycosidic bond and steric factors have been investigated (67, 140,179).

In kraft pulping the reaction rate of noncellulosic carbohydrates, such as xylan, glucomannan, and galactoglucomannan, varies with the accessibility, branching, type of sugars, and glycosidic bonds involved. Hamilton and Thompson (116) studied the behavior of purified individual hemicellulose species in alkaline digestion to augment their earlier findings (114) concerning the structure of hemicelluloses present in different pulps. The conventional kraft process converts the 4-O-methylglucuronoxylan of hardwoods to xylan and 4-O-methylglucuronoarabinoxylan of the coniferous woods to an arabinoxylan. The arabinoxylan obtained from a southern pine kraft pulp had a degree of polymerization of 76 to 90 and, at intervals of 12 to 18 anhydroxylose units, an arabinofuranose was linked by a $1 \rightarrow 3$ glycosidic bond. The prehydrolyzed kraft pulp from the same wood contains only xylan where all the arabinose units are cleaved during the acid hydrolysis stage, as in acid sulfite pulping.

The instability of the glycosidic bond between uronic acid units

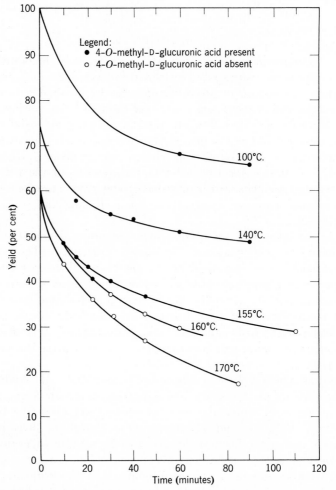

Fig. 5. The variation of yield of 4-O-methylglucuronoxylan with temperature and duration of kraft cook [Hamilton and Thompson (116)].

and xylose chain to alkaline hydrolysis is demonstrated in Fig. 5. The 4-O-methylglucuronoxylan obtained from red alder neutral sulfite semichemical pulp lost all of the uronic acid groups after 10 min. of heating with kraft liquor at 170°C. Croon and Enström (58a,58b) and Meier (200a,200b), after studying thoroughly the behavior of xylan containing hemicelluloses from both coniferous and deciduous woods in kraft pulping, concluded that when a cooking liquor containing not too much excess active alkali is used, at the most 60–70% but not all of the 4-0-methyl-D-glucuronic acid residues are split off at the end of the digestion.

The arabinofuranose unit attached to carbon 3 of the anhydroxylose unit of the arabinoxylan polymer causes the end-group peeling reaction to be terminated at that point by the formation of a stable metasaccharinic acid during alkaline digestion. Such an explanation has been postulated (263) and confirmed by the model experiments upon 3-0-methyl-D-xylose (57). Hamilton and Thompson (116) followed the degradation rate of arabinoxylan in kraft liquor and compared it with that of xylan and glucuronoxylan, demonstrating the relative stability of this polymer toward alkaline hydrolysis. The retention and accumulation of short-chain molecules, however, causes the average degree of polymerization of the arabinoxylan to drop more quickly than the other two polymers.

The glucomannan has been found more susceptible to alkaline degradation than the xylan family of polymers, and a smaller fraction of the original glucomannan survives the kraft digestion (58b,116, 200b). When the carbonyl end groups of the wood polysaccharides were reduced by the addition of sodium borohydride to the kraft cooking liquor, the retention of glucomannan was more than doubled (119). The yield increase must be due to the reduced rate of peeling-off degradation of this polymer, especially during the earlier part of the digestion.

The galactoglucomannan residues remaining in the kraft pulps of southern pine species indicate the relative stability of this polymer to alkaline digestion. Arabinogalactans, pectins, and gums, on the other hand, are dissolved and rapidly degraded in kraft liquor (116).

The retention of xylan in kraft pulps has a great deal of interest, especially regarding the strength of these pulps which has been attributed to high xylan content. McKinney (197) theorized that xylan is retained by transglycosidation involving lignin-xylan glycosidic linkages where xylan chains are grafted on one another by a glycosidic bond. Häggroth and Lindberg (111) confirmed the possibility of this hypothesis, using phenyl-β-D-xyloside as model compound for lignin-hemicellulose complex. They were able to effect the substitution of simple alcohols and cotton cellulose by alkaline transglycosidation. No direct evidence, however, was found of such reaction occurring during alkaline pulping and, if there were any linkages between cellulose and xylan formed, their number must be very small.

The recent studies on the adsorption of xylan on cellulose fibers

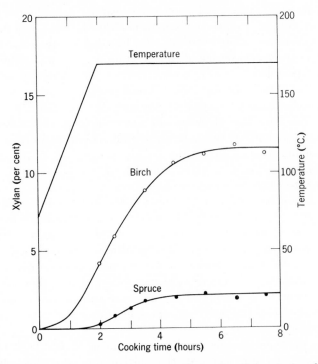

Fig. 6. Amount of xylan adsorbed on purified cotton linters during the kraft digestion of birch and spruce wood [Yllner and Enström (325)].

during kraft cooking, however, produced a better explanation of the mechanism of xylan retention. The addition of dissolved hemicellulose to the cooking liquor during kraft pulping is known to increase the pulp yield under certain conditions (247). Yllner and Enström (325,326) found that cotton and purified sulfite pulp adsorb a large amount of xylan when cooked together with birch, spruce wood, or birch holocellulose in kraft liquor, Figs. 6, 7, and 8. The xylan content of these cellulose samples reaches a maximum value after several hours digestion at 170°C. and remains constant after that. The xylan content of the cooking liquor reaches a maximum value near to top temperature and, then, decreases continuously. Apparently, the adsorption of xylan increases with decreasing alkali concentration in the black liquor and with increasing degradation of

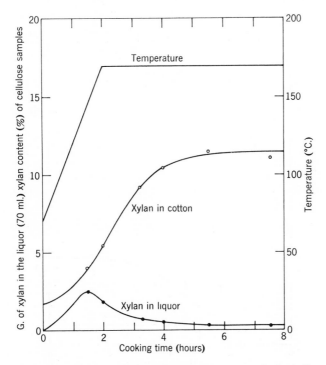

Fig. 7. The adsorption of xylan on a sample of raw cotton in kraft digestion of birch holocellulose [Yllner and Enström (326)].

the xylose-containing hemicellulose dissolved in the liquor. About 20% of the adsorbed xylan is resistant to extraction with cold sodium hydroxide in a concentration of 10 to 20%. The adsorbed xylan is also found very resistant to heterogeneous acid hydrolysis. The uronic acid content of the adsorbed xylan is much lower than that of the native polysaccharide. From these observations, it is concluded that, upon the elimination of uronic acid branches and shortening of the polymer, xylan is adsorbed and possibly crystallized on the surface of cellulosic fibrils. Such a process of dissolution, degradation, and adsorption must be taking place continuously during the kraft process.

Saarnio and Gustafsson (258) found that hexosans dissolved in the kraft cooking liquor are rapidly destroyed, while pentosans are more resistant and are the main carbohydrate constituents in the cooking liquor. Therefore, the possibility of their adsorption back on

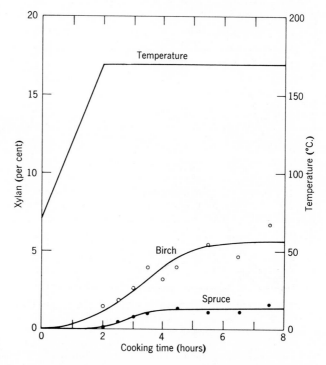

Fig. 8. Amount of xylan adsorbed by purified sulfite pulp during kraft digestion of birch and spruce wood [Yllner and Enström (325)].

the pulp is good, especially during the second half of the digestion as the alkali concentration goes down. Additional indirect evidence of this phenomenon is supplied by the data obtained by Schwartz and Bray (278), in which the kraft pulps produced with continuous liquor flow contained low pentosan and high alpha-cellulose. Here, in order to maintain constant chemical concentration, the preheated fresh liquor, in the concentration range of 23 to 70 g./l. active alkali, was continuously injected, and the liquor, discharged at the same rate, carried away the dissolved xylan, preventing its adsorption. In similar experiments, Yllner, Östberg, and Stockman (327), using constant flow of liquor in the concentration range of 8 to 35 g./l. active alkali in cooking of pine, found that the loss in pulp yield above 23 g./l. active alkali and the loss in xylan above 15 g./l. active alkali became very appreciable. The loss of mannan was almost complete before reaching maximum cooking temperature, and was about the same for all cooking liquors: nearly 80% of the original mannan. The analysis of xylan and glucan in cooking liquor in the course of digestion corresponded well to the pulp analysis, but the mannan was nearly completely destroyed upon dissolution. The pulps at 45% yield contained only 4 to 6% xylan, which corresponds to about 8 to 10% xylan in pulps prepared by the ordinary kraft digestion. Therefore, it may be assumed that almost one half of the xylan in kraft pulp is of the "adsorbed" type.

E. PREHYDROLYSIS KRAFT AND SODA PROCESS

The prehydrolysis kraft or soda process was originally developed for the production of dissolving grade high-alpha pulp from hardwoods and other material rich in pentosan (66). The wood chips are subjected to acid hydrolysis in dilute mineral acid solutions or with steam alone at elevated temperature. In the latter case, the wood acid formed catalyzes the hydrolysis of hemicellulose, especially preventing the adsorption of xylan during the subsequent kraft pulping. The prehydrolysis kraft process has become a standard pulping process for making dissolving pulp from hardwoods as well as from pine.

F. MODIFICATION OF ALKALINE PROCESSES WITH ELEMENTAL SULFUR, POLYSULFIDE, BOROHYDRIDE, AND HYDROGENATION

The addition of 1 to 2% elemental sulfur on the weight of wood to soda liquor results in higher yield and pulp strength, nearly equal to kraft (309,35). The sulfur is converted to thiosulfate, sulfide and, possibly, to polysulfide upon dissolution in sodium hydroxide. In pulping of coniferous woods, the addition of sulfur to kraft liquor or replacement of sodium sulfide with sodium polysulfide produces up to 5% higher yield with little or no change in pulp quality (106,162,19).

This process appears to be economically feasible if the method for the regeneration of elemental sulfur used in a sulfite-type recovery system can be adapted (138). The mechanism of yield increase in polysulfide pulping has not been fully explored. Since nearly all of the polysulfide sulfur is converted to sulfide during early stages of the cook, the use of high active alkali and low cooking temperature appears to be favorable. (See also the Addendum, page 534.)

Schuerch and co-workers (9,20) conducted soda pulping experiments under catalytic hydrogenation conditions in which lignin is continuously hydrogenated and stabilized as soon as it is dissolved in the cooking liquor, producing low melting phenolic and acidic compounds as possible valuable byproducts.

The addition of sodium borohydride to kraft liquor results in an appreciable increase in pulp yield from pine because of more efficient retention of glucomannan (119). It is easily conceivable that the carbonyl end groups of this polymer are reduced by borohydride and stabilized toward alkaline degradation. Apparently, the effective retention of glucomannan reduces the surface area available for the readsorption of xylan, as indicated by the low xylan content of these pulps. With birch, 1% sodium borohydride on wood caused 7 to 8% increase in pulp yield involving improved retention of glucomannan, xylan, and cellulose (219a).

G. BY-PRODUCTS OF ALKALINE PULPING

1. Volatile Compounds

A portion of the methoxyl groups of the wood splits during the alkaline digestion. Methanol only is formed in the soda process. In the kraft process, in addition to methanol, methyl mercaptan, dimethyl sulfide, and dimethyl disulfide are formed, producing the characteristic kraft mill odor. These compounds are continuously discharged from the digester with the relief gases. They partly remain in the cooking liquor and also continue to form until the end of the digestion. When the digester is blown, they escape into the atmosphere in large quantities. Some still remain in the black liquor, however, and collect in the condensate from the evaporators in the recovery plant. The collection and burning or the absorption and eventual oxidation of these compounds appear to be effective in reducing the air pollution in the vicinity of kraft mills.

The conversion of additional methoxyl to dimethyl sulfide may be achieved by heating the black liquor at elevated temperatures with additional sulfur (102). Its oxidation product, dimethyl sulfoxide, has interesting solvent properties. The resinous woods produce turpentine during alkaline pulping, which distills out of the digester with the relief gases. The turpentine is recovered by condensation, then purified by fractional distillation and washing with sulfuric acid and sodium hydroxide. Depending on the wood species used, the amount of turpentine varies from 1 to 2.5 gallons per ton of pulp.

2. Tall Oil

In alkaline pulping of resinous woods, the resin acids and fatty acids are removed by the cooking liquor, and their sodium salt with small amounts of unsaponifiable material rises to the surface of the partly evaporated black liquor as "sulfate soap." The soap is collected by skimming. It is then treated with sulfuric acid, washed with warm water, and dried. The crude tall oil product is a dark, oily liquid containing an 8 to 10% unsaponifiable part, 30 to 50% resin acids, and 40 to 60% fatty acids, varying with the location in the tree and species of wood (320). The unsaponifiable part contains largely esters of fatty acids, sterols, higher alcohols, and hydrocarbons.

The crude tall oil is further refined by vacuum distillation to improve its color and to eliminate the objectionable odors. The two main fractions of tall oil, the resin and fatty acids, are separated by fractional distillation before or after partial or total esterification. There are also other methods of separation based on the solubility differences of these acids or their derivatives. The relatively pure fractions are desirable for a variety of industrial applications. The fatty acid fraction of tall oil is composed of oleic, linoleic, linolenic, palmitic, and ricinoleic acids, in decreasing order of importance (45). The principal constituent of the resin acid fraction is abietic acid. The largest use of resin acids is in the sizing of paper. (See also Chapter 7.)

3. Alkali Lignin and Other Constituents of the Black Liquor

Nearly all of the carbohydrates dissolved in the black liquor are further degraded to hydroxy carboxylic acids which, thus far, have not been recovered on a commercial scale. However, there have been suggestions for dry distillation of black liquor solids (248) or for treatment of black liquor, with or without the addition of alkali, at elevated temperature and pressure (101) to convert the organic material to simple compounds, such as methanol, acetone, methyl ethyl ketone, acetic acid, and low-melting oils.

Two thirds of the alkali lignin can be precipitated from the black liquor by lowering the pH to 7 to 9 with carbon dioxide in flue gases or with mineral acids. The precipitate is coagulated by heating, then filtered, and washed, producing the sodium salt of alkali lignin. This impure product is suspended in dilute acid solution and further washed to eliminate the residual ash. The alkali lignin contains substantial amounts of phenolic groups with an equivalent weight of 200 to 250 gm. A limited amount of alkali lignin is produced commercially, and some of its actual and suggested uses include laminated paper plastics, asphalt emulsions, dispersing agent, foundry core binder, latex-saturated products, and reinforcing rubber.

H. CHEMICAL RECOVERY IN ALKALINE PROCESSES

The alkaline pulp mills cannot operate economically without an efficient recovery system. The black liquor is evaporated and burned in specially designed furnaces to recover alkali, sulfur, and heat. In the kraft process, alkali is recovered as sodium carbonate and sodium sulfide. The chemical losses in alkaline processes are about 5 to 7% in alkali and nearly 30% in sulfur. In the kraft process, sodium sulfate is added at the furnace to make up for losses of alkali as well as sulfur. The green liquor obtained by dissolving and clarifying the smelt is causticized with lime and filtered to convert it to white liquor for starting a new cook. In the soda process, sodium carbonate is added for makeup to the smelt-dissolving tank and causticized as in the kraft process.

VI. Miscellaneous Chemical Pulping Processes

There have been numerous studies and claims of novel methods of chemical pulping of wood, but none have successfully come into commercial practice. This is largely because the present pulping processes use relatively inexpensive and abundant chemicals, such as sodium hydroxide, sulfur, and lime, which are difficult to supplant.

Besides the requirement of selectivity of a pulping agent toward lignin, its recovery and re-use is, of course, essential for economic feasibility. A majority of the proposed pulping processes use relatively expensive chemicals with no possibility of chemical recovery or with large chemical losses.

Among these, the nitric acid process has been the one most thoroughly investigated. It has been known for some time that wood can be delignified with dilute nitric acid solution at high temperature or with concentrated acid solution at low temperature. The oxidation and fragmentation of lignin is the primary reaction in nitric acid pulping of wood. For dissolution of the degraded lignin, however, the wood has to be washed with water after nitric acid digestion and treated with dilute sodium hydroxide (80,64). In Germany, the process is used in the production of high-alpha pulp from beech. Apparently the hydrolytic action of acid on wood carbohydrates is quite severe, so the strength of the paper pulps is generally comparable to that of sulfite pulp. The nitric acid consumption has been found to be excessive for commercial use of the process (323), and it may become practical only when inexpensive nitric acid is available as a byproduct or waste (257).

Another oxidizing agent proposed for pulping wood is chlorine. The selectivity of aqueous chlorine toward lignin is well known, and the chlorinated lignin can be dissolved in dilute alkali. After several chlorinations and alkali extractions, wood can be fiberized to pulp, but the chemical cost is very high. Therefore, it is useful only in postdelignification of chemical pulps during bleaching.

The solvolysis of lignin with hydroxy organic compounds has been investigated for pulping of wood. Among these, n-butyl alcohol, n-amyl alcohol, ethylene glycol, and triethylene glycol are relatively good solvents (11,94). The reaction of these solvents depends on the catalytic action of wood acids formed at elevated temperature or on an acid catalyst added. The rate and efficiency of the delignification is governed by the solvent power of these alcohols toward lignin. The delignification of wood can also be accomplished by heating with hydrotropic solutions (142,196), such as xylene sulfonate, that require the presence of an acid catalyst. The delignification of hardwoods with organic solvents is accomplished more easily than that of softwoods, which may be attributed to the heteropolymeric nature of the hardwood lignin.

VII. Semichemical Pulping

It is not necessary to use highly delignified pulps in making many grades of paper and paperboard. Further, the use of pulps with relatively high lignin content is desirable from the point of view of effective utilization of wood. Semidelignified pulps can be produced by a suitable adaptation of any one of the well-known chemical pulping processes. Both the sulfite and kraft processes have been found suitable for making semichemical pulps from a variety of wood species. In these processes, the wood is only partially delignified, for example, 30 to 60% of lignin is removed compared to 60 to 90% in chemical pulping, and the pulping is completed by mechanical fiberization. Since the lignin is extensively modified during digestion, it is likely that the mechanical fiberization and subsequent refining removes, to a large extent, the middle lamella and primary wall and the S_1 layer of the secondary wall from the fiber surfaces. This should greatly improve the possibility of fiber bonding, which is essential for good mechanical strength in paper.

The most prominent among these processes is the neutral sulfite semichemical (NSSC) process (50,253), which is widely used for the production of high yield pulps from hardwoods. The neutral sulfite semichemical pulp is especially useful in the manufacture of high rigidity boards for corrugating medium and other purposes.

Pulps obtained from acid sulfite or bisulfite digestion of northern coniferous woods in yields of 60 to 65% were found suitable for the manufacture of newsprint. The yield of kraft pulp from coniferous woods that is used unbleached in the manufacture of paperboard is being continuously increased. This may also be considered as a type of semichemical pulping.

Because of the very large lignin content, the bleaching of the pulps made from coniferous woods is costly. Therefore, they are mostly used without bleaching or sometimes after partial bleaching. However, because of their relatively lower lignin content, the bleaching of hardwood semichemical pulps has been found feasible under certain circumstances.

VIII. Chemimechanical Pulping

In these processes, the fiberization of wood is accomplished primarily by mechanical means. The mild chemical treatments are employed to improve the physical properties of the pulps over those of purely mechanical pulps. Such treatments may include steaming or mild digestion with water, bisulfite, neutral sulfite, or bicarbonate solutions. These pretreatment methods have been especially useful in better and easier fiberization of dense hardwoods by mechanical processes that are otherwise not suited for grinding.

A. CHEMIGROUNDWOOD

The production of groundwood from relatively high-density hardwoods has not been very successful. However, upon impregnating and digesting the bolts of these woods in neutral sulfite liquor, they can be successfully reduced to pulp by grinding (270). The variables of the so-called "chemigroundwood" process has been thoroughly investigated (177). A wide range of pulp properties can be obtained by changing the severity of the chemical treatment.

B. COLD SODA PULPING

In this class, the "cold soda" process has been the most successful in the production of groundwood type of pulp from hardwoods. The results of extensive studies initiated at the U.S. Forest Products Laboratory indicate that pulps of varying bulk and strength characteristics can be obtained by simply changing the amount of alkali used (41,42). Here, the wood chips are treated with dilute caustic solution, 2 to 6%, at room temperature and the softened chips are reduced to pulp by disk milling. The pulp can be bleached by the methods used for groundwood. The microscopic examination of these fibers also indicates that the middle lamella and primary wall and S_1 layer of the secondary wall are extensively removed from the fiber surfaces during mechanical treatment (194,310), which is prerequisite for the development of mechanical strength of the pulp.

C. SULFITE PRETREATMENT

The use of hot neutral or bisulfite liquor in the treatment of the chips prior to mechanical fiberizing is also an effective method in softening of hardwoods. Similarly, this type of treatment also provides a method for the production of relatively light-colored pulps from softwoods, which can be much stronger than groundwood (51).

D. COARSE FIBER PULPS

For the manufacture of structural boards, hardboards, and insulation board, the wood is mechanically reduced to a fiber pulp after steaming at high temperature and pressure (12,27). Under the conditions used, wood acids are generated, which promote the hydrolysis and dissolution of some of the hemicelluloses. The pulp produced has very little fiber bonding capacity and is relatively dark in color.

IX. Mechanical Pulping

The manufacture of groundwood is one of the oldest of pulping processes. Most coniferous woods and a few low-density hardwoods, such as aspen and cottonwood, are suitable for making good quality groundwood. In this process, the blocks of wood are fiberized by pressing them against the periphery of a rotating abrasive stone. The surface of the stone is continuously sprayed with a jet of water to keep the abrasive surface clean and dissipate the friction heat developed. Apparently, the effective wetting of the fibers in the wood near to the grinding surface is a requirement for proper fiberization. The temperature on the grinding surface is near to the boiling point of water, but the zone next to the surface in the wood may have a temperature as high as 170 to 180°C. (187). It is likely that the presence of adequate moisture in this zone is the key to fiber separation. The lack of adequate water penetration and swelling in hardwoods of relatively high specific gravity near the grinding zone might be the cause of their poor fiberization characteristics.

In mechanical pulping, little or no change in chemical composition of wood occurs when the pulp yield is about 95%. Although a majority of fibers are separated with slight damage, a great number of the fibers are torn across the cell wall and disintegrated into a fine fraction. It is likely that the fiber separation occurs at the edge of compound middle lamella, thereby exposing some secondary wall surface.

X. Bleaching and Purification of Wood Pulp

A. INTRODUCTION

The color of unbleached wood pulps varies with the pulping process and the species used. The brightness of sulfite and groundwood pulps made from many woods is adequate for their use in newsprint and some other grades of paper without further treatment. For some purposes, pulps can be partially bleached or brightened by treatment with reducing and oxidizing agents that destroy only the coloring compounds or groups without removing the residual lignin. The color of mechanical and chemimechanical pulps can be improved only by this method, using peroxides, hydrosulfites, or hypochlorite. Although the chemical and semichemical pulps can also be bleached partially by a single-stage hypochlorite or peroxide treatment, the practice finds only limited use in producing semibleached pulps. On the other hand, the pulps used in permanent white papers and in the production of regenerated cellulose and cellulose derivatives have to be bleached by complete removal of residual lignin and coloring materials. Further pulp purification is primarily used to reduce the hemicellulose content of dissolving pulps, and it is achieved by hot alkali refining incorporated into bleaching operation.

B. MULTISTAGE BLEACHING

Although a patent was granted to Watt and Burgess (311) in 1854 for the bleaching of soda pulp by chlorination and a subsequent hypochlorite treatment, the process was not used because of technical difficulties involved in handling chlorine.

Similarly, Fremy and Terreil (84) and Cross and Bevan (59) demonstrated the suitability of alternate chlorination and alkaline extraction for complete delignification of wood. The method, however, was not suitable for pulp bleaching because of the low brightness and yellow color of the pulp produced. At the turn of this century, the development of modern pulp bleaching technology was started by the incorporation of a hypochlorite stage. The chlorination, alkaline extraction, and hypochlorite bleaching still remain the basic three stages of most common multistage bleaching in the industry. At present, the highest permanent brightness and quality of pulps are produced by the use of additional bleaching stages employing chlorine dioxide and peroxide. These developments have been especially useful in bleaching kraft pulps to a very high brightness without a loss in pulp strength.

Since the chemicals used in bleaching are costly and no chemical recovery can be contemplated, it is desirable that most of the lignin be removed in pulping. In all pulping processes, however, the delignification rates toward the end of digestion generally slow down, and the degradation of carbohydrates is accelerated. Therefore, the optimum in pulp yield and residual lignin in a given process is determined by the pulp quality and the bleaching cost. The lignin content of sulfite pulp from coniferous woods is about 4 to 5% and that of kraft pulp 6 to 8%. The sulfite pulps respond to a three-stage bleaching, but kraft pulps are bleached to a comparable brightness in 5 to 6 stages, generally including two chlorine dioxide stages. In fact, the strength of the kraft pulps can be preserved only by reducing the amount of active chlorine applied in the hypochlorite stage or by completely eliminating this stage from the bleaching sequence.

C. CHEMISTRY OF BLEACHING

An interesting review of the chemistry of bleaching and oxidizing agents was made by Holst (131), which included halogen oxygen compounds, ozone, and peroxide. As a brief review, the color of organic substances is associated with the presence of mobile π electrons in chromophoric systems of conjugated double bonds. In unbleached pulps, these systems may involve the carbonyl, phenyl, p-hydroxyphenyl, quinone, and adjacent carbonyl groups of the degradation products of lignin or carbohydrates adsorbed on the pulp, especially in the kraft process. The color developed by the absorption of light in the visible spectra is due to electron transition from the ground state to an excited state of the molecule. The bleaching process eliminates such mobile electrons as a result of the reaction or rupture of the conjugated double bonds of primarily mesomeric type. The active compounds used in bleaching are either the reducing agents, which produce an active or nascent hydrogen, or oxidants containing highly electronegative elements, such as halogen, halogen oxygen compounds, ozone, and hydrogen peroxide. The bleaching with oxidizing agents is by far technically the most prevalent and, among these, the treatment with aqueous solution of chlorine is basic to postdelignification and remains most important in pulp bleaching.

When chlorine gas is dissolved in water, a reversible hydrolysis occurs according to the following equilibrium:

$$Cl_2 + H_2O \rightleftharpoons H^+ + Cl^- + HOCl \tag{1}$$

and whose constant at 25°C. was found to be (139):

$$K = \frac{(H^+)(Cl^-)(HOCl)}{Cl_2} = 4.84 \times 10^{-4} \tag{2}$$

The degree of hydrolysis increases with increasing temperature. The hypochlorous acid formed is a very weak acid and dissociates

$$HOCl \rightleftharpoons H^+ + OCl^- \tag{3}$$

with an ionization constant of

$$K = \frac{(H^+)(OCl^-)}{HOCl} = 3.7 \times 10^{-8} \tag{4}$$

at 18°C. (62). From the examination of these equilibria, it is evident that the relative concentrations of molecular chlorine, hypochlorous acid, and hypochlorite ion in a solution are affected by the hydrogen ion concentration. By the simultaneous solution of equations 2 and 4, the approximate composition of aqueous solutions of chlorine can be estimated (62,129). The variations in the composition of a $0.1N$ solution of chlorine at varying pH values are shown in Fig. 9. It is

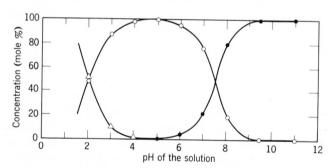

Fig. 9. Composition of aqueous solutions of chlorine at various pH values [Hibbert *et al.* (315)]. Key: △, Cl₂ ; ○, HOCl; and ●, OCl⁻.

apparent that molecular chlorine predominates only below pH 2, hypochlorous acid between pH 2 and 7.5, and hypochlorite ions above pH 7.5. Consequently, the pH of the system determines the type and the rate of the reactions to which the pulp components are subjected during bleaching.

Substitution is the primary reaction of chlorine with lignin in acid solution. Therefore, the treatment of unbleached pulps with acidic solution of chlorine is called chlorination. In alkaline solutions, the chlorine present as hypochlorite acts primarily as an oxidizing agent, which may be accompanied by a slow and limited amount of chlorination.

1. Mechanism of Acidic Chlorination

The so-called chlorination reaction of lignin of unbleached pulps in acidic chlorine solution is, by far, the most important reaction in bleaching that requires the complete delignification. In this reaction, the major portion of residual lignin is degraded and converted into water or alkali-soluble products with little or no detriment to carbohydrates. Chlorination alone cannot impart the desired whiteness to the pulp without bleaching with hypochlorite or chlorine dioxide. After chlorination, however, the response of the pulp to bleaching is improved manyfold because of the modification of the residual lignin.

The mechanism of the chlorination of lignin was extensively studied by Hibbert and his co-workers (315), and a general concept was developed of the reactions involved in bleaching wood pulps. Their concept was proved and further developed by Dence and Sarkanen (63,268) and Strauss and Sarkanen (297). Accordingly, in the treatment of softwood pulps or lignins with acidic chlorine solution, four types of reactions are thought to take place. The first reaction is a rapid substitution of chlorine in the guaiacyl nucleus at the six position, and primarily at the five position, if the phenolic hydroxyl groups are free. The second is a demethylation reaction that is slower and must take place consecutively with substitution. These two reactions are rapid at low pH and the rate increases with increasing amounts of chlorine, but they both slow down when the pH is increased to the alkaline side. Apparently the demethylation reaction is catalyzed by the elemental chlorine in the presence of moisture, which results in the formation of methanol and free phenolic hydroxyls.

The third type of reaction involves the electrophilic displacement of the side chain in the guaiacyl nucleus by chlorine, resulting in the liberation of one mole of hydrochloric acid for each mole of chlorine consumed. The rate of this reaction is favorably affected by the presence of free benzyl alcohol in the side chain and phenolic hydroxyl groups in para position to the side chain. The residual lignin in the pulps from kraft and sulfite processes must contain such nuclei predisposed to this type of scission. In fact, this reaction might be the one that causes the fragmentation and eventual solubilization of lignin in the later stages of pulp bleaching.

The fourth and final reaction in acid chlorination involves the oxidation of catechols, formed as result of demethylation, and their conversion to corresponding orthobenzoquinone. If these compounds survive the alkaline extraction stage, they are further degraded to aliphatic carboxylic acids in the hypochlorite stage. The rate of this oxidative reaction is probably governed by the amount of hypochlorous acid, since it is known that, even at pH 1, up to 20% of the total chlorine is present as hypochlorous acid. The concentration of this acid, however, must be very low after a short period of pulp chlorination, because the concentration of chlorine diminishes rapidly and the hydrolysis of chlorine is suppressed by the formation of hydrochloric acid.

The kinetic studies indicated that, during chlorination stage, two different reactions take place (47,273): one is rapid, which is thought to be a substitution reaction, and the other, a slower reaction, is presumed to be an oxidation reaction. From the rate of hydrochloric acid formation and the change in chlorine concentration, the velocity of these reactions can be estimated. Giertz (87) studied chlorination of sulfite pulp and found that, after about 15 min., the substitution reaction is terminated, while the oxidation reaction continues at a relatively constant rate after a rapid initial rate. After a 45-min. chlorination, the amount of alkali-soluble lignin was unchanged. The solubility of chlorinated lignin is increased by increasing the amount of total chlorine but, beyond certain chlorine dosage, the solubility of lignin remains constant. Therefore, it is not possible to delignify the pulp completely in a single chlorination. After an alkaline extraction, however, the pulp can be further chlorinated, and the chlorinated lignin must be dissolved before it is possible to chlorinate the residual lignin any further. This topochemical effect is explained partly by the assumption that the accessibility of lignin to chlorine is limited as a result of the submicroscopic structure of fiber and of lignin and, partly, by the inability of the chlorine molecule to penetrate through the chlorinated layer of lignin. Since lignin can be chlorinated almost completely in a single step with gaseous chlorine, the cause of limited chlorination in an aqueous system may be due to poor wetting and solvent power of water toward lignin as suggested by Nakano and Schuerch (211).

It is estimated that one third to one half of the chlorine consumed in acidic chlorination of pulp reacts by oxidation (124,166). By maintaining very low pH at the beginning of chlorination, the amount of chlorine used by oxidation can be reduced but with little benefit. The chlorinated, demethylated, and partially depolymerized lignin becomes soluble in dilute alkali and is washed out by digesting with warm sodium hydroxide. This treatment reduces the lignin content of the pulp to a level of 10 to 25% of that of unbleached pulp. Complete removal of this residual lignin, along with the coloring substances, is achieved during the subsequent treatment with oxidants.

2. Oxidative Bleaching Agents

The hypochlorites, chlorine dioxide, and hydrogen peroxide, are the most important oxidants used in pulp bleaching. The reaction of these compounds with wood carbohydrates is as important as that with residual lignin. This is especially true for the hypochlorites and peroxide where they attack polysaccharides under certain conditions, and the mechanism of these reactions is a primary concern in pulp bleaching.

a. Hypochlorite

Although the oxidation potential of hypochlorous acid increases with increasing acidity, the oxidizing power of the aqueous solution of chlorine at low pH values is not very great. This is partly because of the faster rate of the competing chlorination reaction that results in the depletion of chlorine, causing the hydrolysis equilibrium shift to the left in equation 1, thereby the concentration of hypochlorous acid remains very low. After an initial reaction period, the hydrogen and chloride ions formed in the chlorination of lignin further suppress the chlorine hydrolysis. The oxidation mechanism of organic compounds, however, is quite complex, and the type and rate of oxidation depend not only on the oxidation reduction potential, but also on the mutual structure and the types of linkages of the systems involved. For instance, during the chlorination stage, a small amount of chlorine is consumed rapidly for oxidation even before the substitution reaction commences (124). Otherwise, the rate of the subsequent oxidation reaction during pulp chlorination, as already mentioned, is relatively slow and probably dependent largely on the prior substitution and demethylation of lignin.

The bleaching power of aqueous chlorine reaches a maximum at a pH 7.0. However, the attack of aqueous chlorine on carbohydrates also reaches a maximum at about pH 7.0, indicating that the presence of both hypochlorous acid and chloride ion in bleaching liquors is not desirable (53). The oxidation of carbohydrates is generally severe in a pH range of 4 to 8, and hypochlorite bleaching in this range is avoided. The formation of oxycellulose during chlorination, as well as alkaline hypochlorite bleaching, cannot be avoided entirely, as indicated by the rise in copper number and drop in viscosity of the pulp after these stages. The extent of the oxidation of carbohydrates below pH 2 and in the absence of too much excess chorine during pulp chlorination is relatively low because of the short duration of the stage and the low reaction temperature. In hypochlorite bleaching, on the other hand, even above pH 10, the oxidative attack on cellulose is considerable, as indicated by the loss in pulp viscosity and strength. This stage is generally longer and requires somewhat higher temperature, which might account for the damage.

The degradation of polysaccharides by hypochlorite involves primarily the stepwise oxidation of hydroxyl groups in which the primary hydroxyl may be converted first to an aldehyde, and the secondary hydroxyls to keto groups (299). Further oxidation of these carbonyl groups leads to complete fission of the sugar residue and depolymerization of the polysaccharide. Depending on the type of sugar residue and the glycosidic bond involved, the fission products may include glyoxalic, glyceric, oxalic, and erythronic acids, simple sugars, and carbon dioxide (125,299,314). It is well known that the presence of keto sugar residues formed during hypochlorite bleaching contributes to the increased reducing power of the pulp. The pulps containing such oxo-sugar residues are susceptible to alkaline degradation and further oxidation and, if an alkaline extraction or purification stage follows a drastic hypochlorite treatment, the loss in yield and strength can be very appreciable because of further degradation of polysaccharides. It also has been shown that such carbonyl groups introduced into the sugar residues during bleaching with hypochlorite at low pH, 7 to 8, cause severe color reversion in bleached pulps upon aging (90,151,234).

Another form of oxidation of polysaccharides may involve the direct scission of glucosidic linkages in treating pulp with aqueous chlorine at any pH. The studies on the oxidation of methylglycosides of sugars and cellobiose indicated that nonhydrolytic cleavage of glycosidic linkages takes place in chlorine water as well as in hypochlorite. The gluconic acid and other corresponding acids obtained from these glycosides were apparently the major acidic products (68,69,180,299), indicating that the oxidation of the reducing groups of each sugar takes place without any preceding attack on the hydroxyl groups. The highest yield of gluconic acid was obtained under acidic chlorination conditions in which the amount of erythronic and glyoxalic acids was very small. The latter acids are the major components of the degradation product from hypochlorite oxidation, which may indicate that the keto glycosides are intermediates in the formation of these acids.

The rate of oxidation of the polysaccharides during bleaching is undoubtedly governed by the accessibility of these polymers, by the kind and configuration of the monomers, and by the glycosidic bonds involved. It is probable that, because of their less crystalline nature, the hemicelluloses are easily accessible and are attacked more rapidly. However, this does not result in any great loss of these polymers, since they are already subjected to severe treatment during pulping processes and highly degraded. Further degradation of these short chain polymers would not change their quantity, composition, location, or sorption characteristics to any great extent so as to influence the pulp properties. On the other hand, a slight oxidative attack on cellulose weakens the mechanical strength of the fiber and causes a measurable loss in pulp viscosity.

In order to minimize the carbohydrate oxidation during hypochlorite bleaching, the concentration of active chlorine and the temperature must be kept low and the pH high. Under these conditions, the rate of bleaching is also retarded and, therefore, it is necessary to use a very long hypochlorite stage. By injecting hypochlorite and alkali for buffer at several intervals, the alkalinity and strength of the bleach liquor is controlled. It is also common practice to divide the hypochlorite stage and to have an alkaline extraction between the stages to assure maximum permanent brightness with minimum carbohydrate oxidation.

The foregoing observations explain why the single-stage hypochlorite bleaching of chemical pulps has always been detrimental to strength. Since the lignin cannot be completely oxidized in a single-stage hypochlorite treatment, the brightness of the resulting pulps is neither high nor permanent. Even at high pH, the lignin is partially chlorinated with attendant limited amount of demethylation and solubilization (315). Upon aging, this residual chlorinated lignin in the pulp is likely to release some of its bound chlorine as hydrogen chloride, with attendant discoloration due to the change in the lignin structure. Therefore, the chemical pulps of reasonably permanent brightness can be produced by mild hypochlorite bleaching only when it is preceded by an effective chlorination and solubilization of the lignin.

The studies on the hypochlorite oxidation of lignin and lignin model compounds indicated that the aromatic nuclei with free phenolic hydroxyl are attacked rapidly, but the hydrolysis and subsequent destruction of etherified phenolic structure were slow (245). This provides further evidence that the oxidative delignification with hypochlorite is contingent on prior demethylation of lignin by chlorination. Since the limited number of phenolic hydroxyls and keto-enolic groups are probably the primary causes of color in native lignin, their destruction in a single-stage hypochlorite treatment would result in an appreciable improvement in initial brightness, which finds application in bleaching mechanical and chemimechanical pulps.

b. Chlorine Dioxide and Chlorite

Nearly 40 years ago, Schmidt (272) discovered that chlorine dioxide is a highly selective delignification agent for wood, but only during the past decade has it become an important commercial bleaching agent. Because of its relatively high cost, chlorine dioxide is used in small quantities and only in the later stages of pulp bleaching. Under the normal bleaching conditions, chlorine dioxide attacks wood carbohydrates very slowly (261,262). When the pulp has been overbleached with chlorine so as to produce carbonyl groups, however, chlorine dioxide treatment causes large increases in carboxyl content and decreases in the carbonyl content of the pulp with attendant loss in pulp strength. This indicates that carbonyl groups are quite susceptible to attack by chlorine dioxide. The treatment with large excess chlorine dioxide and under drastic conditions, however, can also result in the degradation of wood carbohydrates (287,288).

Somsen (282) studied the kinetics of the reaction of chlorine dioxide with simple organic compounds, each containing functional groupings presumed to be present in oxidized cellulose. The various functional groups to chlorine dioxide attack were ranked in the following order of decreasing stability: primary alcohol > α-glycol > α-hydroxy ketone > α-diketone > aldehyde. The stability of hydroxyl groups toward chlorine dioxide was higher at near neutral pH than at pH 1, while the reverse was true for carbonyl groups. These observations support the view that the degradation of carbohydrates by chlorine dioxide may be slight in case of normally bleached pulps but very appreciable for overbleached pulps. When the hypochlorite stage is eliminated from the bleaching sequence, little danger will exist of overbleaching the pulp.

The reaction of chlorine dioxide with lignin and model compounds has been studied (16,134,154,186), and the result should also apply to the reaction mechanism involved in bleaching pulp with this agent. Chlorine dioxide rapidly attacks the aromatic nuclei with free phenolic hydroxyl group and converts it to quinones and cyclic peroxides. On the other hand, the compounds with methylated phenolic hydroxyl are demethylated and subsequently oxidized, but at a much slower rate.

Levitin, Thompson, and Purves (176) studied the chlorine dioxide oxidation of periodate lignin and found that lignin is slowly demethylated, chlorinated, and depolymerized into soluble products. In successive stages of oxidation, lignin became soluble first in dilute sodium hydroxide, then in water and, finally, in strongly acidic solutions. The same authors also treated the lignin with acidified sodium chlorite solution. They found that the course of oxidation was similar to that found with chlorine dioxide, but it proceeded at a slower rate. In order to determine whether the oxidation by chlorite could be attributed primarily to the chlorine dioxide formed, they bubbled nitrogen through the reaction mixture to continuously purge the system of the chlorine dioxide. Although the reduction of chlorite was at first rapid, it came to a standstill halfway through the reaction, leaving a lignin that was bleached but could not be dissolved. When the flow of nitrogen was discontinued and the chlorine dioxide was allowed to accumulate, the reaction began again and the lignin was dissolved extensively. These observations support the view of Giertz (88) that, in bleaching with sodium chlorite, the chlorine dioxide is the principal active delignification agent.

The sodium chlorite is still more expensive than chlorine dioxide, and its use in pulp bleaching is very limited. Chlorite solutions are stable and do not show any bleaching action under neutral or alkaline conditions. By adding oxidizing or reducing agents, or by acidifying and raising the temperature, the chlorite solution can be activated, which basically involves the chlorine dioxide generation. The preparation of holocellulose (322) from wood with acidified chlorite solution also depends on such activation in which the reaction takes place at a pH about 4 and at 70 to 80°C. and in the presence of reducing groups of wood carbohydrates. Recently, Zienius and Purves (329) have shown that the degradation of pectic acid with chlorite and chlorine dioxide is more severe than that with chlorine under the conditions used in holocellulose preparation. In the oxidation with chlorite, the degradation was more severe at pH 2 than at pH 4, but the degradation caused by chlorine dioxide was almost independent of acidity. At pH 4, the rate of degradation for both oxidants was about the same. The different mechanism of oxidation for chlorite solution is likely to involve chlorous acid, the concentration of which would be expected to increase with decreasing pH because of more complete hydrolysis of chlorite ions. Near neutral pH, only chlorite ions would be present that are apparently ineffective in the oxidative degradation of pectic acid. Another specific reaction of acidic chlorite solution involves the oxidation of reducing sugars to aldonic acids (148). The oxidation of the reducing end groups in a similar reaction by chlorous acid increases the stability of cellulose toward alkaline hydrolysis, which cannot be done with chlorine dioxide (201).

The addition of oxidizing agents, such as chlorine and hypochlorites, activates the chlorite in slightly alkaline solutions, producing good bleaching effect (39). Certain reducing agents, such as aldehydes but not ketones, also activate chlorite in neutral or slightly acidic solutions (316) in which the hypochlorous acid, formed as an intermediate product, reacts with more chlorite, producing chlorine dioxide. From these observations, it may be concluded that, although the oxidizing action of chlorite depends primarily on the generation of chlorine dioxide, there is some specific activity of chlorous acid toward certain reducing groups that might be useful in some cases. In relation to this, it is interesting to note that, in an alkaline solution, the chlorine dioxide is reduced only to chlorite, using one fifth of its potential oxidizing power for bleaching.

$$ClO_2 + e \rightarrow ClO_2^- \tag{5}$$

The chlorite formed can be activated and used in a second stage. In pulp bleaching, chlorine dioxide is used in weakly acidic solutions, preferably at pH 4 to 5 where its entire oxidizing power may be utilized. Equation 6, however, represents only the most important half reaction involving the reduction of chlorine dioxide.

$$ClO_2 + 4H^+ + 5e \rightarrow Cl^- + 2H_2O \qquad (6)$$

In the presence of organic compounds formed by various side reactions, the reaction mechanism may become complicated; for example, in the formation of chloric acid (253).

Starting with an unbuffered system near neutrality, which is commonly practiced, the pH drops to a level of 4 to 5 because of the formation of hydrogen chloride and other acid reaction products. Chlorine dioxide solutions buffered at pH 7 are unstable (282) and, after a rapid initial decomposition, the solution is stabilized. The following mechanisms have been proposed for the decomposition of chlorine dioxide solution (38,298).

$$2ClO_2 + H_2O \rightleftharpoons HClO_2 + HClO_3 \qquad (7)$$
$$6ClO_2 + 3H_2O \rightleftharpoons 5HClO_3 + HCl \qquad (8)$$
$$ClO_2 \rightleftharpoons \tfrac{1}{2}Cl_2 + O_2 \qquad (9)$$

According to Brown (43), equation 8 primarily accounts for the decomposition in solutions, and equation 9 for that in the gas phase, which also concerns the processing technology of chlorine dioxide.

Chlorine dioxide is generated in the bleach plant by the reduction of chloric acid with sulfur dioxide or methanol in a solution of 4 to $5M$ sulfuric acid with hydrochloric acid, or by electrolytic reduction using mostly continuous processes (318). Although there are many possible reactions that may take place in these processes, Rapson (229,230) proposed that the primary reaction common to all of them is the one between chloric acid and hydrochloric acid that results in the formation of chlorine dioxide.

$$HClO_3 + HCl \rightleftharpoons HClO_2 + HClO \qquad (10)$$
$$HClO_2 + HClO_3 \rightleftharpoons 2ClO_2 + H_2O \qquad (11)$$
$$HClO + HCl \rightleftharpoons Cl_2 + H_2O \qquad (12)$$

The chlorine dioxide removed from the reaction zone contains appreciable quantities of chlorine and may be further purified by countercurrent absorption in water, since chlorine dioxide is approximately 10 times as soluble as chlorine. The presence of up to 10% chlorine by weight remaining in chlorine dioxide solution, however, is no detriment in pulp bleaching (231).

c. Peroxide

Although the brightening action of peroxide on wood pulp was known for a long time, it did not become practical until an effective method of stabilization of the alkaline peroxide solution was discovered (126). The peroxide process was developed primarily for bleaching of groundwood, but it also found increasing use in bleaching all kinds of mechanical and chemimechanical pulps since its inception in 1940. The process, however, can be used as the final stage in bleaching of chemical pulps to extremely high brightness. The peroxide does not have any extensive delignification action on pulp, but it is instrumental in the elimination of color that is caused by the presence of compounds of natural origin or those formed during pulping or bleaching.

Hydrogen peroxide is a weak acid with a dissociation constant of 1.78×10^{-12} at 20°C. (275), and the hydroperoxyl ions formed in solution

$$H_2O_2 \rightleftharpoons H^+ + HO_2^- \tag{13}$$

are the bleaching agents. Since peroxide bleaching of pulps is done in an alkaline solution, pH 10 to 11.5, the equilibrium shifts to the right. Although the formation of HO_2^- ions and the rate of bleaching increases with increasing alkalinity, the decomposition of hydrogen peroxide into water and oxygen gas is also accelerated by higher alkali concentration, and its chemistry constitutes an important facet of bleaching technology.

The wasteful decomposition of peroxide is catalyzed by a great number of metallic impurities, which include silver, platinum, copper, manganese, chromium, cobalt, molybdenum, and tungsten (275). The catalysis can be homogeneous as well as heterogeneous and surface catalysis. In the alkaline bleach liquors, these metals are most likely present as the colloidal hydroxides. Biochemical catalysis of the bleach liquor decomposition may also take place by enzyme catalase produced by bacteria (208,240).

The use of peroxide bleaching depends on the prevention of this wasteful decomposition that is accomplished by the inactivation of the catalysts with stabilizers (239). The inactivation of these catalysts may involve adsorption or complexing with appropriate additive used in the bleach liquors, such as sodium silicate or stannate and magnesium sulfate or sodium pyrophosphate. The colloidal silicic or stannic acid or magnesium hydroxide formed inactivates by adsorption. The addition of a molecularly dehydrated alkali metal phosphate, such as sodium tripolyphosphate, is likely to inactivate the catalytic impurities by complexing (280). The use of chelating agents, ethylenediamine tetraacetic acid (EDTA) and others, has been proposed, but apparently the quantities needed have to be in excess of that required by the total hardness present in water (120). Therefore, the use of chelating agents would be practical if they are highly specific for the catalyst ions involved.

The most common stabilizers used in pulp bleaching are sodium silicate and magnesium sulfate. The sodium silicate added to the bleach liquor acts not only as a stabilizer but also as a buffering agent, a corrosion inhibitor and a detergent as well. The presence of magnesium hydroxide in addition to silicate extends the stability of the peroxide solution toward higher alkalinity, from pH 11 to 12. The activity of the catalyst, however, changes with pH, and the mutual deactivation of these colloidal materials by adsorption could also take place. Therefore, the stability and the effectiveness of peroxide bleach liquor often vary with wood, processing water, and the purity of the chemicals used, and they are not always easy to predict.

The reaction of hydrogen peroxide with the coloring compounds is the primary concern in bleaching groundwood. It is known that some of the naturally occurring wood colors, especially in the heartwood of certain deciduous woods, do not respond to peroxide bleaching. The woods presently used in the manufacture of groundwood are light colored and easy to bleach. Besides these extraneous compounds, lignin is also an important source of color, especially in regard to fading and yellowing of mechanical pulps with aging. The unbleached, as well as bleached groundwood, turns yellow upon exposure to sunlight, which appears to result from photochemically induced oxidation of wood components. The accelerated oxidation of carbohydrates also apparently takes place only in the presence of lignin and extraneous wood components, as in groundwood. Here, the role of noncarbohydrate components is somewhat reminiscent of the cellulose degradation caused by the anthraquinone dyes in light tendering or accelerated oxidation in hypochlorite bleaching (274). Lignin is slowly demethylated and degraded during yellowing of groundwood, forming new chromophoric groups and thereby acting as a reservoir of yellow color.

Jones (149) studied the effect of peroxide bleaching on the lignin of spruce groundwood as well as on Brauns' native lignin. He found no change in lignin content after bleaching and, as expected, there was some loss in acetyl content and an increase in organic acidity. Upon methylation of groundwood or native lignin with diazomethane, peroxide consumption was significantly decreased, indicating that the acidic hydroxyls of lignin might primarily be involved in peroxide bleaching. Since the brightness of kraft and sulfite pulps increases after similar methylation (32), it would indicate that the lignin nuclei carrying these groups are responsible for color of unbleached pulps.

In groundwood bleaching, the effect of peroxide on wood polysaccharides is likely to be negligible and of little consequence. On the other hand, the degradation of cellulose, because of peroxide applied in the last stage in the multistage bleaching of chemical pulps, could be measurable if the pulp is oxidized earlier in hypochlorite stage. The pulps treated with peroxide in the final stage possess good brightness stability, which is not due to reduction of the amount of carbonyl groups in the pulp (121). In fact, the number of carbonyl groups increases proportionately to the viscosity drop. However, the newly formed carbonyl groups could be only end-group type, and the carbonyls originally present along the chain rather than at the end of the molecule might have been destroyed, which would result in improved color stability.

3. Reducing Agents

A relatively permanent brightening of groundwood is obtained with zinc or sodium hydrosulfite, the industrial applications of which started in 1932 (128) and preceded the use of peroxide by some years. Hydrosulfite is especially useful when it is used in a second stage following a peroxide pretreatment in a two-stage bleaching of mechanical and chemimechanical pulps (138). The reductive action of hydrosulfite on coloring compounds in wood is likely to involve carbonyl, quinonoid, and other unsaturated systems conjugated with the aromatic ring in a manner similar to one encountered in the reduction of vat dyes to leucoform with this reagent. The hydrosulfites in solution are easily oxidized upon contact with air oxygen and during bleaching, and a closed system has to be used for attaining maximum efficiency. The decomposition of hydrosulfite is apparently catalyzed also by heavy metals, and the addition of sodium tripolyphosphate and ethylenediamine tetraacetic acid (EDTA) to the bleach liquor or to the acid-washing liquors used in pretreating the pulp somewhat suppresses the rate of decomposition (283).

Recent laboratory studies have indicated that sodium borohydride is an effective brightening agent for groundwood (195) and cold soda pulps (189). The use of this chemical in pulp bleaching is not likely to be practical for some time because of its high cost. The reducing mechanism of lignin with borohydride would be expected to be similar to that proposed for hydrosulfite. During bleaching, 75% of the borohydride is lost by hydrolysis that is catalyzed by the heavy metal ions. The treatment of chemical pulps of high brightness with sodium borohydride improves their brightness stability by reducing the carbonyl groups of carbohydrates oxidized in earlier stages of bleaching.

A solution of sulfurous acid, or its sodium salt, is also used to brighten mechanical pulp, but the effect is small and not permanent. The reaction of these agents probably involves the blocking of carbonyl groups in lignin by the formation of hydroxysulfonic acids that are not very stable compounds.

D. PRACTICAL ASPECTS OF BLEACHING

1. General

The bleaching characteristics of wood pulps vary with the wood species and the pulping process used. Generally, the pulps from hardwoods are easier to bleach and require less chemical because these pulps contain much less residual lignin than softwood pulps. Also, the heteropolymeric nature of the hardwood lignin and its less tendency to condense during pulping is expected to contribute to the ease of response of these pulps toward bleaching. On the other hand, the hardwoods generally contain more coloring compounds, especially in their heartwoods, that are responsible for the difficulty in bleaching the mechanical pulps from some species, although they are mostly rendered soluble in chemical pulping processes. The bleaching of hardwood kraft pulps to a very high brightness, however, may sometimes require as many stages as softwood kraft pulps. The sulfite pulps can be bleached much more easily than kraft pulps, partly because of the sulfonic acid groups and partly because of less condensed structure of sulfonated lignin.

In the multistage bleaching of wood pulps, the efficiencies and the effects of chemical treatments in different stages are interdependent. Therefore, it is desirable to discuss the variables of basic bleaching stages collectively. In any given stage, the use of a minimum amount of chemical is essential not only for economical reasons but also for preserving the quality of paper pulps. However, in the production of dissolving pulp, the removal of hemicelluloses and the control of desired viscosity and molecular weight distribution of alpha-cellulose is conveniently attained by adjusting the concentration of excess chemicals in various stages of bleaching.

2. Chlorination

A large portion of postdelignification is achieved by chlorination alone, while 70 to 80% of the remaining lignin in pulp is rendered extractable, and the rest becomes susceptible to complete oxidative degradation in later bleaching stages. The amount of chlorine required in acid chlorination stage is determined primarily by the residual lignin in the pulp and the pulping process involved. The total bleach or chlorine demand estimated from pulp permanganate number is distributed between chlorination and hypochlorite stage or other oxidative bleaching stages, estimated on equivalent chlorine basis. The appropriate amount of chlorine to be applied in chlorination stage is determined experimentally for each pulp. Here, the criterion is to dissolve a maximum amount of lignin in a subsequent extraction stage with the application of least amount chlorine. The amount of extractable lignin increases with increasing amounts of chlorine but, above a certain level of chlorine input, the extractable lignin remains constant, and more chlorine is left unconsumed. Depending on the type of pulp and number of stages in bleaching, the quantity of chlorine varies between 55 to 70% of the total chlorine demand. The pulp is chlorinated using a suspension of about 3.5% at room temperature for 60 min. The rate of chlorination varies with the kind of pulp, the temperature, and the pH. Sulfite pulps are chlorinated much faster than kraft pulps, probably because the sulfonated lignin in the pulp is more swollen and easily accessible and wettable by the acidic solution of chlorine than the lignin in kraft pulp. Although some of the sulfonic acid groups are split as the chlorination of sulfite pulp advances (166), the solubility of the intermediate products would be greatly influenced by the residual sulfonic acid groups. In the chlorination of sulfite pulps, 90% of the applied chlorine is consumed in 10 to 15 min., while kraft pulps require 30 to 40 min. Although the prolonged time of chlorination may not materially affect the quantity of extractable lignin, it improves the response of the pulp to subsequent oxidative bleaching that increases the final pulp brightness.

The rate of chlorination increases with increasing temperature but.

above room temperature, the effect on the amount of extractable lignin is very small while the degradation of carbohydrates becomes very appreciable (79). Therefore, in order to avoid carbohydrate degradation during chlorination above 20 to 25°C., the time of chlorination must be proportionately curtailed (308). The high temperature of chlorination is especially detrimental when the amount of chlorine used is much in excess of that needed for rapid substitution and oxidation. The hydrolysis of chlorine to hypochlorous acid being more rapid at elevated temperature results in the oxidation of carbohydrates. The acid-catalyzed hydrolysis of pulps, particularly from alkaline processes, may also become significant, if the temperature of chlorination is too high. In modern bleach plants, the gaseous chlorine is injected and thoroughly mixed with the pulp suspension in a very short time at the bottom of an upflow chlorination tower. Because of the presence of a hydrostatic head, the solubility and the rate of pulp chlorination are enhanced.

As the acidity of pulp suspension increases, first because of hydrolysis of chlorine and later because of reaction with lignin, the substitution and demethylation reactions are accelerated where the concentration of molecular chlorine is the rate-determining factor. Therefore, lowering the pH of the suspension before addition of chlorine shortens the length of this stage by suppressing the hydrolysis of chlorine. At the end of chlorination, the pulp is washed to eliminate the hydrochloric acid and dissolved acidic lignin degradation products formed. A major part of the sulfite lignin is washed out in this operation, and a somewhat smaller portion of lignin is removed in bleaching kraft pulps. Because of the lack of a reliable method, a true estimate of the residual lignin in the pulps from different bleaching stages cannot be made.

3. Alkaline Extraction

Alkaline extraction following the chlorination stage is primarily used to remove the lignin degradation products whose solubility in dilute alkali is governed largely by the presence of phenolic and possibly by the carboxyl groups. The conditions of alkaline extraction may cover the following ranges: pulp consistency about 12 to 18%, sodium hydroxide 0.5 to 2.5% on pulp, digestion temperature 40 to 70°C., and time 1 to 3 hours. Since sulfite pulp lignin is easily soluble, these pulps require relatively mild conditions in comparison with kraft pulps. The efficiency of extraction increases with increasing temperature and the amount of alkali up to a certain level above which loss of pulp yield and quality becomes appreciable with no further improvement in extraction efficiency. At the start, a major portion of alkali is rapidly used up by the residual hydrochloric acid and other acidic products. In bleaching kraft pulps, the amount of alkali is adjusted to reach a final pH of 10 to 11 and the temperature is maintained at 60 to 70°C. With sulfite pulp, the extraction may be carried out slightly above neutral pH and at 40 to 60°C.

No other bases but sodium hydroxide have found wide commercial use in pulp extraction. Calcium hydroxide is not effective, since even the dissolved chlorolignin forms a precipitate with lime, especially at near or above neutral pH, resulting in increased chlorine demand in hypochlorite stage (10,166,224). Sodium sulfite has been found an effective extractant when applied to chlorinated sulfite (251) and neutral sulfite semichemical pulps (305). The temperature coefficient of extraction with sodium sulfite is higher than sodium hydroxide, which suggests that, in addition to the hydrolysis of this salt at elevated temperatures, some chemical reaction may occur, possibly involving the formation of hydroxy sulfonic acid with carbonyl groups.

4. Hypochlorite Stage

The hypochlorite stage constitutes the most common and, in a sense, a truly bleaching treatment in which the pulp is rendered bright. The alkaline solution of chlorine accomplishes this by destroying the degradation products of lignin and other coloring compounds and, then, converting them primarily to carbon dioxide and soluble organic acid. Of relatively low cost, calcium hypochlorite is most commonly prepared by dissolving chlorine gas in milk of lime. An excess of lime is left in the bleach liquor to act as buffer, keeping the pH of the pulp slurry at the desired level of alkalinity for the duration of the bleaching stage. The amount of active chlorine, in every case, is experimentally determined and, depending on the pulp and the brightness desired, it may vary between 1 to 1.5%. A pulp consistency of 10 to 15% and a temperature of 30 to 40°C. are commonly employed when the length of the stage is about 3 to 4 hours. The pH during hypochlorite bleaching must be kept above 9 to limit the attack on carbohydrates. With increasing temperature and chlorine and decreasing pH, the attack on carbohydrates increases, resulting in a loss of pulp strength and low brightness stability. An excess of hypochlorite residual and a relatively high temperature, however, are essential to complete the bleaching in a reasonable time. Therefore, the third variable, namely the alkalinity of bleach liquor, is the most important factor. When the pH is increased from 7 to 11, the final brightness, alpha-cellulose, and carboxyl content increase while copper number and yellowing of pulp decrease (170). At the end of the hypochlorite stage, the pulp is acidified with sulfur dioxide and further washed for improved brightness stability.

The yield of carbohydrates in bleaching of fully cooked paper pulps is nearly quantitative, and the loss of polysaccharides in different bleaching stages is nil, although they might be degraded and somewhat modified, depending on the severity of bleaching conditions. On the other hand, only partly cooked high-yield or semichemical pulps are subject to measurable losses in their hemicellulose content during bleaching. This especially concerns the neutral sulfite semichemical pulps from hardwoods, which contain highest quantities of hemicellulose, and the changes in carbohydrate composition of these pulps during bleaching have been subjects of several investigations (25,26,141). During a regular three-stage bleaching of these pulps, the loss of carbohydrates is apparently small; probably not more than 1 to 2%, and it is primarily confined to noncellulosic polysaccharides. The loss, however, is expected to vary, depending on the unbleached pulp yield and the degree of delignification attained during pulping. This would be particularly apparent when one considers the large polysaccharide losses unavoidable during the preparation of lignin-free holocellulose from wood, even when the most selective delignifying agents are used (44).

5. Other Bleaching Stages

The easy bleaching pulps, such as sulfite pulps in general and neutral sulfite and alkaline pulps from hardwoods, can be bleached satisfactorily in three stages, as outlined above. However, for bleaching these pulps to a very high brightness and particularly for bleaching alkaline pulps from softwoods, the number of stages has to be increased and chlorine dioxide or hydrogen peroxide has to be used, especially in later stages. The relatively high brightness can also be obtained without the use of the last two agents by applying larger quantities of chlorine. In this case, either chlorination or hypochlorite stage or both are divided into two parts, with an alkaline extraction between these stages in order to reduce the maximum concentration of chlorine that would come in contact with the pulp. Still better results, however, are obtained by using one or two chlorine dioxide stages in bleaching sequences containing five or more stages. The following combinations of stages are examples of common bleaching sequences:

1. Cl_2, NaOH, hypochlorite, ClO_2, NaOH, ClO_2
2. Cl_2, NaOH, hypochlorite, ClO_2, H_2O_2
3. Cl_2, NaOH, ClO_2, NaOH, ClO_2
4. Cl_2, NaOH, ClO_2, NaOH/Cl_2, ClO_2

Since chlorine dioxide and hydrogen peroxide do not attack the carbohydrates, the pulp strength improves with the use of these chemicals and the reduction of the total chlorine applied in earlier stages. The elimination of the hypochlorite stage or application of very small quantities of chlorine in extraction stage, as shown in sequence 4, would be beneficial from the point of view of pulp strength. The use of peroxide in the final stage produces more permanent brightness (121). In the chlorine dioxide bleaching, 0.3 to 0.8% chlorine dioxide is applied, using a pulp consistency of 12 to 15%, pH of 4 to 5, temperature of 55 to 75°C., and a reaction time of 2 to 4 hours. The conditions used in peroxide bleaching are generally the following: 0.3 to 0.5% hydrogen peroxide; 3 to 5% sodium silicate; 0.05% magnesium sulfate on pulp; pH of 10 to 11; consistency of 12 to 15%; temperature of 70 to 80°C.; and time of 2 to 3 hours.

In producing extremely high brightness, the loss in pulp strength may be kept to a minimum by adding a small amount of chlorine dioxide in the chlorination stage (232). No mechanism has been suggested for this synergistic effect that apparently reduces the oxidative degradation of carbohydrates in this stage, thereby permitting the application of increased quantities of chlorine and a longer time of treatment.

E. BRIGHTNESS REVERSION

The brightness of the bleached pulps is not permanent and, depending on the wood species and the processing methods used, more or less yellowing occurs upon aging. It has been known that pulps bleached to high brightness by using several hypochlorite stages are less stable than those bleached with chlorine dioxide or peroxide. In order to test the stability of pulp brightness, the bleached pulps are subjected to an accelerated aging test by heating in the air at 110 to 120°C., and for a given length of time.

Rollinson (249) showed that colored material extracted with water from bleached kraft pulps subjected to accelerated aging is not lignin but possibly hemicellulosic in origin. Giertz and McPherson (90) were able to extract most of the coloring compounds from aged sulfite pulp with lithium hydroxide that was largely concentrated in the gamma-cellulose fraction. The amount of yellowing reaches a maximum when the hypochlorite bleaching is performed near neutral pH and a large excess of chlorine is used. Apparently, the pulps containing large quantities of hemicellulose are more susceptible to color reversion because of the high accessibility of these polysaccharides to the oxidant. The colored material extracted from the aged pulp is characterized by a high carbonyl content and is strongly acidic. However, because of their instability, especially in alkaline solutions, the isolated compounds are not likely to be the same as those existing in the pulp. Since the dialdehydes, such as glyoxal, upon heating in acidic solutions, produce colored condensation products, it is not difficult to envision a similar mechanism in the formation of coloring compounds from the fission products of oxidized carbohydrates. It has been shown that color reversion can be minimized through the elimination of carbonyl groups by reduction with sodium borohydride and, to a much lesser extent, by oxidation with chlorous acid to carboxyl groups (151,152,234). The carbonyl groups responsible for brightness reversion can be associated with hemicellulose as well as cellulose. Carboxyl groups, as such, are not involved in color reversion as the brightness stability of the borohydride reduced oxycellulose indicates, nor is the shortening of the cellulose molecules accompanying the oxidation with hypochlorite (233).

When wood pulp is bleached with hypochlorite, the pH should be kept as high as possible and the quantity of active chlorine low to minimize the color reversion, hot-alkali solubility, and loss of strength of the pulp. Although the first two detrimental effects can be largely corrected by the borohydride treatment, this is by no means an economically feasible method at the present.

F. PURIFICATION OF DISSOLVING PULP

In the manufacture of dissolving pulp, the cooking conditions are so adjusted as to effectively remove not only lignin but also the wood hemicelluloses. This is generally achieved by using low combined sulfur dioxide and prolonged cooking in sulfite process and by the prehydrolysis stage in the kraft process. The resulting pulps, however, contain not too much more than 90% alpha-cellulose, which varies with the wood species and the severity of the cooking conditions used.

In order to increase the alpha-cellulose content to above 95%, these pulps are subjected to hot-alkali refining, generally following the chlorination stage during bleaching. Unfortunately, neither the drastic conditions used in pulping nor the extraction with hot-dilute sodium hydroxide is entirely specific for hemicellulose, and an appreciable amount of alpha-cellulose originally present in the wood is also degraded and lost. The hot-alkali purification sometimes follows a chlorination preceded by an oxidative prebleaching step in order to increase the efficiency of extraction, especially in regard to wood resins. The production and purification of high alpha-cellulose wood pulps and the variables involved are discussed in an excellent paper by Richter (243).

The concentration of sodium hydroxide used in pulp purification is about 1 to 2%, which is around 10 times that used in the extraction of paper pulps.

The temperature used in purification is also much higher, varying from 90 to 170°C. In bleaching of paper pulps, most of the alkali used in the extraction stage is consumed for the neutralization of the acids originating from lignin but, in hot-alkali refining of dissolving pulp, it is primarily used for the degradation of carbohydrates. The relatively high rate of alkali degradation of hemicellulose components of the pulp in comparison with that of alpha-cellulose fraction is the primary factor in determining the usefulness of this purification method.

Apparently, the hemicelluloses are degraded and dissolved much faster because of their low molecular weight and higher accessibility, the nature and susceptibility of glucosidic bonds involved and, finally, because of their molecular structure involving branching and carboxyl groups. The cellulose will, however, also undergo some degradation to give either soluble products or products insoluble in the hot diluted alkali, but soluble in cold, strong alkali used in the alpha-cellulose determination. The mechanism of hot-alkali degradation of carbohydrates involves either the reducing end groups or the hydrolytic chain scission, which is thoroughly reviewed by Meller (202).

The reduction with sodium borohydride or oxidation with chlorous acid stabilizes the reducing end groups of polysaccharides toward hot alkali. Such treatments apparently improve the relative stability of cellulosic fraction more than that of the hemicellulosic components resulting in increased alpha-cellulose yield (13).

It has long been known that the purification with a strong solution of sodium hydroxide, 10 to 15%, at room temperature results in better yield of pulp with much higher alpha-cellulose content. By such treatment, the alpha-cellulose content of a dissolving pulp already purified with hot-dilute alkali can be increased from about 95% to more than 99% (313). However, because of the high cost of complex chemical recovery involved, the method has found only limited application in the production of highest grade of dissolving pulps. In this connection, the type and degree of association of hemicelluloses with cellulose in wood pulps have provided a great deal of theoretical interest, and numerous attempts were made to prepare pure wood cellulose free of xylan and mannan. Several methods employing multiple extraction techniques have been successfully used to prepare pulps containing up to 99.9% glucan (235).

Purification of dissolving pulp is also concerned with the removal of wood resins, especially those composed of fatty acids and their esters that survive the sulfite pulping. Since the fats and fatty acids are the main constituents of the extractives in hardwoods, the resins of sulfite pulps from these species are particularly troublesome. The presence of wood resin, especially the ether soluble fraction in the pulps, causes "pitch" problem in the pulp and paper mills, but its presence in dissolving pulps is very detrimental to several operations in the viscose rayon process, causing filtration trouble, clogging of spinnerets, and other difficulties.

The large part of the resin is associated with ray parenchyma in the wood, and the elimination of all parenchyma cells from the pulp by "deflouring" effectively reduces the resin content. This, however, also entails an appreciable loss in pulp yield that is not always tolerable.

The deresination of dissolving pulps by chemical means has been subject of several investigations (210,228,241). The use of nonionic surfactants in conjunction with hot-alkali refining has been found very effective in extracting these resins and, among these compounds, the condensation products of alkyl phenols with ethylene oxide have been used with a great deal of success (236,260).

The elimination of resins from hardwood sulfite pulps by hot-alkali extraction after chlorination is relatively ineffective. This is largely the result of the more neutral nature of the residual resins found in these pulps, which are essentially composed of fats and unsaponifiables. It has been shown by Leopold and Mutton (175) that the chlorination of the unsaturated bonds of these fats renders them more hydrophobic and resistant to saponification with dilute alkali. On the other hand, the use of chlorine dioxide and, to a lesser extent, hypochlorite or peroxide treatment instead of chlorine in the first stage causes the oxidation and cleavage of double bonds in fats, increasing their susceptibility toward saponification and emulsification in hot dilute alkali. Apparently, such an oxidative bleaching stage preceding the chlorination would be most advantageous from the point of view of deresination as well as delignification.

XI. Composition and Physical Properties of Pulps

The chemical and physical properties of wood pulps vary with the wood species and the pulping process used. In the manufacture of dissolving pulps, the purity and a relatively definite distribution of the molecular weights in the cellulose are the chief requirements, but also present are more subtle and probably less understood properties that influence the dissolving, acetylation, spinning, and other processing characteristics of these pulps. In the case of paper pulps, the physical properties are of prime importance where the strength and bonding characteristics of individual fibers in a complex fashion determine the quality of paper. Therefore, the rheological properties of pulp fibers, as related to mechanical properties, such as strength, toughness, stiffness, elasticity, and resilience, give good indication of their end use. These properties are largely dependent on the morphology, the microscopic or submicroscopic structure and composition of the fibers, and the structure and distribution of chemical constituents in the cell wall. The bonding characteristics of fibers are also influenced to some extent by the physical properties as well as by the physicochemical properties, the specific surface area and, possibly, by the texture of the fiber surfaces.

The morphology of pulp fibers is primarily dependent on the wood species used, and large variations exist between different woods. The fibers from coniferous woods are essentially uniform and comprised chiefly of tracheids, more than 95% by weight. On the other hand, the pulps from hardwoods contain highly heterogeneous elements that include parechyma and ray cells, vessel elements, and fibers. In comparison with the tracheids of coniferous woods, the hardwood fibers are much shorter and smaller in diameters. A large variation between the species of these two classes of woods also exists. An extreme example of this is the contrast between the thick-walled larger diameter fibers of southern pine and the thin-walled slender fibers of spruce and hemlock. Since the pulps from spruce and hemlock contain a larger number of fibers in a given weight and larger surface area for bonding, they produce stronger papers. The pulp from southern pine, on the other hand, does not develop as much interfiber bonding but, because of the higher strength of individual fibers, imparts better tearing resistance to the paper.

Pulp properties are of course greatly influenced by the degree of delignification. The fibers become more stiff and have low bonding capacity as the lignin content of the pulps increases. The chemical composition and structure of the carbohydrate components as well as the physical structure of cell wall and of the cellulose itself vary with the pulping processes.

In papermaking, the capacity of interfiber bonding of pulps is increased by beating, refining, or so-called hydration. In beating extensively delignified pulps, first the loosely held primary wall is completely disintegrated and fibrillated. When the mechanical treatment is continued, the S_1 layer of the secondary wall is peeled off and fibrillated. The maximum pulp strength is reached before any extensive fibrillation of S_2 layer occurs. Moreover, for the retention of adequate fiber strength, this layer should remain relatively intact, possibly with the elimination or distribution of internal stresses and with some internal swelling. Initial and maximum specific surface area or bonding capacity, mechanical properties, and hydration characteristics of the pulps vary with the pulping processes. The complex interrelation of these properties with the chemical composition of the pulps remains a largely unsolved problem.

Although the major aspects of the structure of various hemicelluloses in wood and their behavior during different pulping processes have been studied, more subtle differences between the chemical constituents of these pulps are yet to be elucidated. Hamilton and Thompson (116) compared the carbohydrate constituents of kraft, sulfite, and neutral sulfite semichemical pulps from several wood species. These results are summarized in Fig. 10. In this respect, the differences between kraft and sulfite pulps have been of great interest. The kraft pulps generally produce stronger paper, but they are difficult to hydrate. Many suggestions have been made to explain the differences between these pulps on the basis of chemical and morpho-

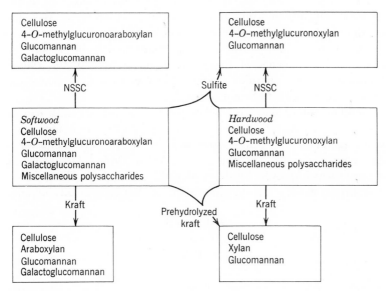

Fig. 10. The behavior of major polysaccharides of wood during pulping [Hamilton and Thompson (116)]. (Xylan of kraft pulps also contain glucuronic acid residues.)

logical factors (89,116,143,321). Not only the type, quantity, and structure of the hemicelluloses, but also their location, crystallinity, and interaction with cellulose in the fiber wall would influence the rheological properties of the pulps. Jayme and v. Koppen (145) and Kallmes (155) obtained information on the topochemistry of pulp fibers that is especially valuable in estimating the chemical composition of fiber surfaces. This kind of information may lead to a better understanding of the mechanism of the fiber bonding.

The localized attack of acid across the cell wall has long been suspected as the cause of the low strength of sulfite pulp fibers, and this is still the most plausible explanation of the weakness of these pulps. More recent evidence, however, suggests that the changes taking place in the submicroscopic structure of cellulose in different pulping processes may also influence the properties of pulp fibers. In comparison with sulfite pulps, the cellulose of kraft pulps shows higher lateral order and crystallite width (213), and the diameter of the fibril bundles is larger (144,153). These observations are consistent with the behavior of kraft pulps. For example, the resistance to hydration and swelling probably indicates strong interfibrillar bonding in the fiber wall which, also, would result in higher fiber strength. Although the differences in the physical structures can be attributed mostly to the acidity or alkalinity of the cooking liquors used in the preparation of pulps, the influence of the hemicellulose, especially the xylose-containing polysaccharides, on the physicochemical properties of these pulps remains to be elucidated.

Modified sulfite pulps of higher yield or higher strength can be obtained by changing the acidity of the cooking liquors in multistage processes (266). The composition and physical properties of a series of such pulps from jack pine are shown in Table VII. The pulp strength was improved by decreasing the acidity of cooking liquor. The strongest pulp was obtained with the use of a weakly alkaline

TABLE VII

The Effect of Pulping Conditions on the Composition
and Properties of Jack Pine Pulps (266)

	Kraft	Bi-sulfite	Two-stage sulfite		
Final cooking pH					
1st stage	11–12	2.9	3.0	5.6	3.0
2nd stage	—	—	1.8	1.9	8.4
Permanganate number	17.4	20.3	18.0	20.2	22.2
Bleached pulp yield (%)	41.9	45.7	46.4	50.2	43.6
Carbohydrate composition (%)					
Glucose, galactose	82.4	84.3	81.2	79.5	87.0
Mannose, arabinose	7.0	7.1	8.4	12.7	5.9
Xylose	9.2	7.0	8.7	6.1	5.6
Uronic anhydride	1.4	1.6	1.7	1.7	1.5
Pulp strength (at 500 ml. freeness)					
Tear factor	134	86	104	65	121
Burst factor	95	66	70	58	81
Breaking length (meters)	12,200	10,400	10,500	10,000	10,600
MIT fold	1,450	720	1,050	500	1,350

sulfite in the second stage. This pulp contained the least amount of hemicellulose and was lowest in yield. The highest yield of pulp was obtained when the pH of the first stage was nearly neutral, but this pulp contained the highest amount of glucomannan and was the weakest. Apparently, besides the effect of acidity of the cooking liquor, the hemicellulose retention also influences the pulp strength. The high hemicellulose content of the high-yield pulp would contribute little to the fiber strength and detract from over-all pulp strength, since the number of fibers in a given weight would diminish. On the other hand, the lowest yield pulp contains the largest number of fibers and, probably, the strongest ones also, where the weakly alkaline cooking liquor may have produced a physical change similar to that of kraft pulping.

REFERENCES

1. Adler, E., *Svensk Papperstidn.*, **49**, 339 (1946).
2. Adler, E., *Svensk Papperstidn.*, **50**, 11B, 9 (1947).
3. Adler, E., *Svensk Papperstidn.*, **50**, 261 (1947).
4. Adler, E., *Ind. Eng. Chem.*, **49**, 1377 (1957).
5. Adler, E., and B. Lindgren, *Svensk Papperstidn.*, **55**, 563 (1952).
6. Ahlm, C. E., *Paper Trade J.*, **113**, No. 13, 115 (1941).
7. Annergren, G. E., and S. A. Rydholm, *Svensk Papperstidn.*, **62**, 737 (1959).
8. Annergren, G. E., and S. A. Rydholm, *Svensk Papperstidn.*, **63**, 591 (1960).
8a. Annergren, G. E., I. Croon, B. F. Enström, and S. A. Rydholm, *Svensk Papperstidn.*, **64**, 386 (1961).
8b. Annergren, G. E., and I. Croon, *Svensk Papperstidn.*, **64**, 618 (1961).
9. Arlt, H. G., and C. Schuerch, *Tappi*, **41**, 64 (1958).
10. Arnold, G. C., F. A. Simmonds, and C. E. Curran, *Paper Trade J.*, **107**, No. 10, 32 (1938).
11. Aronovsky, S. I., and R. A. Gortner, *Ind. Eng. Chem.*, **28**, 1270 (1936).
12. Asplund, A. T. A., U.S. Pat. 2,008,892 (1935).
13. Assarsson, A., L. Stockman, and O. Theander, *Svensk Papperstidn.*, **62**, 865 (1959).
14. Aulin-Erdtman, G., *Svensk Papperstidn.*, **59**, 363 (1956).
15. Bailey, A. J., *Ind. Eng. Chem. Anal. Ed.*, **8**, 52 (1936).
16. Barton, J. S., *Tappi*, **33**, 496 (1950).
17. Baush, H., and N. Hartler, *Svensk Papperstidn.*, **63**, 279 (1960).
18. Beazley, W. B., W. B. Campbell, and O. Maass, "The Physical Properties of Sulfite Liquors," *Dominion Forest Service Bull.*, 93 (1938).
19. Berthier, R., *Assoc. tech. ind. papetière, Bull.*, **4**, 93 (1953).
20. Bhattacharia, A. K., E. Sondheimer, and C. Schuerch, *Tappi*, **42**, 448 (1959).
21. Binger, G. E., and A. G. Norman, *Tappi*, **40**, 755 (1957).
22. Bixler, A. L., *Paper Trade J.*, **107**, No. 15, 29 (1938).

23. Bjorkman, A., *Svensk Papperstidn.*, **59**, 477 (1956); **60**, 243, 329 (1957).

24. Bjorkman, A., and B. Persson, *Svensk Papperstidn.*, **60**, 158, 285 (1957).

25. Bjorkvist, K. J., S. Gustafsson, and L. Jörgensen, *Svensk Papperstidn.*, **56**, 734 (1953).

26. Boehm, R., *Tappi*, **39**, 12 (1956).

27. Boehm, R. M., *Ind. Eng. Chem.*, **22**, 4 (1930).

28. Booker, E., and C. Schuerch, *Tappi*, **41**, 650 (1958).

29. Borlew, P. B., and T. A. Pascoe, *Paper Trade J.*, **122**, No. 10, 31; **123**, No. 15, 178 (1946).

30. Boyer, R. Q., U.S. Pat. 2,862,887 (1958).

31. Bradley, L., and E. P. McKeefe, Can. Pat. 219,557 (1922).

32. Brauns, F. E., *Paper Trade J.*, **103**, No. 5, 36 (1936).

33. Brauns, F. E., and W. S. Grimes, *Paper Trade J.*, **108**, 11, 40 (1939).

34. Bray, M. W., and J. S. Martin, *Paper Trade J.*, **113**, 35 (1941).

35. Bray, M. W., J. S. Martin, and L. A. Carpenter, *Paper Trade J.*, **93**, No. 12, 23 (1931).

36. Bray, M. W., J. S. Martin, and S. L. Schwartz, *Paper Trade J.*, **105**, No. 24, 39 (1937).

37. Bray, M. W., J. S. Martin, and S. L. Schwartz, *Paper Trade J.*, **109**, No. 17, 40 (1939).

38. Bray, W. Z., *Z. anorg. u. allgem. Chem.*, **48**, 217 (1906).

39. Brennan, J. F., J. D. McMahon, and G. P. Vincent, *Paper Trade J.*, **115**, No. 21, 25 (1942).

40. Brink, D. L., R. L. Hossfeld, and W. M. Sandstrom, *J. Am. Chem. Soc.*, **71**, 2275 (1949).

41. Brown, K. J., and J. N. McGovern, *Tappi*, **33**, 364 (1950).

42. Brown, K. J., and J. N. McGovern, *Paper Ind.*, **35**, No. 1, 66 (1953).

43. Brown, R. W., *Tappi*, **35**, 75 (1952).

44. Browning, B. L., and L. O. Bublitz, *Tappi*, **36**, 452 (1953).

45. Browning, B. L., and J. B. Calkin, *Paper Trade J.*, **123**, No. 26, 45 (1946).

46. Calhoun, J. M., F. H. Yorston, and O. Maass, *Can. J. Research*, **B15**, 457 (1957).

47. Carmody, W. R., and J. S. Mears, *Paper Trade J.*, **106**, No. 20, 38 (1938).

48. Casey, J. P., *Pulp and Paper*, Vol. I, Interscience, New York, 1960.

49. Cederquist, K., N. K. G. Ahlborg, B. Lunden, and T. O. Wentworth, *Tappi*, **43**, 702 (1960).

50. Chidester, G. H., *Paper Trade J.*, **129**, No. 21, 84 (1949).

51. Chidester, G. H., J. F. Laundrie, and E. L. Keller, *Tappi*, **43**, 876 (1960).

52. Chidester, G. H., and J. N. McGovern, *Paper Trade J.*, **108**, No. 6, 31 (1939).

53. Clibbens, D. A., and B. P. Ridge, *J. Textile Inst.*, **18**, 135T (1927).

54. Copenhaver, D. E., W. A. Biggs, Jr., W. H. Baxley, and J. T. Wise, U.S. Pat. 2,714,118 (1955).

55. Corbett, W. M., J. Kenner, and G. N. Richards, *J. Chem. Soc.*, **1953**, 57.

56. Corbett, W. M., and G. N. Richards, *Svensk Papperstidn.*, **60**, 791 (1957).

57. Corbett, W. M., G. N. Richards, and R. L. Whistler, *J. Chem. Soc.*, **11** (1957).

58. Croon, I., B. Lindberg, and H. Meier, *Acta Chem. Scand.*, **13**, 1299 (1959).

58a. Croon, I., and B. F. Enström, *Tappi*, **44**, 870 (1961).

58b. Croon, I., and B. F. Enström, *Svensk Papperstidn.*, **65**, 595 (1962).
59. Cross, F. C., and E. J. Bevan, *J. Chem. Soc.*, **38**, 666 (1880).
60. Dahl, C. F., U.S. Pat. 296,935 (1884).
61. Daniels, H. S., and J. L. McCarthy, *Tech. Assoc. Papers*, **31**, 626 (1948).
62. Davidson, G. F., *Shirley Inst. Mem.*, **12**, 1 (1933).
63. Dence, C., and K. Sarkanen, *Tappi*, **43**, 87 (1960).
64. Desorbey, G. M. H., U.S. Pat. 2,571,993 (1951).
65. Dorland, R. M., R. A. Leask, and J. W. McKinney, *Pulp Paper Mag. Can.*, **59**, No. C., 236 (1958).
66. Dorr, R. E., *Papierfabr.*, **37**, 1 (1939).
67. Dryselius, E., B. Lindberg, and O. Theander, *Acta Chem. Scand.*, **12**, 340 (1958).
68. Dyfverman, A., *Acta Chem. Scand.*, **7**, 280 (1953).
69. Dyfverman, A., B. Lindberg, and D. Wood, *Acta Chem. Scand.*, **5**, 253 (1951).
70. Eaton, A. K., U.S. Pats. 106,143 (1870), 119,224 (1871).
71. Enkvist, T., *Svensk Papperstidn.*, **51**, 225 (1948).
72. Enkvist, T., and B. Alfredsson, *Svensk Papperstidn.*, **54**, 185 (1951).
73. Enkvist, T., *Tappi*, **37**, 350 (1954).
74. Enkvist, T., *Svensk Papperstidn.*, **60**, 616 (1957).
75. Erdtman, H., *Svensk Papperstidn.*, **43**, 255 (1940).
76. Erdtman, H., *Svensk Papperstidn.*, **45**, 374 (1942).
77. Erdtman, H., *Svensk Kem. Tidskr.*, **56**, 6, 26, 95 (1944).
78. Erdtman, H., *Svensk Papperstidn.*, **48**, 75 (1945).
79. Eriksson, I., and L. Stockman, *Svensk Papperstidn.*, **59**, 663 (1956).
80. Feldtman, G. A., *Zellstoff u. Papier*, **18**, 55 (1938); through *Chem. Abstracts*, **32**, 2737 (1938).
81. Felicetta, V. F., and J. L. McCarthy, *J. Am. Chem. Soc.*, **78**, 4499 (1957).
82. Field, L., P. E. Drummond, and E. A. Jones, *Tappi*, **41**, 727 (1958).
83. Fischer, J. H., W. C. Hawkins, and H. Hibbert, *J. Am. Chem. Soc.*, **62**, 1412 (1940).
84. Fremy, E., and A. Terreil, *Bull. Soc. Chem.*, **9**, 439 (1868).
85. Freudenburg, K., *Angew. Chem.*, **68**, 84, (1956).
86. Gierer, J., and B. Alfredson, *Svensk Papperstidn.*, **62**, 434 (1959).
87. Giertz, H. W., *Svensk Papperstidn.*, **46**, 152 (1943).
88. Giertz, H. W., *Tappi*, **34**, 209 (1951).
89. Giertz, H. W., *Svensk Papperstidn.*, **56**, 893 (1953).
90. Giertz, H. W., and J. McPherson, *Svensk Papperstidn.*, **59**, 93 (1956).
91. Gishler, P. E., and O. Maass, *Can. J. Research*, **B13**, 308 (1935).
92. Graham, J. A., Brit. Pat. 5365 (1882).
93. Green, H. V., and F. H. Yorston, *Pulp Paper Mag. Can.*, **40**, 244 (1939); **41**, 123 (1940).
93a. Green, H. V., *Pulp Paper Mag. Can.*, **63**, T-155 (1962).
94. Grondal, B. L., and P. Zenczak, U.S. Pat. 2,772,968 (1956).
95. Gross, S. K., and C. Schuerch, *Anal. Chem.*, **30**, 518 (1958).
96. Hägglund, E., *Chemistry of Wood*, pp. 215–218, Academic Press, New York, 1951.
97. Hägglund, E., *Svensk. Kem. Tidskr.*, **37**, 120 (1925).

98. Hägglund, E., *Svensk. Kem. Tidskr.*, **38**, 177 (1926).

99. Hägglund, E., *Svensk Papperstidn.*, **44**, 183 (1941).

100. Hägglund, E., *Svensk Papperstidn.*, **47**, 230 (1944).

101. Hägglund, E., and F. Bergius, German Pat. 311,933 (1917).

102. Hägglund, E., and T. V. E. Enkvist, U.S. reissue Pat. 24293 (1957).

103. Hägglund, E., and R. Hedlund, *Papierfabr.*, **30**, 49, 61 (1932).

104. Hägglund, E., H. Heiwinkee, and T. Bergek, *Cellulosechemie*, **21**, 108 (1943).

105. Hägglund, E., and A. Johansson, *Svensk Papperstidn.*, **35**, 475 (1932).

106. Hägglund, E., and T. Johnson, *Svensk Papperstidn.*, **49**, 204 (1946).

107. Hägglund, E., T. Johnson, and H. Busch, *Finnish Paper and Timber J.*, **16**, 282 (1934).

108. Hägglund, E., T. Johnson, and H. Urban, *Eer.*, **63**, 1387 (1930).

109. Hägglund, E., B. Lindberg, and J. McPherson, *Acta Chem. Scand.*, **10**, 1160 (1956).

110. Hägglund, E., and A. Waller, *Finnish Paper and Timber J.*, **16**, 383 (1934).

111. Häggroth, S., and B. Lindberg, *Svensk Papperstidn.*, **59**, 870 (1956).

112. Häggroth, S., B. Lindberg, and U. Saeden, *Svensk Papperstidn.*, **56**, 660 (1953).

113. Haglund, G., Swedish Pats. 77429 and 79840 (1931).

114. Hamilton, J. K., E. V. Partlow, and N. S. Thompson, *Tappi*, **41**, 803, 811 (1958).

115. Hamilton, J. K., and N. S. Thompson, *Tappi*, **42**, 752 (1959).

116. Hamilton, J. K., and N. S. Thompson, *Pulp Paper Mag. Can.*, **61**, No. 4, T-263 (1960).

117. Hart, J. S., R. K. Strapp, and J. H. Ross, *Pulp Paper Mag. Can.*, **55**, No. 9, 113 (1954).

118. Hart, J. S., and J. M. Wood, *Pulp Paper Mag. Can.*, **56**, No. 9, 95 (1955).

119. Hartler, N., *Svensk Papperstidn.*, **62**, 467 (1959).

120. Hartler, N., E. Lindahl, and C. G. Moberg, *Svensk Papperstidn.*, **62**, 269 (1959).

121. Hartler, N., E. Lindahl, C. G. Moberg, and L. Stockman, *Tappi*, **43**, 806 (1960).

121a. Hartler, N., P. Rönström, and L. Stockman, *Svensk Papperstidn.*, **64**, 699 (1961).

122. Hartler, N., and O. Sandberg, *Svensk Papperstidn.*, **63**, 263 (1960).

123. Heiwinkel, H., *Svensk Papperstidn.*, **47**, 265 (1944).

124. Heiwinkel, H., and E. Hägglund, *Svensk Papperstidn.*, **43**, 391 (1940).

125. Henderson, J. T., *J. Am. Chem. Soc.*, **79**, 5304 (1957).

126. Heritage, C. C., U.S. Pat. 2,125,634 (1938).

127. Hibbert, H., and G. H. Tomlinson, Jr., U.S. Pat. 2,069,185 (1937).

128. Hirschkind, W., *Pulp Paper Mag. Can.*, **33**, 489 (1932).

129. Hisey, W. O., and C. M. Koon, *Paper Trade J.*, **103**, No. 6, 36 (1936).

130. Hoge, W. H., *Tappi*, **37**, 369 (1954).

131. Holst, G., *Chem. Revs.*, **54**, No. 1, 169 (1954).

132. Howard, G. C., U.S. Pats. 1,699,845 (1929), 1,856,558 (1932).

133. Hunter, *Paper Making through Eighteen Centuries*, William Edwin, Rudge 1, New York, 1930.

134. Husband, R. M., C. D. Logan, and C. B. Purves, *Can. J. Chem.*, **33**, 68 (1955).

135. Ingruber, O. V., *Pulp Paper Mag. Can.*, **55**, No. 10, 124 (1954).

136. Ingruber, O. V., *Pulp Paper Mag. Can.*, **58**, No. 13, 161 (1957).

137. Ingruber, O. V., *Pulp Paper Mag. Can.*, **60**, No. 11, T-346 (1959).

137a. Ingruber, O. V., *Svensk Papperstidn.*, **65**, 448 (1962).

138. Jacques, H., and R. W. Barton, *Pulp Paper Mag. Can.*, **59**, No. 10, 154 (1958).

139. Jakowkin, A. A., *Z. physik. Chem.*, **29**, 613 (1899).

140. Janson, J., and B. Lindberg, *Acta Chem. Scand.*, **13**, 138 (1959).

141. Jappe, N., *Tappi*, **41**, 224 (1958).

142. Jayme, G., and K. H. Rosenstock, *Wockenblatt für Papierfabr.*, **86**, 1009 (1958).

143. Jayme, G., *Tappi*, **41**, 178A (November 1958).

144. Jayme, G., and G. Hunger, *Monatsh.*, **87**, 8 (1956).

145. Jayme, G., and A. v. Koeppen, *Das Papier*, **4**, 373, 415, 455 (1950).

146. Jayme, G., and W. Licht, *Holzforschung*, **9**, 33 (1955).

147. Jayme, G., and L. Rothamel, *Cellulosechemie*, **22**, No. 3, 88 (1944).

148. Jeanes, A., and H. C. Isbell, *J. Research Natl. Bur. Standards*, **27**, 125 (1941).

149. Jones, G. W., *Tappi*, **33**, 149 (1950).

150. Johnston, H. W., and O. Maass, *Can. J. Research*, **3**, 140 (1930).

151. Jullander, I., and K. Brune, *Acta Chem. Scand.*, **11**, 570 (1957).

152. Jullander, I., and K. Burke, *Svensk Papperstidn.*, **62**, 728 (1959).

153. Jurbergs, K. A., *Tappi*, **43**, 561 (1960).

154. Kakehi, K., R. A. Murphy, and K. Sarkanen, Abstracts of Papers, Tappi Pulp Bleaching Conference, Chicago, Ill., June 13, 1960.

155. Kallmes, O., *Tappi*, **43**, 143 (1960).

156. Keller, E. L., U.S. Forest Products Laboratory, unpublished results.

157. Keller, E. L., U.S. Forest Products Laboratory, unpublished results.

158. Kerr, W. D., and S. A. Harding, *Pulp Paper Mag. Can.*, **56**, No. 9, 182 (1955).

159. Klason, P., *Svensk Papperstidn.*, **19**, 180 (1916).

160. Kompa, G., and Y. Talvitie, *Chem. Zentr.*, **1931**, II, 2074.

160a. Koshijima, T., *J. Japan Wood Res. Soc.*, **6**, 194 (1960).

161. Kratzl, K., G. Billek, A. Graf, and W. Schweers, *Monatsh.*, **87**, 60 (1956).

162. Kureniemi, T., and J. O. Murto, *Finnish Paper and Timber J.*, **30**, No. 24, 437 (1948).

163. Lange, P. W., *Svensk Papperstidn.*, **48**, 241 (1945).

164. Lange, P. W., *Svensk Papperstidn.*, **57**, 525 (1954).

165. Larocque, G. L., and O. Maass, *Can. J. Research*, **19B**, 1 (1941).

166. Larson, L. L., *Paper Trade J.*, **113**, No. 20, 25 (1941).

167. Lea, D. C., *Tappi*, **37**, 393 (1954).

168. Legg, G. W., and J. S. Hart, *Pulp Paper Mag. Can.*, **61**, T-299 (1960).

169. Legg, G. W., and J. S. Hart, *Tappi*, **43**, 471 (1960).

170. Lekander, K. E., and L. Stockman, *Svensk Papperstidn.*, **58**, 775 (1955).

171. Leonard, R. H., W. H. Peterson, and M. J. Johnson, *Ind. Eng. Chem.*, **40**, 57 (1948).

172. Leopold, B., *Acta Chem. Scand.*, **4**, 1523 (1950).

173. Leopold, B., *Acta Chem. Scand.*, **6**, 38 (1952).

174. Leopold, B., *Acta Chem. Scand.*, **6**, 75 (1952).

175. Leopold, B., and D. B. Mutton, *Tappi*, **42**, 218 (1959).

176. Levitin, N., N. S. Thompson, and C. B. Purves, *Pulp Paper Mag. Can.*, **56**, No. 5, 117 (1955).

177. Libby, C. E., and F. W. O'Neil, *Tappi*, **4**, 161 (1950).

178. Liese, W., *Holz Roh-u Werkstoff*, **15**, No. 11, 449 (1957).

179. Lindberg, B., *Svensk Papperstidn.*, **59**, 531 (1956).

180. Lindberg, B., and D. Wood, *Acta Chem. Scand.*, **6**, 791 (1952).

181. Lindberg, J. J., *Paperi ja Puu*, **42**, 193 (1960).

182. Lindgren, B. O., *Acta Chem. Scand.*, **5**, 603 (1951).

183. Lindgren, B. O., *Svensk Papperstidn.*, **55**, 78 (1952).

184. Lindgren, B. O., *Svensk Papperstidn.*, **61**, 669 (1958).

185. Lindstedt, G., *Acta Chem. Scand.*, **4**, 448 (1950).

186. Logan, C. D., R. M. Husband, and C. B. Purves, *Can. J. Chem.*, **33**, 82 (1955).

187. Luhde, F., *Pulp Paper Mag. Can.*, **60**, T-269 (1959).

188. Luner, P., *Pulp Paper Mag. Can.*, **57**, No. 3, 216 (1956).

189. Luner, P., *Tappi*, **43**, 819 (1960).

190. Maass, O., et al., *Pulp Paper Mag. Can.*, **54**, No. 8, 98–134 (1953).

191. Machell, G., and G. N. Richards, *J. Chem. Soc.*, **1960**, 1924 (1960).

192. Machell, G., G. N. Richards, and H. H. Sephton, *Chem. and Ind.*, 467 (1957).

193. Martin, G. E., *Tappi*, **33**, 90 (1950).

194. Marton, R., *Tappi*, **42**, 948 (1959); **42**, No. 2, 68A (1959).

195. Mayer, W. C., and C. P. Donofrio, *Pulp Paper Mag. Can.*, **59**, No. 10, 157 (1958).

195a. McGovern, J. N., and E. L. Keller, *Pulp Paper Mag. Can.*, **49**, 93 (1948).

196. McKee, R. H., *Ind. Eng. Chem.*, **38**, 382 (1946).

197. McKinney, J. W., *Paper Trade J.*, **12**, No. 4, 58 (1946).

198. Meier, H., *Svensk Papperstidn.*, **62**, 687 (1959).

199. Meier, H., *Acta Chem. Scand.*, **14**, 749 (1960).

200. Meier, H., Abstracts of Papers, Third Cellulose Conference, Syracuse, N. Y. (1960); *J. Polymer Sci.*, **51**, 11 (1961).

200a. Meier, H., *Svensk Papperstidn.*, **65**, 299 (1962).

200b. Meier, H., *Svensk Papperstidn.*, **65**, 589 (1962).

200c. Meier, H., *Acta. Chem. Scand.*, **15**, 1381 (1961).

201. Meller, A., *Tappi*, **34**, 171 (1951); **35**, 72 (1952).

202. Meller, A., *Holzforschung*, **14**, 78 (1960).

203. Merewether, J. W. T., *Holzforschung*, **11**, 65 (1957).

204. Mikawa, H. J., *Chem. Soc. Japan Ind. Chem. Sect.*, **54**, 651 (1951).

205. Mikawa, H., K. Sato, Ch. Takasaki, and H. Okada, *J. Chem. Soc. Japan, Ind. Chem. Sect.*, **54**, 299 (1951), *Chem. Abstracts*, **47**, 2981 (1953).

206. Miller, R. N., and W. H. Swanson, *Paper Trade J.*, **78**, No. 15, 178 (1924).

207. Miller, R. N., and W. H. Swanson, *Ind. Eng. Chem.*, **17**, 843 (1925).

208. Mills, R. T., W. O. Stauffer, and W. S. Hinegardner, *Paper Trade J.*, **122**, No. 20, 54 (1946).

209. Muhlethaler, K., *Biochem. et Biophys. Acta*, **3**, 15 (1949).

210. Mutton, D. B., *Pulp Paper Mag. Can.*, **59**, No. 10, 260 (1958).

211. Nakano, J., and C. Schuerch, *J. Am. Chem. Soc.*, **82**, 1677 (1960).

212. Nelson, R., and C. Schuerch, *Tappi*, **40**, 419 (1957).

213. Nelson, R., Abstracts of Papers, Third Cellulose Conference, Syracuse, N. Y. (1960); *J. Polymer Sci.*, **51**, 27 (1961).

214. Nokihara, E., J. M. Tuttle, V. F. Felicetta, and J. L. McCarthy, *J. Am. Chem. Soc.*, **78**, 4495 (1957).

215. Nolan, W. J., and W. F. Brown, *Tappi*, **35**, 425 (1952).

216. Öhrn, O. E., and I. Croon, *Svensk Papperstidn.*, **63**, 601 (1960).

217. Paranyi, N. I., and W. Rabinovitch, *Pulp Paper Mag. Can.*, **56**, No. 3, 163 (1955).

218. Pascoe, T. A., J. S. Buchanan, E. H. Kennedy, and G. Sivola, *Tappi*, **42**, 265 (1959).

219. Perry, J. H., Manufacture of Mechanical Pulp, in N. J. Stephenson, ed., *Pulp and Paper Manufacture*, McGraw-Hill, New York, 1950.

219a. Pettersson, S. E., and S. A. Rydholm, *Svensk Papperstidn.*, **64**, 4 (1961).

220. Pew, J. C., *Tappi*, **32**, 39 (1949).

221. Pew, J. C., *J. Am. Chem. Soc.*, **73**, 1678 (1951).

222. Pew, J. C., *J. Am. Chem. Soc.*, **74**, 2850 (1952).

223. Pew, J. C., *Tappi*, **40**, 553 (1957).

223a. Pew, J. C., *Nature*, **93**, 250 (1962).

224. Phelps, M. W., and J. Schuber, *Paper Trade J.*, **106**, No. 8, 126 (1938).

225. Picted, R., and G. L. Brelaz, German Pat. 26,331 (1883).

226. Pigman, W. W., and W. R., Csellak, *Tech. Assoc. Paper*, **31**, 393 (1948).

227. Quick, R. H., *Tappi*, **39**, 357 (1956).

228. Rapson, W. H., *Pulp Paper Mag. Can.*, **57**, No. 10, 147 (1956).

229. Rapson, W. H., *Tappi*, **39**, 554 (1956).

230. Rapson, W. H., *Tappi*, **41**, 181 (1958).

231. Rapson, W. H., and C. B. Anderson, *Tappi*, **40**, 307 (1957).

232. Rapson, W. H., and C. B. Anderson, *Tappi*, **41**, 486 (1958).

233. Rapson, W. H., C. B. Anderson, and G. F. King, *Tappi*, **41**, 442 (1958).

234. Rapson, W. H., and K. A. Hakim, *Pulp Paper Mag. Can.*, **58**, No. 8, 151 (1957).

235. Rapson, W. H., and G. K. Morbey, *Tappi*, **42**, 125 (1959).

236. Rapson, W. H., and M. Wayman, U.S. Pat. 2,716,058 (1955).

237. Regestad, S. O., and O. Samuelson, *Svensk Papperstidn.*, **61**, 735 (1958).

238. Regnfors, L., and L. Stockman, *Svensk Papperstidn.*, **59**, 510 (1956).

239. Reichert, J. S., D. J. Campbell, and R. T. Mills, *Paper Trade J.*, **118**, No. 15, 45 (1944).

240. Reichert, J. S., R. T. Mills, and D. J. Campbell, *Paper Trade J.*, **122**, No. 5, 37 (1946).

241. Richter, G. A., *Ind. Eng. Chem.*, **33**, 1518 (1941).

242. Richter, G. A., *Tappi*, **36**, 228 (1953).

243. Richter, G. A., *Tappi*, **38**, 129 (1955).

244. Richter, G. A., and L. H. Pancoast, *Tappi*, **37**, 263 (1954).

245. Richtzenhain, H., and B. Alfredsson, *Acta Chem. Scand.*, **7**, 1177 (1953); **8**, 1519 (1954); **10**, 719 (1956).

246. Richtzenhain, H., B. Abrahamson, and F. Dryselius, *Svensk Papperstidn.*, **57**, 473 (1954).
247. Ringstrom, E., and S. Lindberg; by S. Yllner and Enström, B., *Svensk Papperstidn.*, **59**, 229 (1956).
248. Rinman, E. L., *Svensk Papperstidn.*, **26**, 158 (1923).
249. Rollinson, S., *Tappi*, **38**, 186 (1955).
250. Rosenberger, N. A., *Bumazh. Prom.*, **31**, No. 3, 6 (1956).
251. Ross, J. H., C. R. Mitchell, and F. H. Yorston, *Paper Trade J.*, **91**, No. 20, 53 (1930).
252. Routala, O., and A. Pohjola, *Pappers- och Trävarutidskr. Finland*, **16**, 289 (1934).
253. Rue, J. D., S. D. Wells, F. G. Rawlings, and J. A. Staidl, *Paper Trade J.*, **83**, No. 13, 50 (1926).
254. Rydholm, S., *Svensk Papperstidn.*, **57**, 427 (1954).
255. Rydholm, S., *Svensk Papperstidn.*, **58**, 273 (1955).
256. Rydholm, S., and S. Lagergren, *Svensk Papperstidn.*, **62**, 103 (1959).
257. Ryerson, L. H., U.S. Pat. 2,733,992 (1956).
258. Saarino, J., and C. Gustafsson, *Finnish Paper and Timber J.*, **35**, 65 (1953).
259. Saeman, J. F., E. G. Locke, and G. K. Dickerman, *Paper Trade J.*, **123**, No. 12, 38 (1946).
260. Samuelson, H. O., Swedish Pat. 150,651 (1955).
261. Samuelson, O., and N. Hartler, *Svensk. Kem. Tidskr.*, **62**, 197 (1950).
262. Samuelson, O., and C. Ramsel, *Svensk Papperstidn.*, **53**, 155 (1950).
263. Samuelson, O., and A. Wennerblom, *Svensk Papperstidn.*, **57**, 827 (1954).
264. Samuelson, O., and A. Westlin, *Svensk Papperstidn.*, **50**, 149 (1947).
265. Sandborn, L. T., U.S. Pat. 2,104,701 (1938).
266. Sanyer, N., E. L. Keller, and G. H. Chidester, *Tappi*, **45**, 90 (1962).
267. Sanyer, N., and E. C. Jahn, Abstracts of Papers, XIII Intern. Congr. of Pure and Applied Chem. (1953).
268. Sarkanen, K., and C. Dence, *J. Org. Chem.*, **25**, 715 (1960).
269. Scarth, G. W., *Can. J. Research*, **3**, 107 (1930).
270. Schafer, E. R., and J. C. Pew, *Paper Trade J.*, **116**, No. 4, 25 (1943). Forest Products Laboratory Report No. 1419.
271. Schick, P. E., U.S. Pat. 2,788,273 (1957).
272. Schmidt, E., and E. Graumann, *Ber.*, **54**, 1860 (1921), *Chem. Abstracts*, **16**, 273 (1922).
273. Schmidt-Nielsen, S., *Papir. J.*, **26**, 83 (1938).
274. Scholefield, F., and H. A. Turner, *J. Textile Inst.*, **24**, 330 (1933).
275. Schumb, W. C., C. N. Satterfield, and R. L. Wentworth, *Hydrogen Peroxide*, Reinhold, New York, 1955, pp. 467–499.
276. Schwartz, H., J. L. McCarthy, and H. Hibbert, *Papper Trade J.*, **111**, No. 18. 30 (1940).
277. Schwartz, S. L., and M. W. Bray, *Paper Trade J.*, **107**, No. 12, 24 (1938).
278. Schwartz, S. L., and M. W. Bray, *Paper Trade J.*, **123**, No. 17, 42 (1946).
279. Sivola, G., U.S. Pats. 2,701,763 (1955), 2,730,445 (1956).
280. Smedberg, G. E., Can. Pat. 575,636 (1959).
281. Soderquist, R., *Paper Trade J.*, **139**, No. 42, 30 (1955).
282. Somsen, R. A., *Tappi*, **43**, 154, 157 (1960).

283. Sparrow, D. B., J. J. Eberl, and K. W. Britt, U.S. Pats. 2,707,144 (1955), 2,707,145 (1955).

284. Stamm, A. J., *Phys. Chem.*, **36**, 312 (1932).

285. Stamm, A. J., *J. Physics*, **6**, 334 (1935).

286. Stamm, A. J., and H. K. Burr, *J. Phys. Colloid Chem.*, **51**, 240 (1947).

287. Staudinger, H., and W. Döhle, *J. pract. Chem.*, **161**, 219 (1943).

288. Staudinger, H., and J. Jurisch, *Zellstoff u. Papier*, **18**, No. 12, 690 (1938).

289. Stephenson, N. J., ed., *Pulp and Paper Manufacture*, Vol. I, "Preparation and Treatment of Wood Pulp," McGraw-Hill, New York, 1950.

290. Stockman, L., *Svensk Papperstidn.*, **54**, 621 (1951).

291. Stockman, L., *Das Papier*, **14**, 85 (1960).

292. Stockman, L., and E. Hägglund, *Svensk Papperstidn.*, **54**, 243 (1951).

293. Stone, J. E., *Pulp Paper Mag. Can.*, **57**, No. 7, 139 (1956).

294. Stone, J. E., *Tappi*, **40**, 539 (1957).

295. Stone, J. E., and D. W. Clayton, *Pulp Paper Mag. Can.*, **61**, No. 6, 30T (1960).

296. Stone, J. E., and H. V. Green, *Pulp Paper Mag. Can.*, **59**, No. 10, 223 (1958).

297. Strauss, R. W., and K. Sarkanen, TAPPI meeting, Feb. 21, 1960, New York.

298. Taube, H., and H. Dodgen, *J. Am. Chem. Soc.*, **71**, 3330 (1949).

299. Theander, O., *Svensk Papperstidn.*, **61**, 581 (1958).

300. Tilghman, B. C., Brit. Pat. 2924 (1866); U.S. Pat. 70487 (1867).

301. Timell, T. E., C. P. J. Glaudemans, and J. K. Gillham, *Pulp Paper Mag. Can.*, **59**, No. 10, 242 (1958).

301a. Timell, T. E., *Tappi*, **44**, 88 (1961).

302. Tomlinson, G. H., G. H. Tomlinson, II, J. R. G. Bryce, and N. G. M. Tuck, *Pulp Paper Mag. Can.*, **59**, No. 6, 247 (1958).

303. Tomlinson, G. H., and L. S. Wilcoxon, *Paper Trade J.*, **110**, No. 5, 31 (1940).

304. Traynard, B., A. M. Ayroud, and A. Eymery, *Assoc. tech. ind. papetière Bull.*, **45** (1953).

305. Trivedi, S. A., R. M. Kingsbury, and F. A. Simmonds, *Paper Ind. and Paper World*, **28**, 1443 (1948).

306. Turner, G. B., The Thermal Decomposition of Aqueous Solutions of Sulfur Dioxide, Thesis, London Univ., 1954.

307. Tyden, H., *Svensk Papperstidn.*, **59**, 296 (1956).

308. Virkola, N. E., Y. Hentola, M. Makinen, and R. Soila, *Svensk Papperstidn.*, **62**, 477 (1959).

309. Waite, C. N., and J. Hedin, U.S. Pat. 1,249,287 (1917).

310. Wardrop, A. B., and H. E. Dadswell, *J. Inst. Wood Science*, No. 2, 8 (1958).

310a. Wardrop, A. B., and G. W. Davies, *Holzforschung*, **15**, 129 (1961).

311. Watt, C., and H. Burgess, U.S. Pat. 11343 (1854).

312. Watt, C., and H. Burgess, Brit. Pat. 1942 (1853).

313. Wayman, M., and D. L. Sherk, *Tappi*, **39**, 786 (1956).

314. Whistler, R. L., and R. Schweiger, *J. Am. Chem. Soc.*, **79**, 6460 (1957).

315. White, E. V., T. N. Swartz, Q. P. Peniston, H. Schwartz, J. L. McCarthy, and H. Hibbert, *Paper Trade J.*, **113**, No. 24, 33 (1941).

316. White, J. F., M. C. Taylor, and G. P. Vincent, *Ind. Eng. Chem.*, **34**, 782 (1942).

317. Whitney, R. P., S. T. Han, and J. L. Davis, *Tappi*, **40**, 587 (1957).

318. Wiesner, W., *Pulp Paper Mag. Can.*, **58**, No. 2, 83 (1957).
319. Wiley, A. J., E. McCoy, M. J. Johnson, and W. H. Peterson, *Ind. Eng. Chem.*, **33**, 606 (1941).
320. Wise, L. E., *Paper Ind.*, **24**, 822 (1942).
321. Wise, L. E., *Paper Ind.*, **38**, 1024 (1956).
322. Wise, L. E., M. Murphy, and A. A. D'Addieco, *Paper Trade J.*, **122**, No. 2, 34 (1946).
323. Wither, R. P., and H. A. Captein, *Forest Prods. J.*, **10**, 174 (1960).
324. Woods, N. I., *Pulp Paper Mag. Can.*, **57**, No. 5, 142 (1956).
325. Yllner, S., and B. Enström, *Svensk Papperstidn.*, **59**, 229 (1956).
326. Yllner, S., and Enström, *Svensk Papperstidn.*, **60**, 549 (1957).
327. Yllner, S., K. Osterberg, and L. Stockman, *Svensk Papperstidn.*, **60**, 795 (1957).
328. Yorston, F. H., Studies in Sulfite Pulping, Dominion Forest Service Bull., 97 (1942).
328a. Zhigalov, Yu. V., and D. V. Tishchenko, *Zhur. Priklad. Khim.*, **35**, 147 (1962).
329. Zienius, R. H., and C. B. Purves, *Tappi*, **43**, 27 (1960).

Addendum

More recent studies (N. Sanyer and J. F. Laundrie, Forest Products Laboratory, unpublished results) on the polysulfide process have indicated that the pulp yield reaches a maximum with the addition of increasing amount of polysulfide. The kraft pulp yield from pine at 50 Kappa number is increased from 50 to 62% with the use of 20% polysulfide sulfur on wood. The decomposition of polysulfide in alkali has a large temperature coefficient, and it is desirable to use a cooking schedule which will allow nearly complete penetration and reaction of polysulfide before heating the digester to the maximum temperature. The use of thin or short chips also improves the effectiveness of the polysulfide.

The selectivity of the polysulfide process is due not to the increased rate of delignification, but largely to the protection and retention of hemicelluloses, mainly of glucomannan, and to a lesser extent, xylan and cellulose, in the cooking of pine. With oak, the yield increase is about one-half that of pine. Since the hardwoods contain only small amounts of glucomannan, the yield increase is mainly due to the improved retention of xylan.

CHAPTER 11

Wood as a Chemical Raw Material

J. F. Harris, J. F. Saeman, and E. G. Locke, *Forest Products Laboratory,* Forest Service, United States Department of Agriculture, Madison, Wisconsin*

Enormous quantities of wood are utilized yearly in the form of lumber, fuel, wood, paper, cellulose, and cellulose derivatives (cf. Chapter 1). These products consume wood, either in its original form or as cellulose, both native and regenerated. No products have yet been produced, on a large scale, by disintegration of the original polymeric components of wood. Despite the attractive possibilities for the use of wood as a chemical raw material, it has not been seriously studied, and remains unexploited, from this viewpoint.

The purpose of the present chapter is to acquaint the reader with this potentially important role for wood, and to outline the important economic and chemical principles that should be considered in its development. It is hoped that the discussion will impart an awareness of the many opportunities for profitable research in the area, and

* Maintained at Madison in cooperation with the University of Wisconsin.

provide suitable guidelines for those few who, eventually, become associated with research development concerning wood.

Unfortunately, treatment of the subject is severely limited by the available space, and only selected topics are discussed. The selection is somewhat arbitrary, depending upon the predilections and backgrounds of the authors, and it must not be assumed that topics omitted are unimportant. It is hoped that what is included will be sufficient to accomplish the purpose described.

I. The Raw Material

The primary product of the forest is a fairly expensive material; the better grades of lumber or pulp are comparable to refined sugar in cost. For this reason the raw material to be considered as a chemical source is virtually limited to the residues resulting from the operations of the existing forest industries. Such residues exhibit wide variations in character. They differ in their chemical nature, depending on the species involved; their physical nature varies with the operation by which they are produced; and the concentrations and amounts available show extreme regional variation. Thus, it is not possible to make broad generalizations, and the adequacy of the raw material supply in any locale can only be judged with information at hand on the quantity and character of the available material.

While statistics on specific commercial products are readily available, data on the total product of the nation's forest are gathered infrequently at high cost. The most recent report on the subject is the Forest Resource Report No. 14, "Timber Resources for America's Future" (103), which goes into unusual detail on the kind and amount of residues resulting from logging and manufacture in the various wood industries and in the various regions.

Logging residues, material that is cut or killed during woods operation and left in the woods, amounted to more than 20,000,000 tons in 1952. Included in this estimate are logs missed in yarding or left at landings, pieces resulting from breakage, and unutilized portions of the tree down to 4 inches in diameter. None of this material has commercial application at present.

The distribution of species in the timber cut for 1952 is shown in Table I. The predominant use of softwoods for both pulp and lumber is reflected in the fact that there was three times as much softwood cut as hardwood. It should also be noted that relatively few species

TABLE I

Distribution of Timber Cut in the Unites States
by Species Group, 1952[a]

Species	Per cent of total
Eastern species	
Softwoods	
White, red, and jack pine	1.99
Southern yellow pine	23.77
Spruce, fir	1.37
Other softwoods	1.72
Total, softwoods	28.85
Hardwoods	
Yellow poplar	2.02
Other soft hardwoods	7.97
Oak	10.02
Beech, yellow birch, sugar maple	2.64
Other hard hardwoods	2.36
Total, hardwoods	25.01
Total, eastern species	53.86
Western species	
Softwoods	
Douglas-fir	24.49
Ponderosa and jeffrey pine	7.38
Western hemlock	4.56
White and sugar pine	1.25
Redwood	2.02
Other softwoods	6.28
Total, softwoods	45.98
Hardwoods (total)	0.16
Total, western species	46.14
Total, all species	100.00

[a] Data compiled from "Timber Resources for America's Future" (103). Further information on distribution may be found in the cited reference.

account for all but an insignificant part of the total cut, with the two softwood species—Douglas-fir and southern yellow pine—making up almost one half of the total.

Solid residues from primary manufacturing operations include coarse materials, such as slabs, edgings, and trimmings, and fine material such as sawdust and shavings. These amounted to more than 50,000,000 tons of wood in 1952, of which approximately 60% was utilized as fuel, leaving approximately 20,000,000 tons unused. The principal source of these residues is the lumber industry. In contrast to logging residues, they represent a most attractive source of raw material for chemical conversion because of high concentration and continuing supply.

It is important to consider the many variations in sawmill practices throughout the country, as they have an important effect on the quantity and distribution of manufacturing residues. The New England, Middle Atlantic, and Lake States regions are characterized by small sawmills, and concentration yards in which lumber is dried and finished are uncommon. In the South Atlantic, Southeast, East Gulf, and West Gulf regions, concentration yards are commonly used, and the large accumulation of residues at these locations holds real promise as a raw material for chemical processing. The Northern Rocky Mountain region has a moderate amount of wood residues, and the mills are sufficiently large to hold some promise for utilization.

In the Pacific Northwest region is located the largest concentration of wood residues. The sawmills are very large, and huge quantities of material, uniform in both physical and chemical properties, are available. In addition to primary manufacturing residues, very large amounts of logging residues are also available in high concentration. The introduction of natural gas in this region has resulted in a marked decrease in the use of residues for fuel, further increasing the supply available for chemical processing.

In addition to the residues generated in logging and manufacturing operations, certain areas give promise of providing large quantities of another form of wood for chemical conversion. This is the wood that is removed from forests for the purpose of upgrading the stand and establishing better forest management practices. It includes trees culled from good stands of timber and trees cut from low-grade stands in preparation for replanting. The possibility of operating with a very low harvesting cost in some of the poor forest regions may make this type of material more attractive than the solid residues described previously. The quantity available is difficult to estimate, but it is very large. The Forest Resource Report (103) states that 52,000,000 acres of unstocked or poorly stocked commercial forest area require replanting, and that one-fifth of the entire eastern hardwoods growth is cull material.

The chemical composition of residues varies greatly from region to region, depending primarily on the useful species that predominate in the locality. The chemical analysis of some species is given in Chapter 3, Table IV, page 70. Unfortunately, little analytical information is available, and this table includes values for only a few of the commercially important trees. It can be observed that hardwoods have a lower lignin content than softwoods and a much more variable glucan content. The dominating difference between hardwoods and softwoods lies in the mannan and xylan content. (The term "mannan" or 'xylan," as used here, refers to the amount of that particular sugar obtained by hydrolysis.) In the hardwoods, mannan seldom exceeds 3 to 4%, while the xylan content is normally quite large, ranging from 15 to 25% of the wood. In most softwoods, mannan is the major nonglucan polysaccharide, but some softwood species contain almost equal parts of mannan and xylan. In some species, arabinan and galactan are much more predominant than they are for the species listed.

The ash content, although minor in quantity, frequently plays a large role in process considerations. The cation content of the inorganic ash constituents is principally calcium and potassium. Smaller amounts of silica are also present.

The wood substance solubilized in pulping operations represents another huge source of chemical raw material. In 1955, Wiley (109) estimated that 500,000 tons of carbohydrate material were being produced annually by the nation's pulp mills and that the potential supply of carbohydrates available from this source approached 2,000,000 tons annually. Utilization of these liquors has been under intensive study for many years (81,97,108). In general, however, the problems associated with profitably employing this material are considerably different from those that arise in the utilization of solid wood residues. Information on the location, type, and capacity of wood pulp mills in the United States as well as data for the consumption of various species is issued regularly (102).

II. Product Outlets

Although many materials might profitably be made from wood, consideration of chemical conversion as a forest management tool eliminates examination of those products which, while profitable, do not appear to have the future market capacity to consume significant quantities of wood. Two market areas, into which the potential products from the chemical conversion of wood might enter, appear to have the prerequisite characteristics for good forest management. The rapidly growing organic chemical industry and the food market both seem to have attractive possibilities for exploitation by materials obtainable from wood.

The large carbohydrate content of wood with its potentially large yield of glucose has always been a strong incentive for the development of a process for sugar production. The product, if competitive with other carbohydrate sources, would find outlets in the human food, animal food, and chemical sugar markets. These markets are very large. At the present time, the per capita consumption of food sugar in the United States is approximately 100 pounds per year—a total of 8,000,000 tons annually (33). Most of this is in the form of manufactured goods, such as baked foods, canned goods, and ice cream. Less than one-third of the sugar used reaches the home in sugar bags.

Molasses consumed as a cattle food amounts to approximately 500 million gallons per year, which is equivalent to 1,500,000 tons of sugar per year (101). Feeding molasses competes directly with corn, 6.5 gallons of molasses being equivalent in carbohydrate value to 1 bushel of corn. With the present surplus of agricultural products, there is little incentive to develop processes for the production of low-grade sugar stocks suitable for stock feeding, and the present consumption of sugar in this form is much less than that of the high-quality material used in human consumption. The potential market is very much larger than the present figures indicate. The rapidly increasing American population consumes meat at a per capita rate of 175 pounds a year. As the years pass and the market for grain and other agricultural products begins to strain productive capacity, sugar will undoubtedly play a major role in feed formulation.

The largest users of sugar for chemical manufacture are the producers of yeast, citric acid, and vinegar. The annual consumption of sugar for industrial purposes, including ethanol and pharmaceutical production, is very small, approximately 500,000 tons.

The second major potential outlet for chemically processed wood, the organic chemical market, is very large and extremely complex. The total production of the industry exceeds 15,000,000 tons yearly and includes thousands of different chemical entities (57). Despite its present large size, it continues to grow at a phenomenal rate of 12.5% per year, compared to a 6.2% growth rate for the entire chemical industry and 3.0% for United States industry in general. The growth rate is expected to be sustained at this level by increasing the traditional markets through the improvement of competitive position and by the development of new products, resulting in the capture of other consumer market areas.

At present, the principal raw material sources for organic chemical production are the steel and petroleum industries. They supply huge quantities of the basic building blocks, benzene, toluene, xylene, naphthalene, propylene, and ethylene. Until comparatively recently, these compounds were obtained as by-products, but the rapid expansion of the chemical industry has outstripped the supply, and plants that use petroleum fractions now operate to produce these compounds as primary products. Thus, petroleum has become the major source of organic chemicals. Its predominant position is illustrated by the fact that petroleum-derived chemicals account for more than three-fourths of the total tonnage of organics produced. Chemicals derived from wood also compete in the present-day market. The cellulosics, including rayon, cellulose acetate, and other cellulose derivatives, form the largest single group of polymers marketed. Tall oil and naval stores are also tonnage products that are finding new markets.

The chemical industry produces more than 10,000 products for commercial use. A much larger number of compounds are known and have been made in laboratories—more than 100,000 in the organic field alone. The industry's products, however, are those for which definite uses have been developed. Desirable products are those that perform satisfactorily at the least cost. The actual chemical composition of a product is of little importance, and products with different chemical compositions frequently compete for the same market. Further, because of the versatility of chemical processing methods, products of the same chemical composition are frequently made from different raw materials, and it is generally true that many different products are made from a few basic raw materials. Thus, the industry is characterized by widespread competition between processes, raw materials, and products.

Theoretically, all the consumer products of the organic chemical industry that are available today could be produced from wood, but only a relatively few could be produced competitively. The evaluation of wood as a chemical raw material involves not only consideration of its cost, availability, elemental and molecular composition, but also consideration of products, product markets, and ease of processing to these products.

Although wood can provide chemical products that could conceivably enter all areas of the present-day organics market, the area where it appears to have the most chance of success seems to be in the polymer field. The molecular components of wood are of a type that can be readily transformed into a variety of polyfunctional molecules suitable for the production of plastics, resins, fibers, adhesives, and films. Such products would have a different chemical composition but would compete for the same consumer markets that are now being supplied by chemicals derived from petroleum. Other market areas are of interest, particularly agricultural chemicals and medicinals. The opportunity of successful competition in the production of large tonnage solvents seems more remote; the probability of replacing petroleum with wood as a source of ethyl alcohol, for instance, is extremely small.

III. Processes for the Chemical Conversion of Wood

A. INTRODUCTION

The production of chemical cellulose represents the only large use of wood in the chemical industry. Naval stores and the production of the by-products of charcoal manufacture are small by comparison. The use of wood to produce furfural, ethyl alcohol, crude and refined sugars, acetone, butanol, levulinic acid, oxalic acid, lignocellulose plastics, hydrocarbon fuels, and many others has been suggested and, in many instances, experimental investigations were performed. Oxidation, hydrogenation, fermentation, hydrolysis, and pyrolysis were among the operations proposed to obtain these useful products. Despite the expenditure of large amounts of research and development work, however, chemical conversion of wood has not lived up to expectations. The reasons for economic failure are those common to defunct processes: low yields, high processing costs, and low-quality, low-priced products. In general, reliance was placed on a single product to carry the economic load. Meanwhile, little or no attention was given to fractionation of the major wood components, with subsequent processing of the separated fractions for high yields of high-quality products.

The insistence of chemical buyers for high quality and low price of bulk chemicals precludes the entry into the chemical market of some materials that can be obtained from wood in high yield by using simple processes. Materials, such as mixed aromatics, lignocellulose plastic materials, and crude sugar mixtures of undetermined composition and variable properties, do not find stable bulk markets. On the other hand, monomeric materials of high purity, although more easily marketed, usually originate from only one component of the original wood and are therefore low-yield products. Furfural, for example, is obtained only from the xylan constituent of the hemicellulose, and the maximum theoretical yield that might be obtained is below 10%, even for woods with a high xylan content. Yields of chemical cellulose, which originates from the largest wood fraction, are less than 40%. Some products, such as glucose and ethanol, originate from both the hemicellulose and cellulose fractions, but it seems unlikely that any single product can be obtained in sufficient yield at the necessary low price to establish wood as a bulk organic chemical raw material. Thus, suitable conversion processes must be thought of as multiproduct, and the size and complexity of successfully competing plants become apparent from this fact.

Many process advantages can be gained by solubilizing and separating the major components before they are processed to the final products. Wood, being a low-density solid, suffers several disadvantages as a raw material when contrasted with gas or liquid materials. If it is to be fed continuously to equipment operating at high pressure, the problem of moving it into the reaction zone is extremely difficult. Handling of wood in batch reactors or digesters presents difficulties of temperature and concentration distribution, and equipment costs rise exorbitantly as the process pressure is increased. Reaction times of 10 seconds or less are common when liquid systems are involved, but such times would be quite extraordinary when handling wood. This difficulty puts severe limitations on the reaction conditions that may be employed and, consequently, limits yields and rates. The problem can be circumvented by fractionally solubilizing the wood at moderately low pressures prior to final processing.

In the event that several products are to be made, it would commonly be true that the processing of one fraction in the presence of another would result in a decrease in yield from both fractions, even in the case where a single product is obtained from two fractions. A decrease in product purity normally accompanies the drop in yield.

Thus, preliminary separation of fractions can be expected to result in better yields and simpler purification procedures for obtaining the final products.

In some cases, the presence of a second component, even if inert, introduces a dilution effect that has a detrimental result on the economy of production. The increased cost may be due to an increased heat requirement or loss of reagent or product.

B. SEPARATION OF WOOD COMPONENTS

The suitability of a particular method of separation or fractionation of the wood components can only be critically judged with a knowledge of the over-all conversion process. In general, however, it should effect a high degree of separation at a low cost and rapid rate. The residue should be chemically unchanged and free of undesirable impurities. If possible, it should be tailored to the subsequent processing of the fractions involved. No such ideal processes exist, but separation methods are available that approach the ideal to varying degrees, and it is these that are important in chemical utilization.

The interplay of products and method of separation can best be illustrated by example. Furfural can be obtained from the hemicellulose portion of hardwoods. In the presence of catalytic quantities of mineral acids, xylan is hydrolyzed to xylose, which is in turn converted to furfural. The reaction does not produce furfural in stoichiometric quantities but yields also sizable quantities of humic materials. If furfural is produced from the wood in situ, by steaming acid impregnated chips, a large part of the original hemicellulose fraction is converted to a black amorphous solid that remains as a contaminant in the resulting lignocellulose residue. As furfural yields are not large enough to bear the entire cost of the process, it is necessary to process the residue. It could perhaps be processed to charcoal, in which event this method of separation would be satisfactory. If the residue, however, is being considered as a source of glucosan for chemical utilization, it is considerably inferior to a product that might be obtained by mild hydrolysis of the wood and solubilization of the hemicellulose fraction before processing to furfural. This solubilization of the hemicellulose fraction can be accomplished by using either dilute acid or base solutions. If the end product is to be furfural, the advantage of using acidic solutions is obvious. Utilization of the hemicellulose fraction by means of oxidation to organic acids might dictate the use of caustic solutions or dilute nitric acid, depending on the subsequent processing. In the case of nitric acid, the oxidizing power of the acid could be used in the subsequent oxidation step.

1. Hemicellulose and Lignin Removal

Because of the very labile character of the lignin and hemicellulose fractions, it is desirable to remove these constituents before dissolution of the more resistant cellulose. The lignin, in particular, is extremely sensitive to chemical treatment, being easily transformed to a heterogeneous mixture of cyclic and acyclic compounds. In acidic medium, the hemicellulose is depolymerized through the cleaving of glycosidic linkages, and the carbohydrate fragments thus formed are relatively stable in the medium. The action of alkali on hemicelluloses is not so specific and, if dissolution is done in a basic medium, chemical degradation occurs, along with alkaline hydrolysis of the glycosidic linkages, resulting in a much more complex mixture than that obtained from acid hydrolysis. It should be emphasized that the character of the solution resulting from any of the many processes that might be used is highly dependent on the conditions employed and the extent to which the reaction is allowed to proceed.

Efficient utilization of the complex heterogeneous mixtures frequently obtained from the lignin fraction is extremely difficult; so difficult that the most fruitful approach to utilization of this fraction appears to be through a study of separation processes directed toward obtaining a product with uniform properties. Thus, reagents that remove lignin either by means of specific chemical attack or by a solubilizing effect are of particular interest; the conventional processes now in use for pulp production are of little interest because of the drastic chemical modifications they inflict upon the lignin.

Although none reached the commercial stage of development, a number of reagents were suggested for pulp production that have desirable properties from the chemical utilization viewpoint. These include the hydrotropic solvents, such as sodium xylene sulfonate and sodium benzoate, nitric acid, glycerol and glycols, halogen-substituted aliphatic aldehydes (21), dimethylsulfoxide, tetrahydrofuran (20), and ethylene chlorohydrin (5). None of these are specific solvents for lignin, but they do remove some of the hemicellulose fraction simultaneously, particularly when used in aqueous solution. In some instances, this was the reason for failure to gain commercial status;

others include undesirable pulp properties, high cost, and incomplete lignin removal. Their interesting characteristic here is the possibility that the lignin fraction obtained from their use will be amenable to utilization.

The term hydrotropy was introduced by Neuberg (68) to describe the increase in solvent power of water toward other molecules that results from the presence of (usually) large amounts of a third material dissolved in water. He investigated the hydrotropic effects of 20% solutions of sodium benzoate, sodium salicylate, and several more salts and found enhanced solubility therein for a number of organic liquids. McKee (60) cites a large number of examples of the use of hydrotropic action in industrial processes, and holds several patents on industrial applications of the phenomenon (59). Included among these is one dealing with the delignification of wood, a process that was studied extensively by McKee and his students (51,74).

In this process, the wood is treated in a digester with a concentrated solution of hydrotropic salt at a temperature between 140 to 170°C. for periods ranging from 2 to 12 hours. The major portion of the lignin is thus dissolved. The liquor may be reused six or seven times for the treatment of fresh chips until it is saturated with lignin. The lignin may then be recovered by diluting the solution. After it is filtered, the liquor is concentrated and returned to the digester. The hydrotropic salt is thus recirculated, because the salt is costly as compared with the usual reagents used for delignification. No provision seems to have been made to withdraw the dissolved sugars from the recirculating liquor. These evidently end up as humic materials that are removed from the system, either with the pulp or the lignin, or are precipitated during the evaporation step. A difficulty of the process is the washing of the cellulose residue that must be done with a fresh solution of the hydrotropic salt to avoid precipitation of the dissolved lignin.

The salt originally chosen by McKee was sodium xylene sulfonate, which has a strong hydrotropic action at a relatively low concentration level (23%) and needs only to be diluted to 10% to lose most of its solvent power. Thus, the cost of evaporation after precipitating the lignin is lower than for other salts. Sodium xylene sulfonate is inexpensive, readily available, and stable. Most of the subsequent investigations of this method have used this same salt.

Recent studies of this process were made by Gromovs and Odincovs (26), Traynard and Cymery (99), Jayme and Rosentstock (44), and

Migita and co-workers (65). In no case was the range of cooking conditions investigated widely different from that originally proposed, but various raw materials were investigated. In each case, it was claimed that the lignin fractions showed a minimum amount of degradation, and high-quality, high-yield pulps were obtained. At the present time, the process is not well enough understood to be evaluated as a delignifying process for the purpose under consideration.

Many polyols are effective delignifying reagents, and experimental work has been done using glycerol (17,23,43), ethylene glycol (17,43, 49), ethyldiethylene glycol (23), and triethylene glycol (110). These reagents exhibit many desirable characteristics, but have the disadvantage of being much more expensive and must be used in the anhydrous condition. Development studies based on their use would be warranted only if a superior lignin fraction could be obtained. The lignin-glycol solution could possibly be used directly without recovery of the solvent, but there is no indication that this is the case. The attractiveness of phenol as a pulping reagent originates from a similar prospect: that the phenolic mixture could be used directly as a glue or resin material.

A powerful delignifying reagent that is less expensive than any of the polyhydric compounds is dimethyl sulfoxide. Hossain (40) has recently obtained patents on a process for pulping lignocellulose materials that employs acidic aqueous solutions of this material. Wood is heated at 160 to 175°C. with an aqueous solution containing dimethyl sulfoxide in a concentration of up to 75% in the presence of 0.2% of mineral acid for a period of 2.5 to 4 hours. The acid catalyst, either hydrochloric acid or sulfuric acid, need be used only in very small quantities, but it is an essential ingredient, as no delignification occurs in the unacidified solution, which is very slightly alkaline. Hossain (41) believes that it may serve to cleave a lignocarbohydrate bond that might be a necessary step before the hemicellulose or lignin can be brought into solution. Björkman (7), however, found that "lignocarbohydrate complexes" could be extracted directly from finely divided wood when dimethyl sulfoxide was used. Other acidic catalysts, sulfur dioxide, nitrogen dioxide, and chlorine, promote the reaction effectively. A recent publication (13) gives data on the effect of cooking time, cooking temperature, catalyst concentration, and dimethyl sulfoxide concentration on the pulp yield and concentration of lignin and pentosans in the pulp when sulfur dioxide, chlorine, and nitrogen dioxide are used as catalysts. Pulps with high alpha-cellulose content and high viscosity could be obtained from both aspen and black spruce, which were the only woods studied.

Hemicelluloses as well as lignin are dissolved in both aqueous and anhydrous solutions of the reagent. In fact, the original work in this area was done with the hope of isolating undenatured polysaccharides for structural studies (22,28,62). The dissolved lignin may be recovered in high yield by diluting the spent liquor with water. In the

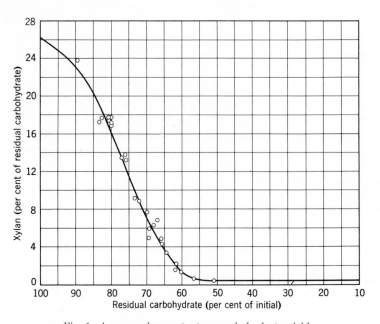

Fig. 1. Aspen: xylan content vs. carbohydrate yield.

patented process, the cooking liquor is diluted to 15% of dimethyl sulfoxide, and a recovery of more than 90% of the lignin fraction is claimed. It is thought to be particularly amenable to utilization, since it undergoes relatively little degradation during isolation and appears to be quite homogeneous. In these respects, it is similar to the lignins obtained by using hydrotropic solvents. The properties of these materials are, undoubtedly, very dependent on the acid concentration in the delignifying solution and on the duration of the reaction.

The carbohydrate fragments originating from the hemicellulose fraction remain in the dilute solution after precipitation of the lignin.

Dimethyl sulfoxide is an unusual solvent, and several patents (34,64) have been issued for its use as a reaction medium for carbohydrate conversions. It may be possible to take advantage of this fact when consideration is given to the utilization of the hemicellulose fraction. In any event, it would be necessary to recover a relatively pure dimethyl sulfoxide solution for reuse, as the reagent is expensive.

At the present time, it does not appear that the utilization of the

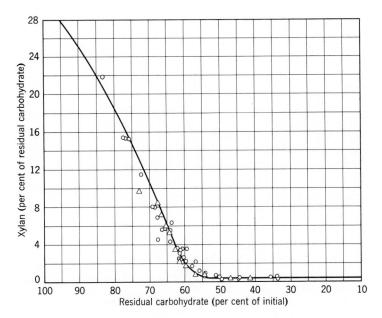

Fig. 2. Southern red oak: xylan content vs. carbohydrate yield.

lignin fraction is a prerequisite to the development of economic processes. The large carbohydrate portions alone may yield products that can compete economically in the current markets. Thus, reagents, such as sodium hydroxide and various inorganic and organic acids, which are capable of solubilizing a portion of the carbohydrate fractions while the lignin is retained in the residue, are also of interest.

The action of catalytic quantities of both organic and inorganic acid on wood results in saccharification of the carbohydrate fraction. If the acid is employed at moderate temperatures in aqueous solution, the process is termed "prehydrolysis." When used in the presence of a lignin solvent, it is similar to an acid pulping process and leaves a residue consisting primarily of cellulose. Analysis of the residues that result from the hydrolysis of various woods and holocelluloses using dilute sulfuric acid in aqueous solution and also acidified solutions of sodium xylenesulfonate has revealed some important facts about the removal of hemicellulose from wood.

In Figs. 1 to 4, the variation in the carbohydrate composition of hydrolyzed residues as a function of total carbohydrate yield is shown

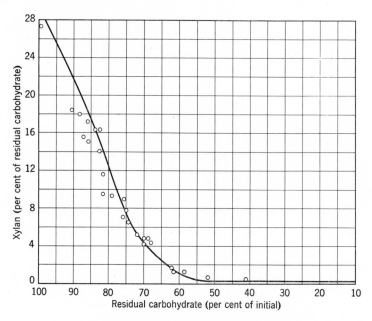

Fig. 3. Sweetgum: xylan content vs. carbohydrate yield.

for four wood species. (The original compositions of the samples are included in Table IV, Chapter 3.) The data points represent a random selection from a large mass of analytical information gathered on residues that were produced over widely varying conditions of hydrolysis. The wood samples were reacted with the hydrolysis solution in small glass ampoules, and the composition and yields of the insoluble fraction were determined at various times, temperatures, and acid concentration levels. The ratio of liquid to solid was 8 to 1 in all experiments; the temperature level varied from 170 to 190°C.; and the acid catalyst concentration ranged from 0.0 to 1.6% of sulfuric acid. In some cases, the hydrolysis was performed in aqueous

solution and the lignin remained in the residue. In others, the hydrolyzing solution was able to dissolve the lignin simultaneously. Analyses were made for lignin and for the individual carbohydrates,
glucose, mannose, and xylose that comprise the insoluble residue.

The ordinate in each figure is the major hemicellulose component
for that particular species. The curves drawn are not curves with an
arbitrary shape but, rather, of a particular functional form. This

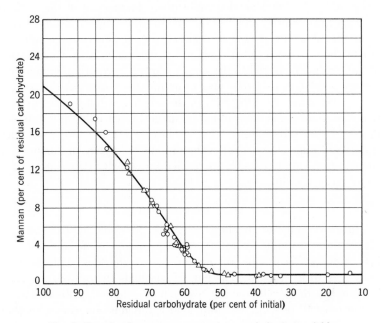

Fig. 4. Douglas-fir: mannan content vs. carbohydrate yield.

form was derived by assuming, for purposes of the correlation, that
the total carbohydrate content of the wood consists of two components of fixed composition (one, the hemicellulose easily hydrolyzed;
the other, the cellulose hydrolyzed with difficulty), which hydrolyze
at the same relative rate regardless of acid concentration. These
generalizations are of value for process design calculations because
they can be used in conjunction with kinetic information on the
system to predict yields and compositions of the various products as
conditions of processing are changed. In this connection, a paper by
Harris and others (31) is of interest. It should not be assumed that
the author is suggesting homogeneity of the hemicellulose fraction.

On the contrary, convincing evidence is available (4) to prove the existence of several polysaccharides of different composition in the hemicellulose fraction of any plant.

It is evident that there is an emphatic correlation between carbohydrate yield and carbohydrate composition in all species. Thus, within the precision indicated and regardless of the conditions of hydrolysis chosen, the residual carbohydrate has a definite fixed composition that is dependent only upon the amount of the original carbohydrate solubilized. The important processing criterion derived from this observation is that variation in the processing conditions affects the rate but results in only minor variations in the composition of the residue, if cooked to the same yield level. Another outstanding feature is the fact that the xylan or mannan is present in all residues. In the case of fir, even after 87% of the original carbohydrate has been removed, mannan is still present. Further, as carbohydrate removal proceeds, the residue composition reaches a constant value from which it does not appear to decline. The presence of xylan and mannan in the resistant cellulose has been verified by other workers (58,66) and seems to be a well-established fact.

2. Saccharification

The conversion of cellulosic materials to sugar appears, at first glance, to be a simple hydrolytic cleavage of glycosidic bonds. Cellulose, however, is unique among the polysaccharides in its extreme resistance to hydrolysis. The glucosidic bonds themselves are easily broken, but the crystalline organization of cellulose results in a much slower over-all rate for the dilute acid heterogeneous hydrolysis than for the dilute acid homogeneous hydrolysis of related noncrystalline carbohydrates. The kinetic mechanism of the heterogeneous hydrolysis has not been established, although various mechanisms have been proposed (25,73,89). The theoretical and practical difficulties involved in the experimental work hindered the development of an exact kinetic theory, and most workers were satisfied to present their results in the form of empirical equations.

Processes suggested for commercial saccharification of cellulose can be grouped into the following categories: (1) simple dilute acid hydrolysis without separation of product as it is formed (46,76,90,104); (2) percolation processes with continuous removal of products during the reaction period (2,18,38,72); and (3) concentrated or anhydrous acid processes in which the crystalline organization of the cellulose is destroyed, the carbohydrate solubilized, and finally completely hydrolyzed in homogeneous solution (47,48,71).

Analysis of the economic and technical aspects of these processes (30,55) reveals that they are marginal at best and hold little promise of commercial success in their present stage of development. Much more effort has been spent on pilot plant studies and technology than on the basic chemistry of the process. The development of satisfactory saccharification processes will require much chemical research, particularly on the fractionation of cellulosic materials, the kinetics of sugar hydrolysis and sugar decomposition, and the modification of cellulose prior to hydrolysis. This type of information is also of importance in designing processes for the production of chemicals other than sugar because the cellulose conversion to sugar is frequently the rate- and yield-controlling step.

The first work on the kinetics of batch saccharification with dilute acid was done by Luers (56), which is believed to be among the first effective applications of chemical kinetics to practical processes. In that early work, it was discovered that the yield of sugar from cellulose followed a growth and decay curve that was well represented by the simple case of consecutive first-order reactions. It was believed that changing reaction conditions affected the reaction rates but not the maximum yield obtainable. In more recent work, Saeman (83) has shown that the maximum yield does change with varying reaction conditions.

While the true reaction mechanism for the heterogeneous hydrolysis of fibrous material is undoubtedly complex, the experimental results of Saeman's work can be quite accurately represented by the simple mathematical equations that describe first-order consecutive reactions:

$$A \xrightarrow{k_1} B \xrightarrow{k_2} C$$

where k_1 and k_2 are first-order rate constants.

In this case, it can be mathematically shown (24) that the maximum concentration of component B is a function only of the ratio of the rates, and may be expressed as follows:

$$(C_B)_{\max} = C_{AO}(1/k_r)^{\frac{1}{k_r - 1}} \tag{1}$$

where C_{AO} is the original concentration of component A, and k_r is the

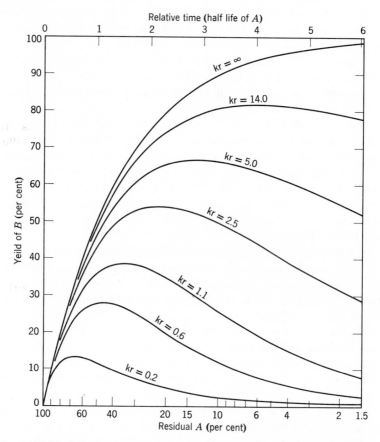

Fig. 5. Yield of the intermediate component in consecutive first-order reactions.

ratio of k_1 to k_2. Fig. 5 is a graphical presentation of equation 1 that shows the accumulation of B as a function of the amount of A consumed with various values of k_r as parameters.

The increase in the maximum yield of sugar with increasing reaction temperature is clearly shown in Fig. 6, taken from Saeman's work. Figs. 7 and 8 illustrate the effect of reaction conditions on sugar yields and time to maximum yield when operating a simple batch hydrolysis, or a continuous single-pass reactor where the sugar is not removed from the reaction medium during the reaction. These values were calculated using the equations for the reaction rate constants obtained by Saeman in the experimental region represented by the

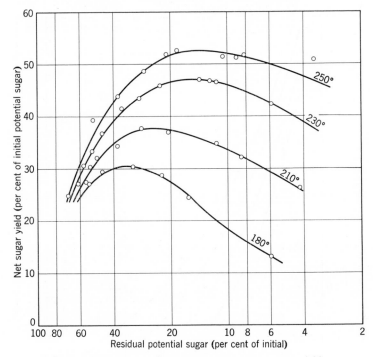

Fig. 6. Effect of reaction temperature on net sugar yield.

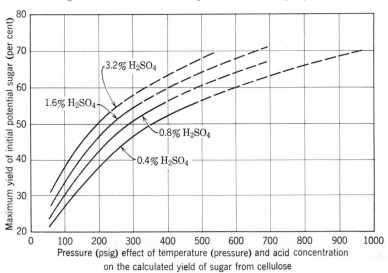

Fig. 7. Sugar yields from cellulose at various reaction conditions

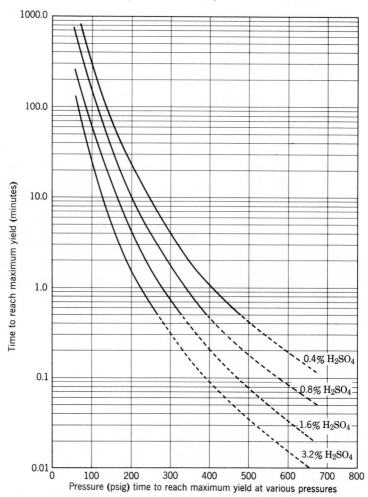

Fig. 8. Time of maximum sugar yield as a function of temperature and acid concentration.

solid lines. The dotted lines are extrapolated values. These figures clearly indicate the marked advantages in sugar yield, product purity, and equipment size that might be obtained if hydrolysis is carried out at high pressures. Problems of equipment and control have prevented development of a batch high-pressure dilute acid hydrolysis process.

The percolation processes avoid the destruction of the sugar by removing it from the reaction site as it is formed. This results in a considerable yield increase when operating at moderate conditions of pressure and temperature; yields of 65% of theoretical can be obtained at an operating temperature of 180°C. The resulting solutions, however, are dilute and, consequently, expensive to concentrate or process. This fact, coupled with the large plant investment required, makes the process uneconomical in the United States. Plants of this type have operated in Western Europe, and many are currently operating in Russia.

Processes employing strong acids give good yields of sugar of high quality. The highly polar concentrated acids cause extreme swelling and solution of the cellulose, which very favorably affect the ratio of the hydrolysis reaction rate to the degradation reaction rates. Hydrofluoric, hydrochloric, and sulfuric acids have received attention as possible saccharification reagents. In all cases, the large amount of acid used requires that efficient methods of separation and recovery of the components of the resulting acid-sugar mixture be available. The strong acid method that has received the most attention is the Rheinau or Bergius method, using fuming hydrochloric acid. Here, the acid is recovered by distillation. The high energy requirement and the necessity of using acid resistant equipment in most of the plant components result in noncompetitive sugar costs.

Work done by Kobayashi (47,48) in Japan on the kinetics of wood saccharification at low temperatures with strong sulfuric acid resulted in the construction of a small pilot plant. In this process, the sulfuric acid is not recovered but is converted to gypsum, which is sold as a high-grade product for use in the production of a bean curd. The carbohydrate products consist of crystalline glucose and a highly concentrated sugar solution similar to corn syrup; both are sold in the edible food market. Kobayashi's reports contain extensive data on the decomposition rates of sugar in sulfuric acid, in phosphoric acid, and in aqueous ammonia solutions.

The problems associated with the development of an economic saccharification process for cellulosic materials are numerous and complex, but they appear no more difficult than those that faced many of the present chemical industries during their development. The saccharification processes developed to date have met these problems in various ways, but in none has complete cognizance been taken of all the difficulties, with the result that none have been economically successful without subsidy. The following discussion will cover the major points that should be borne in mind while weighing the merits of proposed processes and, also, suggest the general direction in which research could be done.

Wood as a raw material, although superior to the annual crops in the general aspect, has many disadvantages. It has a low bulk density and the cost of handling and preparing wood for the saccharification step is high, even when using the best methods and equipment available. The low density of wood is also an important factor in plant cost, especially when batch processes are considered. The available form of the wood is frequently important. In some processes, there are limitations on the type of raw material that may be used; sawdust, which is often available at low cost, is unsuitable for some methods of hydrolysis. Any process that requires bark-free chips incurs a large increase in raw material cost.

The only practical path from cellulose to sugar appears to be acid hydrolysis. The type of acid and its concentration have a most important effect on plant cost. In the strong hydrochloric acid process, the major portion of the plant must be acid resistant, and the estimates of investment cost (30) indicate that such plants would require an investment per annual ton of product similar to that of expensive chemical plants. Plants using dilute sulfuric acid require much less corrosion-resistant equipment, and investment costs are somewhat less than one-half of that required for the strong hydrochloric acid process.

Plant heat requirements depend largely on the end use of the hydrolyzate. In the case where the product is crystalline glucose or molasses, the heat load is enormous. In the Bergius process, heat is required to recover the strong acid used for the primary hydrolysis while in the dilute acid process the main consumption is in the evaporation of the dilute solutions to molasses. Methods for increasing the sugar concentration in the hydrolyzates of the dilute-acid process have been employed (30), and this gives an economic advantage to the dilute-acid process. In the event that the sugar is to be used in solution for the production of yeast, alcohol, or other product easily separable from dilute solution, the heat load is greatly decreased, giving dilute-acid processes a decided advantage over strong-acid processes.

Chemical cost for the dilute-acid processes is small. In the strong-acid processes they become significant, even after full advantage is taken of modern recovery methods. The chemical cost of saccharifying with strong sulfuric acid makes the process unattractive except under certain circumstances where the acid might have further use. The Japanese (47) have studied the possibility of coupling the production of sugar and ammonium sulfate fertilizer, thus effectively cancelling out the cost of catalyst acid and neutralizing reagent.

Waste disposal problems in an efficient saccharification process could be made small; molasses for stock feed and the concentration and burning of much of the other unwanted organics would solve most of the problems at moderate costs. One point worthy of mention here is the production of alcohol. The organic solubles and unfermented sugars in the bottoms of the stills have a high biological demand for oxygen. This is a case in which the waste disposal problem would be greatly reduced, if the pentosan fraction were utilized.

In considering the high costs of handling the raw material, the chemical costs, and the heating load, it is apparent that every effort should be made to obtain full utilization of all the products available, and these should be obtained in the highest possible quality compatible with cost. No commercial ventures have succeeded in such utilization.

The basic reason for the resistance exhibited by cellulose toward hydrolysis is its crystalline organization, hence reduction in the crystallinity of cellulose results in increased yield of sugar. Attempts to use ultrasonic energy for this purpose were unsuccessful. Extreme grinding of cellulose was effective in causing large changes in the rate of reaction and in yield. While grinding of dry cellulose is expensive, some novel method combining extreme attrition and hydrolysis might be useful.

Irradiation with cathode rays causes chemical changes in organic materials. The cellulose crystallite surface is not a barrier to the rays, and chemical changes are brought about throughout the crystallite. This has the effect of increasing the accessibility of cellulose and, hence, increasing the rate of hydrolysis. Such increases in rate of hydrolysis are brought about at the expense of conversion of some carbohydrate to noncarbohydrate material. The net effect, however, is very favorable.

Large changes can be effected in the crystallinity of cellulose by treatment with amines and other reagents that are capable of breaking the hydrogen bonding. The potential usefulness of such a process has not been evaluated in the field of wood saccharification. It should be emphasized that an urgent need exists for more research of the sort that broadens our understanding of this problem, irrespective of practical application.

The immediate outlook for wood saccharification is not highly encouraging. Available processes are suited mainly to special situations. Processes of greater general utility should be developed. Extensive and well-coordinated research is required to accomplish this end. The technology of existing processes might be improved, but it is important to encourage work on new techniques and new approaches to this long-standing problem.

C. UTILIZATION OF HEMICELLULOSES

In their native state, the hemicelluloses are intimately associated with the other wood components. Partial separation can be accomplished by extraction with aqueous alkali solutions, resulting in removal as polymeric fragments, or by hydrolysis with dilute acidic solutions. Acid solutions readily hydrolyze the structural glycosidic linkages, bringing into solution simple carbohydrate units. The utilization can be conveniently discussed in two parts; utilization of the material where its polymeric nature is retained, and utilization of solutions of mixed monomers which are either recovered as pure components or processed to various derivatives.

The outstanding characteristic of hemicellulose is its heterogeneity. This complicates the problem of utilization by precluding the possibility of directly substituting for glucose, sucrose, or starch in the present markets. On the other hand, the hemicelluloses are a readily available source of varied carbohydrate compounds that have only been investigated for utility in a most cursory manner. Hopes for their efficient utilization rest with the possibility of producing unique products that cannot be economically obtained from other sources.

The comparatively recent development of powerful chromatographic procedures for separation of products of partial acid hydrolysis of polysaccharides has resulted in a fast-moving advance in our knowledge of the hemicelluloses. The previous definition of the term, as the components solubilized by extraction with alkali, was recently replaced by a classification based on the main chemical features (4). The similarities and differences of hemicellulose from various sources are being recognized. The main structural features of the xylans and other polysaccharides of wood are fairly well elucidated.

These advances in techniques and chemistry should form the foundation for well-oriented utilization studies, as it is now possible to evaluate separation processes much more precisely than was previously possible. The effect of changing processing variables can be evaluated not only in terms of yield but also in terms of their effect on the polymeric products. The utility of the products can be judged in light of their chemical structure, and studies can be carried on to modify them to suit particular uses. Little work of this type, directed toward utilization, has been done, but the large potential value of studies of this type indicates that such activity is imminent. The carbohydrate polymers of the hemicellulose fraction can undoubtedly find outlets in the market areas now supplied by other natural products, such as gums, mucilages, and starch derivatives. New products resulting from modification of natural polymers will undoubtedly penetrate markets that now are supplied by the synthetic polymers (39,92,107). Tonnage uses can be found as adhesives and binders, food products of all types, drilling fluids, paper additives, soil stabilizers, textile sizing, and foundry sands.

The solutions obtained upon separating the hemicellulose by hydrolysis are complex mixtures that contain various sugars, inorganic components from the ash constituents of the wood, dissolved lignin, and various extraneous components. No one component of these solutions comprises more than one-third of the total solids content. The useful components are the sugars and acetic acid. The minor components, although small in amount, should be considered in evaluating any process operations, since they introduce a buffered character to the solution, and complicate problems when solutions are concentrated or components are crystallized from concentrated magma. They may also be the source of organic or inorganic fouling problems.

The solution from acidic prehydrolysis can be utilized by concentrating and marketing as cattle-feed molasses. The product is comparable to blackstrap molasses from the cane sugar industry and, in general, would command the same price at the point of consumption. It has a disadvantage when compared to blackstrap in that the pentose sugar can be utilized only by ruminants. The acetic acid, always present in this molasses, is also utilized by ruminants. Although this way of utilizing the hemicellulose has the advantage of being a simple process that consumes the entire fraction directly without further refining, and presents no waste disposal problem, it fails to take advantage of the unique character of the solution components, and the product competes directly with a very inexpensive material.

TABLE II

Biochemical Products from Xylose

Product	Organism employed	Reference
Acetone-butanol	*Clostridium acetobutylicum*	a, b
	Clostridium felsincum	b
	Butanolo-acetoni	c
	Granulobacter pectinovorum	c
2,3-Butylene glycol	*Aerobacter faeni*	d
Citric acid	*Aspergillus fumaricus*	e
	Citromyces	f
Fumaric acid	*Rhizopus oryzae*	g
Glycoaldehyde	*Acetobacter acetigenum*	h
Isopropyl alcohol	*Clostridium butylicum*	b
Kojic acid	*Aspergillus flavus*	j
	Aspergillus tamarii	k
Lactic acid	*Streptococcus lactis*	l
	Lactobacillus pentoaceticus	m
Propionic acid	*Propionibacterium pentosaceum*	n
d-Xylonic acid	*Aerobacter aerogenes*	o
	Acetobacter melanogenum	p
	Fusarium sp.	q
Yeast	*Torula utilis*	r
	Monilia candida	r
	Torulopsis xylinus	s
	Torula utilis	t

[a] L. A. Underkofler, E. I. Fulmer, and M. M. Rayman, *Ind. Eng. Chem.*, **29**, 1290 (1937).

[b] N. O. Sjolander, A. F. Langlykke, and W. H. Peterson, *Ind. Eng. Chem.*, **30**, 1251 (1938).

[c] S. Horie, *J. Agr. Chem. Soc., Japan*, **15**, 1097 (1939).

[d] C. R. Breden, and E. I. Fulmer, *Iowa State Coll. J. Sci.*, **5**, 133 (1931).

[e] H. D. Sen, and R. H. Sankhala, *Intern. Sugar J.*, **55**, 273 (1953).

[f] A. Frey, *Z. angew. Chem.*, **44**, 161 (1931).

[g] A. H. Romano, *Tappi*, **41**, 687 (1958).

[h] R. Kavshal, P. Jowett, and T. K. Walker, *Nature*, **167**, 949 (1951).

[j] A. Corbellini, and B. Gregorini, *Gazz. chim. ital.*, **60**, 244 (1930).

[k] B. S. Gould, *Biochem. J.*, **32**, 797 (1938).

[l] M. Toyozawa, and Y. Kaneyuki, *J. Ferm. Technosl., Japan*, **27**, 90 (1949).

[m] L. Weinstein, and L. F. Rettger, *J. Bacteriol.* **24**, 1 (1932).

[n] C. H. Werkman, et al., *Proc. Iowa Acad. Sci.*, **36**, 111 (1929).

[o] E. Masuo and Y. Nozaki, *Ann. Rep. Shionogi Res. Lab.*, **6**, 110 (1956); through *Chem. Abstracts*, **51**, 5192 (1957).

[p] K. Bernhauer, and E. Riedl-Tumova *Biochem. Z.*, **321**, 26 (1950); through *Chem. Abstracts*, **45**, 709 (1951).

[q] A. Hayasida, *Biochem. Z.*, **298**, 169 (1938); through *Chem. Abstracts*, **33**, 199 (1939).

[r] R. Lechner, *Angew. Chem.*, **53**, 163 (1940).

[s] H. Katagiri, C. Tatsumi, and Y. Fugii, *Bull. Inst. Chem. Research, Kyoto Univ.*, **27**, 74 (1951); through *Chem. Abstracts*, **46**, 4167 (1952).

[t] O. W. Winter, *Svensk Papperstidn.*, **48**, 395 (1945).

An appreciable amount of exploratory development work has been done on the application of fermentation processes to the utilization of xylose and mannose in both pure and crude solutions. Much of this work was directed toward the utilization of pulping residues that contain carbohydrates derived from the hemicellulose fraction. Table II is a partial list of biochemical products that can be obtained from xylose. Of this group only the production of yeast has proved to be economically sound. Except for xylonic acid, all of them can be produced directly from glucose by the same organism and, in general, with better yields. Thus, no unique, desirable product, not available more economically by other means, has yet been found.

It would be unfortunate if this fact were the basis for pessimism, because examination of the experimental work reveals that much of it was not oriented toward the utilization of the type of solution being considered in this discussion. Frequently, crude feed stocks of unknown composition with various toxic materials were used; in other cases, the organisms were investigated primarily to determine their action on glucose, and xylose was investigated only at the optimum conditions for glucose. The wonderful versatility and selectivity of the microorgansims certainly warrants that further work be done, not only reworking the processes already suggested, but also in the areas where new unique products might be found.

The production of yeast from spent sulfite liquors is an expanding industry. The current American production is approximately 50 tons per day of all grades. Most of this material is being sold for use as animal feed supplements, but the proportion finding its way into human foods is increasing. The dry yeast (*Torulopsis utilis*) is produced in yields of 45 to 50% of the sugar that is consumed. The culture utilizes both the pentose and hexose sugars and, thus, is well suited for use on wood sugars. The dried product contains about 50% of protein and 3 to 7% of fat. The protein and food values surpass that of leavening yeasts. Much of the present production of yeast from spent liquor goes into pharmaceutical and human food products. Experimental work on the use of torula yeasts in human nutrition will undoubtedly lead to increased markets.

The yeast process is simple, consisting of feed preparation by stripping the sulfur dioxide from the pulping liquor, fermentation in a continuous unit to which nutrients are added, separation of the yeast cream by centrifuging and final drum drying and packaging of the product. The heart of the process is the continuous aerobic

Waldhof fermentor, named after the German company that developed it during World War II. It is essentially an open tank equipped with a draft tube and aeration wheel that mechanically control foaming. Under equilibrium conditions, the material in the fermentor is in the form of an emulsion with a specific gravity of 0.40 to 0.45. No anti-foaming reagent is required. This equipment supplies an enormous free surface for oxygen absorption and, surprisingly, it has not found greater use in the fermentation industry where aerobic conditions are required. Descriptions of the fermentor and the yeast process are available (16,82,78).

The possibility of recovering crystalline xylose and mannose deserves little consideration here, as uses for such pure materials appear to be quite limited. The reactions of mannose are, in general, quite similar to those of glucose and, thus, the compound would have advantage over glucose only in rare instances. Xylose was considered as a possible dietetic food (106), but its sweetening power is so low that it probably could not compete successfully with the other non-fattening sugar substitutes. The separation and recovery of pure sugars by reacting with acetone also was investigated (108).

In some cases, the possibility is good that the xylose, being more labile than the mannose and glucose, can be converted to some easily separated compound, and the residual hexoses could be utilized along with the cellulose portion of the wood. The possibility of oxidizing xylose to glyceraldehyde and trihydroxyglutaric acid (12,96) was considered. Trihydroxyglutaric acid is obtained in rather high yield and could find use as a substitute for other hydroxy acids. The Russians have considered its use in various food products (91).

One of the most promising outlets for the xylose portion of the hemicelluloses of hardwoods is furfural. This inexpensive and useful chemical is undoubtedly destined to have an increasingly important role in the chemical industry. Its potential usefulness rests on the great versatility of the furans (14) and the multiplicity of their derivatives. The possibility of producing furfural from the crude xylose solutions obtained from wood received intensive study recently (79,80,93).

When an aqueous acidified xylose solution is heated, the furfural content of the solution increases to a maximum and then decreases as the furfural decomposes. The shape of the curve for concentration versus time is quite similar to those shown in Fig. 6. Several investigators have found that the disappearance of xylose follows a first-order reaction, with the temperature effect on the reaction-rate constant correlated well by the usual Arrhenius equation. Furfural disappearance in the absence of furfural precursors follows a more complex mechanism which, however, can be closely approximated as a first-order reaction; the temperature effect also is correlated by the Arrhenius equation. The effect of catalyst acid concentration on the rate of disappearance of both xylose and furfural is nearly directly proportional to acid strength for concentrations above $0.1N$. It was found, however, that furfural yields are much lower than the yields that would be predicted, assuming the mechanism to be simple first-order consecutive reactions. This clearly indicates a yield that reduces side reaction, which is believed to be a reaction between furfural and one of its precursors.

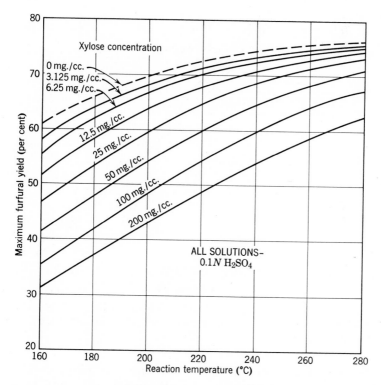

Fig. 9. Maximum furfural yields at various initial xylose concentrations and reacting temperatures. Curves apply to all sulfuric acid concentrations greater than $0.1N$.

Results for the isothermal conversion of xylose to furfural are summarized in Figs. 9 and 10 from which maximum furfural yield and the time at which it occurs may be determined for a given set of reaction conditions with a catalyst concentration of $0.1N$. The yields

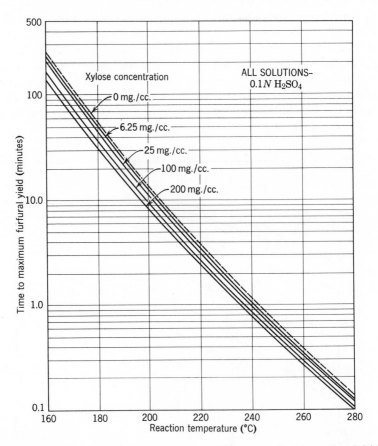

Fig. 10. Time at which maximum yield of furfural is reached for various initial xylose concentrations and reacting temperatures. Catalyst acid concentration, $0.1N$ sulfuric acid.

taken from Fig. 9 are valid for all sulfuric acid strengths greater than $0.1N$; stronger acid merely increases the rate of reaction. The beneficial effect of increasing yield by increasing reaction temperature or decreasing initial xylose concentration is clearly illustrated in Fig. 9.

For catalyst concentrations below 0.1N, the maximum yield is below that shown.

The reaction time required to reach maximum yield for various reaction conditions, with a catalyst concentration of 0.1N sulfuric acid, is shown in Fig. 10. The reaction rate is very nearly proportional to acid concentration for solutions above 0.1N; thus, time to maximum yield can be obtained by applying the appropriate proportionality factor.

The curves in Figs. 9 and 10 were calculated from a semiempirical mathematical correlation developed by Root (79,80). Expressed in differential form, the correlation can be used to predict yields when the reaction proceeds under nonisothermal conditions, which is the usual case in commercial reactors.

The maximum yields of furfural and time to maximum yield when the solution is a commercial hydrolyzate are shown in Figs. 11 and 12.

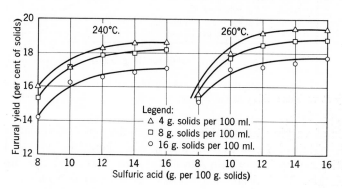

Fig. 11. Maximum yield of furfural as a function of the acidity at various solids concentrations.

The units here were chosen to facilitate experimental design and subsequent economic comparisons, hence require a word of explanation. The concentration units are stated in terms of the total solids in the solution. These solids contained 44% of xylose, 12% of glucose, 9.0% of lignin, and 3.85% of ash; the remainder was unidentified. A portion of the unidentified material was acetic acid. The acidity definition, in particular, may seem somewhat unorthodox since, for economic comparisons, it is expressed in per cent of sulfuric acid based on the solids (not including the sulfuric acid). As a consequence, the effective catalyst concentration increases as solids concentration increases. Most of the acid is required to overcome the buffer capacity of the solutions, which is proportional to the solids content.

A comparison of the yields shown in Figs. 11 and 12 reveals that the

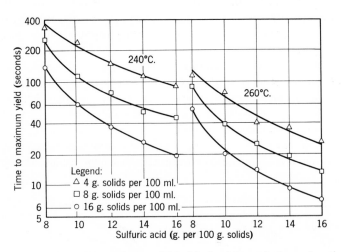

Fig. 12. Time at which maximum yield of furfural is reached as a function of acidity at various solids concentrations.

effects of varying temperature and concentration are similar. The yields obtained from the commercial solution (Fig. 11) at high acidities approach to within 3 to 6% of those predicted from Root's correlation. With decreasing ratios of acid to solid, yields are decreased similarly to that which would be predicted from Root's correlation for acid concentrations below $0.1N$. This effect is due to the large buffer capacity of the solution. An estimate of the buffer capacity obtained by titration of the ash from the hydrolyzate showed that 6.7 pounds of acid per 100 pounds of solids would be neutralized before primary hydrogens of the sulfuric acid became available for catalytic activity. Yields are very low below this level of acidity.

The presence of acetic acid does not have an appreciable effect on the reaction rate or yield of furfural. Because of the small ionization constant of acetic acid, a solution more concentrated than $3.2N$ is required to produce catalytic activity that is comparable to a $0.01N$ sulfuric acid solution. Thus, when sulfuric acid is present as a catalyst, the increase in hydrogen ion content caused by the acetic acid is negligible. Glucose can have a detrimental effect on furfural yields. Root (80) has shown that at low temperatures this reduction in yield can amount to as much as 17%. At the temperatures and concentrations used to obtain the data in Fig. 11, however, it is estimated that the presence of the glucose accounts for a reduction in yield of less than 1%. The results of the study with the commercial hydrolyzate have proved that there is no important reduction in furfural yield because of extraneous materials in the solution.

The economical and technological aspects of furfural production from crude xylose solutions were evaluated in detail by Smuk (93). The conclusion was reached that furfural can be an important product from an integrated wood chemical plant that utilizes the entire carbohydrate fraction. In pilot plant operation, no important engineering problems were encountered, except calcium sulfate scaling, which can be alleviated by various means.

D. UTILIZATION OF CELLULOSE

Glucose, in its various forms, is the most widely used organic chemical in the world. Regenerated forms of cellulose, viscose rayon and cellophane, and cellulose derivatives, usually the acetate or nitrate, appear in many familiar consumer products. The annual consumption of chemical cellulose exceeds 2.5 million tons. Although used primarily as a food, starch and its derivatives find extensive outlets in the paper and adhesive fields. Much is marketed in modified forms prepared by the oxidation, pyrolysis, or hydrolysis of the raw starch. The enhanced properties of the modified starches greatly increase the available markets. The chief nonfood uses for starch products depend on the ability of these products to form water soluble pastes and gels. The total annual consumption of water soluble polymers derived from starch is around 500 million pounds. Approximately one-half of the starch milled in the United States is hydrolyzed to glucose, which is used primarily for food, with only a small amount going to the chemical industry. In this market, it must compete with sucrose, which is available in various forms that range from pure crystals to crude blackstrap molasses. Some of the inexpensive forms of sucrose are used as animal feeds and fermentation substrates. In rare instances, high quality sucrose is employed as a chemical raw material.

The rapid development of synthetic polymers in recent years has resulted in the loss of some cellulose and starch markets, but the future utility of these natural polymers cannot be doubted. In fact, the intensive research in polymer chemistry, responsible for the development of high quality synthetics, will lead to the creation of new markets and the recapture of some of the old by increasing our understanding of the natural polymers.

The usefulness of the cellulose fraction obtained from wood by the separation processes previously considered depends primarily on its suitability for a particular process when contrasted to other raw materials available. In the polymeric form, it is in competition with chemical cellulose and starch; solutions of glucose obtained by hydrolysis must compete with sucrose, glucose made from starch, and various crude molasses available. The principal points of comparison for these raw materials are price, purity, and concentration and, in addition, in the case of the glucan, the molecular weight and structure. Upgrading the crude material that normally will contain residual lignin and degradation products from the hemicellulose fraction will increase its cost. In many instances, this results in a noncompetitive price. Thus, the most promising outlets are in processes where the cheap, crude stocks can be utilized as they are received from the separation process, without complicating the process or incurring loss in product yield or quality.

The remainder of this section is devoted to a discussion of processes and reactions of general interest. These have been selected as representative of the type of utilization schemes that have received attention in the past or show promise of being more important in the future. No attempt is made to describe the general usefulness of glucose, cellulose, and starch; this subject is much too large for discussion here.

Although it was proved that all types of cellulase exert their action by hydrolysis (39), the enzymatic degradation of cellulose is poorly understood. This is not for lack of interest, as cellulolysis has great practical significance. In the digestive systems of animals, cellulose breakdown occurs through the action of microorganisms, and these rumen microorganisms have been employed in studies directed toward fermentative utilization of cellulose. Other types of organisms, thermophilic bacteria, have also been superficially investigated as possible useful agents for conversion (29). In these studies, organic acids, acetic, butyric, and lactic, were found to be the principal products. Yields of approximately 50% of the carbohydrate consumed were found, but utilization of the cellulose was low, and the fermentation required several days.

Wood substance as such is not suitable for the feeding of ruminants; it is believed that the digestion of the carbohydrate component is inhibited by the close association of the cellulose and lignin in the wood. The decomposition of lignocellulose residue by microorganisms, however, is not completely beyond possibility. If the carbohydrates in wood could in some way be converted into a completely digestible state, the wood then would have approximately the same value as grain. Such feed would contain virtually no proteins or vitamins, and these would have to be added in greater quantities than are normal with other forms of fodder. It was shown that rumen microorganisms can decompose some woods directly (95), as well as wood irradiated with high energy cathode rays (52), and various pulps (69).

Starch and cellulose can be partially oxidized to provide commercially valuable modifications of these materials. Further oxidation of the polymers or oxidation of simple sugars yield mixtures of organic acids, many of which have good potential markets. Two such acids, which are now of commercial importance, are ascorbic and gluconic acids. The oxidation mechanisms by which these various compounds are formed have not been firmly established but, in most cases, plausible explanations are given. Relatively few oxidants act in a single manner or give high yields of one product. Methods of controlling the specificity of particular oxidants have not been developed.

The oxidative action of periodic acid on starch and cellulose is highly specific, each glucose unit of the chain being converted to a dialdehyde unit. The acid is not only specific in its chemical attack but reacts with both the amorphous and crystalline regions of cellulose. The properties of the dialdehyde starch product are such that it should find applications in the paper, tobacco, and leather industries. Previously, industrial exploitation of periodic acid as an oxidant was limited by its high cost but, recently, an efficient method of recovering and regenerating the iodic acid was developed (75). This development is of interest here, as the technology for starch can obviously have application to the oxidation of other carbohydrate materials.

Periodic acid is prepared from crude iodine and spent oxidant solution in a metal-free electrolytic cell. The fresh oxidant is added with starch slurry to a separate system where oxidation of the starch occurs. The resulting dialdehyde starch is thoroughly washed, the effluent concentrated, and the iodine in the form of iodic acid is returned to the electrolytic cell to be reoxidized to periodic acid. This two-stage process permits good control of the reactions, resulting in savings in oxidant cost and a high-quality product. Although plant costs are extremely high, primarily because of the electrical installation, it appears that at moderate production levels, dialdehyde starch should compete successfully with modified starches made with cheaper, less selective oxidants.

A similar process in which an expensive oxidant is recovered and regenerated by electrolytic oxidation was patented by Isbell (42) for the production of gluconic acid. In this case, the oxidation of the sugar and bromine oxidant is carried out in the electrolytic cell, which contains an aqueous solution of sugar, calcium carbonate, and a small amount of bromide. Free bromine that is formed at the anode oxidizes the sugar and is reduced to bromide. The gluconic acid precipitates from the electrolyte as the calcium salt. Then the crystalline product is removed and separated from the electrolyte, which is returned to the cell. A wide variety of sugar oxidation products can be obtained by this same technique, but the high cost of electrolytic processing limits its applicability.

The biological oxidation of glucose was investigated for the production of gluconic, 5-ketogluconic, kojic, and itaconic acids (100,77). Although these materials might find widespread markets at low prices, it has been estimated that they can only be produced as intermediate-priced chemicals. Little attention has been given to lowering production costs by improving recovery processes, increasing efficiency of the fermentation, or utilizing cheap raw materials of the type being considered here.

The industrial ethanol marketed in the United States originates primarily from petroleum sources; less than 10% of the total production is obtained by fermentation. It is produced from ethylene in large synthetic-alcohol plants, some of which have a capacity of 40 million gallons per year. The tremendous surge in growth of the petrochemical industry is reflected in the fact that, over the past 25 years, the portion of the ethanol market supplied by the fermentation industries has dropped from 90% to the present low level. Only one manufacturer who uses molasses continues to compete, and it is forecast that fermentation alcohol (except in distilled spirits or by-product recovery) will probably disappear from the market entirely.

To compete effectively as a raw material for alcohol production, sugar must be available at approximately one third the price of ethylene. This is a stringent requirement; ethylene is produced in large efficient plants at low cost, and has an exceptionally stable price level. The cheapest carbohydrate source available, blackstrap molasses, suffers competitively because of its extreme price fluctuations. Economical production of ethanol from blackstrap is obtained through skillful purchase of molasses at times of low prices. Surplus agricultural products, although frequently considered as possible raw materials, have little chance of producing competitively priced ethanol, except through government subsidy. Thus, ethanol appears to be an unlikely outlet for profitably utilizing carbohydrates, and any process for its production from the carbohydrates of wood should be viewed more as a scavenging operation than a promising way to obtain tonnage outlets for wood.

Throughout the world, many plants are producing alcohol from spent sulfite pulping liquors. Most of these are located in the Scandinavian countries and Russia. In Russia, where ethanol is produced by the fermentation of starch, a large number of hydrolysis plants are also found that produce alcohol from wood. In North America are located three sulfite-alcohol plants; two in Canada (50) and one at Bellingham, Washington (105). These plants apparently offer a profitable solution to the problem of waste disposal, satisfactorily lowering the biological oxygen demand so that plant effluents legally can be put into the stream. The sugar-free lignosulfonates can be sold at a premium over the crude mixture.

The technology of the alcoholic fermentation was thoroughly investigated (100) for blackstrap molasses and other substrates that contain monosaccharides. Except for minor differences due to the presence of extraneous materials, the processing of sulfite liquors and wood hydrolyzates is similar to that of molasses. Some of the minor components have a toxic and inhibitory effect on the yeast. The sulfur dioxide in sulfite liquor not only lowers the rate of fermentation, but decreases the alcohol yield, partly because of a complex formed between sulfur dioxide and acetaldehyde, one of the intermediates in the yeast metabolism. The problem of toxicity is met by recycling the yeast cream to develop a well-acclimated organism. The yeast concentration in the fermentors is maintained at a maximum level resulting in a high production rate and little loss of sugar by yeast growth. Contamination of the innoculum by other microorganisms has not been a serious problem.

The most important economic factor in the process is the concentration of fermentable sugars in the feed stock; this affects both capital investment and processing cost. The usual concentration level for sulfite liquors is below 2% as compared to 14 to 18% feed concentrations used for the normal blackstrap molasses fermentation. The cost of steam to recover the alcohol from the dilute beer amounts to as much as 50% of the entire processing cost, and increases exponentially as the alcohol concentration decreases. Steam economy can be obtained by resorting to multiple effect distillation and similar techniques used for dilute solutions, but this is only done by increasing the already high capital investment. Pulping plants with by-product alcohol production have special pulp-washing equipment, designed to recover a maximum of dissolved solids with minimum dilution.

Prominent among the effects of mineral acids on sugars is one of dehydration in which three molecules of water are eliminated from the sugar molecule to give the furan ring. Depending on the kind of sugar, various furan compounds are formed: xylose yields furfural; rhamnose gives methylfurfural; and glucose produces hydroxymethylfurfural. These furans and the intermediate compounds formed in the dehydration are extremely reactive and, consequently, a large number of chemical species are formed. In the case of glucose reacting in an aqueous acidic medium, the presence of hydroxymethylfurfural, levulinic acid, formic acid, hydroxyacetylfuran, and oxy-bis-5-methylene furfural, as well as polymeric humins, is established.

Interest in these compounds is widespread, since they are found in many solutions of industrial importance. Hydroxymethylfurfural is produced during the hydrolysis of starch. In addition, it is present as one of the reacting materials that produce the discoloration of sugar solutions during heating, a phenomenon referred to as "nonenzymatic browning." Hydroxymethylfurfural and related compounds are also present in acid pulping liquors. The low quality of wood sugar solutions produced by the dilute acid hydrolysis of wood is due primarily to the presence of large amounts of impurities made up of chemical components of this type.

Both levulinic acid and hydroxymethylfurfural have attracted interest as possible industrial organic chemicals. Levulinic acid (4-ketopentanoic acid) reacts normally as both a fatty acid and a ketone. The stereochemical relationship of the functional groups permits cyclization, resulting in the formation of many interesting heterocyclic compounds. In addition, the presence of active methylene groups allows its use for the preparation of various compounds by condensation reactions. This chemical versatility coupled with the prospect that it could be obtained from cellulosic residues at low cost has resulted in extensive work to exploit the commercial possibilities of levulinic acid. The literature, which is quite extensive, was reviewed by Bordenca (8), Leonard (53), and Morton (67). Only two compounds produced from levulinic acid are being marketed; calcium levulinate, because of its high solubility in water, is used for the intravenous injection of calcium and diphenolic acid (4,4-bis-4-hydroxyphenyl pentanoic acid), which finds use in the production of resins and coatings. Projected uses that appear to have merit include the production of sebacic acid (45) and nylon-type polymers (27).

The production of levulinic acid from cellulose and crude sugar stocks was explored by several investigators (15,35,63). They found that the mineral acid catalyst used has a marked effect on yield. Hydrobromic acid is a superior catalyst, but the increased yield attained does not compensate for the increased cost of the catalyst when compared to processing with sulfuric and hydrochloric acids. With these latter acids, yields of 50 to 60% of theory can be obtained. McKibbins (61) recently studied the kinetics of glucose degradation and related reactions to elucidate the problems associated with producing high-quality sugar solutions by wood saccharification when employing dilute sulfuric acid solutions. Yields of levulinic acid were found to increase as the concentration of catalyst acid increased and to decrease with increasing processing temperature and increasing sugar concentration. The highest yield obtained was 54%. Despite the low cost of the raw material that can be used to produce levulinic acid, it has not been marketed as an inexpensive chemical intermediate. The controlling economic factor appears to be the high cost of recovery from dilute impure solutions.

Hydroxymethylfurfural is also polyfunctional and, like levulinic acid, can be used to synthesize a wide variety of compounds. It behaves like a normal primary alcohol and, in some instances, as an aromatic aldehyde, although the presence of a substituent at position 5 in the ring modifies the molecule so that its behavior is not analogous to that of furfural. Ring reactions include addition, ring cleavage and, in more complex reactions, ring cleavage followed by closure to give

6-membered hetrocyclic rings. Little attention was given to exploiting this interesting compound, probably because of the difficulty of obtaining sizable quantities of high-quality material (32). It was recently made available in pilot plant quantities.

E. UTILIZATION OF LIGNIN

The utilization of lignin presents problems much different from those encountered in the utilization of carbohydrates. The most fundamental of these stems from the complexity of the chemical structure of the lignin polymer, which far exceeds that of the carbohydrates. The effect of most chemical treatments on lignin is usually manifold, with the result that many different chemical fragments are produced. The situation is complicated not only by the large number of different linkages that exist in the lignin structure, but also

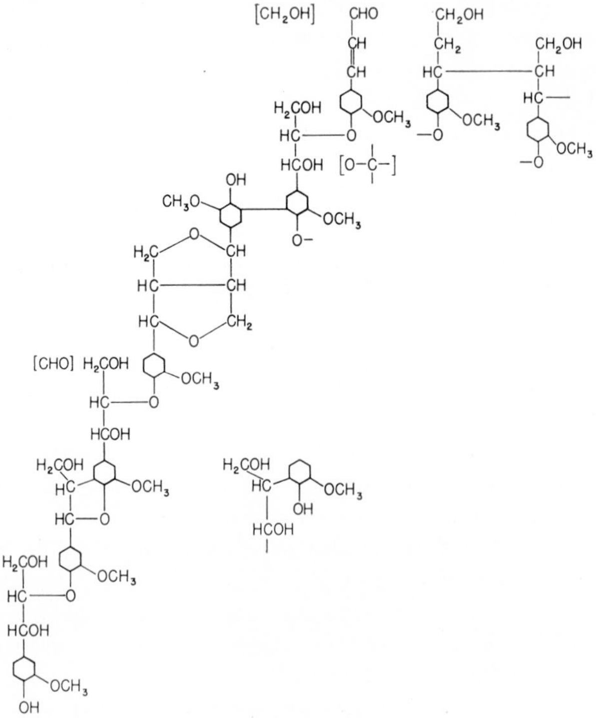

Fig. 13. Pictorial representation of proven linkages in lignin (1).

by the sensitivity of the material. The large number of complex labile compounds, encountered in any experimental work with lignin, places great importance on analytical techniques. The advent of chromatography has greatly helped the elucidation of the chemical structure of lignin and its transformation under chemical attack.

Today, little doubt exists that the lignin of softwoods is composed of guaiacylpropane units joined into a three-dimensional amorphous mass by several types of chemical linkages. The extreme complexity of the material is apparent from examination of Fig. 13, reproduced from a paper by Adler (1). This diagram is a pictorial representation of the proved structural information available, and should not be interpreted as a structural formula in the usual sense. The propane side chains are linked to each other and to aromatic nuclei by various ether and C—C bonds. There is also C—C bonding between nuclei. The three-dimensional character of the polymer is the result of branching brought about through etherification of the phenolic nucleus, as indicated in the figure.

The diversity of chemical bonding results in a highly intricate network, despite the fact that only one type of building unit is used. In hardwood lignins, there are two additional building units and, therefore, a much greater number of possible combinations. No evidence is found of a repetitive pattern in the polymeric structure. Most of the reactive groups of the monomeric precursor are blocked; those remaining account for the characteristic color reactions of lignin.

Perhaps the major impediment to progress in lignin utilization is the highly variable character of the material. Although the in situ nature of lignin is unknown, it undoubtedly is not homogeneous in any piece of wood, and any isolated fraction is not representative of the material as a whole. Variations occur also within and between species. In addition, changes are brought about by the means employed in removal. These include changes before or during solvolytic cleavage, as well as changes occurring as a result of reactions that follow solubilization. These fluctuations in properties, coupled with the fact that few readily applicable analytical tests are available to determine the variations, seriously jeopardize the success of an empirical approach to utilization.

Most of the past work related to the utilization of lignin was done with the lignosulfonic acids that occur in the effluent stream from the sulfite pulping process. The strong pressures from civic groups for the abatement of stream pollution, the need for conservation, and the urge for higher profits spurred the research in this particular industry. The waste disposal problems of the kraft pulping process are not as acute; nevertheless, some of these mills are trying to improve their economic position by reclaiming values from their lignin wastes. Very little has been done with lignin material separated from the wood by processes other than by these conventional pulping methods.

In addition to the lignosulfonic acids, the crude sulfite liquor contains sugars, carbohydrate degradation products, organic acids, and extractives. When concentrated, the crude liquor has limited, low-value markets as a paste or binder, but profitable utilization depends on first obtaining a partially purified lignosulfonate material. This is done by either removing the sugars and processing the upgraded solution for its lignin values, or isolating the lignosulfonic acids by precipitation with calcium. Some attempts were made to fractionate the liquor into lignosulfonate and carbohydrate fractions by means of dialysis or ion exchange. Desugared materials are obtained, with profitable utilization of the carbohydrates, by fermenting the sugars to yeast or alcohol.

Lignosulfonates, in particular the carbohydrate-free products, have found a variety of profitable applications. The most notable of these are their uses in oil well-drilling muds and in the production of synthetic rubber. There are growing uses for the material as a dispersant and an adhesive. Many metallic ions are strongly sequestered by or complexed with lignosulfonates and, consequently, they may be used to replace more expensive sequestering agents for some purposes, especially in agricultural applications. Extensive periodic reviews covering the progress in this field are available (81).

So far, the use of lignin as a chemical raw material has been limited to the production of vanillin and dimethyl sulfoxide. The oxidation product, vanillin, is sold almost exclusively in the flavoring market where it competes successfully with the higher priced natural product and vanillin produced by other methods. Several coproducts from the oxidation process are available in pilot plant quantities but, as yet, they have not found significant markets. The hydrogenation of lignin to produce phenolic materials holds promise for commercial exploitation and was recently the subject of considerable research in Japan.

The only source of lignin presently used for vanillin production is waste sulfite liquor from a softwood sulfite digestion process. Waste liquors from the pulping of deciduous woods are undesirable because of the lower vanillin yield, resulting from the different lignin structure. Only carbohydrate-free material is suitable, and the crude sulfite liquor is either treated with lime to precipitate calcium lignosulfonates, which are used as feed stock, or passed through a fermentation process and stripped of fermentable carbohydrates. The effluent from the alcohol fermentation is approximately 4% of solids, and this is advantageously concentrated to 12% of solids. The lignin content of these carbohydrate-poor solids will normally be about 50%.

The feed stock is made highly alkaline by the addition of lime or sodium hydroxide. The requirement, when using sodium hydroxide, is roughly 80% by weight of the total solids in solution. Various catalysts, such as copper sulfate or copper oxide, may also be added, but it is doubtful whether they are beneficial. The mixture is then charged to the oxidation reactor where it is contacted with air.

The optimum temperature and pressure to be used for the oxidation are not well established. The range of conditions, taken from various patents (11,19,37,85,86,87), varies from 150 pounds per square inch and 160°C. to 1,500 pounds per square inch and 250°C., and the corresponding times of residence range from 4 hours to 4 minutes. The mechanism of the reaction was never established and, consequently, proper operating conditions for each type of equipment were established in a highly empirical manner. Several patents (11,19) infer that the maximum vanillin yield is very dependent on the partial pressure of oxygen maintained in the reactor, and suggest that it should be varied throughout the course of the reaction.

Under proper conditions, the vanillin yield may be as high as 20%, based on the lignin content of the charge solution, and the concentration of vanillin leaving the reactor is about 1%. Vanillic acid is also present in concentrations as high as 0.25%. These two components account for less than 15% of the total oxygen consumed in the reaction. The reaction mechanism is complex and poorly understood.

The sodium vanillate is extracted with butanol by a conventional countercurrent process. Further purification is effected by treating an aqueous solution of sodium vanillate with sulfur dioxide; undesirable phenolic materials are precipitated while the product is retained in solution. The liquor is then filtered, acidified, and the sulfur dioxide expelled. The vanillin is separated from solution by crystallization. Approximately 80% of the vanillin in the reactor effluent is recovered, giving an over-all yield of 16%, based on lignin.

Although its present market is almost entirely food flavoring, oxidation may be considered as a suitable process for manufacturing vanillin and related compounds for the chemical market. From this viewpoint, the present commercial process has several economic deficiencies. The plant investment per ton of product is exceptionally high, being severalfold greater than that encountered for the general type of chemicals with which vanillin would compete. This is a result, in part, of the very dilute solutions employed and partly because of the low rate of oxidation encountered at the conditions of the optimum yield. The recovery of the product from the extremely dilute solution is costly and inefficient. Yields are considerably lower than those obtained on a laboratory scale, using more efficient oxidants and catalysts. The large consumption of caustic, approximately 20 pounds per pound of product, adds a significant increase to the production cost unless it is recovered or reused in some manner.

Despite these shortcomings, oxidation could possibly be a suitable process for converting lignin to marketable chemical monomers. The separation of a more suitable lignin fraction for processing is an obvious step; although it is an undesirable one for the operating pulp mill. It is, however, an important consideration in developing a chemical utilization scheme. A fundamental understanding of the oxidation mechanisms involved would, undoubtedly, result in a much improved process. Although much work was done in this area (9,10), it was largely oriented toward elucidation of the lignin structure, and the knowledge gained was not applied to process improvement. Development work has been highly empirical and, in most instances, the results are inconclusive or unsuited for use in scale-up to plant size.

The use of hydrogenation as a method for the destructive degradation of lignin is of recent origin. The first reported work was done by Lundblad, who obtained two Swedish patents (54) in 1930; these dealt with the production of industrial oils by the catalytic hydrogenation of wood and lignin. Although the chief objective of the investigation was to convert waste wood into more valuable derivatives, the results were of distinct scientific interest. Subsequent studies (9,10) established hydrogenation as one of the important techniques for studying lignin structure. The most recent applied research was done by Schuerch and others (3,6,88,94), which deals with the use of hydrogenation as a pulping method, and that by several Japanese workers attempting to produce phenolic materials suitable for commerce (84,98).

Lignin may be hydrogenated in a hydrogen atmosphere with a catalyst or in the presence of a suitable hydrogen donor, such as tetralin, decalin, or cyclohexane, with or without a catalyst. In the pressure hydrogenation, which has had the most attention, four types of reactions occur: hydrolysis, hydrogenation, reduction, and thermal degradation. In hydrolysis, ether linkages and oxygen rings are cleaved; in hydrogenation, double bonds, radicals, or aromatic rings are saturated; on reduction, carboxyl groups are converted to hydroxyl groups or oxygen is completely removed; and during thermal decomposition, carbon-to-carbon bonds are cleaved with the formation of reactive radicals.

The products obtained from particular raw material depend upon the relative extent to which each of these reactions proceeds, and this is controlled by the specific set of reaction conditions that are employed. The more important system parameters are: the solvent medium; the catalyst, including its carrier, physical form, additives; the temperature; and the duration of the reaction period.

Most of the development work was directed toward the use of lignins obtained as secondary products from the pulping industry but, in recent years, some studies were made using hydrolysis lignins. The presence of calcium and sulfur in these lignins seriously restricts the choice of catalysts. Various effective catalysts are Raney nickel, copper chromium oxide, tin sulfide, iron sulfide, iron sulfate, and molybdenum sulfide, but none of these are entirely satisfactory from a cost and performance standpoint. It is perhaps true that the catalytic effect on those reactions, other than hydrogenation, is of prime importance. A recent Japanese patent application (70) reveals the discovery of a catalyst priced low enough to be discarded after a single use. Such a discovery would have a pronounced effect on the economics of lignin hydrogenation.

The products of hydrogenation are characterized in most studies as residue, heavy oil, and light oil. Little work has been done on characterizing the residue and heavy oil fractions. The light oil fraction may be separated into catechol, phenolic fraction, and a neutral oil containing various oxygen compounds with low molecular weights. The catechol and phenolics are the important marketable products and, under suitable conditions, the total yield of these may reach 50%.

Studies on the composition of the heavy residual fractions might well lead to a better understanding of the hydrogenation process, and point the way to increasing yields of marketable products.

Unfortunately, the phenolics obtained are either ortho- or para-substituted compounds and not suitable for use in the phenol-formaldehyde type polymerization. Thus, the marketing problem restricts the development, and it will be necessary to work in this area before commercializing the process.

A process based on the utilization of the methoxyl content of kraft lignin is the recently developed dimethyl sulfide process (36). Kraft black liquor of 50% solids is mixed with inorganic sulfur compounds, such as sodium sulfide, and heated to 450°F. The reacted solution is relieved to a flash tank, and the volatile dimethyl sulfide and some methyl mercaptan are recovered from the condensate. The yields are about 2.5%, based on the black liquor solids, or approximately 50% on the basis of the methoxyl groups in the lignin.

Uses for this material are not yet well exploited. The most promising outlets are those based on its solvent properties, which are similar to diethyl ether, and its distinctive odor, which makes it useful in odorizing formulas for fuel gas distribution. Its availability at low cost may lead to its use as a chemical raw material but, as yet, no promising outlets have appeared.

REFERENCES

1. Adler, E., *Tappi*, **40**, 294 (1957).
2. Ant-Wuorinen, O., *Suomen Kemistilehti*, **15A**, 31 (1942).
3. Arlt, H. G., K. G. Sonja, and C. Schuerch, *Tappi*, **41**, 64 (1958).
4. Aspinall, G. O., *Advances in Carbohydrate Chem.*, **14**, 429 (1959).
5. Bate, S. C., W. A. Rogerson, and F. G. Peach, Brit. Pat. 686,311, "Production of Cellulose from Lignocellulosic Materials" (Jan. 21, 1953).
6. Bhattacharya, A., E. Sondheimer, and C. Schuerch, *Tappi*, **42**, 446 (1959).
7. Björkman, A., *Svensk Papperstidn.*, **60**, 243 (1957).
8. Bordenca, C., *Forest Prod. J.*, **7**, 435 (1957).
9. Brauns, F. E., *The Chemistry of Lignin*, Academic Press, New York, 1952.
10. Brauns, F. E., and D. A. Brauns, *The Chemistry of Lignin*, Supplement volume, p. 804, Academic Press, New York, 1960.
11. Bryan, C. C., U.S. Pat. 2,692,291 (Oct. 19, 1954).
12. Chalov, N. V., and E. F. Goryachikh, *Gidroliz. i. Lesokhim. Prom.*, **9**, 10 (1956): USSR Pat. 101,202 (Nov. 30, 1955); *Zhur. Priklad. Khim.*, **21**, 486 (1948).
13. Clermont, L. P., and F. Bender, *Pulp & Paper Mag. Can.*, **62**, No. 1, T-29 (1961).
14. Dunlop, A. P., and F. N. Peters, *The Furans*, p. 867, Reinhold, New York, 1953.
15. Dunlop, A. P., and P. A. Wells, U.S. Pat. 2,813,900 (Nov. 19, 1957).

16. Dyck, A. W. J., *Paper Ind.*, **39**, 26 (1957).

17. Erbring, H., *Papier-Fabr.*, **37**, 168 (1939).

18. Faith, W. L., *Ind. Eng. Chem.*, **37**, 9 (1945).

19. Fisher, J. H., et al., U.S. Pat. 2,576,752 (Nov. 27, 1951): U.S. Pat. 2,576,754 (Nov. 27, 1951).

20. Freudenberg, K., German Pat. 836,351, "Method of Obtaining Soluble Unaltered Lignin" (April 10, 1952).

21. Furman, K. E., and P. C. Watt, U.S. Pat. 2,760,861, "Digestion of Ligno-cellulosic Material with Halogen-Substituted, Saturated, Aliphatic Alde-hydes" (Aug. 28, 1956).

22. Giertz, H. W., and J. A. McPherson, *Norsk Skogind.*, **10**, 348 (1956).

23. Gillet, A., and J. Urlings, *Ind. chim. belge*, **17**, No. 3, 273 (1952).

24. Glasstone, S., *Textbook of Physical Chemistry*, 2d ed., pp. 1075 and 1320, Van Nostrand, New York, (1946).

25. Grassie, N., *Chemistry of High Polymer Degradation Processes*, p. 335, Butterworths, London, 1956.

26. Gromovs, V., and P. Odincovs, *Voprosy Lesokhim i Khim. Drevesiny.*, **12**, 63, 79, 91 (in Russ.); *Chem. Abstracts*, **52**, 21080 (1957); *Bumazh. Prom.*, **32**, 11 (1957).

27. Hachihama, Y., and I. Hayashi, *Makromol. Chem.*, **17**, 43 (1955); **13**, 201 (1954).

28. Hägglund, E., B. Lindberg, and J. McPherson, *Acta Chem. Scand.*, **10**, 1160 (1956).

29. Hajny, G. J., C. H. Gardner, and G. J. Ritter, *Ind. Eng. Chem.*, **43**, 1384 (1951).

30. Hall, J. A., J. F. Saeman, and J. F. Harris, *Unasylva*, **10**, 7 (1956).

31. Harris, J. F., J. F. Saeman, and E. G. Locke, *Forest Prod. J.*, **8**, 248 (1958).

32. Harris, J. F., J. F. Saeman, and L. L. Zoch, *Forest Prod. J.*, **10**, 125 (1960).

33. Hass, H. B., and O. H. Lamborn, *Ind. Eng. Chem.*, **47**, 1392 (1955).

34. Haas, H. B., et al., U.S. Pat. 2,893,990 (July 7, 1959).

35. Haworth, W., and W. Jones, *J. Chem. Soc.*, **1944**, 667.

36. Hearon, W. M., *Forest Prod. J.*, **7**, 432 (1957).

37. Hibbert, H., and G. H. Tomlinson, U.S. Pat. 2,069,185 (Jan. 26, 1937).

38. Hignett, T. P., and N. Gilbert, U.S. Pat. 2,801,939 (Aug. 6, 1957).

39. Honeyman, J., ed., *Recent Advances in the Chemistry of Cellulose and Starch*, p. 358, Interscience, New York, 1959.

40. Hossain, S. U., U.S. Pat. 2,901,389 (Aug. 25, 1959); Can. Pat. 537,329 (March 31, 1959).

41. Hossain, S. U., *Pulp & Paper Mag. Can.*, **59**, No. 8, 127 (1958).

42. Isbell, H. S., U.S. Pat. 1,976,731 (Oct. 16, 1934).

43. Janovskii, V. V., et al., *Zhur. Priklad. Khim.*, **27**, 334 (1953); *Zhur. Priklad. Khim.*, **24**, 1100 (1951).

44. Jayme, G., and K. H. Rosenstock, *Wochbl. Papierfabrik.*, **86**, 1009 (1958).

45. Kamlet, J., Can. Pat. 565,455 (Oct. 28, 1958).

46. Katzen, R., et al., *Tappi*, **33**, 67 (1950); *Ind. Eng. Chem.*, **37**, 442 (1945).

47. Kobayashi, T., *Bull. Agr. Chem. Soc., Japan*, **24**, 449 (1960).

48. Kobayashi, T., and K. Mitachi, *Report of the Hokkaido For. Prod. Res. Inst.*, **15**, 149 (1959).

49. Konkin, A. A., and Z. A. Rogovin, *Bumazh. Prom.*, **28**, 15 (1953).

50. Kure, A. R., *Can. J. Chem. Eng.*, **35**, 86 (1957).

51. Lau, H., *Paper Ind. and Paper World*, **23**, 247 (1941).

52. Lawton, E. J., et al., *Science*, **113L**, 380 (1951).

53. Leonard, R. H., *Ind. Eng. Chem.*, **48**, 1330 (1956).

54. Lindblad, A. R., Swedish Pat. 70,589 (Nov. 11, 1930); Swedish Pat. 70,795 (Dec. 16, 1930).

55. Lloyd, R. A., and J. F. Harris, *U.S. Dep. Agr., Forest Ser., Forest Prods. Lab. Repts. No.* **2029**, (April, 1959).

56. Lüers, H. Z., *Angew. Chem.*, **45**, 369 (1932); **43**, 455 (1930).

57. Manufacturing Chemists' Association of the United States, *Chemical Industry Facts Book*, 4th ed. (1959).

58. Matsuzaki, K., et al., *Bull. Chem. Soc., Japan*, **27**, 483 (1954).

59. McKee, R. H., U.S. Pat. 2,784,203 (Jan. 5, 1957); U.S. Pat. 2,308,564 (Jan. 19, 1943); U.S. Pat. 2,298,800 (Oct. 13, 1942); U.S. Pat. 1,932,903 (Oct. 31, 1933); U.S. Pat. 1,929,438 (Oct. 10, 1933).

60. McKee, R. H., *Pulp & Paper Mag. Can.*, **55**, No. 2, 64 (1954); *Ind. Eng. Chem.*, **38**, 382 (1946).

61. McKibbins, S. W., unpublished Ph.D. thesis, University of Wisconsin, 1958.

62. McPherson, J. A., *Acta Chem. Scand.*, **12**, 779 (1958).

63. Meyer, W. G., U.S. Pat. 2,382,572 (Aug. 14, 1945).

64. Micheel, F., and W. Gresser, *Chem. Ber.*, **91**, 1214 (1958).

65. Migita, N., et al., *Sen-i Gakkaishi*, **12**, 632 (1956); *J. Japan. Forestry Soc.*, **36**, No. 11, 343 (1954).

66. Mitchell, R. L., et al., *Tappi*, **39**, 571 (1956).

67. Morton, A. A., "Levulinic Acid as a Source of Heterocyclic Compounds," Scientific Report, No. 8, Sugar Research Foundation, New York, p. 28 (1947).

68. Neuberg, C., *Biochem. Z.*, **76**, 107 (1916).

69. Opderbeck, F., and G. Woerner, *Das Papier*, **14**, 131 (1960).

70. Oshima, M., and K. Kashima, "Lignification of Lignin," *Ann. Rep. Noguchi Inst.*, Tokyo, Japan, Eng. ed. No. 9 (1960).

71. Oshima, M., et al., U.S. Pat. 2,900,284 (Aug. 18, 1959).

72. Ostertag, A., *Schweiz. Bauztg.*, **73**, 287 (1955).

73. Pacsu, E., *J. Polymer Sci.*, **2**, 565 (1947).

74. Pelipetz, M. G., *Ph.D. dissertation*, Columbia University, 1937.

75. Pfeifer, V. F., and others, *Ind. Eng. Chem.*, **52**, 201 (1960).

76. Plow, R. H., and others, *Ind. Eng. Chem.*, **37**, 36 (1945).

77. Prescott, S. C., and C. G. Dunn, *Industrial Microbiology*, p. 923, 3rd ed., McGraw-Hill, New York, 1960.

78. Reiser, C. O., *J. Agr. Food Chem.*, **2**, 70 (1954).

79. Root, D. F., et al., *Forest Prod. J.*, **9**, 158 (1959).

80. Root, D. F., "Kinetics of the Acid-Catalyzed Conversion of Xylose to Furfural," unpublished Ph.D. thesis, University of Wisconsin, 1956.

81. Rowe, J. W., and I. A. Pearl, *Forest Prod. J.*, **11**, 85 (1961).

82. Saeman, J. F., *Ind. Eng. Chem., Anal. Ed.*, **19**, 913 (1947).

83. Saeman, J. F., *Ind. Eng. Chem.*, **37**, 43 (1945).

84. Sakakibara, A., et al., *Ringyô Shinkenjô Kenkyû Hôkoku*, **93**, 113, 123 (1957); *Chem. Abstracts*, **51**, 18589 (1957).
85. Salvesen, J. R., et al., U.S. Pat. 2,434,626 (Jan. 13, 1948).
86. Sandborn, L. T., U.S. Pat. 2,104,701 (Jan. 4, 1938).
87. Sandborn, L. T., U.S. Pat. 2,057,117 (Oct. 13, 1936).
88. Schuerch, C., *J. Am. Chem. Soc.*, **72**, 3838 (1950).
89. Sharples, A., *Trans. Faraday. Soc.*, **54**, 913 (1958); *Trans. Faraday Soc.*, **53**, 1003 (1957); *J. Polymer Sci.*, **14**, 95 (1954); **13**, 393 (1954).
90. Sherrard, E. C., and F. W. Kressman, *Ind. Eng. Chem.*, **37**, 5 (1945).
91. Shubin, E., *Molochnaya Prom.*, **18**, 32 (1957).
92. Smith, F., and R. Montgomery, *The Chemistry of Plant Gums and Mucilages*, p. 627, Reinhold, New York, 1959.
93. Smuk, J. M., "Engineering Studies on the Production of Furfural from Aqueous Xylose Solutions," unpublished Ph.D. thesis, University of Wisconsin, 1960.
94. Sobolev, I., and C. Schuerch, *Tappi*, **41**, 545 (1958).
95. Stranks, D. W., *Forest Prod. J.*, **9**, 228 (1959).
96. Sychev, N. A., *Zhur. Priklad. Khim.*, **11**, 68 (1958).
97. Symposium, *Pulp & Paper Mag. Can.*, **61**, No. 3, 186 (1960).
98. Takahashi, T., and T. Matsuda, *J. Soc. Textile Cellulose Ind.*, *Japan*, **1**, 648 (1945).
99. Traynard, P. H., and A. Eymery, *Holzforschung*, **10**, 6, 43 (1956); *Holzforschung*, **9**, 172 (1955). *Tappi*, **38**, No. 9, 149A (1955).
100. Underkofler, L. A., and R. J. Hickey, eds., *Industrial Fermentations*, Vols. I and II., Chemical Publishing Co., Inc., New York, 1954.
101. "Molasses, Feed, and Industrial Annual Market Summary," *U.S. Dep. Agr., AMS*, Report No. AMS-79, p. 22, illus. (1960).
102. USDA, Forest Service, Division of Forest Economics Research, "Wood-pulp Mills in the United States by State and Type of Product," p. 20, illus. (1959).
103. "Timber Resources for America's Future," *U.S. Dep. Agr., Forest Resource Rep. No.* **14**, p. 713, illus. (1958).
104. Wallace, L. C., U.S. Pat. 2,681,871 (June 22, 1954).
105. Watson, C. A., *Forest Prod. J.*, **9**, No. 3, 25A (1959).
106. Wennig, F., *Wien. klin. Wochschr.*, **68**, 248 (1956).
107. Whistler, R. L., Ed., *Industrial Gums*, p. 766, Academic Press, New York, 1959.
108. Wiley, A. J., L. M. Whitmore, and L. A. Boggs, *Tappi*, **42**, No. 5, 14A (1959).
109. Wiley, A. J., et al., *Ind. Eng. Chem.*, **47**, 1397 (1955).
110. Zenczak, P., *Northwest Sci.*, **26**, 145 (1952).

CHAPTER 12

The Chemistry of Bark

WALDEMAR JENSEN, K. E. FREMER, P. SIERILÄ, AND V. WARTIOVAARA,
The Finnish Pulp and Paper Research Institute, Helsinki, Finland

In the extensive literature concerned with wood chemistry, the chemistry of wood tissue has, so far, had an almost predominating position, while relatively little interest has been shown in the chemistry of bark. From a chemical point of view, it is possible that bark cannot be said to show any fundamental differences on comparison with wood. Nevertheless, the chemical properties of bark are sufficiently peculiar to require special attention.

The difference between the extractives from bark and those from wood are mainly of only a quantitative character. The general points of view regarding these substances, and the carbohydrates and the lignin, are only briefly mentioned here. The main intention is the elucidation of the chemical properties which are particularly characteristic of bark, chiefly in comparison with wood. For the purpose of clarifying the fundamental anatomical principles, a short survey of the anatomy of bark is given at the outset.

I. The Anatomy of Bark

A. GENERAL

In everyday language the term "bark" means the outer part of the stem and branches which surrounds the wood. From the anatomical point of view, the concept "bark" includes all the tissues which are outside of the cambium (25). On the basis of their anatomical structure and physiological activity, the different types of bark tissues can be divided into two main parts, i.e., the "inner bark" and the "outer bark," or "rhytidome."

According to Chang (25), the inner bark includes all the tissues located between the cambium layer and the last-formed periderm, i.e., the tissues of the secondary phloem region, whereas the outer bark comprises the tissues located outside the last-formed periderm. Since, however, the terms used for the different tissues and parts of the bark are not universally accepted, it is not possible in all cases to draw an exact boundary between the inner and outer bark.

Physiologically, the function of the inner bark is to transport the assimilates and to serve as a storage organ for food reserves, whereas the outer bark principally consists of dead tissues, and is thus physiologically inactive and only forms a protective layer against mechanical and chemical injuries (99).

On the basis of their origin, bark tissues can be divided into primary and secondary types. Primary tissues develop through differentiation from embryonal cells generated in the growing point of the stem apex. Secondary tissues arise through cell divisions in special meristematic layers. The two main subdivisions of bark are thus (25): (1) the primary growth, which includes the epidermis and cortex (together known as the cortical region) and the primary phloem tissues, and (2) the secondary growth, which includes secondary tissues formed from two special meristems, the vascular cambium, and the cork

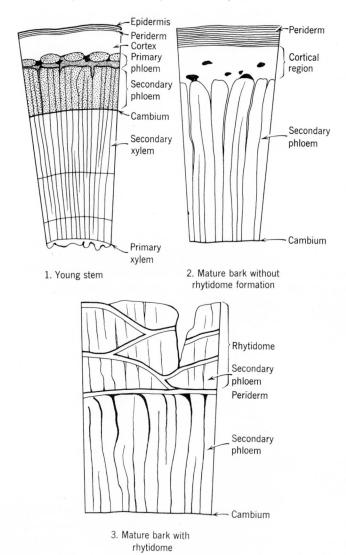

1. Young stem

2. Mature bark without
rhytidome formation

3. Mature bark with
rhytidome

Figs. 1, 2, and 3. Diagrammatic drawings showing the main tissues in different types of bark. 1. Cross section of young branch or stem. 2. Cross-section bark having persistent cortex, such as that in the middle-aged balsam fir and quaking aspen. 3. Mature bark with rhytidome formation (25). (Reproduced by permission of TAPPI.)

cambium. From the former is generated the secondary phloem tissue, also frequently referred to as the "bast," or secondary "Rinde" (in Germany). The phellogen, or cork cambium, gives rise to another tissue: the periderm, or cork.

In the following section, a closer examination of the anatomical structure of the inner and outer barks is given.

B. INNER BARK (BAST, SECONDARY PHLOEM)

The inner bark usually includes the following components: sieve elements, the phloem parenchyma, the sclerenchyma, and the ray parenchyma (43).

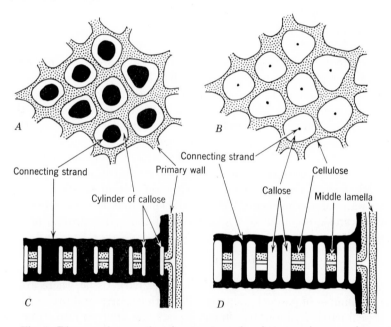

Fig. 4. Diagrams interpreting the structure of a sieve area in an angiosperm sieve tube. Each drawing represents a part of a sieve area with several connecting strands. Surface views in A and B, sectional views in C and D. The protoplasmic contents of the sieve elements covering the sieve areas in C and D are shown in black; so also are the strands connecting these contents across the sieve areas. A and C illustrate younger sieve areas; B and D, older sieve areas. In B and D the amount of callose lining the pores is larger, and the connecting strands thinner than in A and C (44).

1. Sieve Elements

The most important tissue of the inner bark is composed of the sieve elements, i.e., the sieve cells of gymnosperms, and the sieve tubes of angiosperms. The sieve tubes are composed of sieve tube elements connected end to end. Their anatomical structure is, according to Esau (44), as follows.

The sieve elements are formed from longitudinal rows of cells, through the cross walls of which there pass numerous fine connecting strands formed from plasmodesmata, through which the protoplasms of adjacent elements are interconnected. The wall area penetrated by a number of connecting strands is called a sieve area. Each connecting strand is surrounded by a cylinder composed principally of a substance called callose.

The difference between the two types of sieve element, the sieve cells and the sieve tube elements, is that in sieve cells the sieve areas are comparatively undifferentiated. The sieve areas of the sieve tubes are highly differentiated. In shape, the sieve cells are narrower with tapering ends. In angiosperms, the sieve tubes are accompanied by companion cells, which form from the same mother cell as the sieve tube elements themselves, but are smaller in size, parenchymatous in nature, and retain their cell nuclei.

In general, sieve elements retain their function for only one year, in the case of gymnosperms possibly for several years. Then they shrink, probably owing to the dissolution of certain substances from the walls of the elements, the result being that the walls become elastic and are compressed as a result of the active growth of the adjacent parenchymatous tissues (75).

2. Parenchymatous Tissues

Between the sieve elements of the inner bark tissue, there are a great number of parenchymatous cells, both as horizontal rays and as vertical parenchyma which, in many cases, are grouped into strips or bands. The walls of parenchymatous cells are thin and unlignified (43). The horizontal parenchyma cells, the phloem rays, are direct continuations of the xylem rays, both being formed from the vascular cambium. Owing to secondary thickening, strong pressure is exerted outward against the bark, the result being tangential stretching of the tissue and, consequently, general adjustment of the cells as, for example, in the dilatation and redivision of the ray cells. Many tree species, e.g., eucalypts, have in the parenchymatous wedges so formed numbers of different oil glands (27). In comparison with the rays of the xylem, the rays of the phloem are much shorter, owing to the fact that the division of the cambium cells produces substantially more xylem cells than phloem cells [the ratio being about 3:1 in gymnosperms and about 10:1 in angiosperms (72)]. The phloem rays extend, at most, as far as the cork cambium. There is in gymnosperms a special type of ray composed of "albuminous" cells, which resemble companion cells and, in most cases, are associated with the sieve cells (25).

3. Sclerenchymatous Cells

The sclerenchymatous cells, i.e., the bast fibers and sclereids, constitute the supporting tissue of the inner bark. Bast fibers, which vary very much in amount according to the species of tree, sometimes comprising as much as 35 to 48% of the inner bark [Douglas-fir (96)], are in shape oblong [in redwood, 6 to 8 mm. (114)], tapering at both ends—fusiform—their thick walls being more or less lignified or not at all. The bast fibers are usually arranged in tangential rows, the formation of which proceeds in a regular manner; for instance, in redwood, one fiber row is formed during each season of growth, at least in younger stems up to 10 years (114).

Sclereids, or stone cells which, in many cases [balsam fir (59)] form layers between the sieve elements, are short, and are formed from the parenchymatous cells by the thickening as well as by lignification of the wall.

The lignified tissues of the inner bark which, in birch, for example, constitute 20.3% of the whole bast (81), are principally composed of sclerenchymatous tissue. In the inner bark of most tree species, layers can be observed which may correspond to the annual rings of the xylem, their width ranging from 0.1 to 0.7 mm. (72,75).

The width of the inner bark is normally 3 to 10 mm., rarely below 1 mm., or above 13 mm. (99). The proportion of secondary phloem, including the inner bark, in the total bark varies between 72 and 82% in gymnosperms, and between 60 and 88% in angiosperms (25).

C. OUTER BARK (RHYTIDOME)

1. Epidermis

The primary tissue of the outer bark, the epidermis, originates during the primary growth of the tree stem in the outermost tissues of the apical meristem, the dermatogen (43). It consists, in general, of a single cell layer, the individual flat cells of which are cemented together without intercellular space. The walls forming the outer surface of the stem are considerably thicker than the others, and are heavily cutinized, and covered by a waxy cuticular layer (126).

2. Periderm

Secondary meristem of the outer bark, the phellogen or cork cambium, originates, at first, in most cases from the subepidermal parenchymatous cells. In some cases, the epidermis itself gives rise to the phellogen cells. By the periclinal division, the cork cambium produces cork tissue toward the outside. Generally, some division takes place also inward, so that cells are formed which resemble cork cells which are not, however, corky. In this way, the phelloderm tissue is formed,

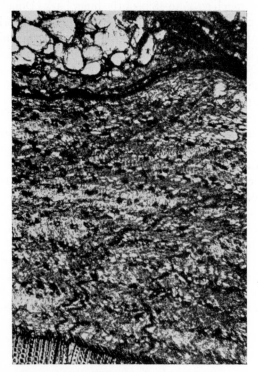

Fig. 5. Cross section of the inner bark and a part of the outer bark of pine Pinus sylvestris), showing the general arrangement of bast tissues and two layers of the periderm (50 X).

which shows a close resemblance to the parenchymatous cells of the bark (43).

The cork tissue, formed from the phellogen outward, consists of scalelike cells, the cork cells, arranged in radial rows. These cells are cemented together by means of an alkali-soluble substance [cf. lignin in middle lamella of wood (64)]. This type of structure makes the

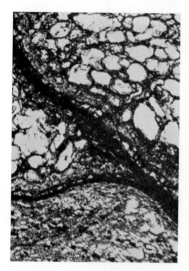

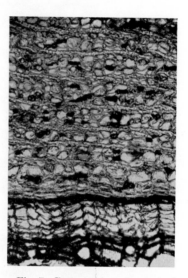

Fig. 6. Cross section of pine (*Pinus sylvestris*), showing a part of the inner bark and rhytidome (50 X).

Fig. 7. Cross section of a part of the inner bark and last-formed periderm layer of pine to show the sieve cells and parenchyma strands (100 X).

cork tissue difficultly penetrable by water and gases. The walls of the cork cells, which are very thin (32) and rarely pitted, consist of three layers, the outermost composed of lignified cellulose, and the innermost of pure cellulose, with an intermediate suberized lamella. In some other tree species (birch), the walls of the cork cells also contain, in addition to suberin, a substance called betulin, which gives the bark its white color (82). The cork cells die at a very early stage, and become filled with air. Primary cork, which for several years covers both branches and stem, grows very thick in some species and differentiates into successive layers, some being tighter and others looser (birch). These layers correspond to the periodic growth of the cork tissue. The separation of the different layers is due to the fact that cork cells formed in the late summer have thicker walls and are more compressed than those formed in the spring (126).

In addition to the periderm formed in the outer surface of the bark, the surface or primary periderm, cork and periderm layers may also

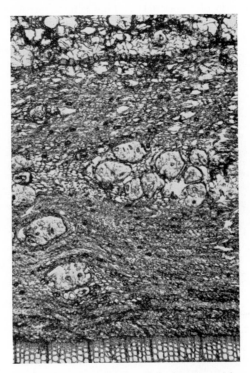

Fig. 8. Cross section of the inner bark and the last-formed layer of rhytidome of black spruce (*Picea mariana*), showing the sclereid groups (50 X).

be formed in the deeper parts of the bark, in the bast tissue. In the transverse section of such an inner or secondary periderm (99), the individual periderms can be seen as curved bands, the new periderm always being connected with previously existing periderms. The interval between the formation of the periderm layers is several years, 4 to 6 years, for instance, in the case of the oak (146). The cork cells are dead and filled with air, consequently the flow of liquids from the inner parts of the stem to the tissues located outside the periderm layer is interrupted, and they also die. The rhytidome thus formed does not constitute a separate tissue type, but contains the remains of all the dead tissues outside the periderm layers, such as cork and parenchymatous cells, bast fibers, sclereids, etc.

Since the rhytidome consists entirely of dead tissue, it cannot expand with the cross-sectional growth of the stem and, therefore,

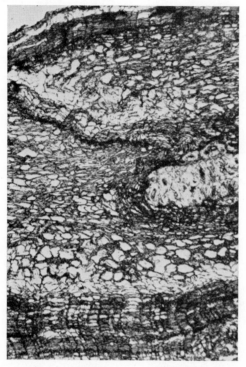

Fig. 9. Cross section of the outer bark of black spruce (*Picea mariana*), showing the periderm bands and a sclereid group (50 X).

cracks into deep fissures and peels off. In each tree species, this takes place in a specific way determined by the anatomical structure of the rhytidome. Accordingly, the rhytidome is described as scalelike, ring-shaped, reticulate (netlike), and fibrous (99).

In the cork tissue, there are areas that allow the penetration of air into the living bark tissue. These mostly roundish, limited spots, where the cork cells are not completely cemented together, are named lenticels (44).

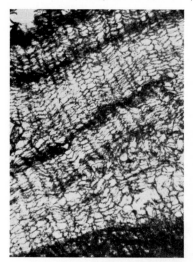

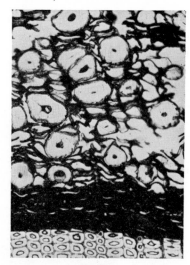

Fig. 10. Cross section of the outer bark of Douglas-fir (*Pseudotsuga taxifolia*) to show the periderms (50 X).

Fig. 11. Cross section of the inner bark of Douglas-fir (*Pseudotsuga taxifolia*). (100 X.)

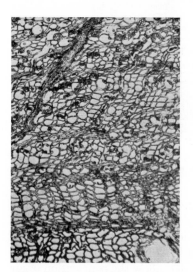

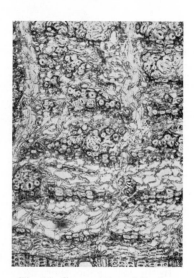

Fig. 12. Cross section of the inner bark of slash pine (*Pinus caribaea*). (50 X.)

Fig. 13. Cross section of the inner bark of silver maple (*Acer saccharinum*) to show the phloem rays and parenchyma strands.

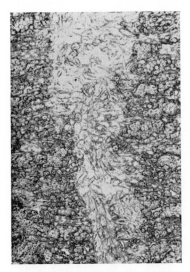

Fig. 14. Cross section of the inner bark of silver maple (*Acer saccharinum*), showing the dilatation of the phloem ray (75 X).

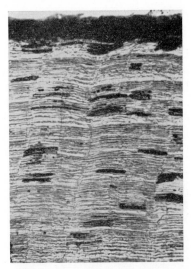

Fig. 15. Cross section of the outer part of outer bark of white birch (*Betula papyrifera*) to show the layers of phellem cells (100 X).

Fig. 16. Flaked off surface layer of outer bark of birch (corresponding to tangential section in relation to trunk). (*Betula verrucosa.*) Extracted with alcohol. (380 X.)

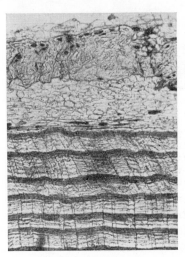

Fig. 17. Cut of outer and inner bark of birch (*Betula verrucosa*), corresponding to cross section in relation to trunk. Extracted with glycerol. (70 X).

3. Cortex

In addition to the tissue types mentioned above, the cortex tissue, i.e., the bark section between the vascular layers and the epidermis, or the periderm (78), can also be considered to belong to the outer bark. The cortex is mainly composed of thin-walled parenchymatous cells, separated by large intercellular spaces, and these cells in many cases lignify, or come to resemble sclereid cells. Cortex tissue may also include resin canals or secretory cells. Between the cortex and the epidermis or periderm, there is often a zone composed of

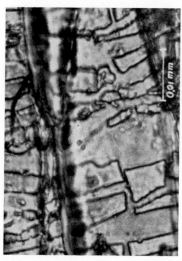
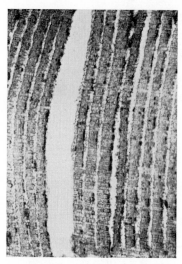

Fig. 18. Flaked off surface of outer bark (corresponding to tangential section in relation to trunk of birch). (*Betula verrucosa.*) Not extracted. (1300 X.)

Fig. 19. Cut through a "lenticel" corresponding to radial section in relation to trunk of birch (*Betula verrucosa*). (70 X.)

collenchymatous or collenchymalike cells. They are regularly aligned, and their walls are often thickened in a special way (25). In certain tree species, among which may be mentioned *Abies balsamea* (balsam fir), and *Betula papyrifera* (white birch), the cortex tissue still persists, when the stem has completely matured (25).

The proportion of outer bark in the whole bark largely depends upon the age of the stem, in addition to the tree species. In a fully mature tree, the limiting values can be considered to be 16 to 25% in gymnosperms, and 12 to 33% in angiosperms. In cases where the cortex tissue persists throughout the life of the tree, it accounts for 7 to 11% (25).

D. DIFFERENCES BETWEEN THE BARKS OF GYMNOSPERMS AND ANGIOSPERMS

In the foregoing, an outline has been given of the typical structure of tree bark. In different tree species and individual trees, however, the order of the structural components of the bark, and their proportions, may vary very greatly. Great differences between gymnosperms and angiosperms can be observed. In gymnosperms there are sieve cells, whereas angiosperms only contain sieve tubes; in addition, the phloem parenchymas of gymnosperms run principally in tangential lines, whereas in angiosperms the parenchymatous cells mainly occur in groups between the sieve tubes; and further, there are distinct differences in structure between the pores in the walls of the phloem rays in gymnosperms and in angiosperms (25).

E. CORRELATION WITH THE STRUCTURE OF THE XYLEM

The structure of the bark is very different from that of the ordinary wood or xylem, the reasons being principally physiological (25). In the wood, there are no tissues corresponding to the periderm and cortex of the outer bark. On the other hand, the secondary phloem layer can well be compared with the secondary xylem layer. In both tissues, growth rings are clearly observable, the relative widths of which correspond to the number of cells that divide into xylem and phloem cells, respectively. The function of both the tracheids and vessels of the wood and the sieve elements of the bark is to transport liquids. The tracheids, however, act simultaneously as supporting tissue. The cell walls of sieve cells and sieve tubes are cellulosic in nature, and the structure of the sieve areas in them is much more complicated than that of the pits of tracheids. There are no cells in the xylem corresponding to the sclereid cells of the bark, whereas bast fibers and the fibers of the wood are very similar.

II. The Analysis of Bark Samples

A. THE FRACTIONATION OF BARK FOR CHEMICAL INVESTIGATION

In a survey of the chemistry of bark, it seems natural to follow the lines of direction given by its anatomical subdivision. However, the chemical investigations carried out to date do not support such an exposition. Relatively little attention has so far been paid to the connection between the anatomy of the bark and its chemical composition. Furthermore, the genetic processes within the bark have been dealt with only to a minor extent. In the main, the aim has been of a purely analytical character, and the bark as a whole has been extensively used as the starting material.

The fractionation of a sample of bark on the basis of the anatomy has, in practice, turned out to be a very difficult undertaking. In many cases, a subdivision into merely "inner" and "outer" bark has been employed. Redwood bark is fractionated mechanically for commercial use into cork flakes, fibrous material, and bark powder. This fractionation, which can also be applied to several other kinds of bark, corresponds to the subdivision of the extractive-free bark in that the suberin is enriched in the cork flakes, the cellulose mainly in the fibers, and a large part of the ligninlike material in the bark powder. The last-mentioned fraction mostly consists of parenchyma cells and fiber fragments. A fractionation of the bark of Douglas-fir, which was carried out in a relatively extended manner, has been described by Kurth and Smith (110) who, by means of screening, divided the inner bark into bark powder (fines) and fibers, and the outer bark into cork, fibers, and bark powder. The pure bast fibers settled in a solution of salt, so that it was possible to separate one further fraction from the impure bast fibers of the outer bark. This fraction consisted of sieve tubes and parenchyma from the phloem of the outer bark. Hossfeld and Kaufert (74) showed that bark of aspen can be subdivided in a relatively easy way into anatomically well-defined layers. After steaming in an autoclave, the bark was fractionated by hand into the four tissue elements given in Table III, i.e., phellem, phelloderm, and the inner and the outer layer of secondary phloem.

B. THE CHEMICAL COMPOSITION OF BARK TISSUES

When bark is analyzed, the result is dependent upon a number of factors, which will be more closely specified in connection with the extractives from bark. Thus far, there exists no commonly accepted detailed method for the analysis of bark, and the methods of different authors vary considerably with respect to the fractionation and the analysis of the material, and also the reporting of the results. The analytical results for bark given by different authors are, therefore, seldom directly comparable with one another. As a rule, it can be said that it is possible to get a fairly reliable comprehension of the chemical differences between various plant tissues only in those cases where these tissues have been investigated under the same conditions.

Tables I to IV give analytical values for a number of bark and wood tissues. Of the physical constituents of the bark, the bast fibers differ least from the wood with regard to chemical composition (Table I),

TABLE I

Percentage Analysis of Bast Fibers
and Wood of Douglas-Fir (96)

	Fiber	Wood
Values based on oven-dry unextracted materials		
Ether soluble	2.92	1.32
Alcohol soluble	8.65	5.46
Hot water soluble	2.58	2.82
Sum of three extractives	14.15	9.60
Values based on oven-dry extractive-free materials		
Ash	0.60	0.17
Lignin	44.80	30.15
Holocellulose	54.58	71.40
Pentosans	8.62	10.11
Methoxyl group	3.89	4.75
Acetyl group	2.39	0.59
Uronic acid anhydride	4.62	2.80
Methoxyl on lignin	7.16	15.20

while the cork cells of the outer bark and the "fines" fraction show much larger deviations. The cork substance is often especially rich in extractives and, in addition, a great part of it is built up from hydroxy acid complexes which have no analogy within the wood tissue. The bark powder consists, to a very great extent, of alkali-soluble material, 88% in bark powder from redwood, for example (13).

As a whole, the bark also differs from the wood with respect to the content of mineral substances, which can be more than ten times higher in bark than in the corresponding wood. On an average, hardwood bark has a higher ash content than softwood bark. In general, the ash of bark has been found to consist of more than 60% of lime.

Potash can also be detected in rather large proportions, up to 30%. Sodium, magnesium, and iron each amount to a few per cent, and the content of manganese is generally less than 1%. Silica can sometimes

TABLE II

Comparative Table of the Most Important Chemical Characteristics of Outer Bark, Inner Bark, and Wood of Birch (83)[a]

No.	Isolation or calculation of fractions	Chemical nature of fractions	Outer bark, %	Inner bark, %	Wood, %
1.	Extracted with ether, 24 hours	Fats, fatty acids, phytosterols, resenes, resin acids, waxes, triterpenes	38.1	1.7	1.3
2.	Extracted with alcohol, 24 hours after extraction with ether	Coloring matter, tannins, phlobaphenes, some water-soluble matter	5.6	13.7	1.8
3.	Saponified with KOH in alcohol after extraction with ether, alcohol, and a solution of sodium sulfite	Suberin	38.7	1.2[b]	c
4.	Substance insoluble after treatment with 72% H_2SO_4, dilution and hydrolysis [calculated from per cent methoxyl (21.1%) in wood lignin]	Lignin	>1.3	20.3	19.5
5.	Substances reducing Fehling's solution and soluble in water after extraction with ether and alcohol	Reducing sugars	—	1.3	—
6.	Furfural formed by distillation with 13.15% HCl and precipitated with barbituric acid	Pentosans	1.1	20.2	25.2
7.	Substances reducing Fehling's solution after total hydrolysis, less the calculated amount of pentoses	Hexosans	>3.4	18.5	43.4
8.	Split off by saturated lime water at 100°C.	Acetyl (as CH_3CO-)	0.24	2.8	4.6
9.	Split off by saturated lime water at 100°C.	Formyl (as HCO—)	0.04	0.1	0.2
10.	6.25 × N	Substances containing nitrogen, calculated as protein	3.8	5.0	1.9
11.	Uncharacterized organic substances		7.3	13.4	1.6
12.	Ash		0.4	1.8	0.3
13.	Total		100.0	100.0	100.0

[a] Values are calculated on unextracted, dry substance.

[b] Uncertain if suberin.

[c] Not determined.

constitute one third of the weight of the ash, and phosphoric acid can be present in quantities amounting to a few per cent.

Table II gives the chemical constituents of outer and inner bark and also of the wood of *Betula verrucosa*. Table III lists the analytical

TABLE III

Distribution of Components in Aspen Bark (74)

	Tissue Elements, %[a]							
					Secondary phloem			
	Phellem 2.0%		Phelloderm 17.2%		Outer layer 67.2%		Inner layer 13.6%	
	Layer	Bark	Layer	Bark	Layer	Bark	Layer	Bark
Ash	8.64	0.17	2.46	0.42	1.59	1.06	2.75	0.37
Petroleum ether ext.	13.30	0.26	14.90	2.56	1.07	0.71	2.59	0.35
Ether ext.	2.92	0.06	3.02	0.52	1.70	1.14	2.52	0.35
Benzene ext.	1.11	0.02	1.28	0.22	0.27	0.18	0.52	0.07
Alcohol ext.	5.72	0.11	31.78	5.45	13.78	9.26	16.48	2.25
Hot water ext.	8.0	0.20	26.50	4.55	9.50	6.38	13.40	1.83
Pentosan	3.28	0.06	21.80	3.74	22.5	15.12	17.50	2.38
Pectin	0.0	0.0	27.40	4.71	3.71	2.49	3.21	0.44

[a] All percentages based on oven-dry weight of original bark or layer.

values of different elements of the bark of aspen. The analyses of tissue elements of black spruce (4) are given in Table I, Chapter 8.

Table IV gives the results of a number of bark analyses selected from publications issued later than 1945. For older reports, reference is made to reviews by Segall and Purves (149), and Kurth (104). The results of analyses of a large number of different kinds of bark have been reported by Chang and Mitchell (26), and by Clermont and Schwartz (29). For a bibliography, see Roth et al. (141). For the sake of comparison, the analytical values for the corresponding wood have also been mentioned in some instances. The solubility values refer to successive extractions, if not otherwise stated.

III. The Extractives of Bark

A. FRACTIONATION OF THE EXTRACTIVES

By the term "extractives," one means such substances as can be dissolved from bark by means of organic solvents or water without

TABLE IV

Some Bark Analysis Results

Bark species and reference	Ash, %	Solubility						Extraction order	Tannin
		1 Hexane	2 Benzene	3 Ether	4 Ethanol	5 Hot water	6 Other solvents		
Abies concolor (white fir) (65)[a]									
Av. tree age, 116 yrs.								1-2-3-5-4	
Bottom sample		2.91	1.02	1.63	2.84	9.85			3.9
Top sample		2.14	0.78	0.41	0.67	14.45			7.8
Av. tree age, 152 yrs.									
Bottom sample		2.44	0.69	1.94	2.70	15.14			4.3
Top sample		2.10	1.03	0.93	0.98	15.67			6.1
Av. tree age, 209 yrs.									
Bottom sample		2.72	1.10	3.80	3.31	10.61			3.5
Top sample		2.46	0.89	2.79	2.31	11.43			4.5
Av. tree age, 209 yrs.									
Bottom samples									
Inner bark		0.53	0.19	0.07	0.98	12.74			
Outer bark phloem		1.23	0.52	1.28	1.90	10.47			
Cork		3.46	1.93	8.98	3.89	7.69			
Wood		0.2	0.03	0.12	3.12	2.11			
Libocedrus decurrens (incense-cedar) (158)[b]									
Tree age, 146–195 yrs.								1-2-3-5-4	
Bottom sample		3.4	1.6	1.2	1.9	8.0			
Top sample		7.7	2.4	0.9	1.1	18.3			
Tree age, 261–285 yrs.									
Bottom sample		3.0	2.2	0.5	1.4	9.5			
Top sample		4.9	1.6	0.6	1.7	12.5			
Tree age, 326–351 yrs.									
Bottom sample		2.5	2.0	1.1	1.6	6.6			
Top sample		3.8	8.8	1.8	2.9	7.6			

Species / Sample								
Chamaecyparis lawsoniana (Port-Orford-cedar) (158)								
Tree age, 242–257 yrs.								
Bottom sample	3.4	0.8	1.5	3.3	8.2		1-2-3-5-4	4.6
Tree age, 285–336 yrs.								
Bottom sample	3.7	1.1	1.6	1.9	7.9			4.9
Thuja plicata (western red-cedar) (158)								
Tree age, 223–282 yrs.								
Bottom sample	2.7	2.0	2.3	1.1	10.0		1-2-3-5-4	4.8
Top sample	7.4	2.9	2.3	0.6	14.5			5.3
Abies grandis (grand fir) (111)[e]	1.80			6.07	7.20	10.02 (ethanol-benzene)	6-4-5	
Abies magnifica (red fir) (8)[d]								
Butt sample	1.21	0.44	1.30	32.15	2.57		1-2-3-4-5	
Top sample	1.53	0.36	0.91	19.95	2.90			
Shasta red fir (8)[e]								
Inner bark	1.26	0.34	0.31	4.24	27.60		1-2-3-4-5	
Outer bark	1.69	0.73	0.90	25.10	4.30			
Pinus elliottii (slash pine) (21)[f]	2.22	4.6			10.9		2-5-NaOH (1%)-NaOH (4%)	
Pinus contorta (lodgepole pine) (62)		2.87	0.90	2.02	16.42	6.94 (pet. ether)	6-2-3-5-4	
Pinus ponderosa (ponderosa pine) (107)[g]	3.4	1.3	0.83	8.3	12.13		1-2-3-4-5 6-3-5	
Pinus echinata (shortleaf pine) (122)[h]								
Bark	1.6		4.6		8.5	7.2		
Wood	0.5		2.2		2.8	3.3 (ethanol-benzene)		
Pinus sylvestris (2)[i]			4.44	1.31	18.25		3-5-4 3-4-5	
Tsuga mertensiana (mountain hemlock) (105)[i]								
Bark								
Bottom sample	1.83		7.53	26.25	4.39			
Top sample	1.36		7.31	21.65	10.49			
Inner bark	2.35		3.90	23.92	1.59			
Wood	0.47		1.47	3.96	1.18			

(continued)

TABLE IV (continued)
Some Bark Analysis Results

Bark species and reference	Ash, %	Solubility						Extraction order	Tannin
		1 Hexane	2 Benzene	3 Ether	4 Ethanol	5 Hot water	6 Other solvents		
Pseudotsuga taxifolia (Douglas-fir) (103)[j]									
Whole bark	0.73[k]			7.80	13.97	2.31		3-4-5	
Bark needles	0.63[k]			5.43	9.69	2.61			
Bark powder	1.83[k]			4.61	24.31	4.37			
Cork flakes				24.55	9.22	2.46			
Betula verrucosa (birch) (2)[l]				12.29	1.08	15.51		3-5-4	
Populus tremuloides (quaking aspen) (139)[m]									
Bark	4.05			15.13		23.06	23.52 (ethanol-benzene)		
Wood	0.30			1.00		2.00	1.52 (ethanol-benzene)		
Populus tremuloides (20)								3-6-4-5	
Bark									
Freshly cut				9.6	1.4	4.1	10.8		
Seasoned				3.4	1.0	4.9	7.3		
Wood									
Freshly cut				2.7		1.1	1.1		
Seasoned				1.5		1.8	2.1 (ethanol-benzene)		
Populus tremuloides (74)[n]	2.02		0.49	2.07	17.05	12.89	3.88 (pet. ether)	6-3-2-4-5	
Beech (97)[o]	7.83					5.78	4.56 (benzene-methanol)	6-5	

ᵃ Percentage composition of hexane-soluble wax from whole bark: lignoceryl alcohol 34.7, sterol and unsaturated alcohols 3.1, free acids 36.5, combined acids 23.5%₀.

b The moisture-free extractive-free bark contained 1.0% ash, 46.5% "lignin," 10.7% pentosan, 3.4% methoxyl, 0.7% acetyl, and 51.3% holocellulose.

c "Lignin" 31.01%, pentosans 8.02%, and holocellulose 45.66%.

d Tannin in a butt sample, 16.3%. Composition of a benzene extract: free acids 42.6%, saponified acids 37.0%, neutrals (mainly lignoceryl alcohol and phytosterol) 20.4%.

e Carbohydrate gum in inner bark 16%.

f "Lignin" 52.4%. Soluble in 1% NaOH at 90°C. 21.2%, in 4% NaOH at 170°C. 45.5%, insoluble residue 18.4%. Elementary and functional group analysis of bark fractions and whole bark are given.

g Constituents of hexane extract: free acids 42.1%, combined acids 29.8%, unsaponifiable 28.1%.

h "Lignin" in bark 45.6%, in wood 27.6%; pentosan in bark 7.6%, in wood 8.9%; holocellulose in bark 34.2%, in wood 69.3%.

i Constituents of the ether extract: wax 43.9%, resin acids 8.0%, fatty acids 8.3%, phenols 3.1%, other acids 8.9%, saponifiable 16.2%, unsaponifiable 11.6%.

j Per cent analysis of extractive-free material:

	"lignin" 72% H₂SO₄	Pentosan	Methoxyl	Acetyl
Tsuga mertensiana (105)				
Bark, bottom sample	51.91	6.95	—	0.73
Top sample	49.05	10.61	3.44	0.94
Inner bark	3.58	13.11	3.43	1.16
Wood	31.85	12.03	5.20	1.67
Pseudotsuga taxifolia (103)				
Whole bark	57.54	6.40	3.76	0.83
Bark needles	47.36	7.46	3.89	2.39
Bark powder	73.33	3.55	2.55	0.41
Cork flakes	81.42	—	—	—

k Percentage based on extractive-free material.

l The ether extractables consisted of up to 95% betulinol.

m Each extraction carried out on original material. "Lignin" in bark 23.86%, in wood 17.30%; pentosan in bark 18.54%, in wood 22.50%; holocellulose in bark 60.63%, in wood 79.50%; cellulose in bark 38.72%, in wood 63.50%.

n "Lignin" 23.01%, pentosan 20.30%, and pectin 7.64%.

o "Lignin" 33.30%, holocellulose 51.08%.

undergoing saponification or any other change. In bark, these substances are higher fatty acids and alcohols, resin acids, fats, waxes, hydrocarbons, terpenes, steroids, alkaloids, proteins, pigments, tannin, phlobaphenes, glycosides, and carbohydrates.

Nearly all the groups of substances listed here are represented among the extractives from most types of bark. Although their total part by weight in the bark is large (in general, 20 to 40%) the different individual substances are, with a few exceptions, present in such small amounts that their economically profitable isolation has not been possible.

One of the first systematic series of analyses of bark extractives was carried out by Zellner and co-workers in 1923 to 1934. This series of analyses comprised about 30 species of wood, mostly hardwoods. Zellner's method for isolation of the different groups of substances was based upon their variations in solubility in organic solvents and water (Table V).

TABLE V

Gross Solubilities of Extractives from Barks (55, 149)

Group	Class of substances	Soluble in	Insoluble in
I	Volatile terpenes, aldehydes, etc.		
	Aliphatic oils, fats, waxes	Petroleum ether	
	Higher acids and alcohols	Ethyl ether	Water
	Hydrocarbon resenes, plant sterols	Alcohol	
II	Amorphous resins and resin acids		
	Substances as in Group I, but more highly	Ethyl ether	Water
	hydroxylated	Alcohol	Petroleum ether
III	Phlobaphenes. Sometimes also glycosides	Alcohol	Water
			Petroleum ether
			Ethyl ether
IV	Tannins, simple sugars, glycosides, etc.	Alcohol	Petroleum ether
		Water	Ethyl ether
V	Polysaccharides, gums, and pectins	Water	Petroleum ether
			Ethyl ether
			Alcohol

In successive extractions, the result depends upon the sequence of extractions. A common procedure is that the material is first treated with a nonpolar solvent, such as hexane, ligroin, or petroleum ether, often followed by benzene. In many instances, the other extractives are extracted with ether, ethanol, and water.

In practice, it is of course not possible to achieve a complete fractionation according to Table V. A rather considerable overlapping has to be expected in successive extraction as well as in the precipitation of groups of substances from extracts by the employment of other solvents.

B. THE INFLUENCE OF EXTERNAL FACTORS UPON THE EXTRACTION RESULTS

Large differences usually appear when the results obtained by different authors from extractions of the same kind of bark are compared with one another. Actually, the results from extractions of bark are dependent upon so many external factors that it is probably practically impossible to achieve completely reproducible results. Such factors are, for example, the age and the growing conditions of the tree, the height at which the sample was taken from the trunk, the sampling method, the lapse of time between sampling and analysis, the treatment of the analytical material, and so on. In Table IV, there are given some analytical results that show the influence of variations in the external conditions on the content of extractives of different kinds of bark. In the main, seasoning diminishes the content of extractives of the bark of aspen (20). The content of the extractives of bark samples from white fir (65) and three species of cedar (158), taken at different heights of the trunk from trees of different ages, has been determined. In white fir, in all age groups, the wax and ether extract content of the bark is highest in the lower part of the trunk. In the case of incense-cedar, quite the contrary can be observed. This constitutes an example of the difficulties in drawing conclusions of general validity from bark analyses. In young trees, the content of water extractives is higher in the top samples than in the bottom samples whereas, on the whole, the differences have been counter-balanced in older trees. The content of ether-soluble matter and phlobaphenes increases with age.

C. SOME EXTRANEOUS SUBSTANCES ISOLATED FROM SPECIAL TYPES OF BARK

It is not possible within the scope of this chapter to give a detailed and complete list of the occurrence of different individual substances in bark. Those compounds that can be considered as being derivatives of anthraquinone, and α- and γ-pyrone, are especially to be found in very great number. In the following, some groups of substances that are present in bark are briefly characterized by means of a number of examples. Further information on the properties and the occurrence of these and other natural substances (exclusive of alkaloids) can be obtained from a book by Karrer (94).

1. Alcohols

Besides the alcohols commonly present in wax and fat, i.e., lignoceryl and behenyl alcohol, glycerol, and so on, certain polyalcohols have been detected in bark such as, for example, d-mannite (133) and dulcite (94), and alicyclic alcohols, such as d-quercitol in oak bark (94), quebrachitol (132), and inositol (98).

2. Carboxylic Acids, Amides, and Lactones

Fatty acids and resin acids are dealt with subsequently. Monotropitoside is a glycoside of salicylic acid methyl ester and primverose. This compound has been detected primarily in the bark of *Betula lenta*, according to Bridel and Picard, as a yield of 60 g. from 20 kg. of bark (15). As an example of the presence of carboxylic acids in bark, piperonylic acid, p-coumaric acid, and caffeic acid can further be mentioned (94). Fagaramide has, for example, been detected in the bark of *Xanthoxylum macrophyllum* (51).

I　　　　　　II　　　　　　III

Protocatechuic acid (I) and ellagic acid (II) are obtained as decomposition products from more complicated compounds. Protocatechuic acid is present, rather often also in a free form, in bark and other plant tissues. Ellagic acid has been detected in the bark of spruce and oak, for example.

3. Aldehydes, Ketones

Cinnamaldehyde can be isolated from bark oil from *Cinnamomum zeylonicum*. Salicylic aldehyde has been detected by Koepfli (98) in the bark of *Rauwolfia caffra*. Other aldehydes detected in bark are myristic aldehyde (144), 4-methoxysalicylic aldehyde and gluco-vanillin (in young beech bark).

Picein (ameliaroside) is a glucoside of *p*-hydroxyacetophenone, and is present in several kinds of bark. Bridel et al. isolated picein in amounts of up to 1% from the bark of *Amelanchier vulgaris* (14). Cotoin (III) is present in "coto bark," i.e., in the bark of *Nectandra coto*. In various barks, many compounds closely related to cotoin are present, such as for example hydrocotoin, maclurin, protocotoin, and phloretin. D-Camphor has been isolated from root bark oil from *Cinnamomum zeylonicum* (94).

4. Phenols

Bark of *Salicaceae* contains a group of glucosides of which some were very early detected in bark. Leroux detected salicin, (IV, $R_1 = R_2 = H$), in the bark of *Salix helix* in 1830, and populin (IV, $R_1 = H$, $R_2 = C_6H_5CO$) was isolated in the same year by Braconnot from the bark of *Populus tremula*. Tremuloidin (IV,

$R_1 = C_6H_5CO$, $R_2 = H$) was reported in the bark of *Populus tremuloides* by Pearl and Darling (129), along with a glucoside supposed to be populin, but subsequently found to be salireposide (V) (130).

Salireposide has also been isolated from the bark of *Salicaceae* (134). In the bark from species of birch, primarily *Betula alba*, betuloside (VI) has been detected (159). Plouvier detected coniferin and syringin (VII) in the bark of species of *Fraxinus* (133).

5. Lignans

Like lignin, the lignans can be thought of as being derived from phenylpropane units, although they are not polymeric compounds, but combined from two coniferyl units. Hearon and MacGregor (60) have prepared a review on the lignans occurring in a natural state.

In the bark of species of *Himantandra*, Hughes and Ritchie found four lignans: galbulin and galcatin (VIII), which are phenyltetra-hydronaphthalene derivatives, and galbacin (IX) and galgravin, which are tetrahydrofuran derivatives (76).

A number of lignans of tetrahydrofurofuran type, of close mutual relation, have been detected in different kinds of bark. Eudesmin is present in a gumlike exudate of *Eucalyptus hemiphloia*, phillyrin in the bark of *Phillyrea latifolia*, asarinin in the bark of *Xanthoxylum carolinianum*, and symplocosin in the bark of *Symplocos lucida*.

Dickey (36) has detected liriodendrin (X) in the inner bark of yellow poplar.

6. Quinones, Anthraquinones

Derivatives of quinone are present in bark in small quantities. Here, only some naphthoquinones, such as plumbagin (124), alkannan, and alkannin, can be mentioned.

Derivatives of anthraquinone are more commonly present in bark. As examples, there may be mentioned anthragallol (XI) and different

methyl ethers thereof, rubiadin and its methyl ether, and soranjidiol (19), morindone and morindin (17), and emodin (XII) (94).

7. Derivatives of α- and γ-Pyrone

Among the rather numerous derivatives of α-pyrone isolated from bark, the following examples are given here. Fraxetin (XIII) and esculetin, and the corresponding glucosides, fraxin and esculin, have been isolated from the bark of species of *Fraxinus* (154,155). Fraxinol has also been detected in the bark of ash (155). Other compounds of this type isolated from bark are umbelliferone (28), scopoletin (138), and xanthoxyletin (XIV) (18).

The derivatives of γ-pyrone constitute a very large group of natural substances, including some flavonoids, the most important of which will be described later. As representatives of the derivatives of γ-pyrone of another type, which have been isolated from bark, maltol (XV) (94) from larch tree bark, and rotenone [from root bark of *Piscidia erythrina* (127)] can be mentioned.

D. WAX AND FAT IN BARK

The fraction which can be extracted from bark by means of hydrocarbons is often referred to as wax, despite the fact that besides genuine waxes it generally contains a large proportion of other substances, such as resin acids, triterpenes, nonaliphatic alcohols, and so on. In Fig. 20, the separation of a petroleum ether extract of aspen bark is described.

The proper wax fractions are principally composed of lignoceric and behenic acid, partly in a free form, partly as esterified with lignoceryl

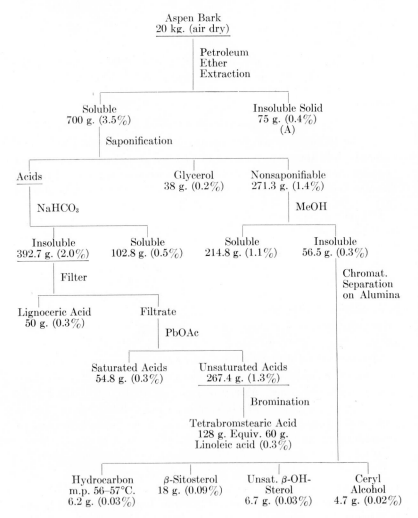

Fig. 20. Separation of the petroleum ether extractives of aspen bark (73).

and behenyl alcohol, and glycerol. In some cases, mention has also been made of the presence of, for example, palmitic, caproic, and azelaic acid, hydroxypalmitic and hydroxymyristic acid, and unsaturated acids, primarily oleic, linoleic, and linolenic acid. Fat is present in bark to a relatively insignificant extent, which is clear from the fact that the amounts of glycerol found are rather small. According to Becker (9), spruce bark contains about 5.3% of crude fat, two thirds of which proved to be digestible in feeding experiments.

By saponification of the benzene-soluble wax from Douglas fir and ponderosa pine bark, rather large amounts of phlobaphene-like material were obtained (64,107). In the opinion of Kurth and Hubbard (107), the phlobaphene is combined with the fatty acids of the wax to make a phlobaphene-fatty acid complex. Hergert and Kurth (65), after saponification, isolated from benzene-soluble wax from white-fir bark phenolic acids of the same type as those described in connection with the bark lignin (Section IV-B).

By means of saponification of the wax extracted from Douglas-fir bark with hexane, there were obtained 60% of lignoceric acid, 20% of lignoceryl alcohol, and 20% of ferulic acid (106; see Section IV, formula XXVIII).

The phenolic component in the bark wax from Douglas-fir gives, by its reactivity, a possibility of influencing the properties of this wax in a number of ways. The melting point of the wax can be raised by 50°C., and its hardness and its ability to retain solvents increased; in doing this, the wax becomes suitable for polishes (106).

There is very little information available on the hydrocarbons in wax. In general, the hydrocarbons found have been of paraffin type. Pajari (128) found n-nonacosane in oil from pine bark. Jermstad (91) found n-docosane in oil from sagrada bark (*Rhamnus purshiana*), and β-phellandrene has been found in cinnamon bark oil (94).

E. TERPENES AND RESIN ACIDS

In the resin ducts of coniferous trees, and in pathologic resin (oleo-resin), which is secreted at the surface of damaged tissues, terpenes are often found together with resin acids (see also Chapter 7).

The volatile oils in the oleoresins mainly consist of terpenes (aldehydes, ketones, alcohols, esters, and so on). The small amounts of volatile oil that have been found in the hydrocarbon extractives of bark consist principally of monoterpenes. Schorger (145) found that the volatile oil of incense-cedar bark consists of α-pinene, dipentene, bornyl acetate, borneol, and small amounts of furfural. The hexane extract of incense-cedar bark (2.5 to 7.7%) contains 0.95% of volatile oil (158). In hexane extract of bark from *Pinus ponderosa* (3.4%), there is 0.2% of a volatile oil (107) with the same properties as the volatile oil in the wood. This oil was found to consist of α- and β-pinene, dipentene, borneol, and bornyl acetate.

The resin acids can be considered as diterpenes, because their skeletal structure is built up of isoprene. Most of the resin acids can be considered as being derived from either abietic acid (XVI) or

pimaric acid (XVII). The natural resin acids constitute complicated mixtures. Because they easily undergo isomerization and other changes, it is difficult to isolate them as individual substances.

The hexane extract of the bark of ponderosa pine (3.4% of the bark) contains 19.5% of free resin acids (107). The benzene extract of incense-cedar bark, after previous extraction with hexane, consists of 72% of resin acids (158), a small part of this being present in a combined form. The amount of benzene extract varies from 1.6 to 8.8%, according to the position on the trunk and the age of the tree.

In oil extracted with petroleum ether from the bark of *Pinus sylvestris*, the resin acids amounted to 4.7 to 9.5% (128). In white spruce bark, resin acids amounting to 1 to 1.5% of the bark were found (11). Also, in the bark of beech (30) and aspen (20), acids that could not be esterified were found.

The terpenes of the bark are mainly of triterpene type. The most plentiful representative of this group of substances is surely betulinol (XVIII). In the outer bark of birch, betulinol is contained in proportions that are unusually large for a compound of this type. Sosa (159) found up to 25% of betulinol in the cork layer of *Betula alba*, and Hirota et al. up to 35% of betulinol in the outer bark layer of *B. platyphylla* (69). Betulinol gives the outer bark of the birch its white color. In smaller amounts, betulinol has been found, for example, in the bark of beech and hazel.

Betulinic acid (—COOH instead of —CH$_2$OH in betulinol) was found by Zellner and Ziffer in the bark of *Platanus orientalis*. Subsequently, betulinic acid has been isolated from, for example, the bark of *Cornus florida* (140) and *Platanus acerifolia* (22), and from the bark of different species of *Melaleuca*. Friedelin (XIX) and cerin (α-hydroxyfriedelin) have been isolated from cork by Drake and Jacobsen, among others; they found these substances in amounts of 1.3 and 0.1 to 0.15% of the cork substance, respectively (38). Jefferies (80) has found friedelin and the corresponding alcohol, epifriedelinol, in the bark of coachwood (*Ceratopetalum apetalum*).

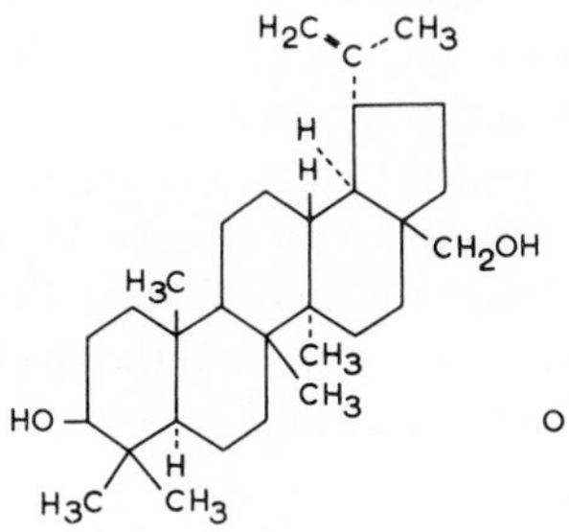

XVIII 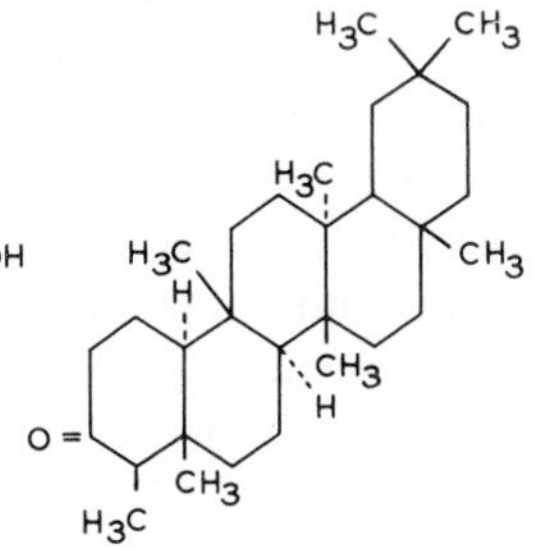   XIX

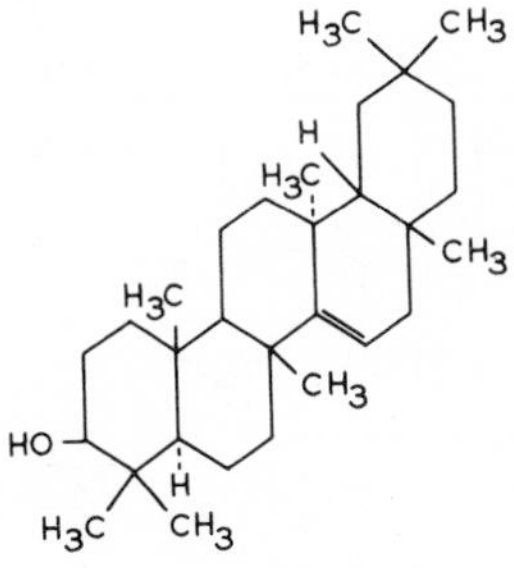

XX

Oleanolic acid acetate has been found in the bark of birch (142) and *Eucalyptus calophylla* up to 0.3% (165). From the bark of *Leptospermum scoparium*, Corbett and McDowell (31) have isolated betulinic acid, oleanolic acid, and ursolic acid acetate. Zellner et al. found taraxerol (alnulin, XX) and the corresponding ketone, taraxerone (protalnulin), in the bark of alder, both *Alnus incana* and *Alnus glutinosa* (167).

Besides the triterpenes mentioned above, hederagenin, chinovic acid, phyllanthol, alnusenone, and melaleucic acid have been found in different kinds of bark. Additional information on the structure and occurrence of these and other terpenes can be obtained from a book by Karrer (94).

F. PHYTOSTEROLS AND DIGITALOIDS

The neutral, nonvolatile part of the oleoresins consists of unsaponifiable matter (higher terpenes and, in some cases, aliphatic hydrocarbons) and esters. The acid components of the esters are fatty acids and resin acids. The alcohol components are higher aliphatic alcohols, higher terpene alcohols, and phytosterols.

The sterols are alcohols, most frequently unsaturated, with 27 to 31 carbon atoms. In accordance with their occurrence in animals or plants, they are subdivided into zoosterols and phytosterols. Among the phytosterols, the mycosterols found in fungi and the sterols of algae constitute separate groups. The chemical differences between these groups are insignificant. With regard to their skeletal structure, the sterols can be derived from sterane (XXI).

$$\underline{XXI} \qquad \underline{XXII}$$

Mixtures of phytosterols have been isolated by saponification of the fractions of wax and resin obtained from the extraction of bark. The yields have, generally, amounted to less than 0.1% of the weight of the bark. β-Sitosterol (XXII) has often been found in these mixtures. In addition, dihydro-β-sitosterol (128), α-sitosterol (not unitary), and stigmasterol (in the bark of elm and ash) have been found in different kinds of bark.

Digitalis glycosides have, in some cases, been detected in bark. The aglycones of these glycosides differ in regard to structure from sterols by having a 5 or 6 ring of lactone type instead of the open side chain at the same carbon atom. As the sugar part, glucose and rhamnose are present, and, in addition, a number of sugars, which have thus far been found only in these glycosides as D-digitalose, L-acovenose, D-cymarose, D-diginose, and so on. They are all methyl pentoses.

The bark of *Nerium odorum* contains a number of digitaloids (138), which are glycosides of digitoxigenin (odoroside H, odorotrioside), or 5-allodigitoxigenin (odoroside B and K; odorobioside K). In the bark of *Periploca graeca*, periplocymarin and periplocin have been detected; these are glycosides of periplogenin. Acovenoside A is a constituent of the bark of *Acocanthera longiflora*.

G. COLORING MATTERS

Flavone, isoflavone, and flavanone derivatives, anthocyanins, and leucoanthocyanins constitute an important group of pigments, which are very widely spread in plants. Many authors use the name "flavonoids" for all these compounds. In accordance with Karrer (94), the anthocyanins and leucoanthocyanins are here dealt with separately, while the other compounds are included in the conception of "flavonoids," or "flavonoid compounds."

1. Flavonoid Compounds

The derivatives of flavone, isoflavone, and flavanone occur naturally as yellow pigments, and they can, with respect to their general structure, be derived from 2- or 3-phenylbenzo-γ-pyrone.

XXIII

Taxifolin: $R_1 = R_2 = OH$, $R_3 = H$
Dihydromyricetin: $R_1 = R_2 = R_3 = OH$
Aromadendrin: $R_1 = R_3 = H$, $R_2 = OH$
Pinobanksin: $R_1 = R_2 = R_3 = H$

XXIV

Quercetin: $R = H$
Myricetin: $R = OH$

Flavonoids are present in rather large amounts in different plant tissues, both as glycosides and in a free state. Some of them are colorless, such as for example the basic substance flavone. A visible color appears when hydroxyl groups are present as substituents.

Mono- , di- , and trisaccharides can be connected to different positions in the aglycone.

There are a large number of flavonoid compounds found in bark. Only a few examples of their occurrence can be given here. Hergert (62) found all the flavonoids listed above in lodgepole pine bark. Kurth et al. (108) found quercetin, pinoquercetin (6-Me-quercetin), pinomyricetin (6-Me-myricetin), and taxifolin in bark from ponderosa pine.

The flavonoids that are most important commercially are quercetin and taxifolin (dihydroquercetin). Quercetin was earlier isolated mainly from the inner bark of American black oak and from the leaves of Australian eucalyptus. In the bark of black oak, quercetin is found in the form of its 3-rhamnoside, quercitrin (35). This glycoside obtained its name when Chevreul proved its presence in the bark of *Quercus tinctoria*. Quercimerithrin (quercetin-7-glucoside) has been found in the bark of a species of *Prunus*. Quercetin is of medical importance, primarily in the form of the glycoside rutin (quercetin-3-rutinoside, quercetin-3-rhamnoglucoside). Rutin is isolated from buckwheat, but is also present in the root bark of *Coprosma rhamnoides* (94), for example.

The dehydrogenation of taxifolin nowadays constitutes an important method for the preparation of quercetin. Taxifolin was found by Pew in 1947 in Douglas-fir which, later, became one of the most important sources for the isolation of taxifolin. Hergert and Kurth (64) found that the cork layer in older specimens of Douglas-fir could contain up to about 22% of taxifolin. Cambie (24) found astilbin (taxifolin-3-rhamnoside) up to a content of 12.5% in the bark of *Quintinnia serrata*. Taxifolin can be extracted with ether after the wax constituents have been removed; hot water has also been used, the taxifolin precipitating upon cooling. Taxifolin can be converted into quercetin by means of sodium bisulfite, but methods based upon oxidation by air have also been employed.

Some authors have tried to clarify the laws, according to which the flavonoids are present in the bark and other parts of the plant, partly free, and partly in a glycoside form. Erdtman (42) has suggested that the flavonoids are formed in the cambium and the cork cambium, from where they are transported to the heartwood and the outer bark, respectively. Hergert and Goldschmid (63) found that, practically speaking, free taxifolin in Douglas-fir was located only in the outer bark and the heartwood, whereas taxifolin-3'-glucoside was present in needles, small branches, cambium, and sapwood and, in trace amounts, in the inner bark. Very small amounts were found of quercetin and quercetin-3'-glucoside, distributed in a corresponding manner. Similar analyses of Atlas-cedar, western larch, and Sitka spruce confirmed that the presence of taxifolin in the heartwood and the outer bark corresponded to the presence of taxifolin-3'-glucoside in needles and sapwood. The authors concluded from this that quercetin and taxifolin are synthesized and transformed into glycosides in the needles or the leaves and transported through the inner bark to the heartwood and the outer bark. The sugar escapes at, or near, the boundaries between the sapwood and the heartwood and, respectively, between the inner and the outer bark.

2. Anthocyanins and Leucoanthocyanins

The anthocyanins are glycosides, whose aglycones, the anthocyanidins, probably do not exist free in a natural state in their monomeric form. Becker and Kurth (8) found, in the bark from red fir, a pigment, which seemed to consist of a polymer of cyanidin. The anthocyanins seem to be present in plants to a less extent than the flavonoids and, generally, are not to be found in bark or wood. The "leucoanthocyanins" are morphologically more commonly distributed in plants. Their aglycones, the leucoanthocyanidins, are chemically something between the flavonols and the anthocyanidins. From taxifolin, a leucoanthocyanidin can be prepared which upon treatment with hydrochloric acid changes into cyanidin chloride (XXV,161).

Pigman et al. have developed a method for the determination of leucoanthocyanins by conversion into anthocyanidins with methanol-

XXV

hydrochloric acid (131). They detected substances that had the properties of leucoanthocyanins in the inner bark and the cambium of black spruce, and in the wood, the inner bark, and the cambium of western hemlock. Hillis (68) used the same method for investigation of some of the types of bark used in tanning. The anthocyanidins, formed on treatment with propanol-hydrochloric acid, were identified as delphinidin, pelargonidin, and cyanidin. The leucoanthocyanins are assumed to cause the red color in leather that has been tanned with extracts of these kinds of bark. In carada bark, Ganguly et al. (50) found a leucoanthocyanidin, which was identified as leucodelphinidin (5,7,3',4',5'-pentahydroxyflavone-3,4-diol).

Krugman (102) investigated the distribution of leucoanthocyanins in species of *Pinus*. Needles and bark were found to contain leucoanthocyanins which, upon acid hydrolysis, gave cyanidin and delphinidin, while the leucoanthocyanins of the roots and the trunk wood gave cyanidin alone.

H. FLAVANOLS

XXVI

Catechin: R = H
Gallocatechin: R = OH

The flavanols, which most commonly occur in a natural state, are *d*-catechin and its *cis* isomer *l*-epicatechin. Mixtures of both of these substances were found by Hergert and Kurth in the bark of white fir, enriched in the cork layer of the outer bark, where their content was up to 16% (65). Mayer and Bauni (123) found *d*-catechin in the bark of oak and chestnut. Gallocatechin and epigallocatechin are also present in many kinds of bark. All of the four flavanols mentioned here proved to be present in the bark of red fir (8).

Regarding the biogenetic formation of flavonoids, anthocyanins, leucoanthocyanins, and flavanols, a number of different theories exist. According to one body of opinion, these compounds are in direct genetic connection, one with the other, so that, for example, anthocyanins are formed from flavonoids or leucoanthocyanins. Another possibility is that the different compounds can be considered as end products of parallel syntheses from common original substances. These different views have been described in detail by Blank (12).

I. PROTEINS

All types of bark contain various amounts of protein. The reason for this is that one of the roles of the bark is the provision of a storage place for these compounds and others. The protein content varies within rather wide limits during the course of the year. Siminovitch and Briggs (156) have studied the variations in the protein content of black locust bark in relation to the power of the cells to resist frost. They found that these variations apply to water-soluble protein alone. The content of nitrogen, originating from water-insoluble protein and nonprotein did not change. The content of sugar decreased in spring more rapidly than the frost hardiness. If the crowns were removed in the winter, the decrease in resistance was delayed and, in proportion to this, the content of water-soluble protein also decreased more slowly, while the content of sugar decreased at a normal rate or more quickly. The composition of the water-soluble proteins was not determined, but their number was found to be at least five (16). The content of these constituents decreased in parallel until May/June, when definite changes in the proportions occurred. By August, the proportions had been almost completely restored for the winter conditions, and a maximum content of proteins was reached in October/November.

Generally, the protein content of bark has been calculated as the product of the nitrogen percentage and the factor 6.25. In accordance with this calculation, the outer bark of birch contains 3.8% and the inner bark 5.0% of protein (Table II). The inner bark of black locust was found to contain exceptionally large amounts of protein, the average being 21.6%, according to Jones and Phillips (92). The values given for the protein content, calculated directly from the nitrogen content, can hardly be considered as completely correct because, in many cases, the bark also contains other nitrogen-containing substances.

It could possibly be expected that the rather large amounts of protein in certain species of bark might be of a certain nutrititional value. Becker (9) carried out feeding experiments with bark from spruce, but found that the proteins, which constituted about 5.5% of this species of bark, were indigestible. The proteins in black locust bark are considered as being the cause of the poisonous effect of this species of bark.

Free amino acids are also present in bark. Szalai and Gracza (162) studied the distribution of tryptophan in the bark and the buds of ash trees during the year, and found that tryptophan is probably stored in the bark to provide for the demand of this amino acid by the buds during development. The investigations of Ziegler on the seasonal variations in the amino acid content in the sieve tube sap of some species of wood are mentioned in Section III-N.

J. THE ALKALOIDS IN BARK

Naturally occurring alkaloids are primarily present in angiosperms, and foremost in dicotyledons, whereas in only a few cases do the monocotyledons contain alkaloids. Only in exceptional cases are the alkaloids present in a free form (narceine, narcotine), such cases probably being dependent upon low basicity. They form salts generally with citric acid, tannic acid, oxalic acid, phosphoric acid, and so on. Examples of alkaloid glycosides exist (solanum and veratrum alkaloids). Members of the tropane series form esters with tropic, atropic, benzoic, and tiglic acid.

TABLE VI

Alkaloids Found in Bark

Group of alkaloids	Individual examples	Sources (examples)
Berberis and Hydrastis alkaloids	Berberine, canadine, hydrastine, berbamine	Berberidaceae Ranunculaceae Rutaceae
Cinchona alkaloids	Quinine, cinchonine, quinidine, aricine	*Cinchona* Rubiaceae
Curare alkaloids (Calabash curare)		*Strychnos toxifera*
Holarrhena alkaloids	Conessine, kurchine	*Holarrhena* species
Pomegranate alkaloids	Pelletierine, pseudopelletierine	*Punica granatum*
Strychnos alkaloids	Strychnine, brucine	Species of *Strychnos*
Yohimbe and Quebracho alkaloids	Yohimbine (quebrachine), aspidospermine	Rubiaceae Apocynaceae
Rauwolfia alkaloids (98)	Rauwolfine, rauwolscine	Apocynaceae

Alkaloids can be present in all the parts of a plant although, in individual cases, they are often found in a special tissue only. In bark, they are often found stored in a solid form, usually as salts (quinine for example). In Table VI there are listed a number of such groups of alkaloids of which the members can, to a considerable extent, be isolated from bark. These and other alkaloids have been described in detail by Cromwell (34).

K. VITAMINS IN BARK

Wodsak and Ueckerman (166) determined the vitamin content of a number of bark species. The results of these determinations are given

TABLE VII

Vitamin Content of Some Bark Species (166)[a]

Bark	Vitamin C		Vitamin B₁		Vitamin B₂		Nicotinic acid	
	Autumn	Spring	Autumn	Spring	Autumn	Spring	Autumn	Spring
Oak	14.8	32.0	0.06	0.074	0.056	0.110	0.870	2.15
Larch	17.6	13.8	0.11	0.100	0	0	0	2.00
Birch	0	2.4	0.03	0.088	0.03	0.068	0.960	0.66
Beech	3.4	5.6	0.17	0.223	0.074	0.156	1.370	2.10
Pine	0	5.0	0.01	0.055	0	0	0	2.80
Spruce	35.1	17.1	0.11	0.083	0	0	0	2.00
Ash	21.6	8.9	0.11	0.140	0.157	0.290	1.400	2.25
Alder		15.6		0.226		0.077		10.00
Lime		6.8		0.145		0.160		0.90

[a] Milligrams of vitamin in 100 g. of bark.

in Table VII. It is apparent from the table that the vitamin content varies considerably between different seasons.

L. CARBOHYDRATES ENTIRELY OR PARTLY SOLUBLE IN WATER

Both the bark and the wood contain, in addition to cellulose, other carbohydrates, which can consist of pectin, polyuronic acids, gums, mucilages, and "hemicellulose." Hemicellulose was originally defined as that part of the carbohydrates which is easily hydrolyzable. Such substances as gums and pectins are often, in everyday usage, included under this conception. The main part of the hemicellulose consists of pentosans and hexosans which are, in comparison with cellulose, easily hydrolyzable but, generally, are not extractable with indifferent solvents.

The pectins mostly consist of partly methoxylated polygalacturonic acids, which are linearily combined in α-1,4-position. On hydrolysis, D-galacturonic acid, D-galactose, L-arabinose, and methanol (from the methoxy groups) are obtained.

When a plant tissue is damaged, sticky substances, known as carbohydrate gums, are secreted. From species of *Acacia*, gum arabic is obtained, which has been used as an adhesive for a long time. Upon hydrolysis of gum from different species of *Acacia*, varying proportions of rhamnose, arabinose, galactose, and glucuronic acid have been obtained (71). Aspinall et al. (5) gave a structural picture for the gum from *Acacia pycnantha*, based upon the results of a controlled hydrolysis.

Becker and Kurth (8) analyzed a carbohydrate gum constituting 16% of the inner bark of red fir. Upon hydrolysis, arabinose and galactose were primarily obtained, and further, glucuronic acid, glucuronolactone, an aldobiouronic acid, and two unknown deoxy-sugars.

Mucilages are not pathological secretions, but their purpose is to serve as reserve nutriment and protective colloids. With water, they form colloidal solutions, and retain water for reserve purposes. The mucilages are present partly in the cell membranes, partly in the vacuoles. Hirst et al. (70) investigated the mucilage in slippery elm bark and, upon hydrolysis of it, found galacturonic acid, galactose, 3-methyl-galactose, and L-rhamnose. After periodate oxidation, 21.6% of galactose, 26.8% of 3-methyl-galactose, and 25.2% of rhamnose were detected. According to Jones and Smith (93), the acid parts of gums generally consist of D-glucuronic acid while, in most cases, the acid properties of the mucilages arise from D-galacturonic acid. Mucilages without acid constituents are also found in plants.

The carbohydrates can be isolated from water extract of bark by precipitation in ethanol. It has, nevertheless, appeared difficult to remove completely the tannin from the carbohydrate preparation in any manner other than by the use of hide powder. The carbohydrate material precipitated from the aqueous extract of incense-cedar bark contained 24% of tannin (158). Upon hydrolysis, the carbohydrates gave 21.6% pentoses, 36.3% galactose, 5.1% mannose, 3.0% uronic acid, and 34.0% glucose (by difference). The carbohydrate material

obtained from grand fir bark by extraction with water was characterized as a polyuronide, possibly with residues of galacturonic acid
(111). Upon hydrolysis, the carbohydrates precipitated from aqueous
extract of *Picea excelsa* bark gave arabinose, glucose, galactose, probably xylose and rhamnose, and D-galacturonic acid, which was said to
amount to 3 to 4% of the solids in the aqueous extract. In these
experiments, the adsorption of polyuronides on hide powder was
investigated (100).

Binko et al. described a method for the determination of pectins,
hexosans, and pentosans in aqueous, alkaline, and sulfite extracts
of bark from chemically barked trees (10).

Free sugar of mono- or disaccharide type is present in small
amounts in many kinds of bark. In pine bark, Schwalbe and
Neumann (147) found 1.87%, in spruce bark 1.32% of such simple
sugars. With regard to the occurrence of sucrose in sieve tube sap,
reference is made to Section III-N.

Starch has also been detected in bark. In black spruce (Table I,
Chapter 8), only the inner bark gave a positive reaction for starch.
The formation of starch in living bark of black locust has been in-
vestigated by Ewart et al. (47).

M. TANNING MATERIALS

By "tanning materials" are meant substances that are able to
convert hide into leather. Each tree or bush contains tanning materials, and they are generally present in all plant tissues. Because of the
great economic importance of tanning materials and their common
occurrence in nature, many publications are devoted to this field.
In spite of the large amount of work that has been done on the clarification of the chemical structure of tanning materials, the structure
is still, to a great extent, unknown.

In many cases, bark is the most suitable source for a commercial
extraction of tanning materials. As examples of the species of bark
utilized for this purpose, the following can be cited: wattle, mangrove,
oak, eucalyptus, hemlock, pine, spruce, larch, and willow. Commercially, tanning materials are also extracted from wood (quebracho,
chestnut, and oak), fruit (myrobalans, valonia, and divi-divi), leaves
(sumac, gambier), and roots (canaigre, palmetto).

Bandekow (7) published a survey of the utility of American species
of wood for the extraction of tanning materials. It is, in general, not

considered as economically profitable to extract plant tissues which contain much less than 10% of tannin, provided that no other useful products can be obtained simultaneously. Among the species of bark which are richest in tannin are wattle and mangrove, both of which can contain 30 to 40% of tannin. The tannin content of other commercially utilized types of bark varies, in general, between 10 and 20%. It should be noticed that the content of tannin is not in itself a deciding factor with regard to the economic value of a raw material for tanning substances. Each extract of tannin gives the leather its own peculiarity, for which reason qualitative variations are considerable.

According to Freudenberg, the natural tanning materials are subdivided into two main groups:

(1) The first group is called hydrolyzable tannins, composed of (a) gallotannins which, upon hydrolysis, decompose into gallic acid and sugar, and (b) ellagitannins which, upon hydrolysis, give ellagic acid and sugar.

O. T. Schmidt has shown that ellagic acid is not present as a primary constituent in the below-named ellagitannins, corilagin, and chebulagic acid, but is formed by the lactonization of hexahydroxydiphenic acid, a dehydrogenation dimer of gallic acid. The gallo- and ellagitannins, thus, appear to be nearly related to one another.

(2) The second group is comprised of condensed tannins or phlobatannins which, when treated with acid, are converted into phlobaphene.

The tannins that can be hydrolyzed constitute complicated mixtures. Only a few constituents of tanning material extracts have been isolated and identified. Thus, for example, an average formula corresponding to penta-m-digalloylglucose could be ascribed to Chinese gallotannin. Hamamelis tannin is a diester of hamamelose and gallic acid. Ellagitannins are present in myrobalans, valonia, divi-divi and also in chestnut and oak bark. Among the ellagitannins, chebulagic acid and corilagin have been isolated and identified by O. T. Schmidt et al.

The main part of the tannin used for tanning could be considered as belonging to the phlobatannin group. These tanning materials have been formed by the dehydrogenation and the condensation of simpler original materials, and they have the ability of being condensed further, resulting in the formation of phlobaphenes, which do not dissolve easily in water. The structure of the phlobaphenes is still largely unknown, but catechin or other flavanes are considered as constituting the building elements for the majority of them. According to Grassmann et al. (52), changes in higher condensed products are a post-mortal process, which can be stopped by means of enzyme poisons, for example. The living bast of spruce bark contains a water-soluble and low-molecular tannin, while the outer bark contains tannin in all the stages of continuing condensation up to the proper phlobaphenes, which can be made water soluble only by means of sulfite.

Hathway (57,58) investigated tannin from oak bark (*Quercus pedunculata*, and *Q. sessiliflora*) for the purpose of clarifying the origin of tannin. In the tannin extract, catechin, gallocatechin, and leucodelphinidin were found. Of these three compounds, gallo-catechin in particular was rapidly oxidized by the polyphenoloxidase enzyme from cambium, which led to the formation of oxidation polymers which highly resembled the phlobatannin from bark. By ringing of the bark, it was found that the phenolic metabolites move downward from the leaves through the sieve tubes of the inner bark. From these experiments, Hathway concluded that pyrogallol phenols, which are formed in the leaves, are transported through the system of sieve tubes to the cambium, where they undergo oxidation into phlobatannin, which is then stored in the bark. Ziegler investigated the occurrence of tannin precursors in the sieve tube liquid of oak (Section III-N).

A large number of investigators have tried to separate the phenolic components in tannin extracts by paper or column chromatography. The number of these components is large, and it is evident from the investigations of spruce bark by Lindstedt and Zacharias (115), that this number is increased if sulfite is used in the extractions. Grass-mann et al. (53) found that perlon powder was very efficient in the separation of tannin extracts from spruce bark by column chroma-tography.

The large amounts of nontannin in aqueous extracts are trouble-some in chromatographic investigations. In the investigations of spruce tannin by Grassmann, the tannin was extracted with ethyl acetate after the removal of wax and fats by means of chloroform (52). Dässler and Urzynicok (39) used the same method of extraction in investigations of the tannin in bast from black alder.

The subdivision of the natural tanning materials described here does not exclude the possibility of the existence of other types of natural tanning materials. Grassmann et al. isolated from bast of spruce bark two substances, which were identified as phenolic stilbene derivatives. One of these substances, whose aglycone was entitled piceatannol, was identical with 2,6,4'-trihydroxy-3,4-tetramethylene-

XXVII

stilbene-5,3'-diglucoside (XXVII) (40). The aglycone of the other substance was identified as dihydropiceatannol (41).

N. CONSTITUENTS OF THE SIEVE TUBE LIQUID OF SOME HARDWOOD TREES

The sieve tubes of the bark can be considered as a system within the tree for the transport of substances which include sugar and amino acids. Ziegler (173) has investigated the composition of the sieve tube liquid of a number of hardwood trees, and the results, which are the most important from a chemical point of view, are given below.

(1) The only carbohydrate in the sieve tube liquid was found to be sucrose. Neither free hexoses nor phosphorylated sugar could be detected. In general, the content of sugar decreased downward in the trunk. After hydrolysis, the monose concentration in sieve tube liquid from bark was as follows: *Quercus borealis*, 186 mg./ml.; *Q. robur*, 175 mg./ml.; and *Tilia platyphyllos*, 188 mg./ml. These values are valid for autumnal conditions. Zimmermann (175) has shown the presence of sugars other than sucrose in the sieve tube liquor of, for instance, American ash where, in addition to sucrose, raffinose and stachyose were also found in substantial proportions.

(2) The protein concentration was independent of the height of the sampling on the trunk, which indicates that the proteins originate from the sieve tube plasma. The content of amino acids, generally, decreased from above downward and, in many cases, increased at the time of protein mobilization in the leaves in autumn. In summer, the only amino acids detectable in sieve tube liquid from oak were glutamic acid, asparaginic acid, and alanine. In autumn, besides

these, there could be detected asparagine, glutamine, serine, methionine, valine and leucine.

(3) While the sugar content of the sieve tube liquid corresponded, on an average, to a solution that was approximately 0.5M, the concentration of inorganic phosphate was less than 0.01M. The variations in the content of phosphate and sugar proved to be in no detectable relation to one another. Readily (7 min.) hydrolyzable phosphate was not present in the sieve tubes. Difficultly hydrolyzable phosphate could, together with the proteins, by reason of the constant content, be considered as originating from the sieve tube plasma.

(4) The reaction of the sieve tube liquid was found to be alkaline; the pH value varied in different instances between 7.45 and 8.66. Despite the fact that sieve tube liquid from *Robinia pseudoacacia* (black locust) was brought to the optimum pH value for invertase, no invertase activity occurred.

(5) In the sieve tube liquid of oak, large quantities of tanning materials and their precursors were detected. Upon storage, a precipitation of phlobaphene gradually takes place. Ziegler is of the opinion that such substances are not present in large amounts in the sieve tube liquid in the tree, but that they have been rinsed out of the bark during the draining of liquid, as well as the fluorescent dyestuffs detected in other trees such as flavone, coumarin and phenol glycosides.

(6) Since only trace amounts of boron could be detected in the sieve tube liquid, boron-sugar complexes cannot be present in considerable amounts.

IV. Extractive-Free Bark

When the extractives have been removed from bark, 60 to 80% of the original bark generally remains. This residual can be divided into: (A) hydroxy acid complexes (suberin), (B) lignin and phenolic acids, and (C) carbohydrates.

A. HYDROXY ACID COMPLEXES

Among the hydroxy acid complexes in extractive-free bark, the most study has been devoted to the suberin isolated from the cork of *Quercus suber* and *Betula verrucosa*. Earlier, suberin was commonly considered as a complex, composed of constituents that were merely or mainly aliphatic. Certain investigations, carried out later, have nevertheless shown that phenolic constituents are also contained in the suberin complex. Here, the investigations that were concerned with the aliphatic part of suberin are dealt with first.

1. The Occurrence of Suberin

Suberin is a constituent of cork cell walls, and its quantity varies considerably in different types of bark. Šarkov (152) found in the bark of pine, fir, aspen, oak, and plane trees 2.0 to 8.3% of suberin, whereas the bark of various birch species contained 19.7 to 38.8% of suberin. The suberin content of the outer bark of cork oak, *Quercus suber* (35 to 40%), and of various birch species is particularly high. For instance, in the outer bark of *Betula verrucosa*, Jensen found 38.7% of suberin (Table II). According to the investigations of cork membranes by Mader (117), a cork cell grows, after it has formed from the phellogen, to the size of older cork cells. Only after this growth has terminated are there formed on both sides of the primary lamella the secondary suberin lamella and the tertiary cellulose lamella. A new cork cell forms from the phellogen only after the preceding cell has passed this stage of development.

2. The Chemical Nature of the Aliphatic Part of Suberin

Suberin has been considered as being in the cork cell walls in the form of a polyestolid of hydroxy acids, and can be dissolved by saponification, for example, by means of alcoholic alkali. The cork substance then loses its elastic properties and breaks up into brown pulp. The acids, which have until now been isolated from the saponification solution, contain two or more functional groups, which make it possible for these acids to form a network bound by ether or ester bonds. It has appeared that this acid mixture, obtained on saponification, readily condenses on heating. Jensen (84) has measured the velocity of the polyestolid formation by means of heating the free acids, and titrating the remaining free carboxyls at stated intervals.

Whether there are any bonds between suberin and cellulose has not been completely clarified. It is not considered to be entirely out of the question that the hydroxy acids of suberin esterify with cellulose in the cork cell walls. There are many indications, however, that this is not the case, but that suberin constitutes a completely free substance. Van Wisselingh showed that the fatty acids of suberin decomposed without cellulosic residues when heated to 300°C. in glycerol. Zetsche et al. (171) discovered that iodine, which did not affect acetyl cellulose, was able to dissolve the suberin from cork. According to the microscopic studies of the cork cell wall by Sitte, the suberin lamellae do not contain cellulose (157).

Some authors have reported small quantities of glycerol in the saponification products of cork [Ribas and Blasco, 6 to 7% (136); Stockar, 1.1% (160)], whereas others have not found glycerol [for instance, Fierz-David and Ulrich (49)]. The different results can, probably, be considered as being due to basic differences in the ages of the cork substances investigated. Ribas-Marqués (135) has shown that there is a 10.5% lower glycerol content in old cork layers than in younger ones. According to Mader (117), a portion of the combined fatty acids in young cork membranes appears to be esterified into triglycerides. Free fatty acids were not detected.

3. Aliphatic Saponification Products of Suberin

Cork substance that has been preextracted and treated with sulfite according to a method developed by Zetsche (168) gives, on saponification, a complicated mixture of higher fatty acids. It is uncertain whether these acids, as such, exist in suberin; it is possible that they are decomposition products of high molecular hydroxy fatty acids. Azelaic acid, $HOOC(CH_2)_7COOH$, and suberic acid, $HOOC(CH_2)_6COOH$, obtained when cork is treated with nitric acid, are thus considered to be decomposition products of suberin.

Below, there is a list of the aliphatic acids isolated to date from cork and birch suberin by means of saponification.

(1) Eicosanedicarboxylic acid was first isolated from cork by Zetsche (169), and from birch bark by Šarkov (152).

(2) Phellonic acid (ω-hydroxybehenic acid) was isolated from cork by Zetsche (169), and from birch bark by Šarkov (152). It was previously considered to be identical with α-hydroxybehenic acid, but Jensen showed that the structure of phellonic acid is identical with that of ω-hydroxybehenic acid (85). At the same time, Guillemonat and Strich also showed this structure of phellonic acid (54).

(3) Phloionic acid (8,9-dihydroxyhexadecane dicarboxylic acid-1,16) was isolated from cork by Zetsche (170).

(4) Phloionolic acid (9,10,18-trihydroxy stearic acid) was isolated from cork by Zetsche and Sonderegger (172). Jensen discovered that

this acid, also, was found in abundance among the saponification products of birch suberin (89).

(5) $C_{18}H_{34}O_4$, an acid with one carboxyl, two hydroxyls, and one double bond, was isolated from birch suberin by Jensen (86).

(6) 18-Hydroxy-9-octadecene carboxylic acid and 8-hexadecene-1,16-dicarboxylic acid were shown by Ribas as being present among the products obtained on the distillation of methyl esters of acids from cork suberin (137). Jensen et al. isolated these acids by means of the countercurrent extraction of methyl esters of suberin acids (88).

In the isolation of saponification products of suberin, Zetsche employed a method based upon the differences in the solubility of the acids and their salts. Jensen made use of a chromatographic method by fractionating the methyl esters of the acids of suberin by means of alumina (84). Subsequently, both of these methods were combined, resulting in yields that were considerably higher than the results obtained in previous experiments (86). Table VIII gives an idea of

TABLE VIII

Substances Isolated from Saponification Mixtures of Suberin
by Column Chromatography (90)

	Birch suberin, %	Cork suberin, %
Acid $C_{18}H_{34}O_4$ $\begin{cases} -OH-OH \\ -COOH \\ -HC=CH- \end{cases}$	15.9	1.9
Phellonic acid	7.4	12.6
1,20-Eicosanedicarboxylic acid	9.7	4.7
Phloionolic acid	7.8	—
Phloionic acid	—	11.0
Acids forming liquid methyl esters	17.2	34.5
Acids in impure methyl ester fractions	22.0	14.3
Losses, mainly substances retained by the chromatographic column	20.0	21.0

the results obtained by means of the chromatographic method. In the suberin of *Quercus suber*, no phloionolic acid could be shown, and phloionic acid could not be isolated from the suberin of *Betula verrucosa*. This was evidently due to difficulties in the elution. Birch suberin appears to contain much phloionolic acid, and little phloionic acid whereas, in cork suberin, the case is possibly to the contrary.

Seoane and Ribas (150) developed a method for the isolation of phloionic acid and phloionolic acid. The results obtained showed that cork suberin contains 12.6 to 12.9% of phloionic acid, and 2.1 to 2.8% of phloionolic acid (135).

The countercurrent extraction has been shown by Jensen et al. to be a method that can very well be applied to the separation of the aliphatic acids obtained on the saponification of suberin (88). The methyl esters of the acids were divided into two fractions, one being soluble and the other insoluble in petroleum ether. These fractions were divided into their components, the former by means of the system petroleum ether/ethanol-water, and the latter with the system benzene-petroleum ether/ethanol-water. The respective compositions of cork and birch suberins were calculated from the theoretical distribution curves. The results are given in Table IX. All

TABLE IX

Substances Isolated from Saponification Mixtures of Suberin
by Countercurrent Distribution (88)

	Birch suberin, %	Cork suberin, %
Acids with methyl esters soluble in petroleum ether		
Acid with unknown constitution	5	4
Acid $C_{18}H_{34}O_4$ { —OH, —OH / —COOH / —HC=CH— }	17	4
Acid $HOCH_2(CH_2)_7CH=CH(CH_2)_7COOH$	11	8
Phellonic acid $HOCH_2(CH_2)_{20}COOH$	10	8
Acid $HOOC(CH_2)_7CH=CH(CH_2)_7COOH$	7	8
Eicosanedicarboxylic acid $HOOC(CH_2)_{20}COOH$	10	9
Acids with methyl esters insoluble in petroleum ether		
Phloionolic acid $HOCH_2(CH_2)_7(CHOH)_2(CH_2)_7COOH$	7	3
Phloionic acid $HOOC(CH_2)_7(CHOH)_2(CH_2)_7COOH$	—	14
Substance with unknown constitution	14	16
Unseparated mixture	19	26

compounds that had previously been isolated chromatographically could also be isolated by means of this method and, in addition, four liquid substances, two of which proved to be the methyl esters of the above-mentioned acids previously identified by Ribas (137).

4. The Formation of Suberin

There are many different opinions as to the formation of suberin lamellae in the cork cell wall. An idea was presented by von Schmidt (143) that suberin is formed by the polymerization and anhydridization of the fatty acids formed by the enzymatic decomposition of glycerides in the young cork cell membrane. Glycerol changes to carbon dioxide and water. Ribas' observation that young cork layers have a higher glycerol content than that of the older ones (Section IV-A2) appears to support this view. According to Mader (118) it is, however, improbable that suberin is synthesized from reserve matter with no contribution of the cell plasma. If a tissue is damaged, the adjoining cells are suberized before phellogen is formed in the underlying layer. This means that cells in general are capable of forming suberin from plasma substances. The decrease in the fat and starch content, which has been observed in damaged tissues, has been explained by Mader (118) as being due to a more lively consumption of energy.

5. Phenolic Constituents of the Suberin Complex

Among the saponification products from extractive-free Douglas-fir cork, Hergert and Kurth (64) found a large proportion of phenolic acids. Hergert (61) later extracted with dioxane-hydrochloric acid a waxlike substance from extractive-free white fir cork, the yield being 48%. Upon saponification, this substance decomposed to 72% of aliphatic hydroxy acids, 6% of mainly ferulic acid (XXVIII), and 22%

$$H_3CO,\ HO-\langle\ \rangle-CH = CH - COOH$$

XXVIII

of high-molecular phenolic acids. According to Hergert, the original complex is composed by ester formation between the carboxyl groups of the hydroxy acid and the aliphatic hydroxyls of the phenolic acids. In addition, the hydroxy acids can be partly combined with one another by polyestolid linkages. In a similar investigation of extractive-free cork from *Quercus suber*, Hergert found, upon saponification of the waxlike substance, 65% of hydroxy acids, 30% of phenolic acids, and 5% of sinapic acid (XXIX). On the basis of these

$$\underline{XXIX}$$

results, Hergert argues that suberin must be considered as an ester of aliphatic hydroxy acids and phenolic acids, and that the cork cell wall consists of a lignocellulose network impregnated with this polyester. As far as these investigations of three species of wood have given results of general validity, it can be said that suberin from gymnospermae contains hydroxy acids with a relatively low molecular weight (hydroxymyristic acid, etc.), phenolic acids related to phlobaphene, and a simple phenolic acid, ferulic acid, which Hergert also detected in extractive-free cork from Douglas-fir. The suberin substance of angiospermae contains hydroxy acids with a larger molecule, phenolic acids of a structure so far unknown, and a monomeric phenolic acid, sinapic acid.

B. LIGNIN AND PHENOLIC ACIDS IN EXTRACTIVE-FREE BARK

Very little is known to date of the processes resulting in the lignification of cells. Šarkov (151) discovered that the lignification in connection with the change of the inner bark bast to the outer bark bast in pine corresponds to a clear reduction in the content of pectins and pentosans, a part of the tannin being simultaneously converted into phlobaphenes. Härtel et al. (77) have shown the lignification in spruce bark tissue which was cultivated *in vitro* in a coniferin-containing medium. Its methoxyl content increased twice as much as did that of tissue cultivated without coniferin. The incorporation of coniferin was discovered to require the action of living cells.

As far as chemical properties are concerned, there are great differences between wood lignin and bark lignin. The lignin of bark cannot be completely dissolved by the same methods as the wood lignin, and isolated bark lignin appears to have a considerably more heterogenous composition than that of wood lignin. In lignin research, most investigations have been concerned with wood lignin, and bark lignin research has generally been limited to the search for connecting points with wood lignin. In this field, softwood bark has, up to now, been studied considerably more comprehensively than has hardwood bark.

1. Phenolic Acids

One of the difficulties occurring in the isolation and investigation of bark lignin is that certain substances interfere with the lignin in the customary determination of lignin content with 72% sulfuric acid. These substances consist of high molecular phenolic acids, and their content in bark substance is substantial. The proportion of extractive-free bark, which is insoluble in 72% sulfuric acid, is in most cases much larger than is the corresponding proportion of wood tissue, and its methoxyl content is lower: 4 to 9% in softwood bark, and 7 to 15% in hardwood bark (37). From the Klason "lignin" of the bark, a part, which varies between one-third and one-half, is in many cases soluble in 1% sodium hydroxide and can also be dissolved directly from extractive-free bark. This part corresponds to the phenolic acids of the bark, their easy solubility in alkali being due to a rather high carboxyl content. The phenolic acids also differ from lignin in their low methoxyl content. It has been shown that the phenolic acids of bark, as opposed to wood lignin, do not give a color reaction with phloroglucinol-hydrochloric acid (110).

Phenolic acids do not exist in living bark, but in dead cork and parenchyma cells, where they can be considered as protecting the bark tissue against bacteria. Kurth and Smith (110) found the

TABLE X

Yields of Phenolic Acid Obtained by 1% Sodium Hydroxide Extraction of Douglas-Fir Bark Components at 25 and 90°C. (110)[a]

Bark component	25°C., %	90°C., %
Inner bark bast fibers	2.9	8.1
Outer bark bast fibers	3.3	9.5
Inner bark fines	0.1	21.6
Outer bark fines	12.0	58.8
Outer bark phloem sieve tubes and parenchyma	5.1	23.9
Cork	21.6	39.2

[a] Percentages based on oven-dry weight of extractive-free bark component.

phenolic acids in Douglas fir bark to be principally localized in cork cells; in addition, they also form a layer on the surface of bast fibers. Table X gives the percentages of phenolic acids in various components of Douglas-fir bark. Phenolic acids were found in cork from Douglas-fir (64), white fir, and Mediterranean oak (61) esterified with hydroxy acids (see Section IV, A5) and also as constituents of the benzene-soluble wax from white fir and Mediterranean oak cork (61,65).

In phenolic acids extracted from various types of bark, the proportions of the functional groups have been found to vary. The content of functional groups has, in general, been determined by means of a method described by Brauns and Lewis (13), based upon selective methylation. Diazomethane methylates only phenolic hydroxyls and carboxyls; dimethyl sulfate in an alkaline medium only affects the aliphatic and phenolic hydroxyls and, by means of the successive employment of the reagents, a completely methylated product is obtained. The initial content of the aliphatic and phenolic hydroxyls and the carboxyls can, respectively, be calculated after the methoxyl determination of the different reaction products. In Table XI are given the characteristics of a number of phenolic acid preparations.

TABLE XI

Characteristics of Phenolic Acid Preparations (Based on Ref. 48)

	Per cent				
Bark tissue	MeO	COOH	Phenolic OH	Aliphatic OH	Ref.
Redwood bastfiber	2.7	4.4	7.8	2.1	13
Redwood fines	0.0	11.0	8.6	3.6	13
Spruce	1.4	7.2		10.5[a]	55
Douglas-fir					
Bast fiber	4.3	5.3	8.3	4.2	96
White fir cork[b]		10.9–13.3	4.4–6.2	3.6–4.1	48
	3.56[d]				
White fir cork[c]		4.8–5.7	10.1–10.7	2.4–3.0	48

[a] Sum of phenolic and aliphatic OH.

[b] Yields, on methylation with Me$_2$SO$_4$, a product soluble in NaOH.

[c] Yields, on methylation with Me$_2$SO$_4$, a product insoluble in NaOH.

[d] Because the two fractions could not be separated before methylation, they are assumed to have the same MeO content.

Despite the fact that the proportions of the functional groups given by different authors vary to some extent, nearly the same value has been calculated for the molecular weight (or the unit of polymerization), approximately 850 to 870. Provided the phenolic acid is monocarboxylic, Kiefer and Kurth composed the following formula for the phenolic acid of Douglas-fir bark (96):

$$
\begin{array}{ll}
\text{HO} & \text{OH} \\
\text{HO} & \text{OH} \\
& C_{36}H_{35}O_{13} \\
\text{HO} & \text{OCH}_3 \\
\text{HO} & \text{COOH}
\end{array}
$$

The yield obtained in the isolation of phenolic acids by means of alkali has proved to be almost independent of the alkali concentration (96). The temperature, on the other hand, is of great importance, as can be seen from Table X. In the paper chromatogram, there are no differences worth mentioning between phenolic acid dissolved, respectively, at 25 and 90°C. (110).

There are no definite lines of demarcation between the phenolic acids and the other substances of bark which resemble lignin. The methods of separation can bring about considerable overlapping, and the uniformity of the preparations isolated can thus be considered uncertain. Kurth and Smith (110) discovered chromatographically that the phenolic acids that they had respectively isolated from the inner and the outer bark bast fiber of Douglas-fir consisted of approximately uniform and similar substances, each of which was mixed with certain impurities. On the basis of the values given in Table XI, Fahey and Kurth (48) concluded that the phenolic acids that they had isolated from white fir cork consisted of at least two components, which could be separated after methylation with dimethyl sulfate.

By their chemical nature, the phenolic acids resemble humic acids rather than lignin. Infrared spectra of native lignin from wood (67), of phlobaphenes, of phenolic acids, and of dioxane lignin from bark (110,65) bear great resemblances to each other. Harwood and Purves discovered that all the nitrogen that remained in white spruce bark, which had been preextracted with methanol and water, was found in the fraction prepared by means of the extraction with 5% sodium hydroxide (55). This gives possibilities of establishing that phenolic acids can, eventually, form protein complexes similar to those formed by humic acids.

The phenolic acids of bark have, to a certain extent, found technical use: for example, as dispersing agents; for viscosity control; for the control of water loss in the use of drilling muds; etc. The pilot plant scale preparation of a phenolic acid product, sodium palconate, has been described by Kottwitz and Forman (101).

2. Alkali-Resistant Bark Lignin

Brauns and Lewis carried out a series of alkaline digestions and a sulfite cooking with redwood bark (13). The pulps obtained contained approximately 30% of matter that did not dissolve in the lignin determination with 72% sulfuric acid. This lignin contained about 14% of methoxyl. After a phenol digestion, such pulp still contained 8% of lignin. Methylation experiments with bark phenol lignin and spruce wood phenol lignin showed a great similarity between these substances.

A part of the alkali-resistant bark lignin can be dissolved with dioxane-hydrochloric acid. The lignin isolated by Kiefer and Kurth from Douglas-fir bast fiber with dioxane-hydrochloric acid contained 2.5% of carboxyl, 14.3% of methoxyl, 4.4% of aliphatic, and 3.2% of phenolic hydroxyl groups (96). This lignin preparation showed a very great similarity with the native lignin from softwood. Kurth and Smith (110) found that the dioxane-hydrochloric acid lignin was considerably more readily separated from the outer bark bast fiber than from the inner bark bast fiber of Douglas-fir. This indicates that bonds between this lignin and the carbohydrate component of fibers weaken when the inner bark bast is converted into outer bark bast, possibly through the influence of cork cambium or because of oxidation by air. From extractive-free Douglas-fir bast fiber, which has been preextracted with sodium hydroxide, 11.8 to 12% of lignin has been extracted with dioxane-hydrochloric acid, calculated on the basis of extractive-free bark (110).

3. Attempts to Decompose Bark and Its Phenolic Acids

The oxidation of wood lignin by means of nitrobenzene in an alkaline medium gives a considerable yield of vanillin. Bark lignin gives a significantly lower yield of vanillin. Wacek and Schön (164) discovered that spruce bark that had been preextracted with alcohol-benzene (30.28% Klason "lignin") gave 2.7% of vanillin in an alkaline nitrobenzene oxidation, on the basis of dry unextracted bark whereas, under identical conditions, spruce wood gave 6.5%.

Kurth and Smith (110) oxidized phenolic acids of Douglas-fir bark with nitrobenzene, and obtained aldehydes, phenols, and acids in the proportions given in Table XII.

TABLE XII

Yield of Products from Alkaline Nitrobenzene Oxidation
of Douglas-Fir Phenolic Acid (110)[a]

| | Per cent | |
| | --- | --- |
Product	Cork phenolic acid	Inner bark bast fiber phenolic acid
Aldehydes	9.11	8.19
Vanillin	0.60	2.60
Protocatechualdehyde	0.66	0.79
Syringaldehyde	absent	trace
p-Hydroxybenzaldehyde	absent	trace
Phenols	1.50	0.79
Acids	10.00	2.72

[a] Percentages based on oven-dry weight of phenolic acid.

Protocatechualdehyde has generally not been mentioned as a product of the oxidation of wood lignin with nitrobenzene. This aldehyde is very unstable, and it may thus be considered possible that a corresponding structural element exists in the initial material in greater quantities than is indicated by the yield of protocatechualdehyde.

Fahey and Kurth (48) studied the phenolic acids of white fir by means of alkaline fusion, and of oxidation with nitrobenzene and with cupric oxide. The result showed a great resemblance to that obtained with the phenolic acids of Douglas-fir bark. Certain similarities with wood lignin could be observed but, simultaneously, there were also differences of significant importance. Such a difference occurred on alkaline fusion in that comparatively large quantities of phloroglucinol were formed. In addition, catechol and protocatechuic acid were identified. The yield of vanillin was low in the nitrobenzene oxidation.

Protocatechualdehyde and p-hydroxybenzaldehyde were also formed on the oxidation of the phenolic acids of white fir bark. From methylated initial matter, 7% of crude vanilloyl formic acid was formed as an oxidation product. From wood lignin, vanilloyl formic acid has only been obtained in small quantities by means of oxidation with cupric oxide or mercuric oxide. Other identified oxidation products of methylated cork phenolic acid were: vanillin, isovanillic acid, vanillic acid, veratric acid, and 5-carboxyvanillin.

TABLE XIII

Results of Paper Chromatography for Nitrobenzene Oxidation Products from Wood and Bark of Gymnosperm and Dicotyledonous Trees (56)

Sample	Substance	Results									
		a	b	c	d	e	f	g	h	i	j
Pinus densiflora	Sapwood	+	±	−	⧺	⧺	⧺	−	⧻	⧺	⧻
	Inner bark	⧺	±	+	+	+	⧺	−	⧺	+	⧺
	Outer bark	⧺	±	⧺	+	⧺	+	−	⧺	+	⧺
Chamaecyparis obtusa	Sapwood	⧺	?	−	+	⧺	⧺	−	⧻	+	⧺
	Inner bark	⧺	?	+	+	+	+	−	⧺	−	⧺
	Outer bark	⧺	?	⧺	+	+	+	−	⧺	−	⧺
Cryptomeria japonica	Sapwood	+	?	?	+	⧺	⧺	−	⧻	+	⧺
	Inner bark	⧺	?	+	+	+	⧺	−	⧺	+	+
	Outer bark	⧺	?	+	+	+	⧺	−	⧺	+	+
Ginkgo biloba	Sapwood	⧺	?	−	+	+	⧺	−	⧻	+	⧺
	Inner bark	⧺	?	+	+	+	⧺	−	⧺	−	⧺
	Outer bark	⧺	?	+	+	⧺	+	−	⧺	−	+
Salix bakko	Sapwood	+	⧺	−	+	+	⧺	⧺	⧻	+	⧺
	Inner bark	⧺	⧺	⧺	+	+	+	⧺	⧺	+	⧺
	Outer bark	⧺	+	+	+	+	+	⧺	⧺	+	⧺
Prunus donarium var. spontanea	Sapwood	⧺	⧺	−	+	−	±	⧺	⧻	−	+
	Inner bark	⧺	+	+	+	±	+	⧺	⧺	−	+
	Outer bark	⧺	⧺	+	+	±	+	⧺	⧺	−	⧺
Cinnamomum camphora	Sapwood	+	⧺	−	+	+	⧺	⧻	⧻	⧺	⧺
	Inner bark	⧺	⧺	±	+	⧺	⧺	⧺	⧺	+	⧺
	Outer bark	⧺	⧺	⧺	+	⧺	⧺	⧺	⧺	+	+
Melia azedarach var. japonica	Sapwood	+	⧺	−	+	+	⧺	⧻	⧻	+	⧺
	Inner bark	⧺	⧺	+	+	⧺	⧺	⧻	⧺	+	+
	Outer bark	⧺	⧺	+	+	+	⧺	⧺	⧺	+	+

a Unknown I.
b Syringic acid.
c Protocatechualdehyde.
d Vanillic acid.
e Formyl vanillic acid.
f *p*-Hydroxybenzaldehyde.
g Syringaldehyde.
h Vanillin.
i Acetoguaiacone.
j *p*-Hydroxyazobenzene.
Key: +, ⧺, ⧻, and ⧻, degree of intensity of identified spots; ±, very faint spots; −, not found; ?, identification uncertain.

Hata and Sogo (56) investigated the products formed, respectively, on the alkaline nitrobenzene oxidation of sapwood, inner bark, and outer bark of eight Japanese tree species, of which the first four (in Table XIII) are coniferous, the other four being deciduous trees.

As can be seen from Table XIII, protocatechualdehyde was formed from all bark samples on oxidation, but not from sapwood, with the exception of one uncertain case. Syringic acid appeared in all experiments with hardwood, but was only found in one certain case in the softwoods. Syringaldehyde is only obtained from hardwood lignin by means of oxidation with nitrobenzene. Table XIII shows that this is the case for both bark and wood lignin. [Leopold and Malmström have, however, chromatographically shown syringaldehyde in small quantities among the nitrobenzene oxidation products of softwood lignin, in particular that of the family *Pinaceae* (113).] According to the results obtained, the existence of the different structural elements in bark and wood lignin are the following:

3-4-Dihydroxyphenyl	exists in bark lignin, but not in wood lignin
p-Hydroxyphenyl	exists in all kinds of lignin
Guaiacyl	exists in all kinds of lignin
Syringyl	exists only in hardwood lignin

5-Formyl vanillic acid is considered as being formed from condensed guaiacyl groups.

C. CARBOHYDRATES OF EXTRACTIVE-FREE BARK

1. Reducing Sugar from the Hydrolysis of Carbohydrates

An examination of the products formed when extractive-free bark is treated with 72% sulfuric acid shows that bark differs, to some extent, from wood with regard to the quantitative composition of the unextractable carbohydrates.

Chang and Mitchell investigated the products of bark hydrolysis of 9 softwood species and 15 hardwood species (26). On the basis of the analytical values obtained, the characteristics of the carbohydrate part of the extractive-free bark can be considered to be as follows. Glucose constitutes the main part of the hydrolysis products of the carbohydrates, or 50 to 70% in both coniferous and deciduous tree bark. Galactose and mannose exist in higher percentages in the hydrolysis products of coniferous tree bark than in those of deciduous tree bark, which is in agreement with the respective proportions in wood. Xylose exists in much higher percentages in deciduous than in coniferous tree bark, and this is also analogous with the relations in wood.

In comparison with wood, the bark of deciduous trees differs in that in many cases its products of hydrolysis contain considerable quantities of arabinose. In many instances, the hydrolysate of coniferous tree bark contains as much arabinose as xylose and, in some cases (lodgepole pine, Engelmann spruce), even substantially more.

2. Cellulose and Pentosans in Extractive-Free Bark

The carbohydrate part of extractive-free bark is principally constituted of cellulose and pentosans. Only scant information is available as far as the other constituents are concerned. In the extractive-free inner bark of white birch, Mian and Timell (125) found 37% of cellulose, 28% neutral unsubstituted β-1,4-linked xylan, 4 to 5% pectic acid, and 4 to 5% of unknown polysaccharides.

In deciduous trees, the pentosan content of both the bark and the wood is higher than in coniferous trees. On the basis of unextracted matter, the bark of deciduous trees usually contains approximately 14 to 17% pentosans, and that of coniferous trees approximately 6 to 9%. As far as the residue is concerned, which is principally cellulose, there are no significant indications of quality differences between the two types of bark. In comparison with wood, the cellulose content of bark is low, the amount of 35 to 40% being seldom exceeded, and values of between 20 and 30% are usual.

The cellulose and pentosans in bark are enriched in bast fibers. The cellulose content of cork cells is very low. In the case of *Betula verrucosa*, the outer bark was found to contain about 4.5% of hexosans and pentosans, whereas the inner bark contained 38.7%, and the wood 68.6% (Table II).

3. Methods for the Purification of the Carbohydrate Part of Extractive-Free Bark

It has been shown in several ways that the standard methods of wood analysis are not suitable for bark. For example, it is clear from the above that the regular determination of lignin with 72% sulfuric acid gives misleading lignin values. The monoethanolamine-chlorination method is often employed in the purification of the

carbohydrate part of wood. Another method consists of sulfite treatment and chlorination, according to Cross and Bevan. Both of these
methods have proved unsuitable for bark, owing to difficulties that
occur in the filtration and washing (96,103,158). Kiefer and Kurth
(96) discovered that the monoethanolamine-chlorination method
could be applied to Douglas-fir bast fiber, if the extractive-free matter
were freed from alkali soluble (1% sodium hydroxide) products,
which consisted of about 50% of the lignin, 21.9% of the pentosans,
and 56.7% of the polyuronides. The holocellulose prepared in this
manner contained 77.8% of alkali-resistant alpha cellulose.

The Kürschner and Hoffer (112) method, which includes treatment
of the substance with alcoholic nitric acid, was applied by Šarkov
(153) who obtained a yield of 25% of carbohydrates from the bark of
birch and aspen. By means of this method, Wacek and Schön (164)
obtained 21.6% of pulp from pine bark.

In a number of instances a method has been used that involves a
treatment with sodium chlorite and acetic acid, in principle according
to Jayme (79). It appeared in experiments with Douglas-fir bast
fiber (96) and with incense-cedar bark (158) that substantial losses
occurred as a result of the degradation of holocellulose, if its lignin
content were by this method reduced below 5.6 to 6%.

It has been found that the holocellulose of bark contains a
substantially high percentage of alkali-resistant alpha cellulose, in
general between 65 and 75%. One must take into account the possibility that the values of holocellulose and alpha cellulose have, in
many cases, not been corrected for lignin.

V. The Commercial and Technical Importance of Bark

A. UTILIZATION OF BARK

Until now, bark has played an exceedingly negative role in the
wood conversion industry. Barking involves expenditure, and the
bark waste collected causes difficulties in disposal. This waste represents 10 to 15% of the total weight of the wood treated and, in the
long run, it is disadvantageous from the economic point of view only
to use it as fuel. Attempts have therefore been made to find a
more advantageous use for bark, in part by endeavoring to attain
better utilization of the physical and chemical components of it, and

in part by including it as a raw material in wood processing. An extensive survey of the literature concerning the properties and the utilization of bark has been given by Marian and Wissing (119).

1. The Use of the Physical and Chemical Components of Bark

The physical components (especially cork, fibers, and bark powder) of many types of bark have been taken into extensive use. Fibers can be used in the manufacture of fiberboard (Section V-B4), and as additions to filling and isolation materials. Bark powder has been used as a carrier for insecticides, and for soil improvement (6,23,116). Short fibers or bark powder have been used as additives to moulding compounds. Fractions of cork have proved suitable for soil improvement and for filling material.

Useful chemicals can be obtained by means of either extraction or pyrolysis. Many of the extractive substances of bark are of medicinal importance, in particular, alkaloids, such as quinine, strychnine, brucine, etc. Tanning agents are obtained from bark and various types of pigment, of which the most important, quercetin, has very great potentialities. The great influence of the phenolic acids on the viscosity of solutions has been employed in various ways.

Numerous attempts have been made to use the phenolic bark extracts for the manufacture of adhesives, by cross-linking the tannins and the polyphenols in these extracts with formaldehyde or phenols. Herrick and Bock (66), and Marian and Wissing (120) have carried out such experiments with the extracts of bark from western hemlock and spruce, respectively. The adhesives obtained were found to be of advantage in the manufacture of plywood. The resistivity of these resin glues to boiling water is low.

2. The Use of Bark in Combustion and Pyrolysis

Table XIV gives the heat of combustion for a number of types of bark, according to Chang and Mitchell (26). The calorific value of bark is approximately equivalent to that of the corresponding wood; in many cases, it is somewhat higher. In general, the bark of coniferous trees has a higher heat of combustion than that of deciduous trees, but the outer bark of birch has an exceptionally high calorific value: 8260 calories per gram, on a moisture-free basis (83).

The advantages gained from the use of bark as fuel are seriously limited by the water content of floated wood. In order to improve the combustion economy, a part of the water is normally pressed out of

TABLE XIV
Heat of Combustion of Barks (26)

Species	Moisture content, %	Calories/ gram[a]	B.t.u./lb.[a]
Balsam fir	6.5	4923	8861
Western larch	6.7	4558	8204
Engelmann spruce	5.5	4644	8359
Black spruce	6.5	4581	8246
Jack pine	6.6	4867	8761
Lodgepole pine	5.6	5661	10190
Slash pine	6.4	5001	9002
Eastern hemlock	6.2	4890	8802
Sugar maple	6.0	4056	7301
Red alder	5.8	4415	7947
Yellow birch	5.2	5042	9076
Paper birch	4.8	5241	9434
Sweetgum	6.2	4139	7450
Blackgum	6.0	4409	7936
American sycamore	6.4	4113	7403
Quaking aspen	5.5	4685	8433
White oak	6.5	3886	6995
Red oak	4.4	4461	8030
Black willow	6.7	3982	7168
American elm	6.7	3845	6921

[a] Values are for samples of the indicated moisture content.

the bark before its use as fuel. The wet combustion method of Zimmerman (174) might be suitable for the direct burning of bark in a wet state.

In pyrolysis, an attempt is made to obtain useful substances by means of dry distillation. To date, the most important product in this respect has been the residue of distillation, or charcoal which, in general, provides a greater yield from bark than from wood. The distillate, however, may also contain utilizable compounds. If the material of pyrolysis is made acid or alkaline, products of the decomposition of wax and phlobaphenes are present in the distillate (45). From pine bark, a phlobaphene fraction has been obtained that is, in its ability to form plastics with polyvinyl chloride, comparable with dimethyl phthalate (46). Charcoal obtained from bark has, usually, too high a content of ash for use as industrial charcoal, and has,

TABLE XV

Pyrolysis of Birch (83)[a]

Product of charring	Element, substance, or group of substances	Outer bark	Inner bark	Wood
	C	12.4	29.5	23.9
	H	0.4	1.0	0.8
Charcoal	O	0.6	2.1	1.6
	Ashes	0.4	2.1	0.2
		13.8	34.7	26.5
	Neutral oil	45.6	2.5	1.4
	Acids	0.8	0.4	0.4
	Phenolic compounds	7.5	2.1	1.6
Tar,	Insoluble in ether	1.1	0.4	0.2
waterfree[b]	Precipitate on soda treatment	1.8	0.3	0.1
	Water soluble tar	0.7	0.8	0.9
	Error in analysis	0.2	0.9	0.0
		57.7	7.4	4.6
	Water soluble tar	0.3	2.8	11.1
	Acids calculated as acetic			
Tar water, exclud-	acid	1.2	5.8	9.7
ing moisture of	Methyl alcohol	0.2	1.0	1.3
charring materi-	Water-soluble neutral com-			
al, including wa-	pounds b.p. < 95°C.	0.4	1.1	1.6
ter of tar	Water, formed in the reac-			
	tions	8.3	22.2	25.2
		10.4	32.9	48.9
	CO_2	5.5	16.9	11.8
	$C_n H_m$ (as C_2H_4)	1.1	0.3	0.5
	CO	2.0	4.5	5.1
Gases	CH_4	2.7	2.1	1.8
	H_2 (remaining)	0.1	0.2	0.1
		11.4	24.0	19.3
	Accounted for	93.3	99.0	99.3
In all	Unaccounted for	6.7	1.0	0.7
		100.0	100.0	100.0

[a] Yields of separate substances or groups of substances in per cent of absolutely dry charring material yielded in charring of outer bark, inner bark, and wood of birch at atmospheric pressure about 4 hours up to 500°C.

[b] Contents of water in the crude tars in per cent of the weight of crude tar as follows: tar from outer bark 3.2%; tar from inner bark 10.6% and tar from wood 21.9%.

instead, been employed for medicinal purposes, for rubber compounding, for use as a reducing agent in metallurgy, and for the making of electrodes, etc.

Table XV shows the products obtained on the pyrolysis of the inner and outer bark and the wood of *Betula verrucosa* at 500°C. In a retort, distillation tar is obtained, which can be considered to have formed as a result of the decomposition and condensation of the original constituents of the bark. The tar obtained on the pyrolysis of birch bark included a 78% neutral fraction, which contained only about 2% oxygen, the remainder being carbon and hydrogen (87). This neutral oil consisted exclusively of aliphatic and alicyclic components, and was probably formed from the suberin and betulinol of the outer bark. Individual substances could not be isolated from the oil by means of chromatography with alumina, or through distillation.

When use was made, in the distillation, of the fluidized bed technique, the condensation of the organic distillate of white spruce bark was prevented to a very great extent. The distillation products were removed as quickly as possible with the aid of carrier gases, for example, with nitrogen, carbon dioxide, or water vapor. The distillate consisted of phenols, fatty acids, aldehydes, and neutral matter (163).

Kurth and Ratnam (109) have investigated the composition of the pyrolysis products of Douglas-fir bark.

B. THE ROLE OF BARK IN THE CONVERSION OF WOOD

1. Increased Pitch Troubles

The large quantities of extractives in bark can, considerably, increase pitch troubles in the manufacture of paper from unbarked wood. Browning and Bublitz (20) found that the content of ether extractives in the bark of aspen is three to four times as high as that in the corresponding wood (Table IV). In a mixture with the resin of the size, or of softwood pulps, these ether solubles bring about the formation of particularly adhesive products. As can be seen from Table IV, seasoning reduces the content of ether extractives in both the bark and the wood.

2. Cooking Experiments with Bark

One of the disadvantages of the cooking of unbarked wood is that the bark considerably increases the consumption of chemicals. This is true in both sulfite and soda cooking. In a soda cooking, the phenolic acids of the bark consume large quantities of alkali. As shown by Brauns and Lewis (13), in their experimental cooking, a great part of the bark lignin remains insoluble, a fact that can possibly be explained by assuming that in bark there is a strong lignin-carbohydrate bond, which does not have any correlation in wood. In the pulping of unbarked wood, the lignin content of pulp thus remains high, a fact that reduces the possibilities of making use of the pulp.

In the pulping of bark, it has been shown that extreme conditions do not give any improvement on the results obtained under normal conditions. Table XVI presents the results of cooking experiments

TABLE XVI

Alkaline Pulping Experiments with Different Types of Bark (29)

Extractive-free bark species	Lignin[c] per cent in extractive-free bark	Pulp yield, %		Lignin[c] in pulp, %		Pentosans in pulp, %	
		I[a]	II[b]	I	II	I	II
Balsam	32.3	39.5	10.3	15.1	19.1	5.1	1.3
Black spruce	27.4	33.7	16.6	8.9	18.4	6.9	5.3
White spruce	27.3	30.3	17.2	5.7	19.0	5.3	2.3
E. hemlock, outer bark	52.7	31.6	13.2	19.6	35.4	4.7	4.5
Douglas-fir, outer bark	55.5	24.9	7.3	7.6	12.7	5.6	1.6

[a] I, 5% NaOH, 1 h, 170°C.
[b] II, 10% NaOH, 4 h, 170°C.
[c] Determined as insoluble in 72% H_2SO_4.

with different types of bark, according to Clermont and Schwartz (29). Stronger liquor and extended cooking time both reduced the yield of pulp and increased the lignin content of the pulp, the reason being that the increased severity of the conditions intensified the degradation of the pulp more than the delignification.

In five successive processes of digestion of western red-cedar outer bark with 5% sodium hydroxide, the lignin content diminished from 12.1% in the first pulp to 3.4% in the fifth and, simultaneously, the yield of pulp dropped from 33.6% to 19.2% (33).

Neutral sulfite semichemical pulping experiments were carried out by Keller (95) with aspen, hickory and slash pine, in part separately with wood and bark, and in part with wood mixed with bark up to 25%. The differences in the consumption of chemicals were highest in the case of slash pine, its bark taking twice as much sulfite from the liquor as an equal weight of wood. With the exception of an increase in the folding endurance of hickory, the strength of the test sheets regularly showed a reduction along with the increase in the proportion of bark. The folding strength appeared to be the most sensitive property, whereas the tearing resistance was the least sensitive. Of these wood species, hickory showed the lowest sensitivity, while aspen pulps lost much in strength and density in consequence of the addition of bark.

Adler and Stockman (1) investigated the sulfite pulping properties of the outermost sap layer of unpeeled, floated logs. A layer approximately 5 mm. thick of the external part of sapwood is difficult to digest, which is considered to be based on the impregnation of this layer with tannin during the flotation.

Martin and Brown (122) gave an illustration of the influence of bark upon the yield and the quality of pulp in sulfate cooking. The bark of shortleaf pine was discovered to contain 10% of parenchymatous and 5% of sclerenchymatous cells. Because of their small size, these cells reduce the strength of the pulp. The long sieve cells, on the other hand, are suitable for paper pulp. Experimental digestions of shortleaf pine showed that high percentages of bark could be used without any considerable deterioration of the pulp, but that sulfate pulps made of bark alone were unsuitable for paper making. The addition of bark increased the consumption of chemicals, and reduced the brightness of the pulp. The reduction of the cellulose content and the increase in the lignin content of the pulp were larger than could be calculated theoretically.

3. The Preparation of Viscose

Kleinert and Wurm (97) investigated the influence of bark upon the preparation of viscose from beech. The fibrous part of the bark reacted in a normal manner, but the preparation of viscose was disturbed by sclerenchymatous cells, which did not dissolve in the sulfite digestion, nor in the alkaline extraction. Wood used for the preparation of viscose must thus be carefully barked, or the pulp must be cleaned of undigested matter.

4. Bark as a Raw Material for the Manufacture of Fiberboard

Many attempts have been made to use bark as an additive in fiberboard manufacture. Certain negative effects have been found in this connection, in particular that in many cases the bark has reduced the strength of the product and influenced its color. In addition, bark has in a number of instances been shown to increase the freeness of the pulp, thus bringing about technical difficulties in board manufacture.

Clermont and Schwartz (29) prepared both softboards and hardboards from western- and eastern-cedar bark. Softboard of insulation type, with a satisfactory tensile strength, could be prepared from the bark of eastern-cedar, whereas western-cedar bark gave a weaker but still useful product (148). An addition of screenings of sulfite pulp or of groundwood somewhat improved the result (29,148). The hardboard prepared was of a considerably lower quality than the minimum requirements for a commercial hardboard.

Hardboards with very good characteristics have been prepared from Douglas-fir mixed with bark (3). In this case, the addition of size is unnecessary as, actually, it has a weakening effect upon the product. The water-repellent property of the Douglas-fir bark is, principally, localized in the benzene soluble wax. Bark additions of 15 or 45% have been used with good results, and differences in the color were negligible.

Anderson and Helge (2) prepared hardboards from spruce (*Picea abies*), pine (*Pinus sylvestris*), and birch (*Betula verrucosa*) with various additions of bark. According to these results, both spruce and pine bark can be used as additives. When 50% pine bark is used, neither heating nor size addition is needed. The sizing effect of the pine bark was found to be based upon the high content of ether soluble wax (1.68% in comparison with 0.31% in spruce bark; the ether extract of birch bark contained 95% of betulinol). The fiber sizing effect can be attributed to this wax alone, as hardboard, prepared with an addition of ether-extracted pine bark, had a very great water absorption value.

Marian and Wissing (121) gave a survey of the attempts that have been made to manufacture fiber board from unbarked wood. Their experiments with the preparation of hardboards from spruce showed that additions of fibrous bark material, amounting to 30 to 40%, can be used without impairment of the product.

REFERENCES

1. Adler, E., and L. Stockman, *Svensk Papperstidn.*, **54**, 477 (1951).

1a. Allison, F. E., and C. J. Klein, *Soil Sci. Soc. Am., Proc.*, **25**, 193 (1961).

2. Anderson, A., and K. Helge, *Forest Prods. J.*, **9**, No. 4, 31A (1959).

2a. Anderson, A. B., R. J. Breuer, and G. A. Nicholls, *Forest Prods. J.*, **11**, 226 (1961).

3. Anderson, A., and W. Runckel, *Proc. Forest Products Res. Soc.*, **4**, 301 (1950).

3a. Arthur, H. R., and C. M. Lee, *J. Chem. Soc.*, **1960**, 4654.

4. Anderson, E., and W. W. Pigman, *Science*, **105**, 601 (1947).

4a. Arya, V. P., C. Enzell, H. Erdtman, and T. Kubota, *Acta Chem. Scand.*, **15**, 225 (1961).

5. Aspinall, G. O., E. L. Hirst, and A. Nicolson, *J. Chem. Soc.*, **1959**, 1697.

5a. Bartlett, F., W. I. Taylor, and Raymond-Hamet, *Compt. rend.*, **249**, 1259 (1959).

6. Aspitarte, T. R., Ph.D. thesis, Oregon State College, 1959; through *Abstr. Bull. Inst. Paper Chem.*, **30**, 379 (1960).

6a. Bertho, A., and M. Koll, *Chem. Ber.*, **94**, 2737 (1961).

7. Bandekow, R. J., *J. Forestry*, **45**, 729 (1947).

7a. Van Blaricom, L. E., and G. M. Tokos, U.S. Pat., 2,975,126 (1961); through *Abstr. Bull. Inst. Paper Chem.*, **31**, 1914 (1961).

8. Becker, E. S., and E. F. Kurth, *Tappi*, **41**, 380 (1958).

8a. Branion, R., *Pulp Paper Mag. Can.*, **62**, T-506 (1961).

9. Becker, M., *Landwirtsch. Forsch.*, **8**, 111 (1955); through *Chem. Abstracts*, **50**, 6705 (1956).

9a. Briggs, L. H., R.C. Cambie, J. B. Lowry, and R. N. Seelye, *J. Chem. Soc.*, **1961**, 642.

10. Binko, I., J. Kolář, Z. Pospichalová, and I. Ivanič, *Věda a Výzkum v Průmyslu Kožedělném*, **2**, 77 (1957); through *Bull. Inst. Paper Chem.*, **29**, 1779 (1959).

10a. Burgon, W. J., and P. Zenczak, U.S. Pat., 2,880,216 (1959); through *Chem. Abstracts*, **54**, 15931 (1960).

11. Bishop, C. T., V. D. Harwood, and C. B. Purves, *Pulp Paper Mag. Can.*, **51**, No. 1, 90 (1950).

11a. Burton, R. E., U.S. Pat., 2,995,434 (1961); through *Abstr. Bull. Inst. Paper Chem.*, **32**, 717 (1962).

12. Blank, F., "Anthocyanins, flavones, xanthones," in W. Ruhland, *Encyclopedia of Plant Physiology*, Vol. X, Springer-Verlag, Berlin-Göttingen-Heidelberg, 1958.

12a. Chatterjee, A., and S. Ghosal, *Sci. and Culture*, **26**, 238 (1960); through *Chem. Abstracts*, **55**, 11450 (1961).

13. Brauns, F. E., and H. F. Lewis, *Tech. Assoc. Papers*, **27**, 460 (1944).

13a. Donoho, C. W. Jr., and D. R. Walker, *Proc. Am. Soc. Hort. Sci.*, **75**, 155 (1960); through *Chem. Abstracts*, **54**, 22872 (1960).

14. Bridel, M., C. Charaux, and J. Rabeté, *Compt. rend.*, **187**, 56 (1928); through ref. 92.

14a. Ely, H., E. F. Kurth, and E. S. Becker, *Corvallis, Oregon Forest Research Center, Rept. No. C-5* (1961); through *Abstr. Bull. Inst. Paper Chem.*, **32**, 1511 (1962).

15. Bridel, M., and P. Picard, *Compt. rend.*, **180**, 1864 (1925); through ref. 94.
15a. Endres, H., *Leder*, **12**, 152 (1961).
16. Briggs, D. R., and D. Siminovitch, *Arch. Biochem.*, **23**, 18 (1949).
16a. Endres, H., and K. Merkle, *Chem. Ber.*, **94**, 431 (1961).
17. Briggs, L. H., and J. C. Dacre, *J. Chem. Soc.*, **1948**, 564.
17a. Endres, H., K. Merkle, and H. Bauriedel, *Chem. Ber.*, **94**, 438 (1961).
18. Briggs, L. H., and R. H. Locker, *J. Chem. Soc.*, **1951**, 3131.
18a. Erdtman, H., and T. Kubota, *Acta Chem. Scand.*, **15**, 1003 (1961).
19. Briggs, L. H., and G. A. Nicholls, *J. Chem. Soc.*, **1949**, 1241.
19a. Faber, H. B. Jr., *Tappi*, **43**, 406 (1960).
20. Browning, B. L., and L. O. Bublitz, *Tappi*, **36**, 418 (1953).
20a. Forest Products Laboratory, Forest Service U.S. Department of Agriculture, *Rept. No. 1666-5* (1961).
21. Browning, B. L., and L. O. Sell, *Tappi*, **40**, 362 (1957).
21a. Gopinath, K. W., T. R. Govindachari, P. C. Parthasarathy, and N. Viswanathan, *Helv. Chim. Acta*, **44**, 1040 (1961).
22. Bruckner, V., J. Kovács, and J. Koczka, *J. Chem. Soc.*, **1948**, 948.
22a. Grillos, S. J., and F. H. Smith, *For. Sci.*, **5**, No. 4, 377 (1959); through *Forstliche Umschau*, **3**, 275 (1960).
23. Burton, R. E., *Forest Prods. J.*, **9**, No. 4, 19A (1959).
23a. Grundon, M. F., and J. E. B. McGarvey, *J. Chem. Soc.*, **1960**, 2739.
24. Cambie, R. C., *J. Chem. Soc.*, **1959**, 848.
24a. Haas, B. R., and R. E. Kremers, *Tappi*, **44**, 747 (1961).
25. Chang, Y.-P., *Anatomy of Common North American Pulpwood Barks*, Tappi Monograph Series, No. 14, New York, 1954.
25a. Hall, R. B., J. H. Leonard, and G. A. Nicholls, *Forest Prods. J.*, **10**, 263 (1960).
26. Chang, Y.-P., and R. L. Mitchell, *Tappi*, **38**, 315 (1955).
26a. Hata, K., and M. Sogo, *Nippon Mokuzai Gakkaishi*, **6**, 71 (1960); through *Chem. Abstracts*, **54**, 25792 (1960).
27. Chattaway, M. M., *Australian J. Botany*, **3**, No. 1, 21 (1955); through *Bull. Inst. Paper Chem.*, **27**, 283 (1956).
27a. Hergert, H. L., *Forest Prods. J.*, **10**, 610 (1960).
28. Chatterjee, A., and S. S. Mitra, *J. Am. Chem. Soc.*, **71**, 606 (1949).
28a. Hergert, H. L., "Economic Importance of Flavonoid Compounds," in T. A. Geissman, *The Chemistry of Flavonoid Compounds*, Pergamon Press, London, 1962.
29. Clermont, L. P., and H. Schwartz, *Proc. Forest Products Res. Soc.*, **2**, 130 (1948).
29a. Herrick, F. W., and R. J. Conca, *Forest Prods. J.*, **10**, 361 (1960).
30. Clotofski, E., H. Weikert, and H. Nick, *Ber.*, **74**, 299 (1941).
30a. Hillis, W. E., and A. Carle, *Biochem. J.*, **82**, 435 (1962).
31. Corbett, R. E., and M. A. McDowell, *J. Chem. Soc.*, **1958**, 3715.
31a. Holmes, G. W., and E. F. Kurth, *Tappi*, **44**, 893 (1961).
32. Crabbe, P., *Ing. Chim.*, **38**, 3 (1956).
32a. Kapil, R. S., and M. M. Dhar, *J. Sci. Ind. Research (India)*, **20B**, 498 (1961).
33. Cram, K. H., J. A. Eastwood, F. W. King, and H. Schwartz, *Pulp Paper Mag. Can.*, **48**, No. 10, 85 (1947).

658   W. JENSEN, K. E. FREMER, P. SIERILÄ, V. WARTIOVAARA

33a. Karrer, P., and H. Schmid, *J. Indian Chem. Soc.*, **38**, 438 (1961).
34. Cromwell, B. T., "The Alkaloids," in K. Paech and M. V. Tracey, *Modern Methods of Plant Analysis*, Vol. IV, Springer-Verlag, Berlin-Göttingen-Heidelberg, 1955.
34a. Kharchenko, R. I., and E. K. Tsaregradskiĭ, *Gidroliz. i Lesohim. Prom.*, *13*, No. 2, 12 (1960); through *Chem. Abstracts*, **54**, 16828 (1960).
35. De Eds, F., and A. N. Booth, U.S. Pat. 2,534,250 (1950); through *Chem. Abstracts*, **45**, 3129 (1951).
35a. Kirrmann, A., and L. Duhamel, *Compt. rend.*, **254**, 1303 (1962).
36. Dickey, E. E., *J. Org. Chem.*, **23**, 179 (1958).
36a. Lawrie, W., J. McLean, and G. R. Taylor, *J. Chem. Soc.*, **1960**, 4303.
37. Doughty, J. B., F. W. Taylor, and W. T. Henerey, *Forest Prods. J.*, **6**, 476 (1956).
37a. McLean, S., K. Palmer, and L. Marion, *Can. J. Chem.*, **38**, 1547 (1960).
38. Drake, N. L., and R. P. Jacobsen, *J. Am. Chem. Soc.*, **57**, 1570 (1935).
38a. Manson, D. W., *Tappi*, **43**, 59 (1960).
39. Dässler, H.-G., and H. Urzynicok, *Holz Roh- u. Werkstoff*, **16**, 327 (1958).
39a. Mian, A. J., and T. E. Timell, *Can. J. Chem.*, **38**, 1191 (1960).
40. Endres, H., *Chem. Ber.* **91**, 636 (1958).
40a. Mian, A. J., and T. E. Timell, *Tappi*, **43**, 775 (1960).
41. Endres, H., W. Grassmann, and H. Mathes, *Chem. Ber.*, **91**, 141 (1958).
41a. Mian, A. J., and T. E. Timell, *Chem. & Ind. (London)*, **1959**, 1552.
42. Erdtman, H., in A. Todd, *Perspectives in Organic Chemistry*, Interscience, New York, 1956; *Proc. Royal Dublin Soc.*, **27**, 129 (1956); through ref. 63.
42a. Murata, T., and N. Takamura, *J. Japan Wood Research Soc.*, **5**, No. 5, 194 (1959); through *Abstr. Bull. Inst. Paper Chem.*, **30**, 950 (1960).
43. Esau, K., *Botan. Rev.*, **5**, 373 (1939).
43a. Narasimhachari, N., and E. v. Rudloff, *Can. J. Chem.*, **39**, 2572 (1961).
44. Esau, K., *Plant Anatomy*, Wiley, New York, 1953.
44a. Nickles, W. C., and J. W. Rowe, *Forest Prods. J.*, **12**, 374 (1962).
45. Euler, H. v., H. Hasselquist, and U. Lööv, *Svensk Papperstidn.*, **50**, No. 11B, 86 (1947).
45a. Okamura, H., and Y. Morohashi, *Nippon Ringaku Kaishi*, **43**, 292 (1961); through *Chem. Abstracts*, **56**, 8890 (1962).
46. Euler, H. v., H. Hasselquist, U. Lööv, and S. Edelö, in *Festskrift J. A. Hedvall*, Gothenburg (1948); *Chem. Abstracts*, **42**, 6341 (1948).
46a. Oksanen, H., *Suomen Kemistilehti*, **B33**, 167 (1960).
47. Ewart, M. H., D. Siminovitch, and D. R. Briggs, *Plant Physiol.*, **29**, 407 (1954); through *Chem. Abstracts*, **49**, 1890 (1955).
47a. Oksanen, H., *Suomen Kemistilehti*, **34B**, 91 (1961).
48. Fahey, M. D., and E. F. Kurth, *Tappi*, **40**, 506 (1957).
48a. Painter, T. J., and C. B. Purves, *Tappi*, **43**, 729 (1960).
49. Fierz-David, H., and C. Ulrich, *Experientia*, **1**, 160 (1945).
49a. Paris, R. R., and R. Letouzey, *J. Agr. Trop. et Botan. Appl.*, **4**, 31 (1957); through *Chem. Abstracts*, **54**, 13275 (1960).
50. Ganguly, A. K., T. R. Seshadri, and P. Subramanian, *Tetrahedron*, **3**, No. 3/4, 225 (1958).

50a. Paris, R. R., and A. Stambouli, *Ann. Pharm. Franc.*, **18**, 873 (1960); through *Chem. Abstracts*, **56**, 1769 (1962).

51. Goodson, J. A., *Biochem. J.*, **15**, 123 (1921); through ref. 94.

51a. Pearl, I. A., D. L. Beyer, D. Laskowski, and D. Whitney, *Tappi*, **43**, 756 (1960).

52. Grassmann, W., G. Deffner, E. Schuster, and W. Pauckner, *Chem. Ber.*, **89**, 2523 (1956).

52a. Pearl, I. A., and S. F. Darling, *J. Org. Chem.*, **27**, 1806 (1962).

53. Grassmann, W., H. Endres, W. Pauckner, and H. Mathes, *Chem. Ber.*, **90**, 1125 (1957).

53a. Pearl, I. A., S. F. Darling, H. De Haas, B. A. Loving, D. A. Scott, R. H. Turley, and R. E. Werth, *Tappi*, **44**, 475 (1961).

54. Guillemonat, A., and A. Strich, *Bull. soc. chim. France*, **1950**, 860; through *Chem. Abstracts*, **45**, 3327 (1951).

54a. Pearl, I. A., O. Justman, D. L. Beyer, and D. Whitney, *Tappi*, **45**, 663 (1962).

55. Harwood, V. D., and C. B. Purves, *Northeastern Wood Utilization Bulletin*, No. 25 (1949); *Paper Trade J.*, **128**, No. 22, 19 (1949).

55a. Pearl, I. A., and J. W. Rowe, *Forest Prods. J.*, **10**, 91 (1960).

56. Hata, K., and M. Sogo, *Mokuzai Gakkaishi*, **4**, 85 (1958); *Chem. Abstracts*, **52**, 19125 (1958).

56a. Pearson, L. C., and D. B. Lawrence, *Am. J. Botany*, **45**, 383 (1958); through *Abstr. Bull. Inst. Paper Chem.*, **31**, 198 (1960).

57. Hathway, D. E., *Biochem. J.*, **70**, 34 (1958).

57a. Pentegov, A. P., and M. A. Chirkova, *Trudy Him.-Metallurg. Inst. Sibirsk. Otdel. Akad. Nauk S.S.S.R.*, No. 13, 11 (1959); *Referat Zur. Him.*, No. 4, 493 (1960); through *Abstr. Bull. Inst. Paper Chem.*, **31**, 27 (1960).

58. Hathway, D. E., *Biochem. J.*, **71**, 533 (1959).

58a. Pouly, P. L., and L. Fauconnet, *Bull. Soc. Vaudoise Sci. Nat.*, **67**, 205 (1960); through *Chem. Abstracts*, **55**, 18803 (1961).

59. Hay, K. D., and H. F. Lewis, *Paper Trade J.*, **111**, No. 25, 39 (1940).

59a. Riggs, N. V., L. Antonaccio, and L. Marion, *Can. J. Chem.*, **39**, 1330 (1961).

60. Hearon, W. M., and W. S. MacGregor, *Chem. Revs.*, **55**, 957 (1955).

60a. Roux, D. G., *Chem. & Ind. (London)*, **1962**, 278.

61. Hergert, H. L., *Forest Prods. J.*, **8**, 335 (1958).

61a. Roux, D. G., and E. A. Maihs, *Biochem. J.*, **74**, 44 (1960).

62. Hergert, H. L., *J. Org. Chem.*, **21**, 534 (1956).

62a. Roux, D. G., E. A. Maihs, and E. Paulus, *Biochem. J.*, **78**, 834 (1961).

63. Hergert, H. L., and O. Goldschmid, *J. Org. Chem.*, **23**, 700 (1958).

63a. Sakai, A., *Nature*, **189**, 416 (1961).

64. Hergert, H. L., and E. F. Kurth, *Tappi*, **35**, 59 (1952).

64a. Sengupta, P., S. N. Choudhuri, and H. N. Khastgir, *Tetrahedron*, **10**, 45 (1960).

65. Hergert, H. L., and E. F. Kurth, *Tappi*, **36**, 137 (1953).

65a. Sitte, P. *Naturwiss.*, **46**, 260 (1959).

66. Herrick, F. W., and L. H. Bock, *Forest Prods. J.*, **8**, 269 (1958).

66a. Thomas, A. F., and J. M. Müller, *Chem. & Ind. (London)*, **1961**, 1794.

660 W. JENSEN, K. E. FREMER, P. SIERILÄ, V. WARTIOVAARA

67. Hess, C. L., *Tappi*, **35**, 312 (1952).
67a. Timell, T. E., *Svensk Papperstidn.*, **64**, 651 (1961).
68. Hillis, W. E., *J. Soc. Leather Trades Chemists*, **38**, 91 (1954).
68a. Timell, T. E., *Svensk Papperstidn.*, **64**, 685 (1961).
69. Hirota, K., T. Takano, K. Taniguichi, and K. Iguchi, *J. Soc. Chem. Ind. Japan*, **47**, 922 (1944); through *Chem. Abstracts*, **42**, 6090 (1948).
69a. Timell, T. E., *Svensk Papperstidn.*, **64**, 744 (1961).
70. Hirst, E. L., L. Hough, and J. K. N. Jones, *J. Chem. Soc.*, **1951**, 323.
70a. Timell, T. E., *Svensk Papperstidn.*, **64**, 748 (1961).
71. Hirst, E. L., and A. S. Perlin, *J. Chem. Soc.*, **1954**, 2622.
71a. Timell, T. E., and A. J. Mian, *Tappi*, **44**, 788 (1961).
72. Holdheide, W., *Holz Roh- u. Werkstoff*, **10**, 263 (1952).
72a. Tschesche, R., and P. Otto, *Chem. Ber.*, **95**, 1144 (1962).
73. Hossfeld, R. L., and W. T. Hunter, *Tappi*, **41**, 359 (1958).
73a. Tunmann, P., and J. Rachor, *Naturwiss.*, **47**, 471 (1960).
74. Hossfeld, R. L., and F. H. Kaufert, *Forest Prods. J.*, **7**, 437 (1957).
74a. Wilson, J. D., *Forest Prods. J.*, **11**, 260 (1961).
75. Huber, B., *Jahrb. Wiss. Bot.*, **88**, 176 (1939).
75a. Ziegler, H., and M. Schnabel, *Flora (Jena)*, **150**, 306 (1961).
76. Hughes, G. K., and E. Ritchie, *Australian J. Chem.*, **7**, 104 (1954); through *Chem. Abstracts*, **49**, 3101 (1955).
76a. Zimmermann, M. H., *Science*, **133**, 73 (1961).
77. Härtel, O., A. v. Wacek, and S. Meralla, *Holzforschung*, **12**, 33 (1958).
78. International Association of Wood Anatomists, Committee on Nomenclature, *International Glossary of Terms Used in Wood Anatomy (Tropical Woods)*, No. **107**, 5 (1957).
79. Jayme, G., *Cellulosechemie*, **20**, 43 (1942).
80. Jefferies, P. R., *J. Chem. Soc.*, **1954**, 473.
81. Jensen, W., *Paperi ja Puu.*, **32B**, No. 4a, 7 (1950).
82. Jensen, W., *Svensk Papperstidn.*, **54**, 739 (1951).
83. Jensen, W., *Acta Acad. Aboensis, Math. Phys.*, **XVI**, 3 (1948).
84. Jensen, W., *Paperi ja Puu*, **32B**, 261 (1950).
85. Jensen, W., *Paperi ja Puu*, **32B**, 293 (1950).
86. Jensen, W., *Paperi ja Puu*, **34**, 467 (1952).
87. Jensen, W., *Paperi ja Puu*, **32B**, 168 (1950).
88. Jensen, W., P. Ihalo, and K. Varsa, *Paperi ja Puu*, **39**, 237 (1957).
89. Jensen, W., and P. Rinne, *Paperi ja Puu*, **36**, 32 (1954).
90. Jensen, W., and R. Östman, *Paperi ja Puu*, **36**, 427 (1954).
91. Jermstad, A., *Pharm. Acta Helv.*, **4**, 90 (1929); through *Chem. Abstracts*, **24**, 4900 (1930).
92. Jones, D. B., and S. Phillips, *J. Am. Chem. Soc.*, **59**, 595 (1937).
93. Jones, J. K. N., and F. Smith, "Plant Gums and Mucilages," in W. W. Pigman and M. L. Wolfrom, *Advances in Carbohydrate Chemistry*, Vol. 4, Academic Press, New York, 1949.
94. Karrer, W., *Konstitution and Vorkommen der Organischen Pflanzenstoffe, (exclusive Alkaloide)*, Birkhäuser Verlag, Basel (1958).
95. Keller, E. L., *Tappi*, **33**, 556 (1950).
96. Kiefer, H. J., and E. F. Kurth, *Tappi*, **36**, 14 (1953).

97. Kleinert, T. N., and P. Wurm, *Svensk Papperstidn.*, **57**, 19 (1954).

98. Koepfli, J. B., *J. Am. Chem. Soc.*, **54**, 2412 (1932).

99. Koljo, B., in E. Treiber, *Die Chemie der Pflanzanzellwand*, Springer-Verlag, Berlin-Göttingen-Heidelberg (1957).

100. Kotasek, Z., *Veda a Vyzkum v Prumyslu Kozedelnem*, **1**, 47 (1956); through *Chem. Abstracts*, **51**, 12525 (1957).

101. Kottwitz, F. A., and L. V. Forman, *Ind. Eng. Chem.*, **40**, 2443 (1948).

102. Krugman, S. L., *Forest Sci.*, **5**, No. 2, 169 (1959); through *Abstr. Bull. Inst. Paper Chem.*, **30**, 26 (1959).

103. Kurth, E. F., *Tappi*, **32**, 175 (1949).

104. Kurth, E. F., *Chem. Revs.*, **40**, 33 (1947).

105. Kurth, E. F., *Tappi*, **41**, 733 (1958).

106. Kurth, E. F., *Tappi*, **36**, No. 7, 119A (1953).

107. Kurth, E. F., and J. K. Hubbard, *Ind. Eng. Chem.*, **43**, 896 (1951).

108. Kurth, E. F., V. Ramanathan, and K. Venkataraman, *J. Sci. Ind. Research (India)*, **15B**, 139 (1956); *Chem. Abstracts*, **50**, 15750 (1956).

109. Kurth, E. F., and C. V. S. Ratnam, *Tappi*, **33**, 517 (1950).

110. Kurth, E. F., and J. E. Smith, *Pulp Paper Mag. Can.*, **55**, No. 12, 125 (1954).

111. Kurth, E. F., and G. M. Tokos, *Tappi*, **36**, 301 (1953).

112. Kürschner, K., and A. Hoffer, *Chemikerzeitung*, **55**, 161, 182 (1931).

113. Leopold, B., and I.-L. Malmström, *Acta Chem. Scand.*, **6**, 49 (1952).

114. Lewis, H. F., *Paper Trade J.*, **130**, No. 14, 18, 22 (1950).

115. Lindstedt, G., and B. Zacharias, *Acta Chem. Scand.*, **9**, 781 (1955).

116. Lunt, O. R., and B. Clark, *Forest Prods. J.*, **9**, No. 4, 39A (1959).

117. Mader, H., *Planta* (Berlin), **43**, 163 (1953/1954).

118. Mader, H., "Kork," in W. Ruhland, *Encyclopedia of Plant Physiology*, Vol. X, Springer-Verlag, Berlin-Göttingen-Heidelberg, 1958.

119. Marian, J. E., and A. Wissing, Index to Bark Literature, Part M, (Contents), *Svensk Papperstidn.*, **60**, 522 (1957).

120. Marian, J. E., and A. Wissing, *Svensk Papperstidn.*, **62**, 187 (1959).

121. Marian, J. E., and A. Wissing, *Svensk Papperstidn.*, **62**, 225 (1959).

122. Martin, J. S., and K. J. Brown, *Tappi*, **35**, 7 (1952).

123. Mayer, W., and G. Bauni, *Leder*, **7**, 33 (1956).

124. Meyer, Th. M., *Rec. Trav. Chim.*, **66**, 193 (1947); through *Chem. Abstracts*, **41**, 6607 (1947).

125. Mian, A. J., and T. E. Timell, *Chem. & Ind.*, **1959**, 1552.

126. Molisch, H., *Anatomie der Pflanze*, Vol. IV, Verlag Gustav Fischer, Jena, 1936.

127. Moore, J. A., and S. Eng, *J. Am. Chem. Soc.*, **78**, 395 (1956).

128. Pajari, K., *Ann. Acad. Sci. Fennicae*, **59A**, No. 6, 7 (1942); *Chem. Abstracts*, **38**, 4648 (1944).

129. Pearl, I. A., and S. F. Darling, *J. Org. Chem.*, **24**, 731 (1959).

130. Pearl, I. A., and S. F. Darling, *J. Org. Chem.*, **24**, 1616 (1959).

131. Pigman, W., E. Anderson, R. Fisher, M. A. Buchanan, and B. L. Browning, *Tappi*, **36**, 4 (1953).

132. Plouvier, V., *Compt. rend.*, **227**, 225 (1948); through ref. 94.

133. Plouvier, V., *Compt. rend.*, **238**, 1835 (1954); through ref. 94.

134. Rabaté, J., *Bull. Soc. Chim. Biol.*, **17**, 328 (1935): through ref. 94.

662   W. JENSEN, K. E. FREMER, P. SIERILÄ, V. WARTIOVAARA

135. Ribas-Marqués, I., *Chimie et industrie*, **68**, 333 (1952).
136. Ribas, I., and E. Blasco, *Anales fis. quím.*, **36**, 248 (1940); through *Chem. Abstracts*, **38**, 4285 (1944).
137. Ribas, I., and E. Seoane, *Anales real soc. españ. fis. quím.*, **50B**, 963, 971 (1954).
138. Rittel, W., A. Hunger, and T. Reichstein, *Helv. Chim. Acta*, **36**, 434 (1953).
139. Ritter, G. J., and R. L. Hossfeld, Lake States Aspen Rept. No. 18, U.S. Dept. Agr., Forest Serv., Lake States Forest Exp. Station, 1947.
140. Robertson, A., G. Soliman, and E. C. Owen, *J. Chem. Soc.*, **1939**, 1267.
141. Roth, L., G. Saeger, F. J. Lynch, and J. Weiner, *Structure, Extractives, and Utilization of Bark*, Bibliographic Series No. 191, The Institute of Paper Chemistry, 1960, 446 pp.
142. Ruzicka, L., G. F. Frame, H. M. Leicester, M. Liguori, and H. Brüngger, *Helv. Chim. Acta*, **17**, 426 (1934).
143. Schmidt, M. v., *Monatsh.*, **31**, 347 (1910).
144. Schmidt, R., and K. Weilinger, *Ber.*, **39**, 652 (1906).
145. Schorger, A. W., *J. Ind. Eng. Chem.*, **8**, 22 (1916).
146. Schulz, H., *Untersuchungen über die Bewertung von Eichenstammholz*, Diss., Hann. Münden (1954).
147. Schwalbe, C. G., and K. E. Neumann, *Cellulosechemie*, **11**, 113 (1930).
148. Schwartz, H., *Paper Trade J.*, **128**, No. 24, 27 (1949).
149. Segall, G. H., and C. B. Purves, *Pulp Paper Mag. Can.*, **47**, No. 3, 149 (1946).
150. Seoane, E., and I. Ribas, *Anales real soc. esp. fis. quim.*, Series B-Quimica XLVII, 61 (1951).
151. Sarkov, V. I., and A. L. Girchits, *Lesokhim. Prom.*, **No. 1**, 14 (1940); through *Chem Abstracts*, **36**, 6576 (1942).
152. Šarkov, V. I., V. N. Kalnina, and S. V. Sobetskij, *Lesokhim. Prom.*, **No. 5**, 8 (1939), Him. Referat. Žurn., No. 7, 121; through *Chem. Abstracts*, **34**, 5273 (1940).
153. Šarkov, V. I., Muromceva, V. N. Kalnina, and Ščegolihina, *Žurn. Priklad. Him.*, **11**, 1659 (1938); through *Chem. Abstracts*, **33**, 5651 (1939).
154. Shimada, H., *J. Pharm. Soc. Japan.*, Japan, **60**, 200 (1940); through *Chem. Zentr.*, **1941 II**, 1867.
155. Shimada, H., *J. Pharm. Soc. Japan*, **72**, 61, 63 (1952); through *Chem. Abstracts*, **46**, 6328 (1952).
156. Siminovitch, D., and D. R. Briggs, *Arch. Biochem.*, **23**, 8 (1949).
157. Sitte, P., *Mikroskopie* (Wien), **10**, 178 (1955); through ref. 118.
158. Smith, J. E., and E. F. Kurth, *Tappi*, **36**, 71 (1953).
159. Sosa, A., *Ann. Chim.*, **14**, 5 (1940); through *Chem. Zentr.*, **1942 I**, 2781.
160. Stockar, G. K., *Uber die Chemie des Korkes*, Diss., Zürich, 1948; through ref. 118.
161. Swain, T., *Chem. and Ind.*, **1954**, 1144.
162. Szalai, J., and L. Gracza, *Phyton*, **11**, No. 2, 111 (1958); through *Abstr. Bull. Inst. Paper Chem.*, **29**, 1646 (1959).
163. Vroom, A. H., *Pulp Paper Mag. Can.*, **53**, No. 5, 121 (1952).
164. Wacek, A. v., and A. Schön, *Holz Roh- u. Werkstoff*, **4**, 18 (1941).
165. White, D. E., and L. S. Zampatti, *J. Chem. Soc.*, **1952**, 5040.

166. Wodsak, W., and E. Ueckermann, *Intern. Z. Vitaminforsch.*, **25**, 379 (1955); *Chem. Abstracts*, **49**, 8409 (1955).
167. Zellner, J., and L. Weiss, *Monatsh.*, **46**, 312 (1925).
168. Zetsche, F., in G. Klein, *Handbuch der Pflanzenanalyse*, Vol. 3, Part 1, Wien, 205 (1932).
169. Zetsche, F., and M. Bähler, *Helv. Chim. Acta*, **14**, 642 (1931).
170. Zetsche, F., and M. Bähler, *Helv. Chim. Acta*, **14**, 846 (1931).
171. Zetsche, F., C. Cholatnikow, and K. Scherz, *Helv. Chim. Acta*, **11**, 272 (1928).
172. Zetsche, F., and G. Sonderegger, *Helv. Chim. Acta*, **14**, 632 (1931).
173. Ziegler, H., *Planta*, **47**, 447 (1956).
174. Zimmerman, F. J., U.S. Pat., 2,665,249 (1954).
175. Zimmermann, M. H., *Plant Physiol.*, **32**, 399 (1957).

Addendum

During the period that has elapsed between the writing of this chapter and its publication, there have been published the findings of more than two hundred new investigations concerned with the chemical composition of bark and its technical utilization. In the review that follows, only a minor part of these new works could be included and, accordingly, it represents a selection which is most immediately intended to exemplify the activity which has in recent times been carried out in this sphere.

Investigations Concerning the Physiological and Genetic Processes in Bark, and General Bark Analyses

Some works have primarily been concerned with the translocation of substances within the bark (76a), and the effect of the external conditions (temperature, season of the year) upon the chemical composition of the bark (63a,13a) and its physiology (22a). A work by Pearson and Lawrence (56a) is concerned with the photosynthetic activity in aspen bark. Ziegler and Schnabel (75a) studied the occurrence of urea derivatives in the phloem sap of some hardwoods. Hillis and Carle (30a) tried to establish the origin of the polyphenols in wood and bark from Eucalyptus species; they concluded that the polyphenols are formed *in situ*, probably from carbohydrates. Holmes and Kurth (31a) have investigated the chemical composition of newly formed inner bark of Douglas-fir. White pine bark has been analyzed by Nickles and Rowe (44a).

The Extractives in Bark

The great majority of the articles published recently deal with bark extractives, and a number of new substances, most of them terpenoids, have been found in different kinds of bark. Mention may here be made of such substances as the diterpene acids, polyalthic acid (21a) and communic acid (4a,43a), the triterpene acid platanic acid (66a), the dihydroxytriterpene mairin, along with a trimethyl ether of ellagic acid (9a) and the coumarin derivative avicennin (3a). Erdtman and Kubota (18a) have analyzed the monoterpene fractions from essential oil from juniper bark. Kapil and Dhar (32a) have established the co-occurrence of the three terpenes lupeol, betulinol and betulinic acid in the bark of *Diospyros montana*, these differ from one another only as regards the oxidation stage of a methyl group. The occurrence of a new binaphthyl derivative called diospyrin in this bark has also been established by the same authors.

The phenolic constituents in pine bark have been studied by Oksanen (46a,47a). Works concerned with the different constituents in the bark of aspen have been carried out by Pearl *et al.* (52a,53a, 54a), and Faber (19a). Mention can further be made of articles dealing with the heterosides in bark of ash tree (50a), terpenoids in the bark of Indian lilac (64a) and mountain ash (36a), and constituents of the volatile oil in Siberian fir bark (57a). A great deal of interest has been devoted to the alkaloids in different kinds of bark (5a,6a, 12a,23a,33a,37a,49a,59a,72a,73a). Also, the steroids in leaves, wood and bark of Nerium oleander have been investigated (58a).

The tannin of certain wood species seems to stand in a very close relationship to substances of flavonoid type. Hergert (27a) found that the distribution of leucocyanidins and catechins in coniferous wood, bark and needles involves a possibility that coniferous tannins are to a great extent derived from these monomers. Roux *et al.* (60a, 61a,62a) found that wattle bark tannin is a polymer of leucorobine-tinidin and leucofisetinidin. Okamura and Morohashi (45a) have separated black wattle bark into nine fractions, the molecular weight of which is within the range 790–2280. Endres *et al.* (15a–17a) have continued their investigation of the polyhydroxyphenols in spruce bark, and isolated and identified 90 to 95 per cent of these (15a). A leucoanthocyanin from the inner bark of black spruce has been investigated by Manson (38a). The occurrence of flavonoids in wood and bark, and their economic importance has been described by Hergert (28a).

Pearl *et al.* (51a) have hydrolyzed bark of various species of *Populus* in alkaline media, and have analyzed the mixtures, primarily of the monomer phenolic acids and aromatic aldehydes obtained thereby.

Carbohydrates in Bark

A great number of investigations into the carbohydrate constituents of bark have been carried out. The polyoses of inner bark have been described by Mian and Timell (white birch, 39a–41a,71a), and also by Painter and Purves (white spruce, 48a). Timell (67a,68a,69a,70a) has studied the carbohydrates in bark of gymnospermae. Wilson (74a) has found out that the preparation of holocellulose from mountain hemlock bark and Douglas-fir bast fiber gives more advantageous results following the previous extraction of the extractive-free bark with alcoholic alkali; this can be thought to be related to the splitting of any possibly existing lignin-carbohydrate bonds during the alkali extraction (see section IV-C-3).

Suberin

A phellonic acid preparation isolated from cork by alkaline hydrolysis (see Section IV-A-3) has been shown to consist, apart from ω-hydroxybehenic acid, of about 20 per cent of ω-hydroxytetracosanoic acid (35a). The suberin lamellae of the cork cell wall have been studied by Sitte (65a), who found support for a structure in which layers of suberin alternate with mono- or bimolecular films of amorphous cork wax.

Bark Lignin

Hata and Sogo (26a) have investigated the lignin in the outer bark of Japanese oak. Haas and Kremers (24a) have isolated stone cells from inner bark of aspen, and found that these cells, as a consequence of their relatively low content of interfering substances, may constitute a suitable material for studies on bark lignin.

Utilization of Bark

There are many publications concerned with the ways of utilizing bark. Attempts have been made to use bark for the manufacture of fiberboard (2a,8a,25a,42a), and the soil-improving ability of bark has been studied (1a,11a). Methods for the preparation of chemicals (7a,10a) and of resins and adhesives from bark (14a,29a,34a) have been described. Reviews on the utilization of bark and the properties of bark which are of technical interest have been compiled (20a,55a).

Subject Index

A

Abies balsamea, see Fir, balsam
Abies concolor, see Fir, white
Abies grandis, see Fir, grand
Abies procera, see Fir, noble
Abietic acid, 327
Abiurara, composition of wood, 72
Acacia melanoxylon, melacacidin from wood, 350
Acacia mollissima, leucoanthocyanin from wood, 350
Acacia senegal, gum arabic from, 360
Acer negundo, β-sitosterol-D-glucoside from, 331
Acer rubrum, see Maple, red
Acer saccharum, see Maple, sugar
Acetic acid, in sulfite-spent liquor, 471
Acetobacter xylinum, 389
Acetyl groups, in wood, 62, 90, 449
Acetyl-coenzyme-A, 374
Acocanthera longiflora, digitaloid in bark, 621
Acovenoside, in bark, 621
Aesculus octandra, see Buckeye, yellow
Afzelin, 347
Alder, red, anatomical features, 36
  ray cells, 20
Alkaline pulping processes, 475–492

Alkaloids, 340
Alkaloids, in bark, 626
Alkannan, in bark, 614
Alkannin, in bark, 614
Allantoic acid, in wood and bark, 379
Alnus glutinosa, lignans in wood, 342
Alnus rubra, see Alder, red
Alnusenone, in bark, 620
Amelanchier vulgaris, picein in bark, 613
Amino acids, in wood and bark, 379
α-Amyrin, 333
β-Amyrin, 333
Angelique, composition of wood, 68
Angiosperms, 9
  bark, 601
Angolensin, 345
Aniba canelilla, 1-nitro-2-phenylethane in wood, 340
Aniba duckei, alkaloids in wood, 340
  cotoin in wood, 353
Aniba rosaeodora, alkaloid in wood, 340
  flavonoids in wood, 346
Anibine, 340
Annual plants, lignin in, 257
Anthragallol, in bark, 615
Apical meristem, 10
Arabinogalactans, in wood, 192, 209, 219–220, 337

Hydroxydammarenone-II, 333
Hydroxyethyl cellulose, 173
Hydroxymethylfurfural, 575

I

Imbauba, composition of wood, 72
Incense-cedar, anatomical features, 27
  bark, analysis of, 606
  carbohydrates in bark, 628
  resin acids in bark, 618
Inositol, 339
Insects, attack on wood, 53
Isoliquiritigenin, 347
Isookanin, 344
Isopimaric acid, 328
Isoprene rule, 317
Isoprenoids, 317

J

Jacareubin, 353
Jarrah, marine borers, resistance, 54
Juglans cinerea, see Butternut
Juglans nigra, see Black walnut
Juniperus virginiana, see Red-cedar,
  eastern

K

Kaempferol, 345, 347
Kakeralli, composition of wood, 68
Kelvin equation, 411
Keyakinin, 338
Keyakinol, 338
Klinki pine, water vapor sorption, 406
Kraft process, 476–483
  active alkali, 476
  bisulfide ion concentration, 480
  black liquor, composition, 491–492
    dimethyl sulfide from, 582
    utilization, 491–492
  borohydride, effect of, 482
  by-products, 490–492
  chemical recovery, 492
  coniferous woods, application to,
    479
  delignification, rate of, 476–477
  delignification mechanism, 480–482
  dimethyl sulfide from liquor, 491
  effective alkali, 478

elemental sulfur in, 489
hardwoods, application to, 479
lignin, reaction of, 292
polysaccharide behavior, 483–489
prehydrolysis, 489
rate of delignification, 480
sodium borohydride addition to
  liquor, 490
sodium polysulfide in, 489
sulfide ion concentration, 480
sulfidity, 476
  effect of, 477–480
tall oil, 357, 491
turpentine, 491
volatile compounds, formation, 490
xylan adsorption during cooking,
  486
Krebs cycle, 380

L

Lactobacillus pentosus, fermentation
  of sulfite liquor, 473
Lanceol, 325
Lapachol, 354
Larch, eastern, heating value, 86
Larch, European, lignans in wood, 342
Larch, western, anatomical features,
  27
  arabinogalactan from, 219
Lariciresinol, 342
Larix laricina, see Tamarack
Larix occidentalis, see Larch, western
Lenticels, 12, 600
Leptospermum scoparium, betulinic
  acid in bark, 619
Leucoanthocyanidins, 349
  in bark, 623
Leucoanthocyanins, 349–351
  determination, 623
Leucodelphinidin, in bark, 624
Leucofisetinidin, 350
Levopimaric acid, 327
Levulinic acid, uses, 575
  wood, production from, 574
Libocedrol, 325
Libocedrus decurrens, see Incense-
  cedar